C0-AJY-615

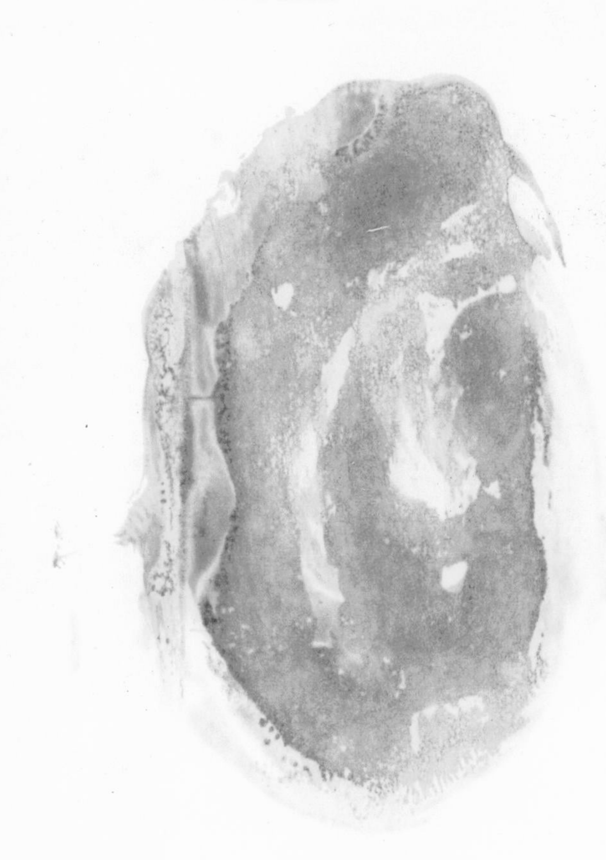

Imperfections in Nearly Perfect Crystals

Imperfections in Nearly Perfect Crystals

SYMPOSIUM HELD AT POCONO MANOR
October 12–14, 1950

Editorial Committee

W. SHOCKLEY, *Chairman*

J. H. HOLLOMON R. MAURER

F. SEITZ

Sponsored by

THE COMMITTEE ON SOLIDS
DIVISION OF PHYSICAL SCIENCES
THE NATIONAL RESEARCH COUNCIL

JOHN WILEY & SONS, INC., NEW YORK
CHAPMAN & HALL, LIMITED, LONDON

Library of Congress Catalog Card Number: 52-5957

PRINTED IN THE UNITED STATES OF AMERICA

Foreword

Realizing that much progress and inspiration in science is due to an exchange and comparison of ideas among investigators in its various branches, the National Research Council, through a Committee on Solids, has striven to promote such a cooperation in the field of solids. This committee, originated by Dr. R. C. Gibbs, Chairman of the Division of Mathematical and Physical Sciences of the National Research Council, was constituted in June, 1947. With the support of the Office of Naval Research, this committee sponsored in August, 1948, at Cornell University, a Conference on "Phase Transformations in Solids." The proceedings of this conference have appeared in the form of a book with the same title as the conference.

The current Committee consists of: M. J. Buerger, Department of Geology, Massachusetts Institute of Technology; P. P. Ewald, Department of Physics, Polytechnic Institute of Brooklyn; W. Shockley, Bell Telephone Laboratories; F. Seitz, Department of Physics, University of Illinois; C. S. Smith, Institute for the Study of Metals, University of Chicago; L. P. Smith, Department of Physics, Cornell University; W. A. Weyl, Department of Mineral Technology, Pennsylvania State College; and R. Smoluchowski, Metals Research Laboratory, Carnegie Institute of Technology, *Chairman*.

The success of this conference prompted the Committee to plan another conference of the same type. W. Shockley of the Bell Telephone Laboratories, with the help of J. H. Hollomon of the General Electric Research Laboratories and R. Maurer and F. Seitz of the University of Illinois and the continuing support of the Office of Naval Research, arranged a conference on the general subject of "Lattice Imperfections," which was held during October 12–14, 1950, in Pocono Manor, Pennsylvania. This group acted also as key panel members in organizing the papers and editing the discussion material for this book.

The subject matter of lattice imperfections is now in the focus of interest of many branches of science which deal with solids, and the vivid and stimulating discussions at the conference contributed materially toward a better understanding of the present state of our knowledge, and pointedly indicated the lack of much vital information. If the conference and this book do not achieve anything else apart from pointing out the major deficiencies in our knowledge of crystalline imperfections, it can be considered a major step towards a better understanding of the solid state.

I am sure that I am expressing the feelings of all members of the National Research Council Committee on Solids in conveying our grateful acknowledgment to Dr. W. Shockley, who, together with Drs. J. H. Hollomon, R. Maurer, and F. Seitz, organized the program of the conference and made this book possible. A particular word of appreciation is due the Office of Naval Research for its helpful support of these conferences, through a contract with the National Academy of Sciences.

R. Smoluchowski

January, 1952

Preface

Our modern civilization is vitally dependent on the strengths of metals. Yet in no case is a definitely established conceptual picture available for the processes that occur when a metal deforms or fractures under stress. All competent thinkers are convinced that dislocations play a vital role in these processes, but no actual deformation that has occurred has been proved to be due to a particular interplay of dislocations.

Dislocations are one of the natural ways in which a crystal can deviate from perfection in the arrangements of its atoms. There are other natural ways: atoms may be missing from their normal positions, they may be squeezed into interstitial positions, atoms of the wrong kind may be present in the right places, and so on. These imperfections are essential in most of the processes in which the atoms or electrons in a crystal move so as to produce observable effects. The symposium papers which furnish the basis for this book deal with a variety of "Imperfections in Nearly Perfect Crystals" from both experimental and theoretical viewpoints. To some degree it has been possible to classify them into four main fields.

Part I, *On the Nature of Imperfections in Nearly Perfect Crystals*, is concerned with the basic concepts. It starts with an attempt to describe and to list systematically the wide variety of imperfections that may occur in crystals. In addition to presenting this "synthesis," Seitz in Paper 1 points out the important ways in which imperfections of one type will have their observable behaviors modified by the presence of imperfections of a second type; in this way, he describes how knowledge of a subtle character has already been obtained and predicts how more should be discovered. The second paper, in Part I, demonstrates how dislocations are one of the few simple ways in which a crystal may deviate from perfection. It also describes the means of classifying dislocations and some of their simplest properties.

The biggest gap in the status of the field discussed at the symposium occurs between Part I and Part II.

Part II, *The Role of Imperfections in Deformation,* is concerned with the deformation of metals. On the basis of the foundation of Part I, it is quite possible to explain deformation; Mott in Paper 6 shows this clearly for several cases. It is not possible, however, to prove the theory correct. There is a gap between the scale and the nature of the experimental observations discussed in Part II and the atomic scale models of the theory presented in Part I and Paper 6. Much promise for a future bridging of the gap is furnished by the papers of Warren and Averbach, and Koehler. Warren and Averbach have developed new techniques for analyzing the details of the deformation patterns of cold-worked metals and perhaps have come closer to giving a picture of a dislocation distribution than has been previously reported. Koehler discusses the role of dislocations as absorbers of mechanical energy from both the theoretical and experimental viewpoint. The other papers by Barrett and Read deal with experimental results concerned with deformations. They are goals towards which the theories must strive.

In Part III, *Diffusion and Related Phenomena,* Apker and Taft deal with the motions of excess electrons and those subtle transient imperfections, *excitons;* Breckenridge discusses dielectric losses due to ionic motion; and the knotty and controversial question of the mechanism of diffusion in alloys is presented from different viewpoints in the report of Bardeen and Herring and that of Zener. The imperfections postulated in Part III involve disturbances localized to only a few atomic sites and on the whole seem more precisely characterized by experiment than do those of Part II; but even in Part III there is debate as to the importance of missing atoms or vacancies in the diffusion process in alloys.

In Part IV, *On the Properties and Effects of External and Internal Surfaces of Crystals,* we find encouragement for believing that a quantitative check of one aspect of dislocation theory is soon to be found. The experiments on small angle grain boundaries, reported as part of the paper by Fisher and Dunn, have reached a state of refinement that almost permits a crucial test of the dislocation model of grain boundaries reported by Read and Shockley. Two of the remaining papers are concerned with the effects of boundaries: Chalmers discusses their effect upon mechanical and chemical properties and Smoluchowski their effect upon diffusion; substructures or imperfections not severe enough to disintegrate single crystals into polycrystals are discussed by Guinier. Interphase interfaces, which play a major role in determining alloy structures and their properties, are discussed by C. S. Smith.

In addition to the papers, many contributions have been submitted in the form of discussion. Some of these have been incorporated in the papers where continuity would be improved thereby, and others follow the papers that they illuminate.

The editors would like to express their appreciation for the cooperation received from the authors and discussers. Special gratitude for aid in handling the manuscripts is due W. T. Read and J. K. Roros. The latter was, in addition, secretary and arranger of the conference, and much of its success was due directly to his care and efforts.

Editorial Committee
W. Shockley, *Chairman*
J. H. Hollomon
R. Maurer
F. Seitz

January, 1952

Contents

I. ON THE NATURE OF IMPERFECTIONS IN NEARLY PERFECT CRYSTALS

Imperfections in Nearly Perfect Crystals: A Synthesis

FREDERICK SEITZ

University of Illinois

ABSTRACT

In this paper an attempt is made to regard the various types of crystal imperfection from a unified viewpoint. This attempt is significant not only for pedagogical purposes, but also for proper appreciation of the genetical relations between crystal imperfections as they appear at the present time. It is pointed out that there are six primary types of crystal imperfection, namely, (*a*) phonons, (*b*) electrons and holes, (*c*) excitons, (*d*) vacant lattice sites and interstitial atoms, (*e*) foreign atoms in either interstitial or substitutional position, and (*f*) dislocations.

It is regarded as unlikely that there are more primary imperfections characteristic of the principal types of solid, although special imperfections may exist in materials with specialized properties, such as ferromagnetic materials. In addition to the primary imperfections, there are three transient imperfections, namely, (*g*) light quanta, (*h*) charged radiations and, (*i*) uncharged radiations. The transient imperfections may have a brief life within the crystal. The individual imperfections are discussed with a brief account of the historical introduction of each type. It is pointed out that two or more imperfections of the same type or of different types may interact to generate other imperfections so that the group forms a closely interlocking family. This feature of the imperfections is regarded as an essential part of their pattern of behavior, intimately related to the normal properties of the imperfections.

The available experimental information concerning the interaction of imperfections is classified in the scheme presented here. Emphasis is placed both on the individual characteristics of imperfections and on the means by which they are generated.

1. BASIS OF SYNTHESIS

Any field of science continues to be developed as long as such development yields new results that are profitable in the sense that they provide a deeper understanding of the laws of nature or of the way in which these laws operate to determine interesting properties of the world about us. As development proceeds, the area within which understanding prevails broadens, and the detailed structure revealed becomes increasingly more intricate. The investigators find that they are able to speak intelligently and accurately about the phenomena in the field to a higher and higher degree of approximation.

At various stages in the development it becomes possible to undertake a coordination or synthesis, in which apparently unrelated facts or concepts are tied together to form a closely interlocking unit. In the most favorable cases this process serves to interrelate almost all the known components of the field, and a great generalization or primary synthesis is obtained. In other cases only portions of the field become interlocked, and the "revelations" associated with the synthesis suggest an excellent guide for further research. The discovery of the laws of nonrelativistic quantum mechanics in the period between 1925 and 1928 represented one of the great primary syntheses in the field of atomic physics, whereas Dirac's formulation of the relativistic theory of the electron or Yukawa's proposal of a meson theory of nuclear forces represented secondary steps in further synthesis of the field. The latter steps leave many important facts uncorrelated, but they do indicate a route for further exploration.

Before the steps of synthesis are taken the uncorrelated components of the field are usually treated by relatively individualistic methods. Often rather arbitrary models are employed to handle particular facets of the subject because they have heuristic or practical value. The step of synthesis serves many purposes. For example, it may show either that the seemingly arbitrary models are actually closely connected and may be treated from a common, general standpoint, or it may show that the values of a model were overrated and that a substitute is more acceptable. Again, the step of synthesis may make it possible for the investigators to employ old models more broadly and with much more assurance than was thought possible previously because the range of applicability is discovered to be much wider than a conservative investigator would have had the courage to admit.

A very great step toward synthesis was achieved in the field of solids during the period between 1930 and 1935, when approximate treatments of the field based upon quantum mechanics provided[1] the connecting link between the various types of ideal solids, namely, metals, salts, valence crystals, and molecular crystals. Even when the approximate methods of solving the Schrödinger equation, such as the Heitler-London or the band scheme, were used, it was found possible to relate such diverse models as the Drude-Sommerfeld model of a metal, the Madelung-Born model of an ionic crystal, and the Baedeker-Wilson model of a semiconductor. In effect, the developments of this period allowed investigators to discuss the intrinsic or intensive properties of an ideally perfect solid from a single coordinated viewpoint and to derive the classical models as special cases. In addition, the new framework was sufficiently broad to permit discussion of the transition types of materials, that is, those which share the properties of two or more ideal types.

After this primary synthesis, investigation in the field of solids centered about the study of properties which are derived from the presence of imperfections. As is usually the case in relatively new explorations, the frontier became compartmentalized into sections, which, at least initially, were studied from rather specialized viewpoints and models. For example, it was recognized[2] that the electrolytic conductivity of salts depended upon the presence of either interstitial ions or vacant lattice sites, which

[1] See, for example, F. Seitz, *Modern Theory of Solids* (McGraw-Hill Book Co., New York, 1940); A. H. Wilson, *Theory of Metals* (Cambridge University Press, London, 1936); *Semi-Conductors and Metals* (Cambridge University Press, 1939); N. F. Mott and H. Jones, *Theory of Metals and Alloys* (Oxford University Press, London, 1935); N. F. Mott and R. W. Gurney, *Electronic Processes in Ionic Crystals* (Oxford University Press, 1940). H. Fröhlich, *Theorie der Metalle* (Springer, Berlin, 1937); A. Sommerfeld and H. Bethe, *Handbuch der Physik*, Vol. XXIV/2 (Springer, 1934); W. Shockley, *Bell System Tech. J.*, **18**, 645 (1939), and *Electrons and Holes in Semi-Conductors* (D. Van Nostrand Co., New York, 1951).

[2] I. Frenkel, *Z. Physik*, **35**, 652 (1926); W. Schottky and C. Wagner, *Z. physik. Chem.*, **11B**, 163 (1930); W. Schottky, *Z. physik. Chem.*, **29B**, 353 (1935).

had been generated as a result of thermal fluctuations. Similarly, it was concluded[3] that the plastic properties of metals depend upon the presence of an imperfection having linear extent, termed a dislocation, which is probably produced in an essentially non-equilibrium manner during crystal growth. Other imperfections were introduced to explain other properties, some of which could be connected with imperfections introduced for different purposes. To illustrate, it was established that the visible absorption bands (Fig. 8) which may be produced[4] in the alkali halides by irradiating them with x-rays, or by introducing a stoichiometric excess of alkali metal (the F-bands), are associated with vacant halogen-ion sites to which electrons have become bound (Fig. 28). Since these vacant lattice sites are also responsible for the migration of the halogen ions when the crystal is acting as an electrolytic conductor, it followed that there is an intimate relation between the imperfections which permit the crystal to conduct an electrolytic current and those which determine its photographic behavior.

A similar synthesis involving the imperfections responsible for the electrolytic and photolytic properties of the silver halides led Mott and Gurney[5] to a very elegant interpretation of the proper-

[3] L. Prandtl, *Z. angew. Math. u. Mech.*, **8**, 85 (1928); U. Dehlinger, *Ann. Physik*, **2**, 749 (1929); E. Orowan, *Z. Physik*, **89**, 634 (1934); G. I. Taylor, *Proc. Roy. Soc. (London)*, **145**, 362 (1934); J. M. Burgers, *Proc. Kon. Ned. Akad. Wet.*, **42**, 294, 378 (1939); F. Seitz and T. A. Read, *J. Appl. Phys.*, **14**, 100, 170, 470, 538 (1941); J. S. Koehler, *Am. J. Phys.*, **10**, 275 (1942); J. S. Koehler and F. Seitz, *J. Appl. Mech.*, **14**, 217 (1947); N. F. Mott, *Research*, **2**, 162 (1949). For more recent and diverse accounts of this subject, see *Carnegie Institute of Technology Symposium on the Plastic Deformation of Crystalline Solids* (Office of Naval Research, 1950); *Report of a Conference on the Strength of Solids*, University of Bristol, England (Physical Society, London, 1948); A. H. Cottrell, *Progress in Metal Physics* (Interscience Press, New York, 1949); A. H. Cottrell and B. A. Bilby, *Phil. Mag.*, **42**, 573 (1951); F. C. Frank, *ibid.*, **43**, 809 (1951).

[4] See the following articles and reviews: R. W. Pohl, *Physik. Z.*, **39**, 36, (1938); J. H. de Boer, *Rec. trav. chim. Pays-Bas*, **56**, 301 (1937); N. F. Mott and R. W. Gurney (*op. cit.*, footnote 1); F. Seitz, *Revs. Modern Phys.*, **18**, 384 (1946); H. U. Harten, *Z. Physik*, **126**, 619 (1949); I. Estermann, W. J. Leivo, and O. Stern, *Phys. Rev.*, **75**, 627 (1949); R. Casler, P. Pringsheim, and P. Yuster, *J. Chem. Phys.*, **18**, 887 (1950); J. Alexander and E. E. Schneider, *Nature*, **164**, 653 (1949); F. Seitz, *Phys. Rev.*, **79**, 529 (1950); E. Burstein and J. J. Oberly, *ibid.*, **79**, 903 (1950).

[5] See Mott and Gurney (*op. cit.*, footnote 1); W. F. Berg, *Report Prog. Phys.*, **11**, 248 (1948); J. W. Mitchell, *Phil. Mag.*, **40**, 249, 667 (1949). Also a sequence of papers by O. Stasiw and J. Teltow, *Ann. Physik*, **1**, 261 (1947);

ties of photographic emulsions. Although these steps of integration were highly important for the progress of the theory, they represented secondary steps of synthesis since they did not provide a single vantage point from which all the properties of solids which are determined by imperfections could be viewed as a coordinated whole. Undoubtedly the greatest obstacle in the path of forming such a coordinated picture was the uncertain knowledge of the imperfections responsible for plastic flow. Very early in the history of the physics of solids it was recognized by Przibram[6] and Smekal[7] that these imperfections were closely linked with those responsible for phenomena such as electrolytic conductivity and the photographic processes. Moreover, by 1935 very explicit models of an imperfection which could explain the rudimentary properties of plastic flow in metals and salts had been introduced by Prandtl, Dehlinger, Orowan, and Taylor,[3] namely, the unit which is now commonly called the Taylor-Orowan or the edge dislocation. However, it required nearly fifteen years of additional investigation and the combined contributions of at least a dozen investigators before the true complex nature of this imperfection and its diverse properties were appreciated with sufficient clarity to make a primary synthesis possible.

The purpose of this article is to attempt the presentation of such an integrated viewpoint in a qualitative manner. It is recognized at the start that, in proposing a general scheme of classification,

Z. anorg. u. allgem. Chem., **257**, 104, 109 (1948). See also J. R. Haynes and W. Shockley, *Report of a Conference on the Strength of Solids*, p. 151. New viewpoints and experiments on this topic are reviewed in considerable detail in the book edited by J. W. Mitchell, *Fundamental Mechanisms of Photographic Sensitivity* (Butterworth Publishing Co., London, 1951). Since this book was prepared, Mitchell has altered his viewpoint somewhat, as expressed in a forthcoming paper, "The Nature of the Sensitivity Centers and the Formation of the Latent Image in the Grains of Chemically Non-sensitized Emulsions," which the writer has had the privilege of seeing prior to publication. Mitchell's views appear to be closely related to those expressed by the writer in a paper bearing the title "Speculations on the Properties of Silver Halide Crystals," to appear in the October 15, 1951, issue of the *Reviews of Modern Physics*, although Mitchell has placed emphasis on polycrystals, whereas the writer has restricted attention to single crystals.

[6] K. Przibram, *Z. Physik*, **41**, 833 (1927); **68**, 403 (1931); and many other papers.

[7] A. Smekal, *Z. Physik*, **55**, 289 (1929); **88**, 204 (1932); **93**, 166 (1934); *Handbuch der Physik*, Vol. XXIV/2; *Report of the International Conference on Physics*, 1934 (Cambridge University Press, 1935).

the writer must make some arbitrary decisions which could be replaced by others which may eventually prove to be less arbitrary. Moreover, the course of events may show that such a synthesis is premature and that it will prove necessary to amplify the classification in highly important ways. Above all, the writer desires to emphasize that a classification of this type is possible only because of contributions from a very large number of investigators who have furnished the bricks, mortar, and part of the architectural planning of which the structure is constituted.

2. THE PERFECT SOLID

We shall regard the perfect solid as an aggregate of atoms arranged in unbroken lattice array (Fig. 1). Each cell of the lattice possesses an identical arrangement of the chemical constituents so

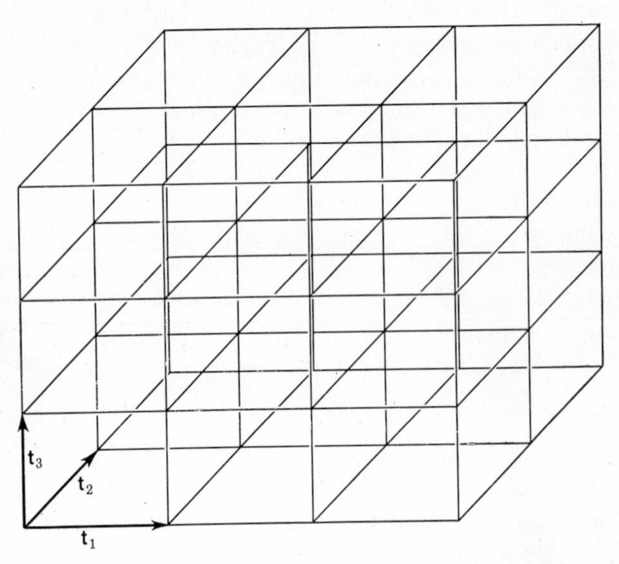

FIG. 1. The ideal crystal consists of a three-dimensional lattice array of identical cells within each of which the atoms are identically arranged. The three independent vectors which constitute the edges of the cell are termed the fundamental translational vectors of the lattice. They are shown as $\mathbf{t}_1$, $\mathbf{t}_2$, and $\mathbf{t}_3$ in the diagram.

that the internal structure is flawless. For further idealization, we shall assume that the system is at the absolute zero of temperature and that all the constituent atoms are at rest except for zero-point oscillation. The surface of the ideal specimen will be regarded as determined by planar crystal faces which provide the aggregate with the lowest surface energy. In addition we shall assume that the electronic configuration of the system is also in the lowest possible energy state compatible with the crystallographic arrangement.

The ideal perfect solid may be an insulator or a metal, depending upon the relative disposition of energy levels. The difference be-

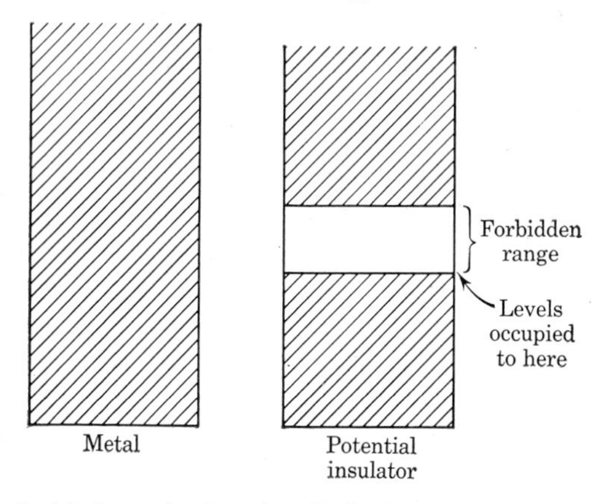

FIG. 2. In the ideal metal, when described with use of the band approximation, the energy levels of the individual electrons form an essentially continuous series above the ground level. In an insulator the series is broken by forbidden ranges or "gaps" and the levels are occupied, in accordance with the Pauli exclusion principle, to the lower edge of one of the gaps. Thus a gap separates the occupied from the unoccupied levels. The solid is a metal if the levels are not occupied to the lower edge of a gap.

tween types may be understood most simply with the use of the band approximation.[1] This associates a wave function, which is very nearly the same as that for a perfectly free electron, and an energy with each electron in the solid. If the electrons were perfectly free, as they would be if the electrostatic potential inside the lattice were constant, the spectrum of energy levels would be essentially continuous, above a well-defined ground state (Fig. 2). As far as its electronic properties are concerned, the solid would behave like a degenerate gas of free electrons and would be unambiguously metallic. The fluctuations in electrostatic potential from atom to atom within the solid produce two effects. First, the wave functions differ from those for perfectly free electrons by a modulation factor which has the periodicity of the lattice; second, the distribution of electronic energy levels deviates from that for perfectly free electrons and may actually have gaps. The system is an insulator, according to this mode of description, if there is at least one gap and if the electronic levels are fully occupied, in accordance with the Pauli exclusion principle, just to this gap and not beyond (Fig. 2). Otherwise the system is metallic. It is a good metal if the density of levels at the top of the occupied region is nearly the same as for a perfect electron gas; it is a poor metal if the density at this region is significantly lower. Most of the good metals of commerce fall in the first category, whereas materials such as graphite and bismuth fall in the second.

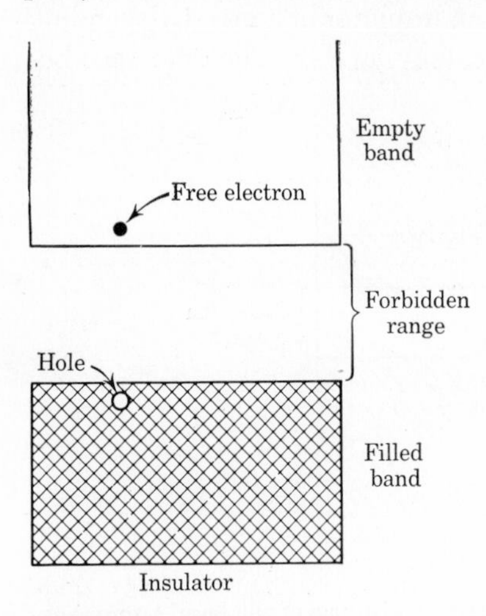

FIG. 3. An insulator becomes conducting, according to the band theory, when an electron is raised from the filled band to the empty band. The current is carried both by the excited, or free, electron and by the hole left behind in the previously filled band.

The three principal types of insulator, namely, salts, valence crystals, and molecular crystals, differ primarily in the distribution of valence electrons about the atoms. In salts there is a preferred distribution about the cations in a more or less spherically symmetrical manner; in valence crystals they are localized along the lines joining nearest neighboring atoms; whereas in molecular crystals they are localized between the lines of atoms in a given molecular unit or "island."

From the standpoint of the band scheme, the insulator becomes conducting as soon as one electron is excited from the filled to the empty band since both the electron and the hole left in the filled band may conduct a current independently (Fig. 3).

The description of the ideal solid on the basis of the band scheme is highly approximate and has semi-quantitative value at most. A more accurate description could be obtained if it were possible to determine the energy levels of the entire solid, regarded as a unified system and not as an aggregate of almost independent electrons. If this description were used, the ground state of the ideal insulator would be separated from the first excited state by an energy gap of the order of 1 ev or more (Fig. 4). The first excited states would not correspond to those obtained from the band scheme by raising an electron from the filled band to the

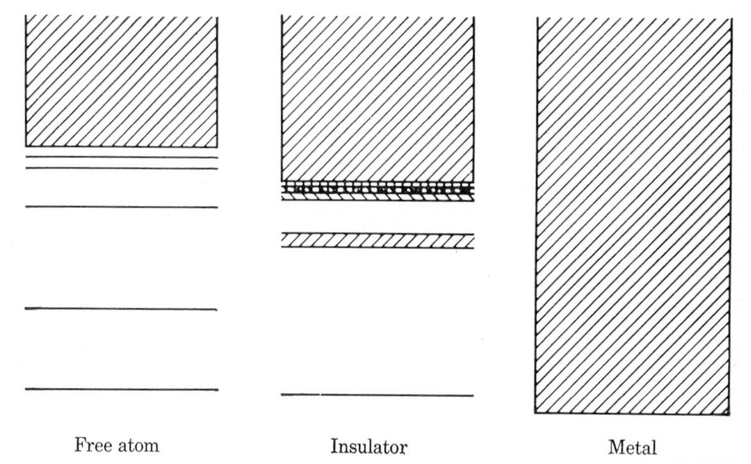

FIG. 4. The energy levels of a solid in the neighborhood of the ground state, when the solid is regarded as a single unit. The levels are treated as characteristic of the entire assemblage of electrons and not merely of one electron, in the manner of the band theory. The diagram on the left shows the energy levels of a typical atom when viewed in this way, discrete levels terminating in an ionization continuum. The insulator has a single lowest level, a group of bands of levels corresponding to non-conducting "exciton" levels, which correspond to the discrete excited states of the free atom, and a continuum corresponding to the ionization continuum of the free atom or to the conducting states of the band theory. Thus there is a close correspondence between the levels of the free atom and of the insulator. The levels of the ideal metal are continuous from the ground state upward.

empty band. Instead, they would be somewhat lower in energy and would correspond to nonconducting states in which the excited electron is accompanied by the hole in the sea of electrons in just such a way that the net motion of charge is zero when the excited electron is displaced. These are commonly termed *exciton states*,[1,8] since they are similar to states which would be obtained

[8] See the books of reference 1 and 17. Also F. Seitz, *Phys. Rev.*, **76**, 1376 (1949); H. Fröhlich and F. Seitz, *ibid.*, **79**, 526 (1950); W. Heller and A. Marcus, forthcoming paper in *Phys. Rev.*

if one atom in a chain or lattice were excited to a state below the ionization limit and if the excitation were to jump from atom to atom in the chain or lattice—a process which is permissible if the atoms are sufficiently close to interact with one another.

In the simplest insulator the lowest level of the entire solid is not degenerate, and the electronic distribution is relatively insensitive to the application of electric or magnetic fields unless the former are of the order of 1 million volts per cm.

The disposition of electronic levels of the entire system is much less clearly understood in an ideal metal than in an ideal insulator, particularly in the region of levels near the lowest. If one overlooks the facts relating to superconductivity, it is possible to assume that the excited levels join the lowest levels continuously in an essentially continuous level as suggested by the band approximation. Low-temperature studies[9] indicate, however, that the lowest level actually may be separated from higher ones by a gap of the order of 10^{-4} ev—a gap far smaller than in ideal insulators. In fact this gap is sufficiently small that it may be ignored if one is idealizing the results of experiments carried on at room temperature when the system is in a highly excited state. Attention must be paid to it in a strict sense only when the properties of metals are considered in the vicinity of 1°K. To a very good approximation, then, the ideal metal may be regarded as if it were composed of an aggregate of electrons which inhabit electronic levels of the type given by the band scheme.

3. THE PRINCIPAL TYPES OF IMPERFECTION

The ideal solid may possess a number of types of imperfection. We shall consider that idealized limit in which the density of imperfections is sufficiently low that they can be regarded as discrete entities which have well-defined individual character. Each unit of imperfection can then be ascribed properties which are independent of the presence of other imperfections of a like or different kind. In this sense, the ideal crystal will be regarded as forming a basic matrix within which the imperfections appear in the role of "particles" in much the same sense that the atoms in an almost perfect gas of low density can be regarded as individual particles with individual characteristics and can be discussed in a

[9] See, for example, the review by K. Mendelssohn, *Report Prog. Phys.*, **10**, 358 (1945); J. C. Slater, *Phys. Rev.*, **51**, 195 (1937); **52**, 214 (1937).

way that does not depend upon the presence of other atoms in the system.

The limit in which the imperfections have a low density corresponds to a "standard" case in physical situations for which a relatively high degree of simplicity occurs. The opposite extreme, wherein the density of particles is so high that each subordinates its individual character to the group character, may also possess a high degree of simplicity. For example, a group of vacancies may cluster together to form a unit in a crystal. This may be treated most simply by regarding it as a single entity, that is, as a bubble or void, and by ascribing to it individual properties, which, although derivable from those of vacancies, possess a degree of simplicity which makes it convenient to treat the assembly as a new unit. Similarly, a group of dislocations may combine to form a unit which is more simply described by the terms *grain boundary* or *mosaic boundary* and can be regarded as having its own properties. We thus avoid the complication of treating the aggregate in terms of its components each time it is considered. We shall, however, restrict attention here to the opposite extreme of high dilution.

The list of *primary imperfections* which we shall consider is:

(A) Phonons.
(B) Electrons and holes.
(C) Excitons.
(D) Vacant lattice sites and interstitial atoms.
(E) Foreign atoms in either interstitial or substitutional positions.
(F) Dislocations.

These imperfections or "particles" may interact with imperfections of the same type or of a different type to generate imperfections of a third type; in fact the scheme of interaction is even more complex, as we shall see below. We shall commonly refer to the last three imperfections in this list as being of the *atomic type* since they frequently represent regions of relatively static atomic distortion in the lattice. Before we enter into a detailed description of the properties of the imperfections and their ability to interact, it is very useful to consider augmenting this list in three ways.

First, it is necessary to adopt an attitude toward the surface of the crystal. We may either regard the surface as an inevitable form of imperfection and add it to the preceding list, or we may include it as part of the normal constitution of an ideal crystal when it possesses the form corresponding to lowest energy and treat deviations from this as the result of imperfection. We shall adopt the second attitude, ignoring the surface whenever feasible in order to focus as much attention as possible on imperfections in the volume of the solid. In spite of this we shall see that the six primary imperfections listed above have special significance in connection with the surface properties of solids, and it will be necessary to touch upon these properties in the following discussion.

Second, we may recognize that it is possible to irradiate perfect or imperfect solids with various radiations such as light or neutrons which can engender imperfections of the six types listed above. At the present state of development of physics, it is convenient to regard such radiations as though constituted of particles. While such particles are in transit through the solid we may regard them as *"transient" imperfections* and add them to the classification:

(G) Light quanta (from radio range to gamma ray range).

(H) Charged radiations (fast positive or negative ions, alpha particles, beta particles, mesons).

(I) Uncharged particles (neutrons, neutrinos).

Third, we may recognize that certain solids, such as the ferromagnetic and ferroelectric solids, have highly individual properties, not widely shared, with which characteristic imperfections may be associated. Consider, for example, an ideal ferromagnetic solid in which all potentially alignable spins (electronic or nuclear) are aligned. An imperfection may be introduced in this structure by reversing one of the spins. If the interaction between spins is sufficient, this imperfection may have the property that, under proper conditions, it can move through the medium in the manner[10] of a spin wave and hence be ascribed dynamic characteristics. It follows that the preceding lists of imperfections can be increased by the addition of other somewhat more specialized types such as spin waves and perhaps the analogous type of imperfection for a ferroelectric[11] material. In the interest of simplicity, we shall

[10] F. Bloch, *Z. Physik*, **61**, 206 (1931); J. C. Slater, *Phys. Rev.*, **52**, 198 (1937).

[11] See the review article by A. von Hippel, *Rev. Mod. Phys.*, **22**, 221 (1950).

omit such topics from detailed consideration, recognizing, however, that there is the possibility of expansion in this direction as the properties of somewhat atypical systems are included.

It is perhaps wise to emphasize at this point that the properties of a single crystal may be affected in an important way by the presence of the crystal surface and imperfections on it. Similarly, grain boundaries, when present, may have a much more important influence on some properties than the imperfections occurring only in single crystals, which are given primary consideration in this review. There is evidence to show, for example, that grain boundaries are better sinks for vacant lattice sites than dislocations are (see Section 6) under conditions in which vacancies are condensing out of the lattice. Nevertheless, a clear understanding of the properties of the most ideally imperfect single crystals available appears to be essential for an understanding of the properties of all crystalline materials found in nature or produced in the laboratory, so that no apology for concentration on single crystals is necessary.

4. THE PRIMARY IMPERFECTIONS AND THE INTERACTION BETWEEN LIKE IMPERFECTIONS

(A) PHONONS

A phonon is the particle associated with unit quantum excitation of one of the modes of elastic vibration of an ideal crystal.[12] Since the forces between atoms obey Hooke's law to a first approximation, the equations of motion of the atoms can be treated by the methods of normal coordinates to yield wave-like solutions. These normal modes of vibration can be classified on the basis of the wavelength, direction of propagation, frequency of vibration, and direction of polarization. The total number of independent modes is equal to three times the number of atoms in the specimen of perfect solid under consideration. For each wavelength and direction of travel there are, in general, three modes of vibration, which in the simplest cases correspond to two transverse and one longitudinal mode. The range of permissible wavelengths for any direction of travel is limited by the fact that the wavelength may not be smaller than the spacing between atoms. The relationship

[12] See for example F. Seitz (*op. cit.*, footnote 1, Chap. 3). The term phonon was apparently coined by I. Tamm.

between frequency and wave number is continuous for waves of given polarization. However, in crystals containing more than one atom per unit cell, which are more normal than exceptional, discontinuities occur (see Fig. 5) in the frequency versus wavelength curve when Bragg's condition for diffraction of waves is satisfied:

$$n\lambda = 2d \sin \theta. \qquad (4.1)$$

Here n is an integer, λ is the wavelength, d is the spacing between atomic planes in the lattice, and θ is the angle of incidence of the wave upon the lattice planes which cause the diffraction.

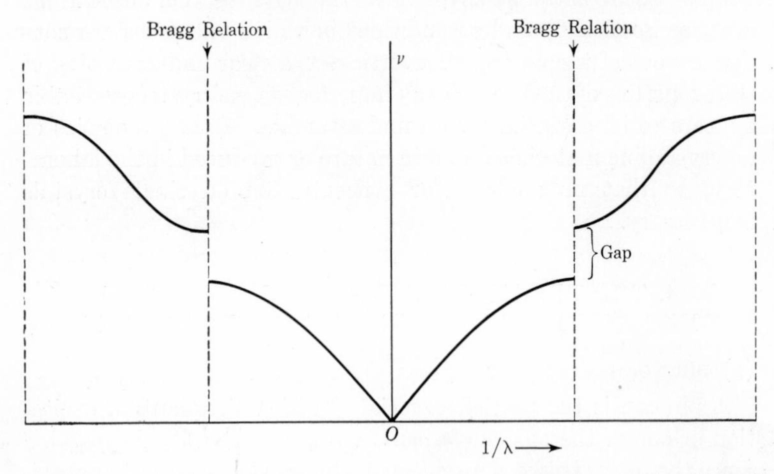

Fig. 5. The relationship between the frequency ν and the wavelength λ of the vibrational waves in a lattice. For simplicity the relation is illustrated for one direction of propagation of the lattice waves and for a single mode of polarization. The gap occurs when the waves satisfy Bragg's condition (Equation 1). Gaps of the type shown occur for all directions of propagation when there is more than one atom per unit cell. The overall range of wavelength is limited by the spacing between atoms; wavelengths shorter than the interatomic spacing have no physical meaning.

If classical mechanics were universally valid, the amplitude of the vibrational waves could be arbitrary. Quantum mechanics, however, imposes restrictions which limit the amplitude of any wave to discrete values which vary as the square root of the quantity $n + \frac{1}{2}$, where n is an integer. This integer specifies the number of phonons of the given wavelength, polarization, and direction of travel that are present in the crystal. In the lowest state of the crystal, attained at absolute zero of temperature, n is zero for all modes, and the limit of the ideal crystal is achieved. Actually the atoms are not completely quiescent under these conditions, for they undergo a small oscillation, termed the zero-point or half-quantum oscillation. In this sense even the ideal crystal contains residual imperfection of phonon character at the absolute zero of temperature.

The waves of longest wavelength correspond to acoustical, or sound, waves. In this range, the frequency varies inversely as the wavelength for given polarization and direction of travel (see Fig. 5), so that the velocity of propagation is constant—an important characteristic of sound waves. This constancy of velocity disappears as the wavelength approaches atomic dimensions.

The simplest way to introduce phonons of a given frequency into a crystal is to link it mechanically with a system vibrating at a fixed frequency which stimulates a specified direction of amplitude of oscillation. For example, a piezoelectric oscillator may be attached to the crystal. Rather specialized modes of vibration may be stimulated with the use of infrared radiation in polar crystals, such as the alkali halides, which develop volume electric polarization when the positive and negative ions are displaced in opposite directions.

A crystal which is at equilibrium at a finite temperature contains a wide spectrum of phonons. The value of the quantum number n associated with a given mode of vibration is given by Planck's relation

$$n = \frac{1}{\exp(h\nu/kT) - 1}, \tag{4.2}$$

in which ν is the frequency associated with the mode of vibration, h is Planck's constant, k is Boltzmann's constant, and T is the absolute temperature. It follows that the number of phonons in a crystal may be increased by placing it in contact with a heat reservoir at a higher temperature than that at which the crystal was initially. The phonons will pour in from the region of contact.

Let us designate by ν_m the maximum frequency associated with the vibrational spectrum. We see from equation (4.2) that n will be of the order of unity or larger when T is larger than $h\nu_m/k$. An essentially equivalent condition is that T should be larger than the characteristic temperature θ, determined by fitting the vibrational component of the specific heat of the solid to the theoretical equation[13] of Debye. θ lies between 200° and 500°K for the great bulk of solids of normal interest, although it is as large as 1800°K for materials such as diamond, in which the velocity of sound is exceedingly high, and as low as 30° for solid helium.[14]

If the forces between atoms obeyed Hooke's law exactly, phonons would not interact with one another, that is, two vibrational waves would pass through one another without producing changes. Actually, the forces between atoms contain an appreciable anharmonic component, so that two or more phonons may interact[13] and cause scattering. In the most general case the number of phonons is changed, and, of course, both the wavelength and direction of propagation of the components are altered. Energy and momentum are conserved in collisions of this type. Since the anharmonic terms in the interaction potential of the atoms contain powers higher than the second in the relative displacement of atoms, the interaction of phonons increases with increasing amplitude of vibration.

One of the most important consequences of the interaction between phonons is its influence upon thermal conductivity. If phonons are generated at the surface of a solid by placing it in contact with an appropriate heat reservoir, they do not flow in an undisturbed manner through the crystal, but will interact both with one another and with the phonons already present. As a result, the migration of the phonons takes place more or less in the manner of diffusion, rather than in the manner of propagation of sound. In the neighborhood of the characteristic temperature the mean free path of the most energetic phonons, which transport most of the energy, is of the order of 10 atomic distances, that is, of the order of $2 \cdot 10^{-7}$ cm, in a typical solid. Phonons in the acoustical range have a far longer mean free path, for sound travels many meters in solids even at room temperature with very little attenuation.

Another important consequence of the interaction between phonons is the fact that they may combine at a localized region of the lattice to produce a large displacement of one or two atoms.

[13] P. Debye, *Vorträge über Kinetishe Theorie* (B. G. Teubner, Leipzig, 1914); C. Kittel, *Phys. Rev.*, **75**, 972 (1949); R. Peierls, *Ann. Physik*, **3**, 1055 (1929); M. Blackman, *Phil. Mag.*, **19**, 989 (1935).

[14] See, for example, W. H. Keesom, *Helium* (Elsevier, Amsterdam, 1942).

In the extreme case, this type of interaction can cause atoms either to vaporize from the surface of the solid or to jump from normal to interstitial positions, thereby producing both interstitial atoms and vacant lattice sites. If the phonons which are responsible for such effects are at thermal equilibrium, the density of imperfections produced in this way can be determined by the laws of statistical mechanics, although the *rate* at which they are formed can be determined only by more detailed consideration[15] of the mechanism of production.

Similarly, phonons may, through localized interaction, stimulate the electronic states of an otherwise perfect crystal, producing free electrons and holes or excitons in insulators, and exciting free electrons to higher states in metals. An otherwise ideally perfect insulator in which electrons and holes are made free by the action of phonons in thermal equilibrium is said to be transformed into an *intrinsic semi-conductor*. This effect has been observed in diamond,[16] silicon, germanium,[17] and tellurium.[18] The density of carriers freed in this way in silicon is shown in Fig. 6.

The fact that two or more imperfections of one type can interact to produce imperfections of an essentially different type in an otherwise perfect crystal indicates, from the standpoint of our scheme of classification, that the imperfections in the list are *not independent of one another*. This raises the interesting question as to whether or not the list of six primary imperfections given in Section 3 is complete in the sense that the group forms a complete interlocking set. We shall return to this highly interesting question later, after discussing the complete family of primary imperfections.

[15] See, for example, S. Glasstone, K. J. Laidler, and H. Eyring, *The Theory of Rate Processes* (McGraw-Hill Book Co., New York, 1941).

[16] R. W. Pohl, *Elektrizitätslehre*, p. 208 (Springer, Berlin, 1949).

[17] The fact that silicon and germanium are intrinsic semi-conductors at elevated temperatures was apparently first appreciated by A. W. Lawson and the writer during wartime research. See the book by H. C. Torrey and C. A. Whitmer, *Crystal Rectifier* (McGraw-Hill Book Co., New York, 1948) for an account of wartime work. See also K. Lark-Horovitz and V. A. Johnson, *Phys. Rev.*, **69**, 258A (1946), and many subsequent papers for an account of work at Purdue University; G. L. Pearson and J. Bardeen, *ibid.*, **75**, 865 (1949); W. Shockley, *Electrons and Holes in Semi-Conductors* (D. Van Nostrand Co., New York, 1951).

[18] J. Bardeen, *Phys. Rev.*, **75**, 1777 (1949).

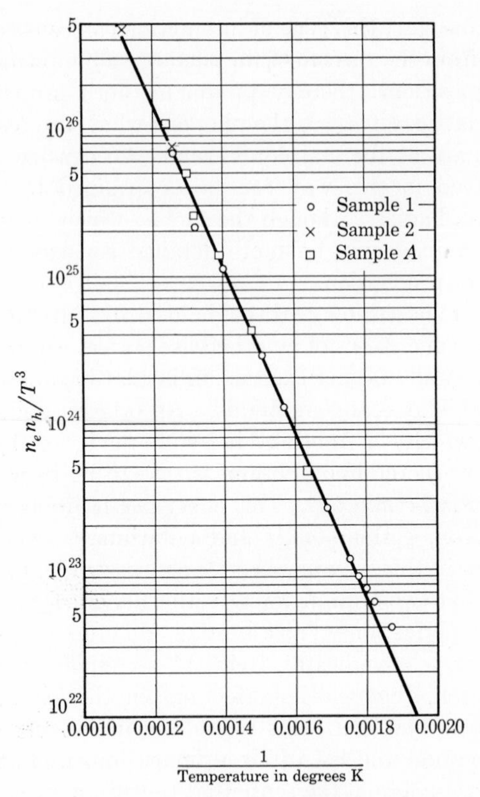

FIG. 6. The density of free electrons and holes in silicon in the intrinsic range of conductivity. The ordinate is the product of the density of electrons and holes divided by the third power of the absolute temperature. The abscissa is the reciprocal of the absolute temperature. The fact that the function is linear when plotted in this manner implies that the electrons and holes are freed as a result of thermal fluctuations. The slope of the line determines the width of the forbidden gap in silicon, namely, 1.1 ev. The density of carriers deviates from a relationship of this type at temperatures lower than those shown in the abscissa because impurities contribute electrons or holes which are freed more easily than those of the bulk solid. (After Pearson and Bardeen, footnote 17.)

(B) FREE ELECTRONS AND HOLES

An ideal metal contains an abundance of free electrons as long as the description given by the band theory is qualitatively correct, which appears to be the case at least above the superconducting temperature. It is possible that the electrons in all metals cease being free in this sense at sufficiently low temperatures and that the metal then resembles an insulator in a highly specialized way (see Section 2). Free electrons or holes may be introduced into insulators in a variety of ways: with the use of high electric gradients near the surface so as to introduce or draw off electrons; as a result of the action of phonons [see (A), page 19]; by the action of ionizing radiations. The ideal insulator becomes an electronic conductor when electrons or holes are introduced into it. Measurements of this conductivity and associated properties, such as the Hall coefficient,[19] can be used to determine the number of carriers and the ease with which they move through the lattice (see Fig. 6).

There does not seem to be a large number of significant observable effects associated with collisions between free electrons or between free holes. Such collisions probably occur very frequently between the free electrons in metals. However, they do not appear to have a significant influence on the electrical resistivity (which, incidentally, is determined primarily by electron-phonon collisions in an otherwise perfect crystal), presumably because the current flowing in the entire crystal is not altered by them. One of the most striking effects of electron-electron collisions has been observed by Dickey[20] in studies of photoelectric emission from the surfaces of alkali metals. It is found that the energy distribution of fast electrons which are emitted from the surface when light quanta having sufficient energy to provide even the electrons at the bottom of the conduction band with ample kinetic energy to surmount the surface barrier does not duplicate the energy density of electrons in the conduction band. Instead, the component of electrons with low energy is enhanced at the expense of those of high energy. An analysis of the results leaves little doubt that many of the fast electrons suffer collisions with the electrons of the conduction band and transfer an appreciable part of their energy to them, giving some sufficient energy to leave the metal.

Electron-hole collisions have great interest and have been studied in the alkali halides[4] and, most particularly, in silicon and germanium.[21] Since the electron and hole have coulomb charges

[19] See the books of footnote 1; also footnote 17.

[20] The writer is indebted to Miss J. Dickey (now Mrs. Apker) for an advanced copy of the manuscript dealing with this work.

[21] H. Suhl and W. Shockley, *Phys. Rev.*, **75**, 1617 (1949); **76**, 180 (1949).

of opposite sign, we might expect them to attract one another and, provided the density of electrons and holes is sufficiently low, to combine to form a hydrogen-like unit. In addition to energy of translation, this unit should possess an internal binding energy, which may be represented, at least as an approximation, by a Rydberg formula of the type[8]

$$E = -\frac{6.77}{\mu^4 n^2} \text{ (ev)}. \quad (4.3)$$

Here μ is the refractive index of the insulator for optical or near infrared frequencies, and n is an integer which may take values from 1 to infinity. Equation (4.3) gives the binding energy relative to the free state. These discrete levels evidently correspond to exciton states[22] of the crystals, so that one effect of combination of a free electron and a free hole can be the formation of an exciton either in the ground state ($n = 1$) or in an excited state ($n = 2, 3, 4 \ldots$). The energy released in this manner could appear either in the form of light or in the form of phonons. The diameter of the orbit in which the electron-hole pair move in the lowest energy state should be of the order of $\mu^2 a_0$, where a_0 is the radius of the first Bohr orbit in atomic hydrogen, that is, 0.53 Å. For $\mu = 2.5$, this is about three atomic distances.

The lowest of the discrete levels (4.3) lies above the ground state of the insulator. Thus a downward transition from these exciton states to the ground state implies complete annihilation of the free electron and hole. Again, the energy released in such complete annihilation can be emitted either in the form of light or in the form of phonons, the latter process being the inverse of the generation of excitons or free electrons and holes by the interaction of phonons. On the other hand, if light is emitted in the complete or partial combination of the electron or hole, the crystal luminesces during the process. We have noted in Section 3 that it may be convenient to regard light quanta of this type, which are

[22] The term exciton was introduced by J. Frenkel, *Phys. Rev.*, **37**, 17, 1276 (1931). The exciton was viewed from the standpoint of the band scheme by G. H. Wannier, *ibid.*, **52**, 191 (1937). See also R. Peierls, *Ann. Physik*, **13**, 905 (1932); J. C. Slater and W. Shockley, *Phys. Rev.*, **50**, 705 (1936). Dr. W. Heller and Miss A. Marcus have recently extended the theory of excitons in the alkali halides in a quantitive way, considering polarization effects (to be published in *The Physical Review*). Similarly, Professor H. Brooks has extended Wannier's work.

passing through the crystal, as transient imperfections (classification G). This procedure is convenient if the light quantum may be absorbed in another portion of the crystal.

The experiments[21] on recombination of electrons and holes in the alkali halides and in silicon and germanium seem to show that direct recombination in the manner described above is rare, presumably because the cross section for the process is exceedingly small. In practical cases recombination occurs through interaction with at least one other type of imperfection, a type of multiple process which will be discussed later at an appropriate place (Section 6).

Free electrons and holes may become self-trapped[23] in polar crystals by producing relative displacement of the positive and negative ions in a radial direction about a point and in a spherically symmetric manner (Fig. 7). The polarization creates a potential well which holds the electron or hole. The energy with which the electron is bound in such a well appears to be only a few tenths of an electron volt in most polar crystals, so that the self-trapped state is not permanently stable at room temperature. In addition, it is possible that the polarization well is able to migrate with relative ease by a thermally activated diffusion process, so that self-trapping does not prevent electrons or holes from moving about the crystal at ordinary temperatures, even though the motion is somewhat inhibited, relative to that of free carriers.

It probably should be emphasized at this point that the free electrons in a metal or a semi-conductor possesses thermal energy of motion at finite temperatures. As a result they may be viewed as possessing quanta of thermal agitation, somewhat analogous to the phonons associated with lattice vibration. If we desired, we could treat such thermal quanta as a new type of imperfection. Since their effects are closely linked with those of phonons, with which they normally are in thermal equilibrium, we shall not add to the list.

[23] L. Landau, *Physik. Sowjetunion*, **3**, 664 (1933); S. Pekar, *J. Phys.* (*U.S.S.R.*), **10**, 341, 347 (1946); J. J. Markham and F. Seitz, *Phys. Rev.*, **74**, 1014 (1948); H. Fröhlich, H. Pelzer, and S. Zienau, *Phil. Mag.*, **41**, 221 (1950). The last group of investigators has pointed out conditions under which self-trapping is impossible, for example, when the orbital frequency of the trapped electron would be long compared to the relaxation time of the lattice.

In this connection, it is very interesting to note that Fröhlich and Bardeen[24] have proposed that superconductivity arises as a result of the coupling between the free electrons in metals and

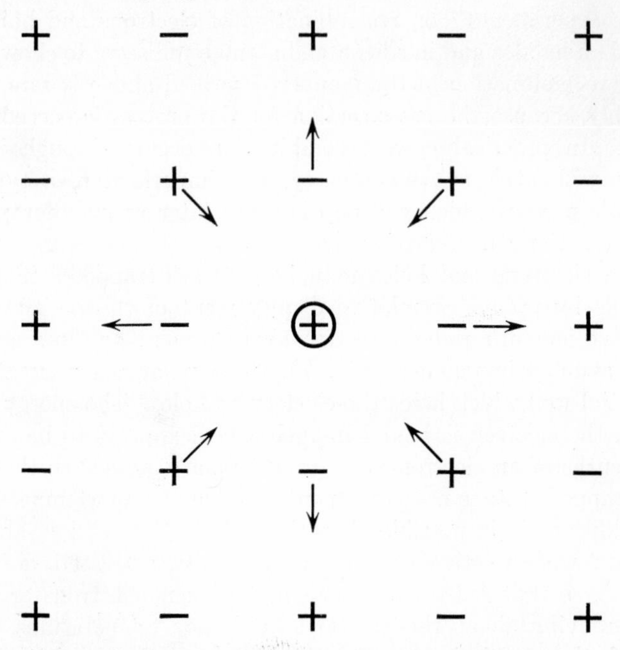

FIG. 7. Schematic diagram of the process by which an electron may become self-trapped. If the electron is held, for example, at the position of a positive ion, the surrounding positive ions will be attracted and the negative ions repelled, as shown. As a result the electron is at the center of a polarized region produced by displacement of the surrounding ions. The potential well formed by such displacement is coulomb-like at large distances, so that it possesses discrete electronic levels. Holes may become self-trapped in a similar way. Calculations show that the energy of self-trapping is usually of the order of a few tenths of an electron volt.

semi-conductors and the lattice vibrational waves responsible for the ordinary resistivity. This point of view, which is being exploited at the time this review is written, is supported by the observations[25] on the shift of the superconducting transition

[24] H. Fröhlich, *Phys. Rev.*, **79**, 845 (1950); J. Bardeen, *ibid.*, **79**, 167 (1950), and other, as yet unpublished, papers. The writer is deeply indebted to Bardeen for the privilege of reading these papers prior to publication.

[25] C. A. Reynolds, B. Serin, W. H. Wright, and L. B. Nesbitt, *Phys. Rev.*, **78**, 487 (1950); E. Maxwell, *ibid.*, p. 477.

temperature with the mass of the atoms of the lattice. Fröhlich has supposed that the coupling permits metastable currents to persist on a microscopic scale, whereas Bardeen has proposed that the coupling distorts the spectrum of electronic energy levels in the ground state of the system in such a way that there are groups of electrons with a very low effective mass. These electrons contribute a very large diamagnetism to the lattice, thereby preventing the magnetic field from penetrating into the interior of the metal. In addition, they behave as if they had such a very long wavelength that they are not restrained near the surface by the attenuated component of magnetic field which does penetrate the surface layers in the manner in which this component of the field would restrain electrons of ordinary mass. This point of view has made it possible for Bardeen to go a very long way in providing a specific model of system which obeys London's phenomonological equations, at least in the case of a simply connected system.

From the point of view presented in this article, the new developments are interesting in the sense that they suggest that superconductivity originates in the interaction of two of the primary imperfections discussed here, namely, free electrons and phonons.

(c) EXCITONS[22]

As we have seen in the preceding sections, an exciton is produced when an insulator is raised to the first, nonconducting excited state of its electronic system. From one point of view the exciton is a neutral particle produced by partial recombination of an electron and a hole without complete annihilation [see (B), page 22]. From another point of view it is the excited state of an atom or ion which may wander from one cell of the lattice to another. In the ideal case it is possible to treat the exciton as though it had two components of energy: an internal energy, represented in one approximate case by equation (4.2), relative to the state in which the electron and hole are free; and a translational energy which can be dissipated like the kinetic energy of a moving electron. A wavelength and direction of propagation can be associated with the various possible states of translational motion of the exciton. In addition, if the angular momentum of the electronic system changes when the exciton is produced, as will usually be the case if the exciton is generated by light, the exciton will have a polarization vector. Heller and Marcus[22] have examined this aspect of exciton theory.

We saw in (A) on page 19 that excitons may be formed by the interaction of phonons. Actually, the simplest and most direct manner to generate excitons is to irradiate the crystal with light in the region of the spectrum corresponding to the first electronic transition. This region, which lies in the ultraviolet for most good

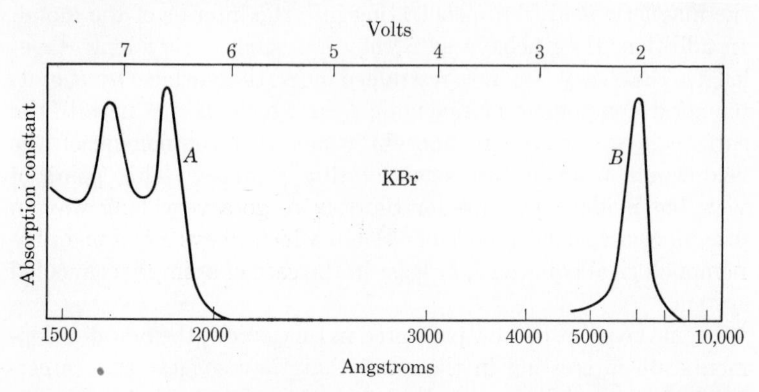

FIG. 8. Position and structure of the fundamental absorption bands in KBr (*A* in the figure). The first peak lies at 1920 Å. The mean free path for light quanta is about 10^{-6} cm at the center of this peak. Curve *B*, which lies in the visible part of the spectrum, shows the *F*-band, associated with electrons trapped in halogen-ion vacancies. The intensity of this band depends upon the concentration of *F*-centers and is greatly exaggerated (of the order of 10,000 times) for normal concentrations of these centers.

insulators, is called the *first fundamental absorption band* of the crystal. It lies below 2200 Å in diamond,[26] is centered at[27] 1580 Å in NaCl, at 1920 Å in NaBr, and at 2200 Å in KI (see Fig. 8). It lies in the near infrared in both silicon and germanium. The absorption of light is so very intense in the center of the first fundamental band in most insulators that the excitons are generated only near the surface of the crystal. For example, the mean free path[28] for light quanta is only $1.0 \cdot 10^{-6}$ cm in NaBr and $1.4 \cdot 10^{-6}$ cm in KI at the center of the bands. Fortunately

[26] F. Peter, *Z. Physik*, **15**, 358 (1932).

[27] R. Hilsch and R. W. Pohl, *Z. Physik*, **59**, 812 (1930); E. G. Schneider and H. M. O'Bryan, *Phys. Rev.*, **51**, 293 (1937).

[28] H. Fesefeldt, *Z. Physik*, **64**, 623 (1950); G. Bauer, *Ann. Physik*, **19**, 434 (1934); A. Kublitsky, *ibid.*, **20**, 749 (1934).

the fundamental band usually has a tail extending toward longer wavelengths in which the mean free path may be much longer. Hilsch and Pohl[4] have found that free electrons are not produced by irradiating the alkali halides in the tail of this band if the crystal is uncolored, thereby demonstrating that the particles produced by excitation are not charged.

Consider now the state of affairs in the neighborhood of the exciton, taking for the moment the viewpoint that the exciton is momentarily localized on a particular atom, such as a halogen ion in a sodium chloride lattice. During the time the exciton spends upon a particular atom, this atom is transformed into a different chemical species, for it does not have the normal configuration of electrons but an excited one. Thus it interacts with its neighbors in a manner different from a normal atom. In particular the interatomic spacing in the neighborhood of the excited atom for which the atom would be at equilibrium is different from that for a normal atom. Should the exciton remain at the particular atom, both this atom and its neighbors would shift their positions to new equilibrium values, emitting phonons during the process. In this case the exciton would become *self-trapped* at the particular atom, since it would be able to move only if the new equilibrium configuration also moved—a relatively slow process. The shift in position of the atoms required to trap the exciton would take about 10^{-13} sec, the characteristic oscillation time of the atoms in a lattice. Hence, if the exciton is able to jump to a neighboring atom in appreciably less than 10^{-13} sec, it will wander on and become trapped only as a result of an unusual fluctuation.[29] The time required for the exciton to migrate from atom to atom is determined by the magnitude of the interaction energy between neighboring atoms when one is excited. This is sufficiently large in salts and valence crystals that the excitons should be able to wander very far before becoming trapped in the manner described above. On the other hand, the first optical absorption bands of some molecular crystals such as naphthalene exhibit a detailed fine structure which indicates that the molecules behave almost exactly as if in the gaseous state. In such cases the interaction between molecules seems to

[29] For discussion of this subject, see: A. von Hippel, *Z. Physik*, **101**, 680 (1936); F. Seitz, *Trans. Faraday Soc.*, **35**, 74 (1939); J. Franck and R. Livingston, *Rev. Modern Phys.*, **21**, 505 (1949).

be sufficiently weak that the molecule undergoes many atomic oscillations before the exciton can jump to a neighbor. Thus the exciton is trapped in the molecule on which it is formed.

This behavior may not be characteristic of all molecular crystals, but only of those for which the component of electronic dipole moment associated with the transition from the ground state to the first excited state is comparatively small; for example, in cases in which the electron clouds on different molecules do not overlap and in which the oscillator strength associated with the transition is 0.1 or less, so that the interaction between the excited molecule and a neighbor is relatively small. It is significant that the time required[30] for an excited naphthalene crystal to emit light is about ten times longer than for a system having an oscillator strength near unity. Other molecular cystals, such as trans-stilbene, have much shorter emission times, and it is possible that the excitons are able to wander much farther in such cases.

Apker and Taft[31] have provided the most direct evidence for the ability of excitons to wander in salts. They have found that excitons produced by irradiation in any part of the first fundamental band of a number of alkali halides (KI, RbI, RbBr) probably can wander at least of the order of 1000 atomic distances and eject electrons from *F*-centers. They have detected electrons of this type that have been ejected through the surface of the crystal. We shall discuss this process somewhat more fully in Section 6.

Relatively little is known about the ultimate fate of excitons in a typical crystal. Three possibilities exist. The energy associated with the exciton could appear as light, in the form of phonons, or be stored, at least in part, in the production or transformation of another type of imperfection. The production of a light quantum, if feasible, requires a minimum time of the order of 10^{-8} sec, during which time the exciton could wander of the order of 10^7 atomic distances if it remains free. Thus the exciton could collide with an imperfection if at least one atom per million is associated with an imperfection. Smakula[32] has found that *F*-centers are formed when a clear, well-annealed specimen of

[30] See, for example, G. B. Collins, *Phys. Rev.*, **74**, 1543 (1948).

[31] L. A. Apker and E. Taft, *Phys. Rev.*, **79**, 964 (1950), **82**, 814, 768 (1951). The writer is deeply indebted to these investigators for detailed discussion of their work.

[32] A. Smakula, *Z. Physik*, **59**, 603 (1930); **63**, 762 (1930).

alkali halide is irradiated with light in the tail of the fundamental band. The production has a quantum yield of unity during the early part of the irradiation. Presumably the excitons created by the light collide with imperfections in this case and generate F-centers, at least during the early phase of the irradiation. We shall discuss this process in more detail in Section 6.

The photoelectric experiments of Apker and Taft,[31] referred to in the foregoing section, support the same point of view and also indicate that the electrons associated with the F-centers become ionized as a result of collision with excitons once the color centers have been formed.[33] Thus the excitons divest themselves of energy in another way at a later stage in the process. The experiments of Apker and Taft also show that the yield of photoelectrons diminishes when the light absorbed in the fundamental band has a very short mean free path, that is, when it lies at the center of the absorption band, and the crystal is at low temperature so that the absorption in this region is very intense. It has been established that a substantial part of this effect arises from the presence of a thin layer on the surface in which there is a stoichiometric excess of halogen atoms. However, it is possible that a component arises from the fact that some of the excitons diffuse to the surface and vanish, probably by emission of phonons. This process was first suggested by Fano[34] in another connection. Since luminescent radiation has apparently never been observed[35] with an appreciable yield when a pure crystal is irradiated in the fundamental band, it seems reasonable to assume that the complete extinction of an exciton by production of light is rare. The most probable explanation is that suggested by the experiments of Apker and Taft, that is, the exciton either transfers its energy to

[33] J. N. Ferguson, *Phys. Rev.*, **66**, 220 (1944) apparently observed photocurrents generated by the freeing of electrons from F-centers by excitons produced in the fundamental band. The F-centers were presumably generated by the excitons during the initial stages of the irradiation.

[34] U. Fano, *Phys. Rev.*, **57**, 564 (1940); **58**, 544 (1940).

[35] See, however, the "edge emission" of CdS described by C. C. Klick, *J. Opt. Soc. Am.*, **41**, 816 (1951). G. C. Farnell, P. C. Burton, and R. Hallama, *Phil. Mag.*, **41**, 157 (1950), report the observation of luminescence in presumably pure silver halides below 145°K. They have not determined the quantum yield. These salts appear to be worth more study. The writer, in a forthcoming paper in *The Reviews of Modern Physics*, under the title, "Speculations on the Properties of Silver Halide Crystals," has suggested that this luminescence arises from $d^9s \rightarrow d^{10}$ transitions in silver ions near dislocations.

an existing imperfection or produces phonons. The writer[29] has pointed out that luminescent radiation may be absent even in an ideally perfect crystal when excitons are produced far from the surface. It is reasonable to assume that an exciton will become self-trapped long before it has diffused about for 10^{-8} sec, produc-

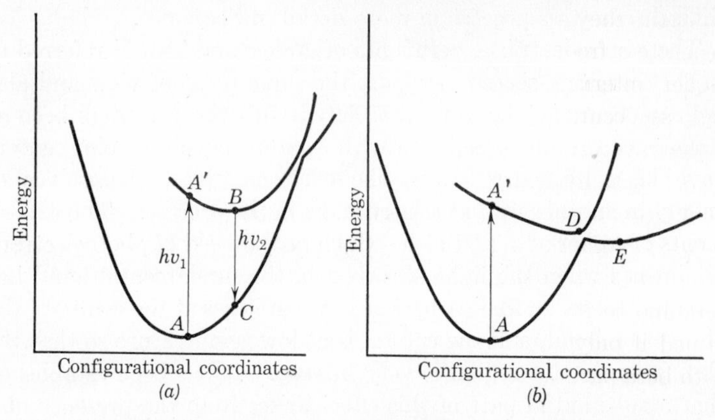

FIG. 9. Two possible arrangements of levels for the normal and first excited state of an insulator. In both cases the abscissa represents the relative positional coordinates of the nuclei of the atoms in the vicinity of the exciton. Case *a* represents that in which light may be emitted. The exciton is formed as a freely moving particle in the transition from A to A', for example, with absorption of light of frequency $h\nu_1$. The system slides to the point having coordinates B when the exciton becomes self-trapped. In this case the system returns to the ground state rapidly by the transition from B to C, for example, by radiation of light of energy $h\nu_2$. In case *b* the ground state and first excited states "cross" at D, and the system ends in a metastable position E when the exciton becomes self-trapped. Thus light cannot be emitted and the system returns to the ground state only when thermal excitation carries the system to the point D, so that it may slide to A.

ing a localized distortion of the lattice. It is entirely possible that the electron configuration associated with the exciton possesses a lower energy for the distorted positions of atoms than the electronic configuration of the normal electronic state of the crystal does for the distorted position. This situation is indicated in Fig. 9*b*, which shows the crystalline analogue of a Franck-Condon diagram in which the normal and excited states cross. This could happen in an alkali halide, for example, if two halogen atoms are drawn very close in the configuration corresponding to a trapped exciton, so that the ions would have a very high repulsive interaction if in the normal, rare-gas state. If this were to occur, the exciton would not be able to emit light after being trapped and would remain metastable until phonons or another type of imperfect upset it.

If two excitons were to collide or become trapped at the same position, they would probably possess sufficient energy either to generate a free electron and hole or to produce a single exciton of higher internal excitation. It has been suggested[36] that this process occurs in naphthalene when it is radiated with natural alpha rays. It is found that the fluorescent yield is much lower under alpha ray excitation than when the crystal is irradiated with beta rays of comparable energy. Since the density of excitation is much higher for alpha rays, which have a short range, it is possible that two excitons frequently occur in the same molecule and combine to form nonluminescent products that could not be obtained if only a single exciton were present, as during excitation with beta particles.

(D) VACANT LATTICE SITES AND INTERSTITIAL ATOMS

We learned in A, page 19, that vacancies and interstitial atoms may be generated as equilibrium imperfections by phonons if the phonons are at temperature equilibrium. The density of vacancies may correspond[37] to 0.01 per cent or larger near the melting

[36] I. Broser and H. Kallman, *Z. Naturforschung*, **2a**, 439, 642 (1947); I. Broser, L. Herforth, H. Kallman, and U. Martius, *ibid.*, **3a**, 6 (1948).

[37] Direct measurements of the density of vacancies in salts were first made by E. Koch and C. Wagner, *Z. physik. Chem.*, **B38**, 295 (1938), in the silver halides with a technique employing the substitutional addition of the halides of divalent metals. The divalent cation requires a vacant cation site to compensate for the extra positive charge. These measurements have been subject to careful re-analysis by O. Stasiw and J. Teltow, *Ann. Physik*, **1**, 261 (1947), who believe they contain evidence for the view that there is appreciable association of the divalent impurities and positive-ion vacancies. In addition, Teltow, *Ann. Physik*, **5**, 63, 71 (1949), *Z. physik. Chem.*, **195**, 197, 213 (1950), has carried out refined extensions of the work of Koch and Wagner on the silver halides, employing several divalent additions, including sulphur. This work, when combined with that of Lawson and Kurnick (footnote 38) and of C. R. Berry [*Phys. Rev.*, **82**, 422 (1951)], provides overwhelming evidence for the existance of Frenkel defects in these salts at temperatures below 300°C. The work of Lawson and Kurnick seems to indicate that Schottky defects predominate near the melting point, whereas that of Berry suggests that the density of Schottky defects is not greater than 0.1 per cent in this range. If the results of Lawson and Kurnick are substantiated they will support the view that

point and produce a very large expansion of the lattice.[38] We shall see later that these imperfections may also be generated in a non-equilibrium way by the action of dislocations and other imperfections.

One of the most important properties possessed by interstitial ions and vacancies is that they usually can migrate about the crystal relatively easily when assisted by thermal fluctuations (that is, interaction with phonons), and hence permit the *diffusion* of matter. In fact, these imperfections were introduced[2] into the theory in order to explain facts concerning diffusion and electrolytic conductivity, the second phenomenon being closely related to the first in salts where the migrating atoms are charged (Fig. 10).

It has now been well demonstrated that vacant positive- and negative-ion sites are normally generated in equal numbers in the alkali halides and that the migration of these imperfections is responsible for the normal electrolytic conductivity of these salts when pure. These imperfections (Fig. 11) are commonly called *Schottky defects,* because Schottky[2] first suggested this mechanism of electrolytic conductivity. Theoretical evidence indicates that

---

oscillational entropy plays an important role in determining the equilibrium density of lattice defects, for the energy required to produce Schottky defects is presumably greater than that required to produce Frenkel defects. Similar measurements have been made in the alkali halides by C. Wagner and P. Hantelmann, *J. Chem. Phys.*, **18**, 72 (1950); H. Kelting and H. Witt, *Z. Physik*, **126**, 697 (1949); H. Etzel and R. J. Maurer, *J. Chem. Phys.*, **18**, 1003 (1950). From this work one may estimate the density of vacancies near the melting point. See also F. Seitz, *Phys. Rev.*, **56**, 1063 (1939). The densities are of the order of 10^{18}/cc (0.01 mole per cent) in the alkali halides at the melting point and of the order of 10^{20}/cc (1 mole per cent) in the silver halides. H. B. Huntington and the writer have estimated the energy required to form a vacant lattice site in metallic copper (see footnote 40). From this one may estimate the density of vacant sites near the melting point in this material. The value is of the order of 0.1 atomic per cent.

[38] The writer is indebted to Lawson and Kurnick for a detailed discussion of their methods of determining the density of lattice defects in the silver halides, based upon the measurement of ionic conductivity at high pressures and temperatures. In this connection it may be pointed out that these investigators have reexamined the work of Strelkow on lattice expansion which had been analyzed initially by Lawson [*Phys. Rev.*, **78**, 185 (1950)] in such a manner as to support the Schottky mechanism and still believe that the Schottky mechanism is not ruled out at elevated temperatures. A forthcoming paper by P. H. Miller on the change in lattice parameter and density produced by lattice imperfections has important bearing on this point.

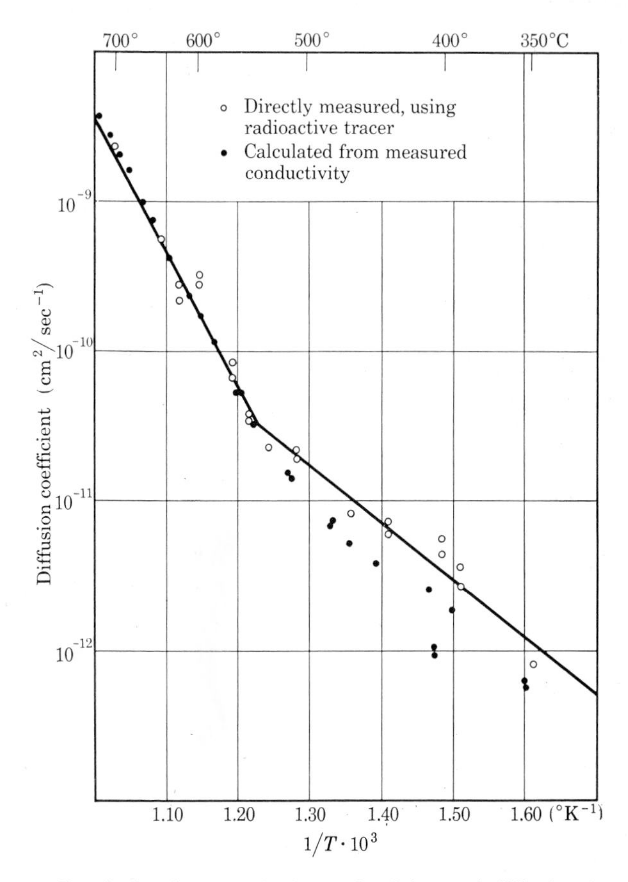

FIG. 10. Correlation between ionic conductivity and diffusion in sodium chloride. The open circles represent the diffusion coefficient of sodium ions, determined by radioactive tracer techniques. The dark circles represent the values of the diffusion coefficient deduced from measurements of the electrolytic conductivity. The knee of the curve occurs at a temperature below which the transport of current is a consequence of the migration of positive-ion vacancies associated with divalent impurity atoms. For temperatures above the knee, the migrating positive-ion vacancies are the normal Schottky type, associated with an almost equal number of negative-ion vacancies. The divergence between the full and open circles, below the knee, implies that the divalent impurities probably migrate in such a way as to stimulate self-diffusion without contributing to the electrolytic current. (After Mapother, Crooks, and Maurer, footnote 91.)

interstitial ions are rare in the alkali halides under equilibrium conditions because more energy is required to form them.

There is also very conclusive evidence that the dominant lattice defects in the silver halides, AgCl and AgBr, are interstitial silver ions and silver-ion vacancies, produced in equal numbers in the pure crystal. The original basis for this viewpoint rested upon calculations of Jost and Nehlep[39] which supported the conclusion

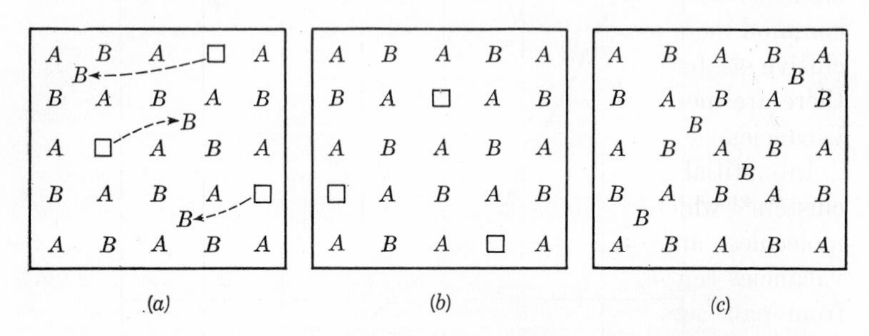

Fig. 11. (a) Frenkel defects, formed by migration of B-atoms from normal to interstitial positions accompanied by formation of vacant sites. It is believed that the silver halides represent an example of this type, the silver ions corresponding to the B-atoms. (b) Schottky defects, formed by the generation of vacant sites in both A and B lattices, either at the surface or at dislocations. Evidence indicates almost conclusively that the defects in the alkali halides are of this type. (c) A modification of (a) in which the B-atoms are present in excess and are not accompanied by vacancies. This probably occurs in ZnO and CdO. The interstitial units are neutral zinc atoms.

that such imperfections, termed Frenkel defects (Fig. 11), are easier to form than Schottky defects. However, Koch and Wagner[37] and, more recently, Teltow[37] and Lawson and Kurnick[38] have provided overwhelming evidence to support this viewpoint. Prior to the work of Teltow and of Lawson and Kurnick, Mitchell[5] suggested that the older work of Jost and Nehlep and of Koch and Wagner might have been subject to error and that Schottky defects are prevalent in the silver salts. The newer work supports the older viewpoint substantially, although it does not eliminate the possibility that Schottky defects are present in large quantity. This work also makes it possible to determine the mobility of the vacancies in the silver salts.

[39] W. Jost, *Z. physik. Chem.*, **A169**, 129 (1934); W. Jost and G. Nehlep, *Z. physik. Chem.*, **B32**, 1 (1936).

Lawson[38] has pointed out that the very large density of lattice defects which are generated in the silver salts near the melting point have a measurable influence upon the thermal expansion of these crystals, and he has proposed a method whereby it may be possible to determine the density of imperfections in other materials.

Theoretical and experimental evidence suggests that vacant lattice sites are formed as a result of phonon interaction in many common metals and alloys,[40] although the evidence is not as conclusive as for the salts. Further investigation may show that there are metals in which interstitial atoms are more likely than vacancies.

Interstitial atoms may interact with one another to form stable clusters[41] which are the analogue of diatomic molecules, triatomic molecules, and, in more extreme cases, of colloids. Similarly, vacancies can combine to form clusters of vacancies which range from pair combinations to large voids in the lattice. Pairs of vacancies of opposite sign appear[42] to be very mobile in the alkali halide crystals (Fig. 12). It is also evident that an interstitial atom or ion can combine with the appropriate type of vacancy to annihilate both types of imperfection, the energy released appearing in the form of phonons.

Breckenridge[43] has pointed out that an associated pair of vacancies of opposite sign possesses a dipole moment, so that such pairs should contribute both to the dielectric constant and to the dielectric loss of the salt in the manner of a relaxation oscillator. The characteristic time associated with the oscillator should be the time required for one of the vacant sites to jump by one atomic position about the other. He has observed losses of this type in

[40] For discussion of present status of this issue, see: F. Seitz, *Acta Crystallographica*, **3**, 355 (1950); C. Zener, *ibid.*, **3**, 346 (1950); J. Bardeen, *Phys. Rev.*, **76**, 1403 (1949); F. Seitz, *ibid.*, **74**, 1513 (1948); H. B. Huntington and F. Seitz, *ibid.*, **61**, 315 (1942); H. B. Huntington, *ibid.*, **61**, 325 (1942). See also R. Smoluchowski and H. Burgess, *ibid.*, **76**, 309 (1949); H. R. Paneth, *Phys. Rev.*, **80**, 708 (1950).

[41] Concerning the formation of clusters in the uncolored alkali halides, see F. Seitz (footnote 4); in the silver halides, see footnote 5.

[42] J. G. Dienes, *J. Chem. Phys.*, **16**, 620 (1948); see also F. Seitz, footnote 4, and *Phys. Rev.*, **79**, 529 (1950).

[43] R. G. Breckenridge, *J. Chem. Phys.*, **16**, 959 (1948); additional work as yet unpublished.

the alkali halides which arise either from pairs or from positive-ion vacancies which are attached to divalent ions (see Section 6, page 71).

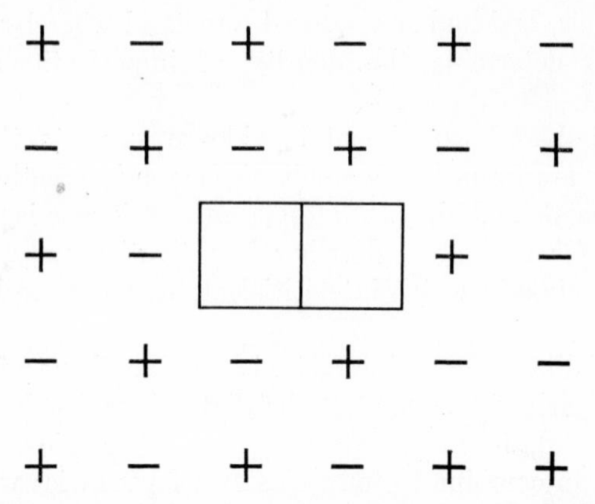

Fig. 12. A coupled pair of vacancies of opposite sign in the alkali halides. This unit is believed to have the ability to diffuse very rapidly. The coupling energy is about 0.9 ev. [J. R. Reitz and J. L. Gammel, *J. Chem. Phys.*, **19**, 894 (1951)].

(E) FOREIGN ATOMS

Foreign atoms may be introduced into an otherwise perfect crystal by a wide variety of methods, for example, as a chemical addition during formation of the crystal. The foreign atoms may occur either in interstitial sites or as a substitute for one or more of the normal atoms of the lattice. To illustrate, carbon and hydrogen may be introduced interstitially in iron and many other metals, whereas substitution is exceedingly common in many salts and in almost all metallic systems, in which it is responsible for the formation of substitutional alloys. Lack of space prevents us from describing in any detail the laws which govern such addition.

The foreign atoms may impart new properties to the solid. They may alter the number of free electrons in a metal or they may introduce new electronic levels in an insulator. Such levels may permit absorption of light in a previously transparent region of the spectrum. For example, the addition[44] of thallous chloride

[44] R. Hilsch, *Z. Physik*, **44**, 860 (1927); H. Lorenz, *ibid.*, **46**, 558 (1928); M. Forro, *ibid.*, **56**, 235, 534 (1949). A survey of the work of the Göttingen school on the alkali halides containing thallium is contained in the paper by

to the alkali halides produces new absorption bands, lying on the long wavelength side of the fundamental band (Fig. 13). The electrons responsible for these new absorption bands are associated with the thallous ion. Pure solids are often contaminated

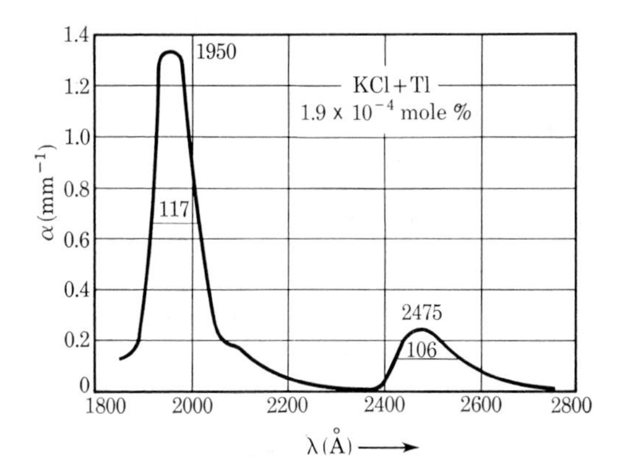

FIG. 13. Absorption bands introduced into the alkali halides by addition of TlCl. The pure crystal of KCl is transparent in the range between 1800 Å and 2800 Å in which the bands appear. It is believed that these bands are associated with excitation of the Tl^+ ion, which occurs substitutionally. (After Koch, footnote 44.)

intentionally to obtain additional characteristics. For example, the electrons or holes associated with the impurity may be freed much more easily than those of the pure material.[45] In such cases the material is transformed into an impurity semi-conductor if the electrons or holes are freed by phonons, or into an impurity photoconductor is they are freed by light quanta absorbed by the

F. Seitz, *J. Chem. Phys.*, **6**, 150 (1938). See also P. Pringsheim, *Revs. Modern Phys.*, **14**, 132 (1942); R. Hofstadter, *Phys. Rev.*, **74**, 100 (1948); *ibid*, .**75**, 796 (1949); F. Williams, *J. Chem. Phys.*, **19**, 457 (1951).

[45] See the books and reviews of footnote 1 for accounts of the influence of foreign atoms on metals and salts. Similarly the material in footnote 17 contains detailed accounts of the influence of foreign atoms in silicon and germanium. See also the many new books on luminescent materials, such as P. Pringsheim, *Fluorescence and Phosphorescence* (Interscience Publishers, New York, 1949); G. F. J. Garlick, *Luminescent Materials* (Oxford University Press, 1949); H. W. Leverenz, *An Introduction to the Luminescence of Solids* (John Wiley and Sons, New York, 1950); G. R. Fonda and F. Seitz, *Preparation and Characteristics of Solid Luminescent Materials* (Conference on Luminescence), (John Wiley and Sons, New York, 1948).

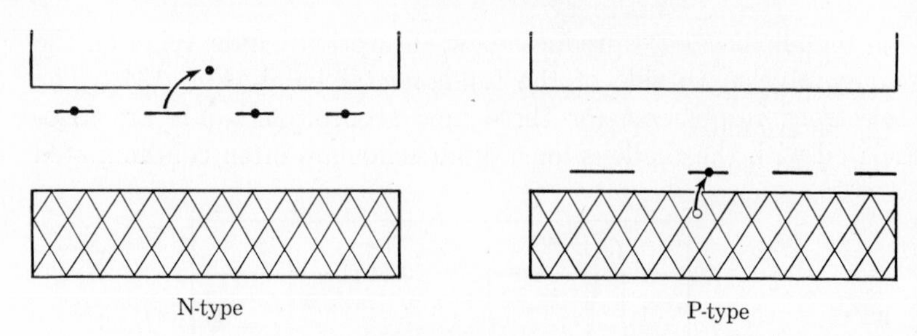

FIG. 14. The impurity may introduce new levels into the solid which may or may not have electrons associated with them. The additional levels are shown in two such cases as horizontal lines lying between the filled and empty bands of an insulator. In the first case the electrons which occupy the levels may evaporate, or be excited by other means, into the empty band, making the insulator an electron or N-type conductor. The levels are termed *donator* levels in this case. In the second case electrons may jump from the filled band to the empty levels and make the insulator a hole or P-type conductor. The levels are designated *acceptor levels* in this case.

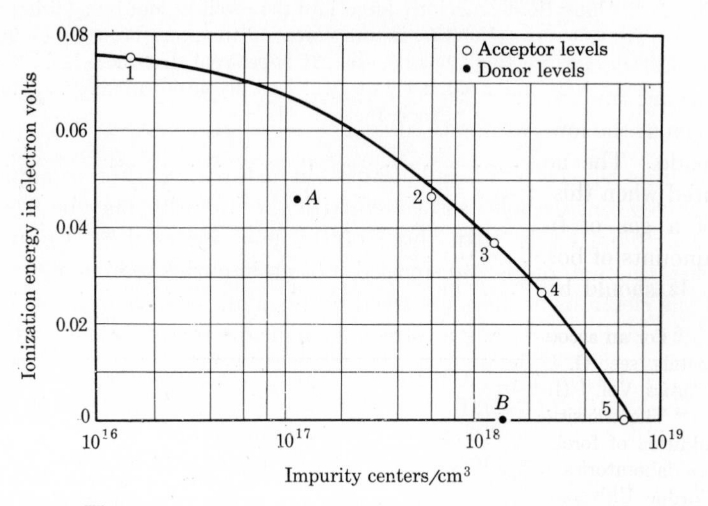

FIG. 15. The transformation from insulating to metallic character in silicon to which impurities have been added. The abscissa is the concentration of phosphorus (dark circles) and boron (open circles). The ordinate represents the energy required to free an electron from a phosphorus atom or to excite an electron from the filled band to the lowest unoccupied level of the boron atom. These energies decrease with increasing concentration and vanish when about one part in 10,000 of impurity is added, indicating the transformation of the material into a metal. (After Pearson and Bardeen, footnote 47.)

impurity or by the base material. Similarly, the impurity may emit characteristic light quanta when its electronic system returns to the ground state after excitation by any means. In this case the solid containing impurities becomes an impurity-sensitized luminescent material.

Foreign atoms sometimes interact with one another to produce clusters ranging in size from atomic dimensions to large aggregates both in metals[46] and in insulators. These may possess their own characteristic absorption spectra or other properties. A particularly interesting type of interaction has been discovered[47] in silicon and germanium. In the ideal, pure form these solids are insulators,[17] the gap between filled and empty bands being 1.1 ev and 0.79 ev, respectively. It is found that many foreign atoms may be introduced substitutionally in the materials. For example, phosphorus is soluble[48] in silicon to amounts of the order of 0.9 atomic per cent. The phosphorus atoms have extra electrons associated with them that occupy discrete levels lying slightly below the conduction band, as in the left-hand side of Fig. 14. When a sufficient density of phosphorus has been added to the crystal, namely, about 7.2 parts in 100,000, the additional electrons become free and the material is transformed into a metal (Fig. 15) even at the lowest temperatures at which measurements have been made. The additional atoms are essentially randomly distributed when this occurs. A similar effect, involving the production of a gas of free holes, has been observed[48] when comparable amounts of boron are added.

It should be added that Schulman[49] and his co-workers have

[46] For an account of the many interesting facts relating to precipitation in metals, see: G. C. Smith, "Age Hardening of Metals," *Progress in Metal Physics,* Vol. I (Interscience Publishers, New York, 1949).

[47] The transition to metallic characteristics in silicon and germanium on addition of foreign atoms was apparently discovered independently in several laboratories during the Second World War, namely the Bell Laboratories, Purdue University, and the University of Pennsylvania. However, G. L. Pearson and W. Shockley, *Phys. Rev.*, **71**, 142A (1947) and K. Lark-Horovitz and V. A. Johnson, *ibid.*, **69**, 258 (1946), appear to have been the first to appreciate the implications of the transition in any quantitative sense. See also the papers by G. L. Pearson and J. Bardeen, *ibid.*, **75**, 865 (1949); F. Seitz and G. Castellan, *Semi-Conducting Materials* (Butterworth Publishing Co., London, 1951), p. 8.

[48] G. L. Pearson and J. Bardeen (footnote 47).

[49] J. H. Schulman, *J. Appl. Phys.*, **17**, 902 (1946); J. H. Schulman, L. W.

observed a number of cases in which different impurities (such as manganese and lead in $CaSiO_3$) combine to form a "complex" which has combined optical absorption and luminescent properties neither would have alone. Systems of this type appear to be exceedingly common among the inorganic phosphors.

(F) DISLOCATIONS

The dislocation is the most complex of the primary imperfections and is probably least completely understood and appreciated at the present time. As mentioned in Section 1, the present knowledge of its properties has been evolved as a result of almost continuous investigation[3] for a period of more than twenty years, and a large number of individuals have contributed.

It is probably worth emphasizing at this point that the dislocation was introduced to explain[3] the ease with which crystals may be deformed plastically. However, convincing evidence has accumulated to show that this is only one of its important properties. For it seems to play a central role in catalyzing processes ranging from crystal growth to the production of color centers in the alkali halides.

Perhaps the most unique characteristic of the dislocation is that it probably is not an equilibrium imperfection and is not formed as an equilibrium product at temperatures appreciably below the melting point, although it may be formed in what approaches an equilibrium manner near the melting point. Frank[50] has pointed out that dislocations catalyze crystal growth so that an otherwise perfect crystal containing dislocations should grow far faster than one which does not. In fact, Frank's analysis shows that the presence of dislocations is almost a necessity for growth of crystals by vapor deposition or from solution in periods of time of everyday or even of geological interest. Hence crystals may grow until at least one dislocation is generated "accidentally" if equilibrium means are not available. We may conclude that at least a fraction

---

Evans, R. J. Ginther, and K. J. Murata, *ibid.*, **18**, 732 (1947); J. B. Merrill and J. H. Schulman, *J. Opt. Soc. Am.*, **38, 471** (1948).

[50] F. C. Frank, *Discussion of the Faraday Society*, No. 5, p. 48 (1949); also forthcoming paper in *Phil. Mag.* (special issue, January, 1952). The writer is indebted to Dr. Frank for a number of stimulating discussions of this topic.

of the dislocations in a crystal are generated during growth and play an important role in such growth—a viewpoint which has received rather dramatic confirmation in the case of natural specimens of beryl, as a result of Griffin's microscopic[51] observations of stepped imperfections on the prism faces of this mineral. Actually most crystals which are grown relatively rapidly from the melt seem to have far more dislocations than are needed to catalyze growth. This appears to indicate[52] that most of the dislocations are formed either because the "accidents" which produce them are far more frequent than is necessary for crystal growth, or as a result of the condensation of vacant lattice sites or interstitial atoms as the specimen is cooled below the melting point. The geometrical relationships between dislocations, vacancies, and interstitial atoms will be discussed further below.

The most general dislocation required to explain[53] phenomena which have been investigated to the present time appears to be that shown schematically in Fig. 16. For purposes of geometric visualization, imagine that the crystal has been cut over a surface S which is bounded by a closed curve C. The curve may intersect the surface in special cases.

Next imagine that the portion of the crystal on one side of the cut is displaced by a vector distance $\mathbf{d}$ relative to that on the other side, $\mathbf{d}$ being the same over the entire surface, and a hypothetical external force being applied to produce the displacement. In practical cases $\mathbf{d}$ is a prominent interatomic distance. Unless the surface S is plane and parallel to $\mathbf{d}$, the relative displacement of the material on each side of the cut either produces a gap or causes the two sides to overlap. In the first case, imagine that one or more atomic layers are added to make the material continuous; in the second, imagine that the overlapping material has

[51] L. J. Griffin, *Phil. Mag.*, **41**, 196 (1950).

[52] F. Seitz, *Phys. Rev.*, **79**, 723, 890, 1002, 1003 (1950); see also special issue of *Phil. Mag.* (January, 1952).

[53] The formation of the general dislocation ring was probably first described by J. M. Burgers (footnote 3). See also the Paper 13, by W. T. Read and W. Shockley, in this book, and by the writer in *Carnegie Institute of Technology Symposium on the Plastic Deformation of Crystalline Solids* (Office of Naval Research, 1950), as well as papers in *Report of a Conference on the Strength of Solids, University of Bristol, England* (Physical Society, London, 1948). See also the paper by F. C. Frank, *Phil. Mag.*, **43**, 809 (1951).

been removed to produce continuity. Then rejoin the crystal and relieve the forces which produced the displacement. The end result is a *general dislocation ring.*

If the vector **d**, which is commonly called the *Burgers vector*, corresponds to the edge of a unit cell of the crystal, the lattice is

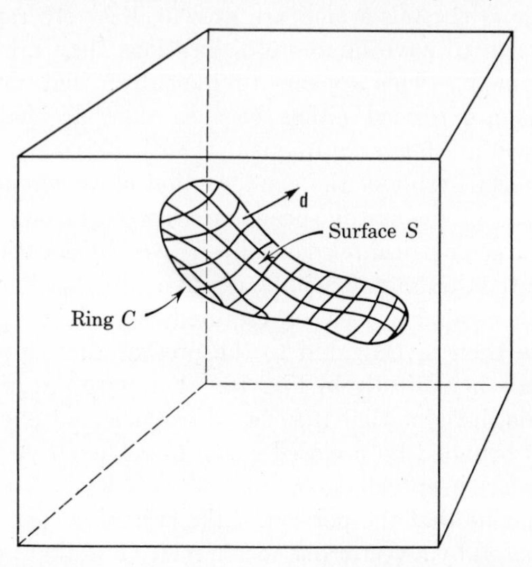

FIG. 16. The general dislocation ring. For purposes of geometrical visualization, imagine that the material is cut over the surface S within the solid. S is bounded by the curve or ring C, which may intersect the surface. The material on one side of the cut is displaced relative to the other by the vector distance **d** (*Burgers vector*) with application of force. The displacement is the same over all of S. Material is added or subtracted until the medium is continuous, and the forces causing the displacement **d** are then relaxed. The result is a dislocation ring. The crystal is in registry everywhere except near C if the material added or subtracted represents layers of unit cells. Otherwise it is in disregistry at regions where the fractional cells are added or subtracted.

in register over all the surface S, except at the region near the boundary curve C, where there is appreciable disregistry and residual strain. If **d** does not correspond to the edge of a unit cell, that is, to a translation vector which sends each atom in the unit cell to an equivalent one in a neighboring cell, the lattice is in disregistry[54] over the entire surface S. While both types of disloca-

[54] Dislocations which produce disregistry over a surface have been discussed by T. A. Read and the writer, *J. Appl. Phys.*, **12**, 470 (1941);

tion ring probably occur in practice, the first one, which is geometrically the simpler, appears to possess all the basic properties needed to explain phenomena which have been investigated thus far. For this reason, we shall focus most of our attention on it, and will recognize that the more complex type exists and may prove to be an indispensable adjunct of the field of crystal imperfections. Since the imperfection is localized near the curve C, this type of dislocation can be regarded as a linear imperfection which forms either a closed loop within the lattice or one that terminates at the surface. The curve C is usually called the *dislocation line* or *ring*.

It is perhaps worth noting that a generalized dislocation ring can be formed by having vacant lattice sites or interstitial atoms condense so as to cover uniformly the surface S, shown in Fig. 16. The vector **d** associated with a general dislocation ring formed in this way will evidently have opposite signs in the two cases. It is possible that this is a very important means by which dislocation rings are generated in practice, for example, during cooling of a melt in which there is a high density of vacancies or interstitial atoms. We saw previously[37] that crystals such as the silver halides may contain as high as one or more per cent of vacant lattice sites near the melting point. These will either condense at existing dislocations or will form new dislocations by condensing in the form of plates[52] or spirals, which are equivalent to dislocations. It should be added that only dislocation rings which have a nonvanishing projection on a plane normal to the Burgers vector can be formed by condensation of vacancies or interstitial atoms. A closed ring which lies entirely in a plane parallel to the Burgers vector cannot be formed in this way.

The first dislocations to be used were not as complex as that shown in Fig. 16, but were special cases of this. Figure 17 shows two important special cases of this type. The first, which is known as a *Taylor-Orowan* or *edge* dislocation, has historical precedence. The second was introduced in 1939 by Burgers as part of a general formulation of dislocation theory from which most of the formal theory has grown. The surface S shown in Fig. 16 can be chosen parallel to the Burgers vector **d** in both cases, and it

---

R. D. Heidenreich and W. Shockley, *Report of a Conference on the Strength of Solids*, p. 57; F. C. Frank, *Proc. Phys. Soc. (London)*, **62**, 202 (1949); A. H. Cottrell and B. A. Bilby, *Phil. Mag.*, **42**, 573 (1951).

extends as a cut through the crystal to a straight bounding line which terminates at opposite surfaces of the crystal. This line is normal to **d** in the first case, whereas it is parallel in the second. In both cases **d** corresponds to an edge of a unit cell so that the plane containing S is an important crystallographic plane, usually called the *slip plane*, for reasons relevant to the theory of plastic flow.

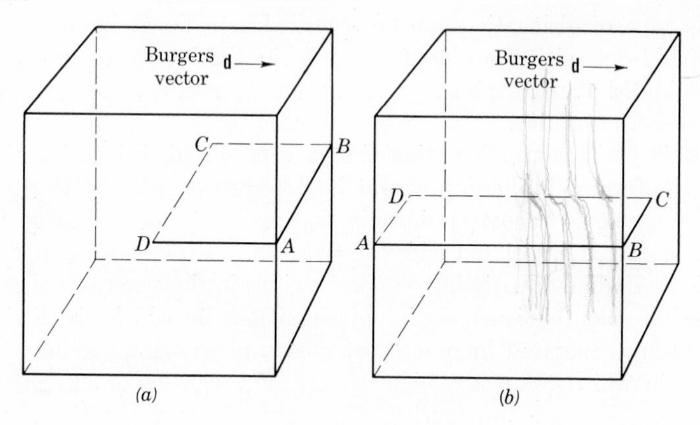

FIG. 17. Two important, simple types of dislocation. (*a*) is the Taylor-Orowan or edge dislocation. The surface S shown in Fig. 16 is a plane, parallel to the Burgers vector **d**, which extends from the line AB at the right-hand side of the block to the line CD midway through the block and *normal* to **d**. (*b*) is the Burgers or screw dislocation. In this case the plane $ABCD$ is also parallel to **d**; however, the interior bounding line CD is also parallel to **d**. Since all sides of the bounding surface $ABCD$, except CD, terminate at the surface in these cases, it is easy to see that the resultant strain is the same in either of the two cases if the side CD is kept fixed and the other three sides are arbitrarily distorted over the outer surface of the block, *provided* **d** *is an allowed translation of the lattice.* The plane parallel to **d** which contains CD is the *slip plane*.

It may be seen that for a given orientation of the lattice, the **d** vector can have either sign for a given magnitude. The strain pattern reverses its sign with reversal of the sign of **d**. Dislocations of a given type for which the **d** vector has the same sign are said to be of *like sign;* those for which it is opposite are said to be of *opposite sign.* Figure 18 shows the strain produced in the lattice along the dislocation line of a Taylor-Orowan dislocation. The diagram represents a cut normal to the line. It can be seen that the lattice is under compression above the slip plane and under tension below it. It is very useful to note that the same strain pattern can be produced by adding an extra half plane to the upper part of the lattice in a direction normal to the slip plane. The extra plane terminates at the dislocation line. Instead, a

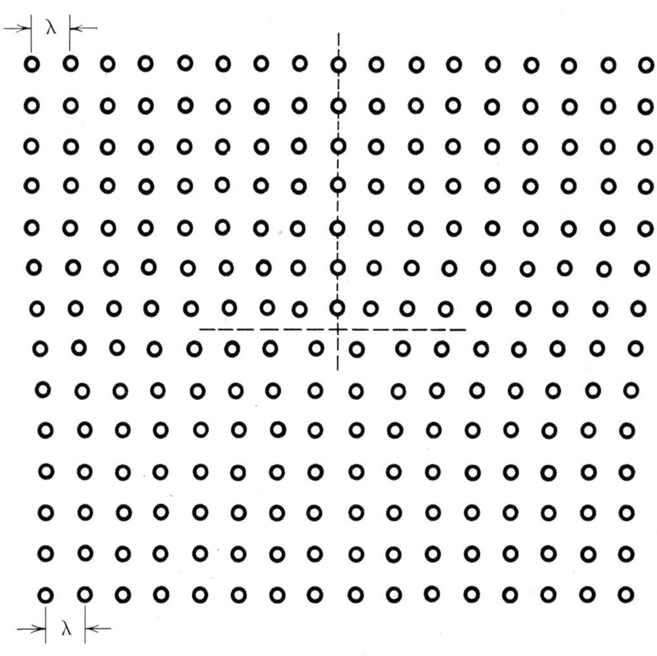

FIG. 18. The disregistry in the vicinity of a Taylor-Orowan, or edge, dislocation line. This figure represents a cut normal to the line CD in Fig. 17a, the horizontal line being parallel to DA. λ is the cell edge, equal in magnitude to **d**. It may be seen that the lattice is under compression above the slip plane and under tension below it. The dislocation can be regarded as formed by adding the vertical dotted half plane, or by subtracting the corresponding half plane in the lower half of the crystal.

half plane could be removed from the lower half of the crystal in such a way that the edge of the removed plane coincides with the dislocation line. These modes of formation correspond to alternate choices of the three edges of the plane $ABCD$ in Fig. 17a which intersect the surface of the crystal.

Figure 19, which is due to Taylor,[3] shows that the motion of a Taylor-Orowan dislocation line across the slip plane produces a shear displacement of amount **d** of the part of the crystal above the slip plane relative to that beneath it. The same result can be produced by moving a dislocation of opposite sign in the opposite direction. It is this ability of the dislocation to produce shear displacement as the result of motion that led to its introduction into the theory of plastic flow—a property which has given it an indispensable position.

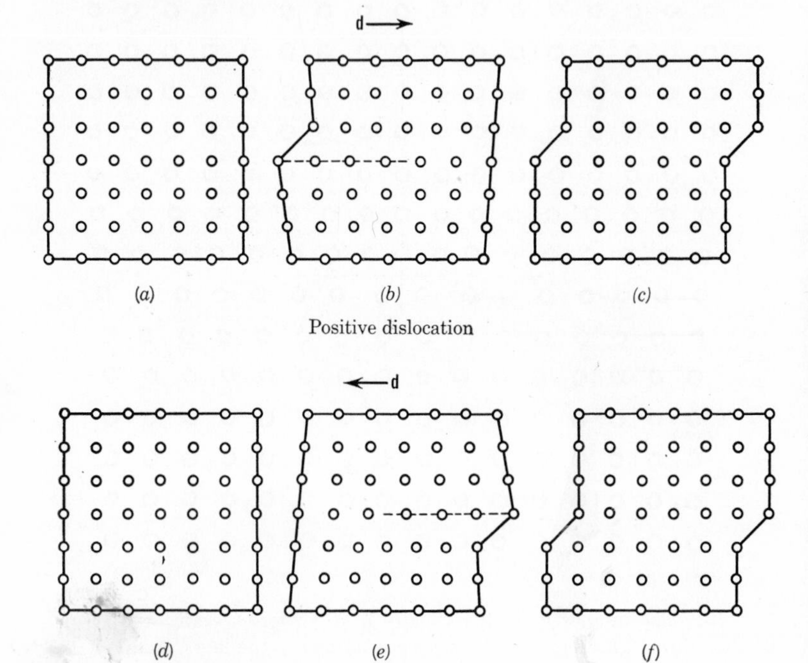

FIG. 19. Schematic diagram showing the manner in which the motion of a Taylor-Orowan dislocation across the slip plane can produce one unit of shear displacement. In the upper sequence the dislocation shown in Fig. 18 is generated on the left and moves across to the right. In the lower sequence a dislocation of opposite sign (reversed sign of the Burgers vector) moves in the reverse direction to produce the same final result. (After Taylor, footnote 3.)

Figure 20 shows the relative positions of rows of atoms above and below the slip plane near a *Burgers* or *screw* dislocation. It is readily seen that motion of a dislocation of this type may also produce shear displacement. In this case the displacement, which is always in the direction of **d**, is normal to the direction of motion of the dislocation line.

If the dislocation ring shown in Fig. 17 lies in the slip plane (Fig. 21), the strain pattern is like that near a Taylor-Orowan dislocation at regions where the ring is normal to **d** and is like that near a Burgers dislocation in regions parallel to **d** (Fig. 22). The strain character is of mixed type at intervening sections of the ring. If a ring of this type starts as a very small loop and

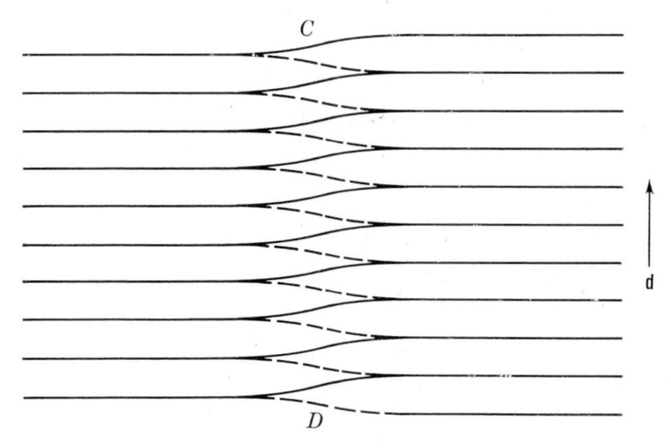

FIG. 20. The relative position of rows of atoms just above and below the slip plane along a Burgers or screw dislocation (Fig. 17*b*). The vertical distance *CD* corresponds to *CD* in Fig. 17*b*. The full line represents rows of atoms above the slip planes whereas the dotted lines, which run into the full lines in regions of registry, represent rows beneath the slip plane. Motion of *CD* perpendicular to itself produces a shear displacement of the upper part of the crystal relative to the lower by the Burgers distance, much as in Fig. 19.

expands to the boundary of the crystal, it produces a shear displacement of the upper part of the crystal relative to the lower along the slip plane, just as the passage of a Taylor-Orowan or a Burgers dislocation does. Thus the ring dislocation lying in the slip plane represents a valuable generalization of the more primitive straight-line dislocations. On the other hand, the dislocation ring shown in Fig. 17, which does not lie in the slip plane, is an even more general imperfection.

Space does not permit us to dwell on the properties of dislocations in complete detail,[3] so we shall be content with the following summary of them.

(1) Calculations show that a ring dislocation lying in the slip plane can be made to expand. Therefore, both a Taylor-Orowan

and a Burgers dislocation line can be made to move parallel to themselves, by very low stresses,[55] probably below 10^5 dynes per cm^2, in an otherwise perfect crystal. Consequently dislocations of this type render a crystal very plastic.

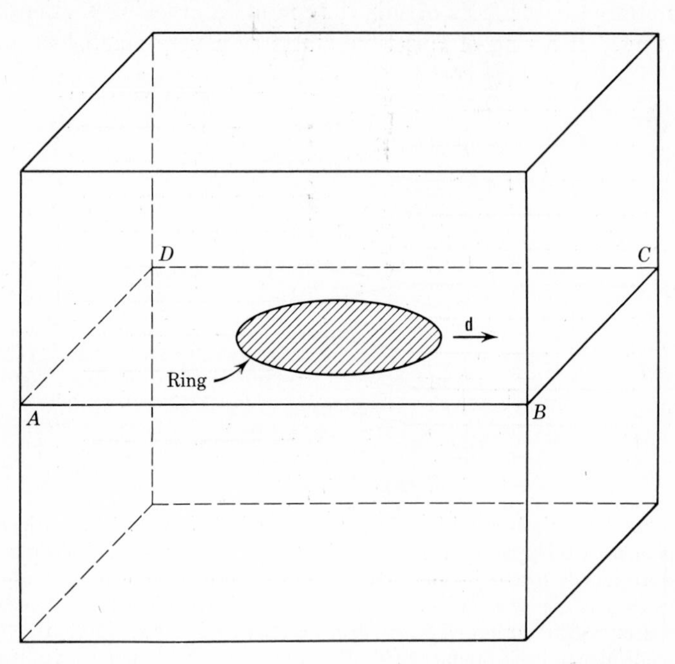

FIG. 21. A dislocation ring, similar to that shown in Fig. 17, but lying in a slip plane, that is, a plane parallel to the Burgers vector. Material does not need to be added or subtracted to the lattice to form this dislocation ring.

(2) The process of plastic flow increases the total length of the dislocation lines in a crystal as a result of the expansion of rings. It is customary to describe the total length of a dislocation line by giving the number of times dislocation lines intersect a unit area in the crystal. This is 10^8 or less per cm^2 in good natural crystals, is near 10^9 per cm^2 in good artificial crystals, and is as

[55] The initial calculations were made by R. Peierls, *Proc. Phys. Soc.* (*London*), **52**, 34 (1939); F. R. N. Nabarro, *ibid.*, **59**, 256 (1947). See also the private communication of W. Shockley referred to in the paper by N. F. Mott and F. R. N. Nabarro, *Report of a Conference on the Strength of Solids*, p. 1; and the paper by the writer, *Carnegie Institute of Technology Symposium on the Plastic Deformation of Crystalline Solids*, Section 4, paragraph *d*.

large as 10^{12} per cm^2 in cold-worked material. In the last case one atom per thousand is near the center of a dislocation line.

(3) A dislocation ring of the type shown in Fig. 17, which does not lie in the slip plane, may move relatively freely[56] in a direction

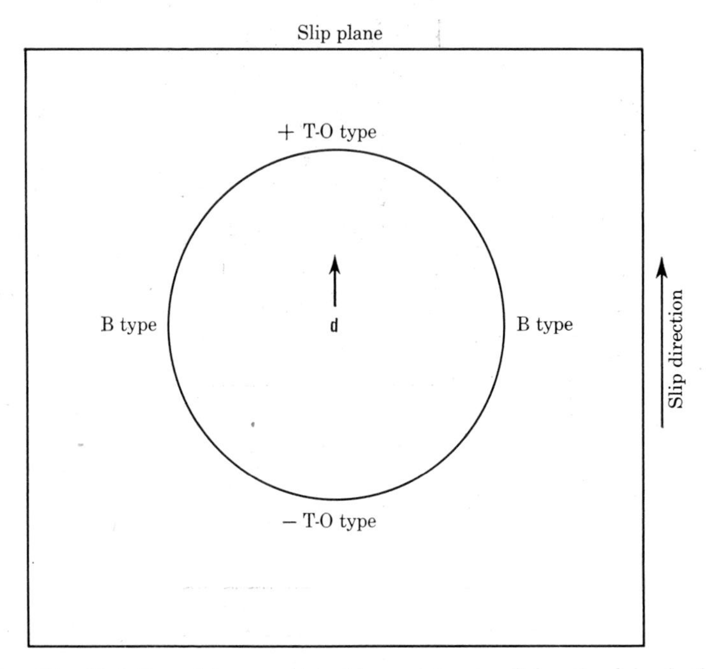

FIG. 22. Variation of the geometrical form of the ring dislocation lying in the slip plane (Fig. 21). The Taylor-Orowan character in regions where the ring is normal to **d** and the Burgers character in regions where the ring is parallel to **d**. The character is mixed in intervening regions. The signs associated with the Taylor-Orowan character are opposite at the upper and lower portions of the ring. If a ring of this type expands or contracts in a direction normal to its perimeter, the portion of the crystal above the slip plane is displaced relative to that below.

parallel to the Burgers vector **d**, that is, on a cylinder generated by passing lines through C parallel to **d** (Fig. 23). Such motion produces a shear displacement of the material inside the cylinder relative to that outside—a form of idealized plastic flow which can

[56] This property of the general dislocation ring was pointed out independently by the writer in a paper in *Carnegie Institute of Technology Symposium on the Plastic Deformation of Crystalline Solids* and by W. Shockley and W. T. Read, Paper 2 of this book.

be observed in punching experiments. The generalized dislocation ring alters its projected area in a plane normal to the cylinder, that is, normal to the Burgers vector, only if material is redistrib-

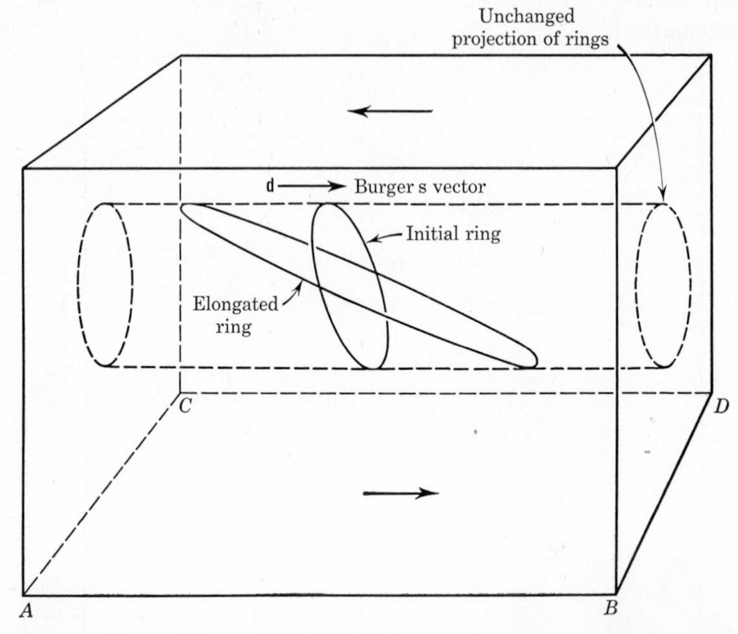

Fig. 23. A general dislocation ring may move freely over the surface of a cylinder formed by passing elements parallel to **d** through it. Such motion does not require redistribution of material by diffusion. For example, the ring may become greatly elongated, as shown, if the crystal is stressed. The material inside the cylinder is displaced relative to that outside if the ring moves along the ring, parallel to itself. This type of motion probably occurs in punching experiments.

uted, for example, by diffusion of atoms. This limitation may be seen from the fact that it is necessary to add or remove material from the crystal in forming the ring not lying in the slip plane.

(4) In addition to displacement and expansion, the general dislocation ring may generate entirely new rings in the slip plane. This process was first pointed out by Frank and Read.[57] It probably accounts for the fact that, at least during the early stages of plastic flow, the strain displacement is localized to rela-

[57] F. C. Frank and W. T. Read, *Phys. Rev.*, **79**, 722 (1950).

tively few atomic planes at which total strains that may be as large as 2000 times **d** are observed.[58] Such planes produce observable discontinuities on the surface of a single crystal known as slip bands. One form of the multiplication process is shown schematically in Fig. 24. Here a portion of a general ring lies

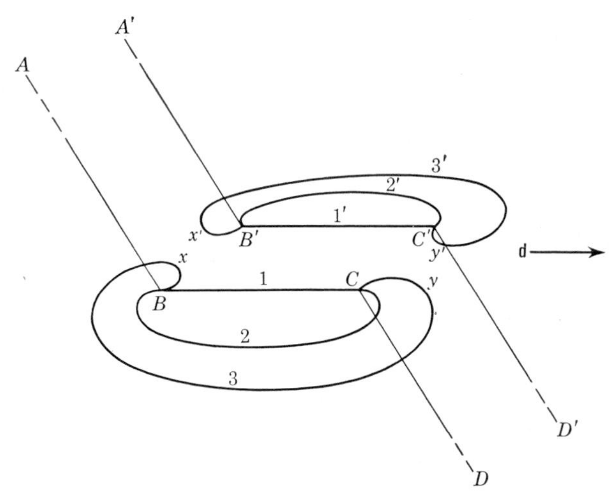

FIG. 24. Schematic diagram showing generation of a dislocation ring by the method of Frank and Read. *ABCD* and *A'B'C'D'* represent portions of a general dislocation ring, the lengths *BD* and *B'C'* lying in the slip plane. The lengths *BC* and *B'C'* may expand through the sequence $1 \rightarrow 2 \rightarrow 3$ and $1' \rightarrow 2' \rightarrow 3'$. Eventually points such as x and x' will meet, as will y and y'. A complete ring may then break off. The original ring will be joined from *A* to *A'* and *B* to *B'*. However, these segments may expand further and join to regenerate the original segments *BC* and *B'C'*, so that the end result is the original ring and a complete ring lying in the slip plane.

in the slip plane and joins two portions which run obliquely. The portion in the slip plane may expand, fold back on itself, and produce both a ring and the original segment.

(5) If a dislocation ring intersects the surface, being cut at two points, there usually is a step on the surface joining the two points of intersection.[50] The height of the step is equal to the projection of **d** normal to the surface, so that the step will be absent only if **d** is parallel to the surface. Figure 25 shows a typical step of the kind which forms the basis for Frank's theory of crystal growth.

[58] R. D. Heindenreich and W. Shockley (footnote 54); A. F. Brown, *Nature*, **163**, 961 (1949).

(6) When a dislocation is made to move, as during the process of plastic flow, heat is generated.[59] This indicates that the motion of a dislocation is able to engender phonons. Experiments show that over 90 per cent of the energy expended in producing extensive plastic flow reappears in the form of phonons so that the

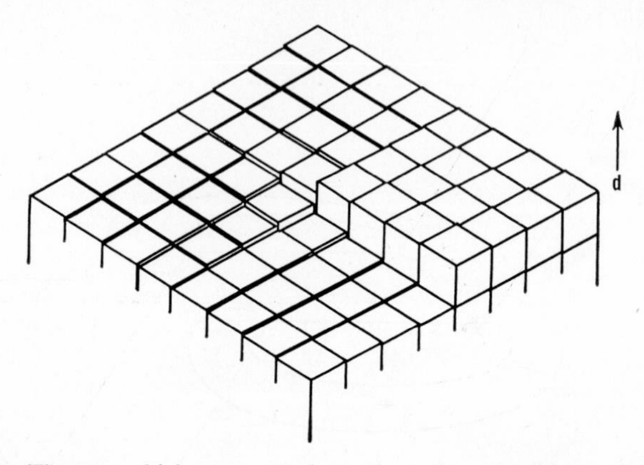

FIG. 25. The step which occurs at the surface of a crystal in a region where a screw dislocation, or a dislocation having some screw character, terminates. This step usually joins the two terminal points of a ring dislocation which cut the surface. The magnitude of the step is equal to the projection of the Burgers vector associated with the ring on the normal to the crystallographic surface. (After Frank, footnote 50.)

conversion process is efficient. There is in 1951 no accurate information on the temperatures produced near the center of a dislocation line when a dislocation moves. However, it seems likely[60] that the dissipation is sufficiently rapid that the dislocation does not achieve a velocity in excess of a few per cent of that of sound in a normal part of the lattice. This dissipation is presumably responsible for internal friction[61] in single crystals.

[59] G. I. Taylor and H. Quinney, *Proc. Roy. Soc.* (*London*), **143**, 307 (1934); **163**, 157 (1937).

[60] G. Leibfried, *Z. Physik*, **127**, 344 (1949); F. Seitz, *Carnegie Institute of Technology Symposium on the Plastic Deformation of Crystalline Solids*; also forthcoming paper in *Phil. Mag.* (special issue, January, 1952).

[61] T. A. Read, *Phys. Rev.*, **58**, 371 (1940); *Trans. AIME*, **143**, 30 (1941); J. Marx and J. S. Koehler, *Carnegie Institute of Technology on the Plastic Deformation of Crystalline Solids;* A. S. Nowick, *Phys. Rev.*, **79** (1950) and also in *Carnegie Institute of Technology on the Plastic Deformation of Crystalline Solids;* J. D. Eshelby, *Proc. Roy. Soc.* (*London*), **197**, 396 (1949).

(7) Dislocation rings interact with one another. This may be seen from the fact that each dislocation is surrounded by a stress-strain field so that the elastic energy of the solid is influenced both by the presence of dislocations and by their proximity to one another. Simple straight-line dislocations of the Taylor-Orowan or Burgers type have relatively simple interactions, dislocations of like sign repelling and those of unlike sign attracting one another in a manner somewhat reminiscent of charged rods, the interaction energy varying inversely as the first power of the distance of separation. If two dislocations of opposite sign moving in opposite directions in the same plane meet, they may annihilate one another with a relatively large release of energy that has been estimated[62] to be of the order of 1 ev per atomic length along the line. This process should produce phonons in densities corresponding to local temperatures of at least 1000°C for times of the order of 10^{-12} sec.

(8) Dislocations may generate vacant lattice sites, and presumably interstitial atoms or ions, as a natural part of their motion. This generation is demonstrated very dramatically by observations of Gyulai[63] on the increase in electrolytic conductivity of sodium chloride during plastic flow. It is found (Fig. 26) that even relatively moderate plastic flow produces a rise in electrolytic conductivity which has been estimated to correspond to the generation of about 10^{18} vacancies per cc. These are produced[64] either as the result of high local temperatures during motion of single dislocation lines, or as the result of the interaction and perhaps partial annihilation of pairs of dislocations. We have seen that a Taylor-Orowan dislocation may be regarded as though produced by the addition of an extra plane of atoms in a direction normal to the slip plane and terminating at the dislocation line (Fig. 18). The additional planes are on opposite sides of the slip planes for dislocations of opposite sign. Thus if two Taylor-Orowan dislocations of opposite sign moving in slip planes which

[62] F. Seitz and T. A. Read, *J. Appl. Phys.* (footnote 3).

[63] Z. Gyulai and D. Hartly, *Z. Physik*, **51**, 378 (1928); Z. Gyulai, *ibid.*, **78**, 630 (1932); A. W. Stepanow, *ibid.*, **81**, 560 (1933). See also the correlating articles by the writer, *Phys. Rev.*, **80**, II, 239 (1950), *Phil Mag.* (special issue, January, 1952).

[64] F. R. N. Nabarro, *Report of a Conference on the Strength of Solids*, p. 75, was the first investigator to make explicit use of the fact that Taylor-Orowan dislocations may act as sources or sinks of vacancies.

are separated by one atomic distance chance to meet, they will recombine, leaving either an extra row of interstitial atoms or a row of vacant sites, depending upon whether the extra planes overlap or are separated by one atomic distance. The interstitial atoms or vacancies should disperse as a result of the high local

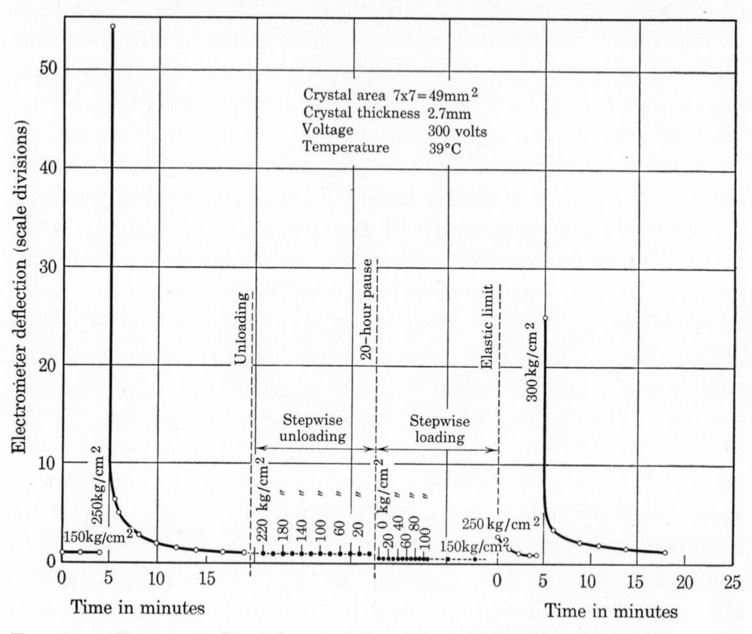

FIG. 26. Current pulses observed in rock salt during plastic flow. The specimen was loaded after the potential had been applied for 5 minutes. A current surge, which dropped continuously in the course of 20 minutes, was observed. A new surge could be generated only by loading again above the elastic limit. (After Gyulai and Hartly, footnote 63.)

temperatures and, in the case of a salt, contribute to the electrolytic conductivity and to any other effects influenced by vacancies or interstitial atoms.

The electrolytic conductivity generated in the alkali halides by plastic flow decreases in about 20 min at room temperature (Fig. 26). Apparently the vacancies combine with one another to form immobile aggregates having a relatively low "vapor pressure" of single vacancies.

It is reasonable to expect dislocations to generate vacancies and interstitial atoms in metals if they may do so in salts, although the method of detecting the presence of such imperfections should not be as easy as in salts. It is possible that studies of the changes in density of solids during cold work will throw light on this matter since the vacancies and interstitial atoms should have the effect of decreasing and increasing the density, respectively, and should give a net contribution, unless by chance their effects accidentally compensate. It should be possible to distinguish this contribution to the density change from that associated with the dislocations, for the vacancies and interstitial atoms probably can be removed by annealing at temperatures below those at which the dislocations are affected appreciably. The evidence concerning the generation of vacancies in metals by moving dislocations is discussed in a paper by the writer in a special (January, 1952) issue of *The Philosophical Magazine*. This evidence is not yet so convincing as that for salts, but is in the main parallel.

(9) Since dislocations possess a strain field which extends to large distances, they may produce disregistry which extends over comparable distances. Heidenreich and Shockley[58] pointed out that the size of the coherent domain responsible for the normal x-ray diffraction pattern can be no larger than the average volume which is free of dislocation lines. Figure 27 shows that a row of Taylor-Orowan dislocations[65] is the equivalent of a wedge of material, producing relative tilting of the portions of the crystals on either side of the row. This is a special case of the development of mosaic structure as a result of the aggregation of dislocations. Apparently grain boundaries can be represented in this way only when the disorientation is a few degrees or less. A general grain boundary is far more complex.

(10) The writer[52] has suggested that screw dislocations which have a Taylor-Orowan component at some region of the lattice, as a result of local curving or bending, may act as sources or sinks for an unlimited number of vacancies or interstitial atoms. When the screw dislocations act as such a source or sink, a new type of dislocation may be generated. This dislocation, called a spiral prismatic dislocation, lies on a double cone formed by abutting

[65] The properties of rows of dislocations of this type have been studied by several investigators: G. I. Taylor (footnote 3); J. S. Koehler, *Am. J. Phys.* (footnote 3); *J. Appl. Mech.* (footnote 3); W. T. Read and W. Shockley *Phys. Rev.*, **76**, 275 (1950); also papers by A. H. Cottrell and F. C. Frank in *Carnegie Institute of Technology Symposium on the Plastic Deformation of Crystalline Solids*.

the bases of two cones whose axes are parallel to the original screw dislocation. The properties of such spiral dislocations have not yet been investigated in any degree of completeness. When

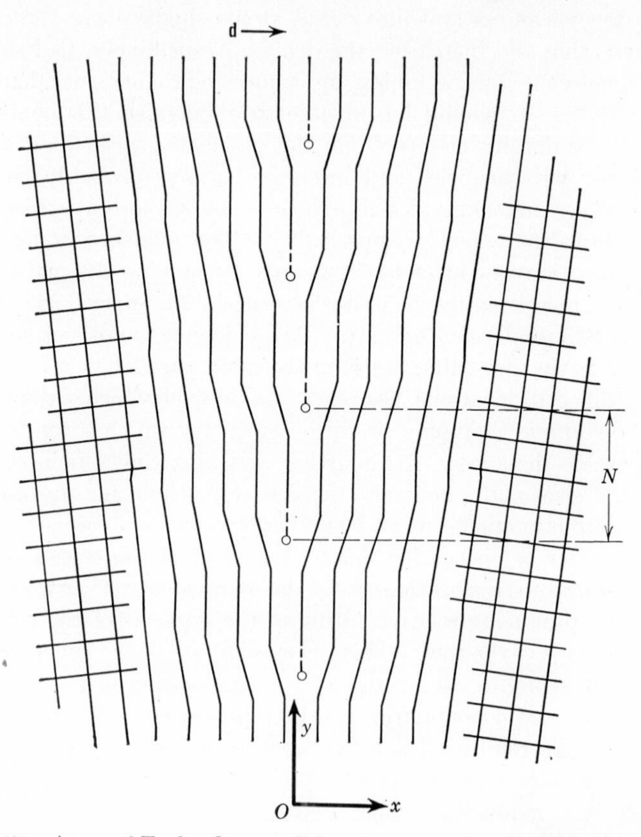

FIG. 27. A row of Taylor-Orowan dislocations extending through the crystal form a mosaic boundary, equivalent to a wedge of added material. The portions of the crystal on either side of the wedge are tilted relative to one another as a result of the row of dislocations, the angle of tilt being of the order $1/N$, where N is the number of atomic distances between neighboring dislocations. (After Burgers, footnote 3.)

formed by the condensation of vacancies, during the cooling of a specimen from the melting point, they may provide voids which are the source of the low rupture strength of well-made crystals.

(11) If a dislocation having some Taylor-Orowan or edge character jogs from one slip plane to another, the region where the

jog occurs has very special properties. For example, it is the place at which a vacancy may disappear with the largest gain in energy, or is the most natural place for generating vacancies by thermal means in a single crystal. The writer has referred[63] to such jogs as the site of "*incipient" vacancies.* Such incipient vacancies have many remarkable properties. For example, they have an effective coulomb field of one-half the electronic charge in a monovalent ionic crystal such as the alkali or silver halides. The writer[35] has proposed that incipient vacancies play an important role in the darkening of single crystals of the silver halides when exposed to light, since they provide natural trapping places for the free electrons and holes generated in these crystals by photons. Elementary reasoning suggests that the density of incipient vacancies should be greatly increased by plastic flow since such flow both generates new dislocations and sets old ones in motion, so that the number of jogs should be increased. This is in general agreement with the observation that the photographic sensitivity of crystals is enhanced by plastic flow.

5. INFLUENCE OF TRANSIENT AND IMPERFECTIONS IN A PERFECT CRYSTAL

Transient imperfections may be introduced either from outside, with use of proper sources, or within the crystal if the crystal is in an excited electronic or nuclear state. Briefly, the properties of these imperfections are as follows.

(G) LIGHT QUANTA

Light quanta of appropriate wavelength may, as we have seen, generate phonons, excitons, or free electrons and holes. The free electrons and holes produced in this way render insulating crystals conducting and make it possible to employ such crystals as ionization counters.[66] This property is valid for other radiations, discussed below, as well. X-rays and gamma rays may generate very fast electrons by the photoelectric process or the Compton process. Gamma rays having energy in excess of 1 Mev may generate both electrons and positrons. In such cases the influence of x-rays and gamma rays is much the same as that of

[66] See, for example, the review by R. J. Hofstadter, *Nucleonics*, **4** (No. 4), p. 2, (No. 5), p. 29 (1949). Also the papers by K. G. McKay, *Phys. Rev.*, **74**, 1006 (1948); **77**, 816 (1950).

cathode rays or beta rays. Gamma rays may also excite nuclei and produce other secondary radiations.

One of the most interesting types of interaction between x-rays and the perfect lattice is that which causes the radiation to be scattered, either elastically or inelastically, by the lattice array. This process is the basis for x-ray diffraction studies,[67] which have yielded such a rich harvest of information concerning the positions of atoms in the lattice and related material, such as the size of coherent domains.

If we desired to expand our synthesis to include the phenomenon of nuclear resonance of crystals[68] in the megacycle and microwave region of the radio spectrum, this topic could be introduced at this point as a natural part of the structure.

(H) CHARGED RADIATIONS

Charged particles which enter the crystal with considerable kinetic energy will dissipate this energy, principally by exciting the electronic system.[69] Thus the main effect is to excite both the free and the inner shell electrons in metals, and to produce excitons and free electrons in insulators. The two types of excitation are roughly equal in insulators. For comparable kinetic energy, a massive charged particle, such as an alpha particle, moves much more slowly than an electron. For example, a 4-Mev alpha particle moves at approximately the same speed as a 500-ev electron. As a result of this fact, a massive ion can transfer[70] a significant fraction of its energy to the vibra-

[67] For accounts of work of this type, see the following books: C. S. Barrett, *Structure of Metals* (McGraw-Hill Book Co., New York, 1943); W. H. Zachariasen, *Theory of X-Ray Diffraction in Crystals* (John Wiley and Sons, 1944); R. W. James, *The Optical Principles of the Diffraction of X-Rays* (Bell and Sons, London, 1949). Also recent papers by B. E. Warren and B. L. Averbach, *J. Appl. Phys.*, **20**, 1066 (1949); **21**, (1950). See also *Carnegie Institute of Technology Symposium on the Plastic Deformation of Crystalline Solids.*

[68] See, for example, N. Bloembergen, *Physica*, **15**, 386 (1949); N. Bloembergen, E. M. Purcell, and R. V. Pound, *Phys. Rev.*, **73**, 679 (1948); J. H. Van Vleck, *ibid.*, **74**, 1169 (1948).

[69] See, for example, the book by N. F. Mott and H. S. W. Massey, *Theory of Atomic Collisions* (Oxford University Press, London, 1934).

[70] This topic is surveyed in the paper by the writer, *Discussions of Faraday Society*, (No. 5), 271 (1949). See also M. Burton, *J. Phys. Chem.*, **51**, 611 (1947). K. Lark-Horovitz, *Semi-Conducting Materials* (footnote 47).

tional system of the lattice, producing phonons. This fraction is of the order of 0.1 per cent for a fast ion having several Mev of energy, but it increases as the velocity decreases and becomes comparable to or greater than the energy lost in exciting the electronic system when the energy of the massive particle decreases to the kilovolt range. The density of phonons along the track of a massive particle is sufficiently large[71] that the temperature becomes very high in a tube surrounding the track. The temperature is of the order of 10,000°K for a distance of several atomic radii, immediately after passage of the ion. The phonons will disperse by diffusion, bringing the local temperature to a normal value in a time of the order of 10^{-9} sec. These *temperature spikes* can produce secondary effects. For example, Siegel[72] has observed disordering in order Cu_3Au specimens irradiated with neutrons that can be ascribed to this influence.

A charged particle may also make "close" encounters with the nuclei of the constituent atoms of the solid and eject the atoms irreversibly from their normal positions, thus producing vacant lattice sites and interstitial atoms. This process, which is termed *displacement*, joins continuously with the process of phonon production. The transition point is determined by the energy required to tear an atom from its normal position and drive it into the lattice—an energy of the order of 25 ev for stable materials. A 4-Mev alpha particle or a 10-Mev proton may produce[70] between 20 and 200 displaced atoms by this procedure. The exact number depends upon the material being irradiated.

If a massive ion comes to rest within the crystal, it constitutes a foreign atom and can be classed as such. Similarly, if it induces nuclear transmutation in the material, it produces foreign atoms and the effects associated with such atoms. For example, the density of free electrons may be altered in a metal, and new electronic absorption bands, associated with the impurity, may be produced in insulating materials. Many effects of this type

[71] The writer first appreciated the importance of the intense heating of the lattice in the wake of a massive particle (thermal spike) during the wartime research (see footnote 70). He has looked unsuccessfully for earlier work in which the significance of such spikes is noted. They are particularly important in metals, in which chemical changes are not readily induced by electronic excitation, since the electrons may dissipate their energy rapidly in the production of phonons which are dispersed over a large area.

[72] S. Siegel, *Phys. Rev.*, **75**, 1823 (1949).

have been observed in the past. Among the most striking studied thus far are those produced in silicon and germanium,[73] in which the influence of the impurities is accentuated by measurement of the changes in semi-conducting properties.

(I) NEUTRAL PARTICLES

The most interesting changes induced by bombardment with neutral particles are those produced by neutrons.[70] The neutron may induce nuclear transmutation, or it may make knock-on collisions with the nuclei and produce motion of massive, charged ions. The first process leads to the introduction of foreign atoms, the second to the effects discussed in (H) on page 59. One of the most interesting features of the knock-on process is that the moving ions produced both directly by the neutron and by secondary collisions of the primary ions with other atoms have relatively low velocity if the neutron has an energy of the order of 1 Mev or less. Thus a large part of the energy is expended in the generation of phonons and displacements. We have already mentioned the changes in ordered Cu_3Au produced[72] by irradiation with neutrons. Many similar effects have been studied.

It should be added, in closing, that the diffraction effects arising from interaction of electrons and neutrons[74] with crystal lattices have, like x-ray diffraction effects, provided very valuable tools for the study of crystal lattices both perfect and otherwise.

6. INTERACTION BETWEEN PAIRS OF IMPERFECTIONS OF DIFFERENT TYPES

Up to this point attention has been focused on the intrinsic properties of imperfections, on their interaction with the ideally perfect crystal, and on the interaction of like imperfections. We

[73] K. Lark-Horovitz, *Phys. Rev.*, **73**, 1256 (1948); R. E. Davis, W. E. Johnson, K. Lark-Horovitz, and S. Siegel, *ibid.*, **74**, 1255 (1948); W. E. Johnson and K. Lark-Horovitz, *ibid.*, **76**, 442 (1949); W. H. Brattain and G. L. Pearson, *Phys. Rev.*, **80**, 846 (1950).

[74] See, for example, the brief review by K. Lonsdale, *Nature*, **164**, 205 (1949). O. Halpern, M. Hammermesh, and M. H. Johnson, *Phys. Rev.*, **59**, 981 (1941); I. Pomeranchuk, *Physik. Z. Sowjeturion*, **13**, 65 (1938); M. L. Goldberger and F. Seitz, *Phys. Rev.*, **71**, 294 (1947*t*); E. Fermi and L. Marshall, *ibid.*, 666; E. Fermi, W. T. Sturm, and R. G. Sachs, *ibid.*, 589; E. O. Wollan and F. B. Shull, *ibid.*, **73**, 830 (1948); F. B. Shull and S. Siegel, *ibid.*, **75**, 1008 (1949).

are now in a position to consider the interaction of unlike imperfections in a systematic way. Since we have used a scheme of classification in which there are six primary and three transient imperfections, it follows that there are twenty-one unlike interaction pairs and a considerably larger number of unlike interactions of higher order such as three- and four-particle interactions. The examination of the various interactions in any detail would require the space of a small volume. Therefore, we shall do no more than outline this subject in order to point out the more interesting interactions and to indicate that the "particle" point of view stressed in this paper has intrinsic merit in the sense that it permits us to view in a unified way what might otherwise appear to be a disconnected group of phenomenon. Attention will be focused on the interaction of unlike pairs in this section. In general, we shall proceed by considering the interaction of each type of imperfection with those below it in the listing introduced in Section 3, deviating from this when special points of interest arise.

It is perhaps worth emphasizing that the interaction of unlike pairs of imperfections provides us with a tool for obtaining information about all. Assume that we know a great deal about one type of imperfection, such as a free electron. From effects induced by interaction with another imperfection we may deduce properties of the second imperfection. From the knowledge gained about the second imperfection and additional information about its interaction with a third imperfection, we may obtain information about the third. This may then be cross-checked by studying the interaction of the third imperfection and an electron. It is noteworthy that the theory of imperfections and the experimental techniques for studying them have finally reached a state in which it is conceivable to undertake interlocking investigations of this type in a systematic way.

(A) INTERACTIONS INVOLVING PHONONS

Phonons are the most ubiquitous of the imperfections, for crystals are usually investigated at temperatures well above the absolute zero. Actually the density may be reduced to a very low value by going to helium temperatures or lower. We have discussed some of the interactions between phonons and other imperfections in the preceding sections. There are, besides, these types of interaction:

(1) Establishment of thermal equilibrium.
(2) Scattering of free particles by phonons.
(3) Distortion of lattice.

Establishment of Thermal Equilibrium. We have seen that non-equilibrium concentrations of phonons may be generated in a portion of the crystal in a number of ways, such as placing it in contact with a heat reservoir that is at a higher or lower temperature, inducing rapid changes in other imperfections as during processes of light absorption, annihilation or self-trapping of electrons, holes and excitons, and placing dislocations in rapid motion. Actually the two most striking properties of phonons are their ability to achieve a state of thermal equilibrium very rapidly through diffusion and phonon-phonon interaction and their very important influence in bringing the crystal to a state of thermal equilibrium through fluctuations. We have seen that such fluctuations can generate equilibrium densities of electrons, holes, excitons, interstitial atoms, and vacancies in an initially perfect crystal. In addition, the phonon atmosphere in a crystal maintains imperfections in a state of Brownian motion which leads to important observable effects. For example, fluctuations in phonon concentration provide the activation energy required to make interstitial atoms and lattice vacancies jump from one lattice site to the next. Processes such as electrolytic conductivity and diffusion of atoms depend directly upon this, as is made evident by the observation that the magnitude of the conductivity and diffusion coefficient depend upon a Boltzmann factor of the form exp $(-E/kT)$, in which E is the activation energy required for motion, k is Boltzmann's constant, and T is the absolute temperature, *even when the density of interstitial atoms or of vacancies is fixed* (see Fig. 10).

In a similar way, phonons may permit self-trapped electrons, holes, and excitons to migrate, either by allowing them to move from one equilibrium position to a neighboring one or by making them completely free. Moreover, the phonons may dissociate excitons into free electrons and holes. This process is particularly important at room temperature when the binding energy of the exciton is 0.1 ev or less, which, according to equation (4.3), occurs when the index of refraction μ is of the order of, or greater than, about 2.8.

Phonons may excite or ionize impurity atoms in insulators. In the second case free electrons or holes may be produced. The electrical conductivity of impurity semi-conductors depends upon this process when the density of carriers varies with temperature through a Boltzmann factor.

Although the dislocation is not an equilibrium imperfection, its properties are strongly affected by the ability of phonons to induce equilibrium conditions and to furnish fluctuations, particularly at elevated temperatures. This conclusion follows from the observation that the plastic properties of crystals, such as their ability to creep under steady load, depend upon temperature through a Boltzmann factor. Moreover, many of the effects induced by plastic flow, such as work hardening and lattice distortion, can be annealed by subjecting the crystal to an annealing process in which the thermal phonons assist the dislocations which have elongated and multiplied during flow to return to something approaching their original condition.

It is very important to note that phonons may free[64] vacancies or interstitial atoms from dislocations having some Taylor-Orowan character. For, as was emphasized in Section 4, the addition of a row of atoms or vacancies to the edge of the "extra" plane, associated with a Taylor-Orowan dislocation, shifts the dislocation line in a direction normal to itself and to the Burgers vector, that is, from one slip plane to the next. It is easily shown that the energy required to produce a vacancy or an interstitial atom at a dislocation is almost exactly the same as that required to form it at the surface. Thus phonons may employ dislocations as sources and sinks of vacancies and interstitial atoms to maintain equilibrium concentrations; it is not necessary to employ the surface of the crystal.

Scattering of Free Particles by Phonons. Consider phonons from their wave aspect. It is clear that whenever a crystal contains one phonon of specified frequency there is superimposed on the periodic lattice of the crystal a secondary periodicity associated with the wavelength of the phonon. The secondary lattice may cause Bragg diffraction of any wave which interacts with the crystal, such as those associated with free electrons, holes, excitons, x-rays, and neutrons, and hence produce scattering. In the case of the charged particles, the diffraction produces scattering which contributes to the electrical resistivity[1] of the medium by compelling the particles to migrate by diffusion. It is significant that the mobility of an electron or hole in a pure solid decreases[75] with temperature in direct proportion to the density of phonons which may interact with the carriers. The scattering of excitons also causes these particles to diffuse through a crystal instead of moving in straight lines. The interaction of x-rays[67] and neutrons[74] with phonons conditions the intensity of Bragg diffraction in a very important, temperature-dependent way.

Conversely, lattice imperfections, particularly those of atomic nature such as impurity atoms and dislocation, may produce both elastic and inelastic scattering of phonons, thereby affecting the component of thermal conductivity which arises from phonon migration. This effect becomes pronounced in insulators at low temperatures, when density of phonons becomes small.

Distortion of Lattice. The presence of phonons causes local distortion of the lattice, which has a number of important effects. For example, the integrated effect of the distortion causes the lattice to expand as the temperature is raised and the density of phonons increases. This is the normal lattice expansion. In addition, the fluctuations in density of phonons shift the spacing[76] between the electronic levels of a solid locally and make it possible for a wider spectrum of light quanta to be absorbed. Much of the temperature broadening of spectral lines in crystals[1] is a result of the interaction of phonons with the exciting radiation in this manner.

(B) INTERACTIONS INVOLVING ELECTRONS AND HOLES

Free electrons and holes may interact with any of the other imperfections. Perhaps the simplest interaction is that in which the particles are scattered during migration—a generalization of the scattering discussed on page 18 in connection with phonon interactions. Consequently, scattering by vacancies, interstitial atoms, or impurities can contribute[77] to the electrical resistivity.

[75] See, for example, the books in footnote 1 for a general account of electrical resistance in pure materials. Also the paper by the writer, *Phys. Rev.*, **73**, 549 (1948).

[76] The local shift of the conduction bands has been employed by W. Shockley and J. Bardeen, *Phys. Rev.*, **77**, 407 (1950), **80**, 72 (1950), in an interesting way to determine the electrical resistivity of silicon and germanium. See also J. Bardeen (footnote 18).

[77] The influence of foreign atoms on the resistivity of metals has been investigated for a number of years (see the books of footnote 1). E. Conwell and

This effect is important at low temperatures in pure crystals and at room temperature in alloys and mixed crystals. In both cases the impurity scattering may predominate over that rising from phonons. Similarly, cold work increases the electrical resistivity of metals,[78] presumably because of the increased concentration of dislocations and vacancies.

Electrons and holes may be captured by vacancies, interstitial ions, impurity atoms, and dislocations. The bound state is cer-

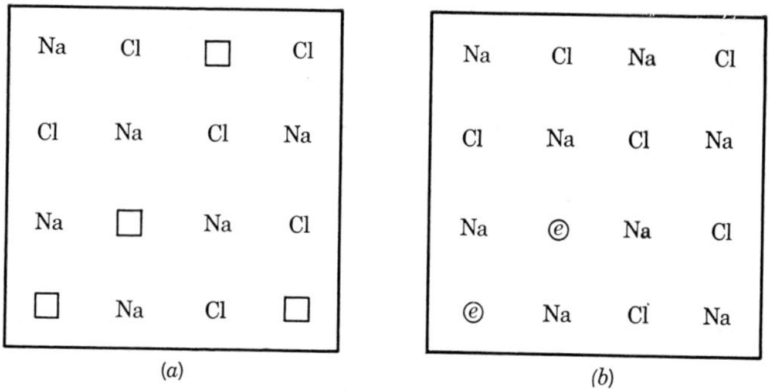

Na Cl □ Cl
Cl Na Cl Na
Na □ Na Cl
□ Na Cl □

(a)

Na Cl Na Cl
Cl Na Cl Na
Na ⓔ Na Cl
ⓔ Na Cl Na

(b)

FIG. 28. The formation of F-centers in the alkali halides by addition of alkali metal to the crystal (schematic). The Schottky defects are altered. The electron from the alkali metal atom occupies the halogen-ion vacancy, and the alkali metal ion occupies the alkali-ion vacancy. (*a*) shows the normal crystal containing Schottky defects, whereas (*b*) shows the crystal containing F-centers, with the vacancies in (*a*) appropriately replaced. The electrons which form F-centers may originate in other ways, such as by ionization of the medium.

tain to be stable if there is a coulomb attraction, as, for example, between an electron and a negative-ion vacancy or an interstitial positive ion in a polar crystal, or between a hole and a positive-ion vacancy or an interstitial negative ion. The F-center, studied so extensively at Göttingen,[4] is undoubtedly the bound state of an electron and negative-ion vacancy in an alkali halide (see Fig. 28).

V. F. Weisskopf, *Phys. Rev.*, **77**, 388 (1950), pointed out that the ionized impurity atoms added to semi-conductors such as silicon and germanium can have an important influence on the mobility of electrons and holes. This effect has been studied experimentally at the Bell Laboratories and at Purdue University (see footnote 47).

[78] See the papers by J. S. Koehler, *Phys. Rev.*, **75**, 106 (1949); J. K. Mackenzie and E. H. Sandheimer, *ibid.*, **77**, 264 (1950).

The counterpart, a hole attached to a positive-ion vacancy, is probably the *V*-center, which absorbs light in the near ultraviolet. This was discovered at liquid air temperatures by Pringsheim[4] and his co-workers, who investigated the structure of a complex of absorption bands in the ultraviolet which probably arise from hole-vacancy aggregates (Fig. 29). An *F*-center may capture a second electron to form the *F′*-center, which is probably the analogue of an H^- ion, two electrons being attached to the same negative-ion vacancy. It is likely that some of the darkening[79] observed when electrons are freed in the silver chlorides is the result of capture of electrons either by incipient vacancies or by interstitial silver ions. However, the darkening studied most extensively in these salts is probably associated with centers obtained by coagulating a number of such vacancies or interstitial silver atoms. It should be added that complex color centers can be observed by allowing *V*-centers and *F*-centers to coagulate in the alkali halides,[80] so that such coagulation is not exceptional, particularly if the crystal is subjected to temperatures at which the centers are mobile.

The ease with which impurity atoms combine with free electrons to form stable centers has been demonstrated by Pick,[81] who has examined the changes in the color centers induced in the alkali halides by free electrons when divalent impurities such as calcium, strontium, and barium are added to the salts.

Apparently free electrons and holes may have an important

[79] This, still controversial, topic has been discussed by Mitchell and the writer (footnote 5).

[80] E. Burstein and J. J. Oberly, *Phys. Rev.*, **76**, 1254 (1949), and St. Petroff, *Z. Physik*, **127**, 443 (1950), have examined in considerable detail the absorption bands produced in the vicinity of the *F*-band and in the near-infra region of the spectrum during coagulation of *F*-centers. The writer described an attempt to identify three of these bands, namely, the bands which the Americans term the M, R_1, and R_2 and St. Petroff terms C, D, and E, in the review article quoted in footnote 4. The investigators quoted above have added at least one more band, designated the *N* band by Burstein and Oberly and the *G* band by St. Petroff. It is probably associated with an aggregate having higher complexity than those responsible for the other bands. No doubt further work will reveal additional structure, since aggregates varying in size from pairs to colloids can be produced.

[81] H. Pick, *Ann. Physik*, **35**, 73 (1939); *Z. Physik*, **114**, 127 (1939). The writer, *Phys. Rev.*, **83**, 134 (1951), has reinterpreted Pick's results in a manner slightly different from that given by Pick.

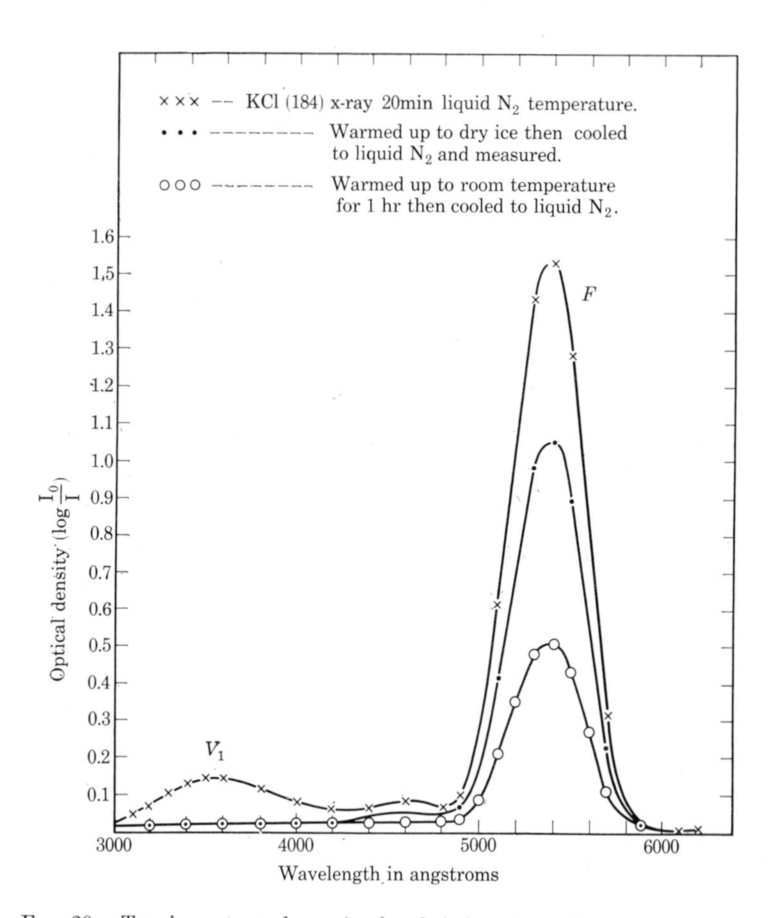

FIG. 29. Two important absorption bands induced in KCl by irradiation at low temperatures with x-rays. The band on the right is the normal F-band, corresponding to an electron in a negative-ion vacancy (see Figs. 8 and 28). The band on the left is the V_1-band. It bleaches when the crystal is warmed, carrying some of the F-band with it. Additional absorption bands, not shown in this figure, occur in the farther ultraviolet. These bands, termed V_2 and V_3, are closely linked with V_1 and grow in intensity when V_1 bleaches. At the present time it seems most reasonable to assume that V_1 is the result of combination of a hole and a positive-ion vacancy. This center is presumably mobile above liquid nitrogen temperature and wanders to form aggregates and to bleach the F-centers. (After Casler, Pringsheim, and Yuster, footnote 4.)

influence on the formation or dissolution of aggregates of interstitial ions or vacancies. For example, Mott and Gurney,[5] have pointed out that the latent image in the silver halides is probably a small clump of silver ions, formed by aggregation of interstitial silver ions. The aggregate grows by trapping free electrons, which have been produced by light quanta or other ionizing agencies, either at incipient halogen vacancies, grain boundaries (if present), or at impurity specks of silver sulphide. The aggregate or speck becomes negatively charged and attracts negative-ion vacancies or interstitial silver ions. In this way a number of neutralized silver atoms are condensed at a point in the crystal. A somewhat inverse state of affairs seems to occur[4] in the alkali halides under appropriate conditions. It is found that *F*-centers and *V*-centers may be formed by irradiating any crystal with ionizing radiation at low temperatures where there are probably no free positive-ion or negative-ion vacancies. The attractive forces between oppositely charged vacancies are apparently sufficient to cause extensive coupling into neutral pairs and probably into larger aggregates at any temperature near or below room temperature. Apparently the electrons and holes produced by the ionizing radiation have a solvent action upon such clusters. It appears as though the cluster captures an electron or a hole and ejects a vacancy having the same sign. Successive capture of this type dissolves the clusters and leaves isolated vacancies from which *F*-centers and *V*-centers may be formed.[82] Incipient vacancies may play an essential role in this process in single crystals in which the clusters of vacancies present are primarily in the form of dislocations. The coulomb charge of the incipient vacancies make them natural traps for electrons and holes.

Dislocations should provide excellent traps for electrons and holes. It will be recalled that the stress field about a Taylor-Orowan dislocation line is tensile on one side and compressive on another. The variation in lattice parameter should produce regions where electrons and holes are more stable[76] than in the undistorted lattice. Actually there seems to be no evidence in the alkali halides, which have been studied most extensively, for unusual centers that might be associated with electrons or holes trapped at dislocations. Only *F*-centers and *V*-centers are observed.[4] It seems necessary to conclude that the electrons and

[82] See in particular the papers by the writer (footnote 4).

holes either interact with clusters of vacancies, which are also trapped near the dislocations, and form the usual centers, or that they generate vacancies from the dislocation itself, probably with the aid of thermal fluctuations, and thereby produce *F*-centers and *V*-centers. This viewpoint is supported by the observation that the density of the crystals decreases during irradiation,[83] exactly as if vacancies were generated from dislocations. One might expect centers formed near dislocations to bear the stamp of their proximity to the dislocation, but there is no strikingly conclusive evidence[84] for this. Incidentally, it is found that alkali halide crystals which have been deformed plastically at room temperature darken much more rapidly than undeformed crystals, presumably because they contain a much higher density of incipient vacancies.

The investigations of Suhl and Shockley[21] on the annihilation of holes in germanium containing free electrons show that such annihilation occurs more easily at the surface than in the volume of the crystal. The results support the viewpoint that the electron and hole have a greater probability of uniting when one is trapped, for example, at the surface, than when in free flight. Presumably the annihilation process occurs when both the electron and the hole are localized in the same region for a time much longer than the 10^{-14} sec which they spend near one another on meeting during free motion.

It is hardly necessary to add that free electrons and holes may interact with transient imperfections, particularly with light quanta. M. Becker, H. Y. Fan, and J. Bardeen[85] have pointed out that the free electrons in semi-conductors may have a strong influence on the optical properties in the part of the spectrum which would be transparent were free electrons absent.

(c) INTERACTIONS INVOLVING EXCITONS

It is evident that excitons can be scattered or trapped by any of the imperfections which produce distortion of the lattice. Those

[83] I. Estermann, W. Leivo, and O. Stern (footnote 4).

[84] St. Petroff (footnote 80) has observed the appearance of a band which lies very close to the *F*-band when coagulates are formed in additively colored crystal. It is possible that this band, which he has termed the *B*-band, is to be associated with *F*-centers near dislocations. In fact St. Petroff's work suggests that the aggregates form near dislocations.

[85] K. Lark-Horovitz and K. W. Meissner, *Phys. Rev.*, **76**, 1530 (1949); M. Becker and H. Y. Fan, *ibid.*, **78**, 178 (1950); J. Bardeen, *ibid.*, **79**, 216 (1950).

which become trapped at impurity atoms may excite or ionize these atoms if there is sufficient energy available. Apker and Taft[31] have demonstrated, for example, that thallium ions in the alkali halides are excited to luminesce with their characteristic emission spectrum when the crystal is irradiated in the fundamental band. Similarly, they have found, as mentioned previously (Section 4, page 28), that the electrons associated with *F*-centers may be ejected from the crystals when it is irradiated in the fundamental band, as if the excitons produced transfer their internal energy to the electrons and cause them to leave the vacancies at relatively high speed, that is, with sufficient energy to surmount the potential barrier at the surface of the crystal.

It seems very likely[86] that the ionizing radiations such as gamma rays, cathode rays, beta rays, and alpha particles excite impurity-activated luminescence in materials by generating excitons which then travel from the point of generation to the luminescent center. This appears to be the only satisfactory way of accounting for the high conversion of energy of the incident particles into light. Fano[34] has employed this hypothesis to explain the variation of efficiency of luminescent materials with bombarding voltage when they are excited with cathode rays. It is assumed that the excitons are destroyed if they reach the surface of the crystal, so that the energy transmitted to the crystal in the form of excitons is lost when these have an opportunity to migrate to the surface.

Smakula[87] has demonstrated that *F*-centers can be produced with a quantum efficiency near unity when the alkali halides are irradiated in the tail on the long-wavelength side of the fundamental band. No photoconductivity is observed.[88] Apker and Taft[31] have concluded that the density of color centers attains a value of about 10^{19} per cc in a thin layer near the surface of the crystal when it is irradiated with light near the center of the fundamental band. The inference of this work is that excitons, generated by the absorption process, are able to engender *F*-centers and *V*-centers. Apparently[82] the excitons are captured by clusters of vacant lattice sites or by dislocations and proceed to do exactly

[86] N. Riehl, *Ann. Physik*, **29**, 636 (1937); F. Seitz, *Trans. Faraday Soc.*, **35**, 74 (1939).

[87] A. Smakula (footnote 32).

[88] R. Hilsch and R. W. Pohl, *Z. Physik*, **68**, 721 (1931).

those things which free electrons and holes may do, in spite of the fact that the electron and hole are closely coupled in an exciton. It is possible that the trapped excitons are highly metastable because of lattice distortion (see Section 4, and Fig. 9) and form F-centers and V-centers from the clusters or dislocations with the aid of thermal fluctuations before the electron and hole can annihilate one another. Dexter and Heller [*Phys. Rev.*, Oct. 15 (1951)] have suggested that the coulomb field of incipient negative-ion vacancies decomposes excitons which pass near by, the electron being captured in the process to form an "incipient" F-center which then diffuses away to form a normal F-center. The hole is eventually captured by an incipient positive-ion vacancy. This suggestion implies that the holes do not give rise to a measurable current.

(D) INTERACTIONS INVOLVING VACANCIES AND INTERSTITIAL ATOMS

Vacancies and interstitial atoms may be attracted to impurity atoms, provided repulsive forces of coulombic or elastic origin are absent. They should always be attracted to a dislocation since the stress field has either sign at some region about the general dislocation line. This is a special case of a general principle, first pointed out by Cottrell[89] and by Koehler and the writer, that dislocations provide excellent regions for condensation of imperfections of the atomic or electronic type. Examples of coupling between vacancies and impurity atoms are well-documented in salts. For example, the divalent alkaline-earth ions have positive-ion vacancies associated with them when dissolved in the alkali halides. One vacancy is needed for each divalent ion to compensate for one unit of the positive charge of the latter. Etzel and Maurer[90] have found that the energy of cohesion of the positive-ion vacancy and divalent ion is of the order of 0.3 ev, so that an appreciable fraction of the vacancies is dissociated even at room temperature for normal concentrations of the divalent impurity. Since the positive-ion vacancies are responsible for most of the electrolytic current in the alkali halides and assist the positive ions to diffuse, we would expect the addition of divalent impurity to enhance both the electrolytic conductivity and the diffusion coefficient of the

[89] A. H. Cottrell, *Report of a Conference on the Strength of Solids*, p. 30; J. S. Koehler and F. Seitz, *J. Appl. Mech.* (footnote 3).

[90] H. Etzel and R. J. Maurer (reference 37).

positive ions. Mapother, Crooks, and Maurer[91] have found this to be the case (Fig. 11). They have also found that the divalent impurity atoms diffuse much more rapidly than the normal ions of the lattice, presumably because they have vacancies near them for a much larger fraction of the time than the normal ions of the lattice do. Johnson[92] and Wagner[93] have used precisely the same concept of association between vacancies and impurity atoms to explain the fact that small amounts of alloying atoms in metals appear to diffuse more rapidly than the normal metal atoms do. There seems to be little doubt that interstitial atoms should also be able to concentrate about appropriate impurity atoms. Associated pairs of positive-ion vacancies and divalent ions should contribute to the type of dielectric loss investigated by Breckenridge.[43]

We saw in (A) on page 63 that phonons can generate vacancies or interstitial atoms at dislocations. It follows that vacancies and interstitial atoms may also disappear at dislocations, causing the dislocation ring to move in the direction normal to the **d** vector. Suppose now that there is a chemical concentration gradient in the solid and that diffusion is taking place as a result of the migration of vacancies or interstitial atoms. In general, we may expect[94] such imperfections to move in a preferred direction in the chemical gradient, much in the manner of diffusing ions in an electrolyte when an electric field is present. The migration should cause an enhancement of the density of the imperfections in one region and a depletion in another. Equilibrium is maintained locally by the action of dislocations, playing the role of sources and sinks. The accompanying change in the dislocation pattern should have the effect of distorting the specimen inhomogeneously. For example, if vacancies are responsible for diffusion, the specimen should expand in regions where there is a net exodus of vacancies and should contract in the region where they condense. If, prior to diffusion, markers through which the vacancies or interstitial atoms do not diffuse are incorporated in the lattice and if they are sufficiently small that they do not inter-

[91] D. E. Mapother, H. N. Crooks, and R. J. Maurer, *J. Chem. Phys.*, **18**, 1231 (1950).

[92] R. P. Johnson, *Phys. Rev.*, **56**, 814 (1939).

[93] C. Wagner, *Z. physik Chem.*, **38**, 325 (1937).

[94] See the papers by the writer and by J. Bardeen (footnote 40).

fere with the flow of vacancies or imperfections, we should expect the relative position of the markers to change in the region where diffusion is occurring. This process, which is now termed the Kirkendall effect, has been observed in brass by Smigelskas and Kirkendall,[95] and has been studied more extensively in a number of alloys by da Silva and Mehl.[96] Since the effect appears to be very general, we may conclude that the coupling between dislocations and vacancies or interstitial atoms plays an exceedingly important role in migrational phenomena of everyday interest. These cannot be understood unless we recognize the part played by dislocations.

Although there does not appear to be incontrovertible proof that vacancies and interstitial atoms concentrate about dislocations, this seems almost certain to be the case. Haynes and Shockley[5] have found that free electrons concentrate about strain lines in the silver halides, as if the carriers found many interstitial silver ions or possibly halogen-ion vacancies there. It is also possible that the electrons are trapped by the dislocations associated with the strain lines and attract the silver ions or negative-ion vacancies from the surrounding medium. This matter could be settled by investigations at low temperatures where the silver ions are not mobile.

Vacancies and interstitial atoms should distort the lattice and, if the distortion has the proper sign, make it easier for light quanta to be absorbed by the base material. Absorption of this type would produce excitons which are trapped near the imperfection. An effect of this kind may explain the observation that the tail of

[95] A. D. Smigelskas and E. O. Kirkendall, *Trans. AIME*, **171**, 130 (1947). Darken, *Trans. AIME*, **175**, 184 (1948), has given a phenomenological treatment of the Kirkendall effect on the assumption that the local density retains its equilibrium value and that each type of atom has its own diffusion coefficient. This treatment represents a valuable link between atomic theories and the experimental observations.

[96] C. da Silva and R. F. Mehl, *J. Metals*, **191**, 155 (1951). This work has also been extended in The Sylvania Electric Laboratories at Bayside, New York, by Alexander and co-workers. These investigators have introduced one of the diffusing constituents by a vapor method under highly "antisceptic" conditions. They seem to avoid porosity observed when experiments are carried out in an atmosphere of gas. Dissolved gas appears to "poison" the dislocations in the sense that they cannot act completely freely as sinks for vacancies. The various experiments show that normal grain boundaries are good sources and sinks.

the fundamental absorption band of most crystals is very sensitive to the state of imperfection of the lattice. Naturally other atomic imperfections, such as dislocations and impurity atoms, should contribute to the effect. This probably provides an explanation of the long absorption tails observed in many salts.

(E) INTERACTIONS INVOLVING IMPURITY ATOMS

Cottrell[89] pointed out that the tendency of impurity atoms to aggregate near dislocations probably provides the explanation of the upper yield-point phenomenon in many metals. The impurity atoms pin the dislocation to the region where it was localized before stress was applied, so that a much larger stress is required than would be the case in a pure material. Once the dislocation is torn free of the atmosphere of impurity atoms, it should move in a relatively unhindered way. Naturally, impurities distributed randomly throughout the lattice should have some inhibiting motion on the dislocations because of the stress fields such atoms produce. Koehler and Marx,[97] who have investigated copper in which hydrogen was dissolved under oscillating as well as static stresses, seem to have evidence to show that the hydrogen atoms pin down the dislocations at room temperature only if the stress is applied rapidly. Otherwise, the hydrogen atoms appear to migrate with the dislocations.

Impurity atoms may also interact with transient imperfections. Here again the most interesting effects[75] are those associated with interaction involving light quanta since they are far more selective than fast charged particles or neutrons. The light quanta may either excite or ionize the impurity atoms. Free electrons or holes are produced in the second case so that the crystal is made photoconducting in a special range of wavelengths as a result of the presence of the impurity atoms. Under favorable circumstances the impurity atoms emit light quanta on returning to the ground state, so that the system is luminescent. Many of the most interesting luminescent crystals are *impurity activated* in this sense. The characteristic luminescent radiation of the impurity may, of course, also be stimulated by excitons or by transient electrons or ions.

[97] J. Marx and J. S. Koehler, paper in *Carnegie Institute of Technology Symposium on the Plastic Deformation of Crystalline Solids.*

(F) INTERACTIONS INVOLVING DISLOCATIONS

Perhaps the only interaction between dislocations and transient imperfections that appears to be of interest at present is that connected with the enhancement of the tail of the fundamental absorption band of insulators because of plastic flow or other sources of distortion. As mentioned in (D) on page 73, the distortion of the lattice and other atomic imperfections apparently makes it possible for light quanta which could not otherwise be absorbed to produce trapped excitons in the neighborhood of the dislocation. The writer[5] has proposed that this effect is of primary importance in the silver halides.

7. TRIPLE AND HIGHER INTERACTIONS

The number of possible triple and higher-order interactions between the imperfections is obviously large. Many of these are not likely to occur as truly simultaneous processes, although they can occur in sequence, granting an elapse of time between stages. We have already discussed some interactions of this type, for example, that between an exciton and the electron trapped in a negative-ion vacancy in one of the alkali halides, thereby producing external photoelectric emission; or that between electrons, holes, or excitons and the vacancies formed by motion of dislocations, with phonons assisting, to generate F-centers. Doubtless many more cases of this type will be discovered as the research in the field is extended. It is sufficient for our purposes to observe that the coupling between the imperfections extends beyond pair interactions. There is little doubt that the imperfections form a very closely related family.

SUMMARY

If the writer were somewhat more pedantic, he would probably complete this discussion by presenting a number of tables which show the relationships between the various imperfections in diagrammatic form. It is evident that these tables would be quite complex in structure because only the interactions of pairs, like and unlike, could be represented readily as a two-dimensional matrix. The interactions of higher order would require either a fairly large number of two-dimensional diagrams or one multidimensional diagram. The reader may have the pleasure of constructing such diagrams.

Perhaps these are the most important summarizing remarks that can be made. The existing status of experimental and theoretical investigation with almost perfect solids seems to imply that we know the basic nature of all the primary imperfections at the present time, that is, the six listed in Section 3. It is very improbable that we are yet familiar with all the intricate properties of these imperfections and with all the ways in which they may combine to impart new and unusual properties to crystals. The field, however, appears to be closed in the sense that we appreciate in a general way the area which is to be exploited. It is highly probable, of course, that new imperfections will be discovered in materials which exhibit usual characteristics, such as ferromagnetism, ferroelectricity, and superconductivity, or other properties metals develop at low temperatures.

2.

On the Geometry of Dislocations

W. T. READ, JR., AND W. SHOCKLEY

Bell Telephone Laboratories, Murray Hill, N. J.

ABSTRACT

This paper points out that dislocations are one of the few types of defects which naturally occur in crystalline substances. All dislocation types are classified according to a simple scheme which makes use of the Burgers circuit and the Burgers vector. Both complete and partial dislocations are considered. Slipping and diffusive motions of dislocations are illustrated, and a dislocation theory of straight versus wavy slip bands is suggested. The intersection of dislocations is discussed and is shown to result in kinks, or jogs, in the dislocation lines which impede the slipping motions and may create vacancies and interstitial atoms. The Frank-Read mechanism of dislocation multiplication is reviewed as a possible explanation of slip bands.

1. DEFINITION OF A NEARLY PERFECT CRYSTAL

It is the purpose of this section to point out that dislocations are one of the few types of defects which will occur naturally in crystalline substances; furthermore, it is shown that all types of dislocations may be classified according to a certain relatively simple scheme which makes use of the lattice vector characterizing the "slip."*

* Although many of the ideas described in this paper have been current in discussions between workers in the theory of dislocations for some time, apparently they have not been presented from a unified viewpoint. For a review of the application of dislocation theory prior to this conference, see references 1, 2, 3. Many of the basic ideas of this paper were introduced by J. M. Burgers, reference 4. (*Note added in proof*: An exposition somewhat similar to this paper has been published by F. C. Frank, "Crystal Dislocations. Elementary Concepts and Definitions," *Phil. Mag.*, **42**, 809 [1951].)

By a nearly perfect crystal we mean a crystal in which only a small percentage of the volume is *bad*, all the rest being *good*. By a good region of the crystal we mean a region in which each atom is properly surrounded by its neighbors. A good region differs from a perfect crystal only in that it may be elastically deformed. Bad regions are those in which the deformation is so large that it may be impossible to tell which of the atoms surrounding another atom are its normal neighbors. The atoms on the edge of the extra plane of a Taylor-type dislocation are evidently in a bad region. For the purpose of discussion, we may imagine that regions in which the strain is larger than 0.2 are classified as bad.

In a nearly perfect crystal we may draw boundary surfaces which separate the bad regions from the good regions. If the crystal is nearly perfect, only a small percentage of the volume is occupied by bad regions; hence any individual bad region must be small in at least one dimension. The case in which the bad region is small in only one dimension represents an extended surface passing through the crystal and can reasonably be supposed to occur only in a crystal grain boundary, a twin boundary, or a stacking fault. We shall exclude the grain and twin boundaries and consider only single crystals. Stacking faults will be discussed in Section 5 in connection with partial dislocations.

We now turn to bad regions whose bounding surfaces are small in at least two dimensions or possibly three. These two cases are considered below.

2. BAD TOPOLOGICAL SPHERES

Consider the case in which the bad region can be surrounded by a closed surface. Next imagine what would happen if we were to remove the material from within this closed surface and replace it with perfect material. If this perfect material were elastically deformed so as to join continuously onto the lattice of good material on the surface of the region, the bad region would be entirely eliminated and only elastically deformed good material would remain. We shall now classify the bad material which was originally within the surface by comparing it with the good material which might replace it.

The simplest way in which the bad material may differ from its good replacement is in the total number of atoms which it contains. For example, if it contained one less atom, the bad material might represent a vacancy. Such a defect is produced by removing one atom from a perfect crystal and allowing the atoms surrounding the vacancy to make minor readjustments. Such a defect could be surrounded by a relatively small sphere, probably only one or two lattice constants in radius. An interstitial atom would similarly be represented by a sphere containing one extra atom.*

Even if the bad region contained the correct number of atoms, it still might represent a defect, and the material inside the sphere might be in a twin orientation as compared to the outside. We shall exclude cases of this sort from the class of nearly perfect crystals and consider them to be examples of polycrystalline material.

Defects of the type discussed in this section merge continuously with those of the next section, as we may see by considering the case in which a number of atoms are removed from the material of the bad region. If we suppose that on a certain crystal plane we remove ten or fifty atoms in the form of a small disc, the crystal can collapse so as to bring the two surfaces on opposite sides of the removed material into contact and into register. It is evident then that this interior contact may well be good material, so that the surface which would initially have been spherical to surround one Schottky defect would extend into a disc-shaped surface, and finally into a torus, since only the atoms at the outer edge of the removed plane would be in bad regions.

3. DISLOCATIONS

Let us next consider the classes of bad regions which must be surrounded by a cylinder with a cross section of atomic dimensions. We may make a closed path about this region, each step of the closed path lying in wholly good material. Such a path is illustrated in Fig. 1. The type of defect inside the bad region can be classified in terms of the closure failure of a particular type of loop called a Burgers circuit.[4]

A Burgers circuit is formed by proceeding through the good material of the crystal in steps which are each lattice translation vectors. We let the three primitive vectors of the crystal lattice be **a**, **b**, and **c**. These vectors are not to be thought of as constant vectors of fixed magnitude and direction, but instead as

* Defects of this type are discussed in Paper 1 by Seitz, which appears in this book.

vectors which vary elastically with the elastic deformation of the good material. A Burgers circuit is given by the equations

$$n_a = 0, \quad n_b = 0, \quad n_c = 0, \tag{3.1}$$

where n_a, n_b, n_c are the total number of steps along the corresponding primitive vectors taken in traversing the loop, proper alge-

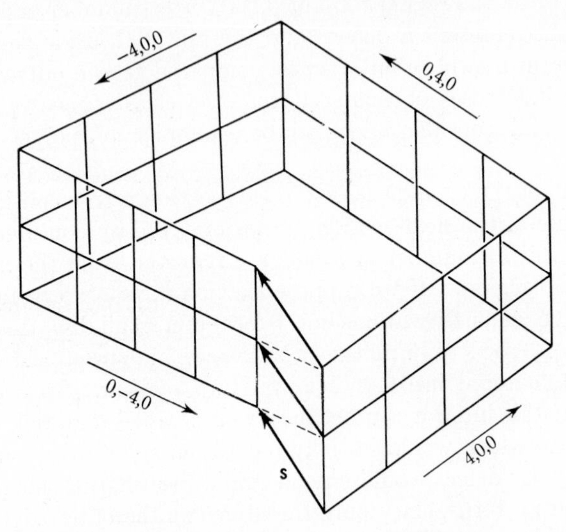

FIG. 1. Definition of the Burgers vector **s**. The Burgers circuit encircles a dislocation with **s** in the [011] direction.

braic allowance being made for the direction of each of the steps. Such a path must evidently close upon itself or fail to close by an amount represented by the vector

$$\mathbf{s} = \Delta n_a\,\mathbf{a} + \Delta n_b\,\mathbf{b} + \Delta n_c\,\mathbf{c}, \tag{3.2}$$

where the quantities Δn_a, etc., are integers. The reason that the closure failure must be represented by such a simple form is that in proceeding through the good material each primitive vector carries the path from a given atom in a unit cell to a corresponding atom in an adjacent unit cell. Therefore, the closure failure at the end of the path can be made up by steps which go from an atom of the final unit cell to the atom of the initial unit cell; and, since these atoms are corresponding atoms of closely adjoining unit cells, the vector separating them must be a combination of the primitive vectors of the crystal. The vector **s** is called the *Burgers vector* or *slip vector* of the bad region.

An alternate procedure is to define the Burgers circuit as a closed curve surrounding the bad region and consisting of atom-to-atom jumps between nearest neighbors. The Burgers vector is then taken to be the closure failure of the corresponding circuit, consisting of the same atom-to-atom jumps, in a perfect crystal.

It is evident that the dislocations most often considered, namely, the Burgers, or screw dislocation, and the Taylor dislocation, are classified by **s** vectors, which are simple translations of the lattice.

It is important to distinguish between cases in which **s** vanishes and those in which it does not. Only when **s** vanishes will it be possible to replace the material inside the surface by elastically strained good material. Consequently, only for the case $\mathbf{s} = 0$ is it possible to define unambiguously the number of atoms missing from the region inside the cylindrical bounding surface. If **s** does not vanish, the cylindrical surface bounding the bad region cannot terminate within the interior of the nearly perfect crystal. This follows from the fact that the Burgers circuit can be continuously deformed so as to slide in along the cylinder. Thus, if the loop starts at a point P and proceeds to a point Q, where P and Q are separated by closure failure **s**, a loop starting at P' which differs from P by an elastic lattice vector **r** will terminate at point Q', which differs from Q also by **r**. Since P, Q, P', and Q' all lie in good material and the parallelogram bounding them does not contain any bad material, it is evident that the lattice vectors of opposite sides are equal, so that the closure failure from P' to Q' is also **s**. By a similar procedure the loop may be deformed by elastic parallelograms so as to show that the closure failure of any loop surrounding the cylindrical surface is the same as any other. In other words, there is a line integral around the circuit which is conserved.

This same theorem may be derived by a consideration of the elastic theory of dislocations founded by Volterra.[5] Volterra's results, however, are somewhat more general than are necessary for periodic crystal structures, and the proof is considerably more involved. In terms of Volterra's theory, the line integral which we have discussed is the integral of the elastic strain; and his theorem states that the closure failure of such a line is represented by the displacement of a rigid body. In a crystalline material the only displacement possible in the good material is that of a lattice vector, so that Volterra's displacement vector reduces to a vector of the class **s**.

This theorem establishes the general topological property associated with a dislocation. Since the vector **s** is conserved along the cylinder, the cylinder must either close upon itself or branch so that the sum of the branches, taking each branch as having its own characteristic **s** value, is equal to the **s** of the original line. The only remaining possibility is that the cylinder may end on the surface or on a grain boundary, which is effectively a surface for a nearly perfect crystal grain.

There are many processes, actual or virtual, which could lead to the formation of the same dislocation. For example, an edge dislocation could be formed by slip over a limited area of the slip plane, the dislocation line being the boundary of the slipped and unslipped areas. The same dislocation could also be formed by adding an extra plane of atoms above the slip plane or removing a plane below the slip plane. Physically, the latter two processes could be realized by a condensation of vacancies or interstitial atoms. Since only pure edge dislocations can be formed by simply adding or removing partial planes of atoms, it is more convenient to think of a dislocation in terms of an actual or virtual slip process, the dislocation being the boundary between slipped and unslipped regions on the slip surface. The virtual slip surface for a given dislocation is defined by the requirement that it contain the dislocation line and be parallel at all points to the slip vector; it may, however, be curved or bent in directions at right angles to the slip vector. It is seen that, for a pure screw dislocation, the slip surface is arbitrary and may be any plane containing the dislocation.

The conservation of the Burgers vector is seen to follow intuitively from the picture of a dislocation as the boundary of a slipped area.

In order to specify the sign of the Burgers vector it is necessary to specify the positive direction of traversing the Burgers circuit, and this in turn specifies the positive direction along the dislocation line as, for example, in the relation of current and lines of force for a wire.

The Burgers vector of a dislocation may be either a lattice translation vector of minimum length or the sum of several such vectors.

Since the observed slip direction in actual metals is parallel to a minimum lattice translation vector, it has been considered that the latter type does not play an important role in plastic deformation. However, in body-centered cubic crystals two [111] type dislocations could combine to form a [100] type, with apparent reduction in elastic energy (elastic energy being assumed proportional to the square of the Burgers vector).*

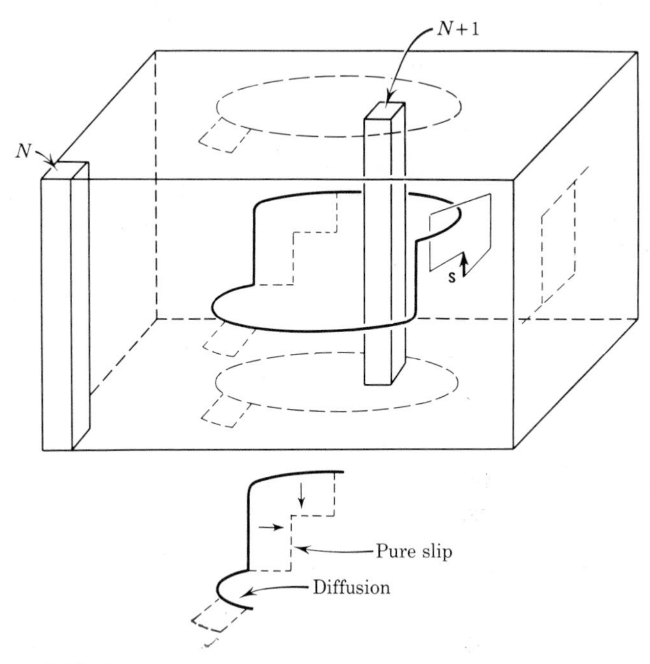

FIG. 2. Diffusive vs. slipping motions. Slip vector is in vertical direction.

4. MOTIONS OF DISLOCATIONS

It is possible to distinguish sharply between two types of motions for dislocations: slipping motions and diffusive motions. These can be understood with the aid of Fig. 2, which shows a dislocation and illustrates the types of motion.

It is supposed that the dislocation in this case has an **s** value corresponding to a minimum translation vector. The dislocation

* This possibility was pointed out to the authors of this paper by F. C. Frank in private communication.

has also been drawn as though it closed upon itself inside the crystal. For purposes of exposition the exterior surface of the crystal has been made parallel to the slip vector **s** of the dislocation. The top and bottom surfaces represent crystal planes, and in Fig. 2 these have been drawn as though they were perpendicular to **s**. Because of the closure failure of any Burgers circuit surrounding the line of the dislocation, it follows that any column of unit cells chosen along the **s** direction will have one more unit cell if the column is encircled by the closed curve of the dislocation than if it is not. From this simple result, it is at once evident that no motion of the dislocation is allowed which will change its projected area upon the top or bottom surface of the crystal unless a mechanism is provided whereby there is a net flux of atoms across the outer surface of the crystal.* If, however, the motion of the dislocation is parallel to the **s** vector as, for example, in the case of a slipping Taylor's dislocation, its projected area is unaltered. Some of the dotted lines representing displacement of the dislocation apply to this case. Also, it is possible to project the screw parts of the dislocation, which show as the vertical straight lines in the figure, without affecting the projected area. These motions are slipping motions, and they can be accomplished simply by sliding unit cells upwards or downwards in the vertical columns of the figure parallel to **s**.

Diffusive motions necessarily accompany changes in the projected area enclosed by the dislocation loop in a plane normal to the Burgers vector. One such motion is indicated by the dotted line shown in the figure. For it there is a net increase of one unit cell per column, through which the dislocation cuts in its motion. These diffusive motions can take place by vacancy diffusion in the crystal, resulting in a net transfer of atoms from the region of the dislocation to the free surface or to a grain boundary, or vice versa, and as a result the dislocation may grow.

The virtual slip surface corresponding to a closed dislocation loop is the surface of a prism having its axis parallel to the slip vector. The dislocation line is the boundary between the slipped and unslipped areas on this prismatic surface. Any slipping motion simply enlarges the slipped area at the expense of the unslipped. Hence the dislocation, by slipping, can shift to any posi-

* This property of a general dislocation ring was pointed out independently by F. Seitz, reference 2, and in Paper 1 by Seitz in this book.

tion or assume any form on the surface of the prism, as illustrated by the slipping motion shown in Fig. 2. Also the screw segments of the dislocation line can move off the prism by slipping, since this does not change the projected area of the loop on a plane normal to the Burgers vector, because a screw dislocation does not have a uniquely defined slip plane.

5. PARTIAL DISLOCATIONS

In some cases a dislocation can lower its energy by splitting into two partial dislocations whose Burgers vectors are not lattice translation vectors; these are necessarily connected by a misfit surface which is a bad region. For a complete dislocation to dissociate into partials connected by a misfit surface it is necessary that the two partials have an elastic energy of repulsion sufficiently intense to overcome the surface tension of the misfit surface. In this case there will be an equilibrium separation of the partials where the repulsive force, which decreases rapidly with distance, is just equal to the constant surface tension of the misfit area. It was first pointed out by Heidenreich and Shockley[1] that a dislocation having a $\frac{1}{2}$ [110] slip vector (taking the lattice constant as unit length) in a face-centered cubic crystal could lower its energy by dissociating into two partials (Shockley partials) having slip vectors $\frac{1}{6}$ $[21\bar{1}]$ and $\frac{1}{6}$ [121], respectively, and connected by a stacking fault, which can be visualized as follows. Consider the crystal to be made up by stacking spheres in close packing. When one close-packed layer has been laid down, the second layer can be added in two ways, corresponding to the two sets of hollows on the first layer. If we call the first layer an A layer, the second layer may be either a B or a C layer, and nearest neighbor requirements will be satisfied. In a face-centered cubic lattice the sequence of layers is . . . $A\ B\ C\ A\ B\ C\ A\ B\ C$ . . . . Now if slip of $\frac{1}{6}$ $[21\bar{1}]$ occurs corresponding to moving a layer into a neighboring set of hollows, then above the fault $A \rightarrow B$, $B \rightarrow C$, and $C \rightarrow A$, so that the sequence of planes is . . . $A\ B\ C\ A\ B\ C\ B\ C\ A\ B\ C$ . . . , the sequence $B\ C\ B\ C$ being of the hexagonal close-packed type and, therefore, defining a stacking fault in face-centered cubic crystals. The energy of this fault is seen to be of the order of the twin boundary energy (possibly twice as large, since a stacking fault is equivalent to a twin one layer thick). This energy is estimated to be comparable to the elastic energy of repulsion of the Shockley partials at a separation of around 50 Å in aluminum. The equilibrium separation of Shockley partials in copper would be somewhat greater because of the lower twin energy in copper. (See Paper 12 by Fisher and Dunn in this book.)

A similar dissociation of a complete dislocation into an extended dislocation consisting of two partial dislocations connected by a stacking fault could occur in hexagonal close-packed crystals.

It is readily seen that Shockley partial dislocations can move in their slip planes by slipping motions, as discussed in the last section. However, they cannot move out of their slip planes either by cross slip in another plane or by diffusion, the reason being that a partial dislocation is necessarily tied to a misfit surface, the misfit of the surface being defined by the vector displacement of the adjoining atomic planes. A stacking fault is defined by a $\frac{1}{6}$ [112]-type displacement, which corresponds to a low energy misfit on the corresponding (111)-type plane but a very high energy misfit on any other plane; hence the partials can move only on the plane of their connecting fault.

In order for a dissociated dislocation to pass out of the hexagonal-type plane, the two partial dislocations must come together. This is also true when the dislocation line consists of segments lying in different (111)-type planes; for example, a dislocation with slip vector $\frac{1}{2}$ $[1\bar{1}0]$ in a face-centered cubic crystal can lie partly in the (111) plane and partly in the $(11\bar{1})$ plane. In the former it will dissociate into partials with slip vectors $\frac{1}{6}$ $[1\bar{2}1]$ and $\frac{1}{6}$ $[2\bar{1}\bar{1}]$, respectively, and in the latter into partials with slip vectors $\frac{1}{6}$ $[1\bar{2}\bar{1}]$ and $\frac{1}{6}$ $[2\bar{1}1]$, respectively; each set of partials comes together at the intersection of the two planes.

F. C. Frank[6] has discussed another type of partial dislocation which is quite different from a Shockley partial. It has been called a *sessile dislocation,* because it cannot move at all by slipping. For example, if a complete $\frac{1}{2}$ [110] dislocation combined with a $\frac{1}{6}$ $[\bar{1}\bar{1}2]$ Shockley partial, the result would be a a $\frac{1}{3}$ [111] partial attached to the stacking fault of the original Shockley partial. This configuration could be made with a sphere model by making a cut part way through the crystal on a (111) plane, spreading the cut open, and inserting a layer of atoms, and then closing the cut so as to produce a . . . *A B C B C A* . . . stacking fault. The slip vector $\frac{1}{3}$ [111] of this partial dislocation on the boundary of the extra plane is at right angles to the plane of the stacking fault; hence, since the dislocation cannot move out of the plane of its fault, it cannot move by slipping but only by diffusion.

6. SLIP BANDS

The formation of slip bands in deformed single crystals probably arises from slipping motion. Sometimes the slip bands are not straight, and after deformation the crystal will have the form shown in Fig. 3. We have here represented a case in which a

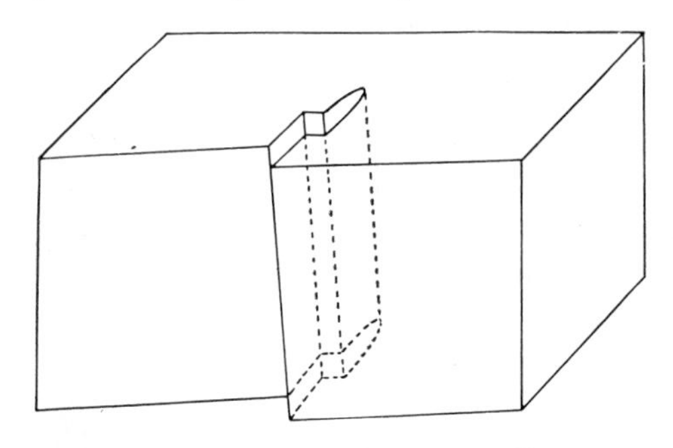

FIG. 3. Screw dislocation with wavy slip plane. Slip has shifted from one plane to another at the small step.

screw dislocation has cut across part but not all of the crystal. The dihedral edges between the two surfaces exposed by the slip are parallel to the vector **s**. It is evident that a motion of this sort can be produced by successive slipping on different planes of atoms parallel to the vector **s**. This is in agreement with observations* on deformed crystals in which slip is seen to have shifted from one plane to another by the sort of transverse slip shown in the small step of Fig. 3. In some cases the transverse steps are distributed relatively uniformly, so that it is impossible to detect them directly.† All that is noticed is that the long straight sections become weaker in one place and stronger on the adjoining line, representing a continuous series of transverse motions of the slip in respect to the main lines of the slip band.

In terms of the slipping motion of dislocations which may shift from one plane to another, as described in connection with Fig. 3, it is possible to suggest a tentative explanation for the phenomena

* See Paper 4 by Read in this book, Fig. 2.

† See Paper 4 by Read in this book, Fig. 3.

of wavy versus straight slip bands observed in different crystals. The slip bands observed on alpha iron are known to be very wavy and irregular.* This crystal is body-centered cubic, and the slip vector is of the form $\frac{1}{2}[111]$, in units of the lattice constant. Motion is observed to take place on slip planes of the forms (110), (112), and (123) so that a given slip vector, such as that just quoted, has the total possibility of three slip planes of the first type, three of the second type, and six of the third type, making twelve altogether. In other words, the slip vector $\mathbf{s}$ may lie on any one of twelve possible slip planes, and for this reason we propose that slip may shift very easily through one slip system to another so as to produce the wavy line.

On the other hand, for the face-centered cubic system, the slip vector is of the form $\frac{1}{2}[101]$, and the slip planes are of the form (111). In this system a given slip vector can lie on only two slip planes. If, furthermore, the slip vector splits up into two partial dislocations connected by a stacking fault, the partial dislocations can themselves lie on only one of the possible slip planes. Therefore, once the dislocation has become extended on a given slip plane, it will have to be squeezed together into a complete dislocation before it can be shifted onto the other slip plane. This would explain the observed fact that slip lines tend to be relatively straight on face-centered cubic crystals.

This discussion of slip bands is intended to show only how the slipping motion of dislocations discussed in connection with Fig. 2 can lead to slip band structures of the form actually observed. It does not explain the fundamental phenomena of slip bands nor their detailed internal structure discussed in the paper on slip bands in this book. In order to explain slip bands, we must show why a large number of dislocations should traverse the single crystal on approximately the same slip plane, and why after this process has proceeded to a certain degree it becomes blocked and slip starts on another system of planes.

7. INTERSECTION OF DISLOCATION LINES

When a dislocation line L_A with slip vector $\mathbf{s}_A$ moves across a slip plane P_A, the part of the crystal above the plane is offset by $\mathbf{s}_A$ relative to the part below. Now imagine a straight line drawn

* See Paper 4 by Read in this book, Fig. 1.

in the crystal along a line of atoms and intersecting P_A. After the dislocation has traversed P_A and cut this line, the line will have an offset, or jog, $\mathbf{s}_A$ where it intersects P_A. This will also be true if the line in question is another dislocation line L_B. Thus, when one dislocation cuts another, each dislocation line acquires a kink or jog at the point of intersection equal to the slip vector of the other dislocation. This jog is a segment of the dislocation line one atomic spacing in length. Since a dislocation line in moving across a slip plane will intersect many other dislocations, it will acquire many such jogs.

We must clearly distinguish two classes of jogs, depending on whether the jog or kink in the dislocation line lies in the slip plane of the dislocation or out of the slip plane. In the first class the jog or kink is immediately eliminated by a slipping motion; this class is therefore trivial. However, in the second class, the jog changes the projected area of the dislocation line on a plane normal to the slip vector, and, therefore, can be removed only by diffusion. Since the jog involves an increase in the length of dislocation line, the energy of the dislocation array is increased whenever two dislocations cut through one another unless the Burgers vector of each lies in the slip plane of the other. This permanent increase in energy is to be distinguished from the energy required to move each dislocation through the stress field of the other.

A jog out of the slip plane is equivalent to a short section of edge dislocation. The jog, therefore, can move by slipping only in the slip direction; otherwise it would change the projected area on a plane normal to the slip vector, as discussed in connection with Fig. 2. Thus, if a dislocation line acquires a jog out of its slip plane, the slipping motion of the line and the jog must be such that the jog moves parallel to the slip vector. The force on the dislocation line due to the applied stresses is at right angles to the line, and is parallel to the slip vector only if the dislocation is pure edge. Consequently, if the dislocation line is not pure edge (that is, not parallel to the horizontal plane of Fig. 2), the force on the line will not be parallel to the permitted motion of the jog. In such a case the jog can move in the direction of motion of the line only by leaving a trail of vacancies or interstitial atoms behind, corresponding to the change in projected area.

These, as well as the drag exerted by the jog, could contribute to the hardening of the slip plane.* The fact that energy is required to make one dislocation cut through another explains the hardening of one slip plane by slip on an intersecting plane.

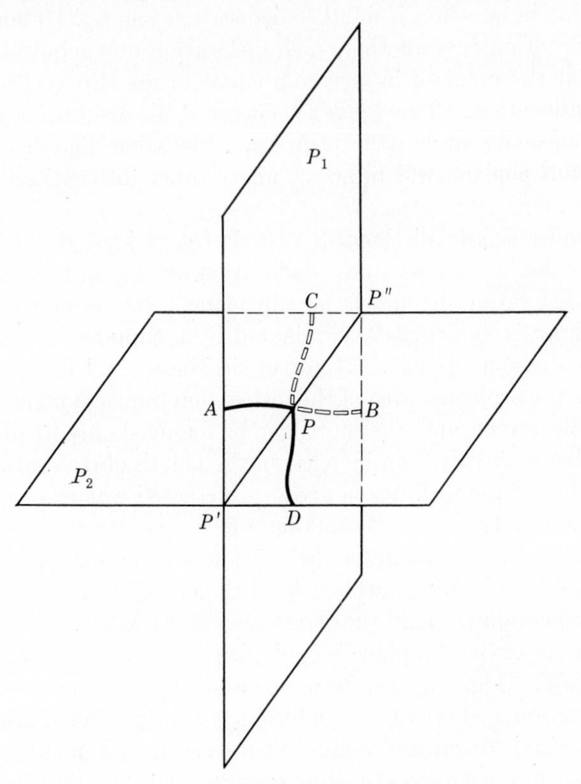

FIG. 4. Intersection and recombination of dislocations. Dislocation line AB in plane P_1 intersects CD in P_2 at point P.

The intersection of two dislocations having a common slip vector may result in a recombination which reduces the total length of dislocation line. For example, in Fig. 4, the segment of dislocation line APB in plane P_1 intersects CPD lying in P_2. There are then four lines going into the intersection point P; AP and CP have Burgers vectors of opposite sign from BP and DP. Thus AP can join onto DP as well as onto BP. After the disloca-

* These ideas were developed as a result of private discussion with F. C. Frank. The importance of jogs in the creation of vacancies has been discussed by F. Seitz, reference 2.

tions recombine and contract under the line tension, the result is two broken lines $AP'D$ and $CP''B$. We shall see in the following section how such an L-shaped dislocation line could produce a slip band.

8. THE MULTIPLICATION OF DISLOCATIONS

The slip bands observed in the plastic deformation of crystals show that on a typical active slip plane there is about one thousand times more slip than would result from the passage of a single dis-

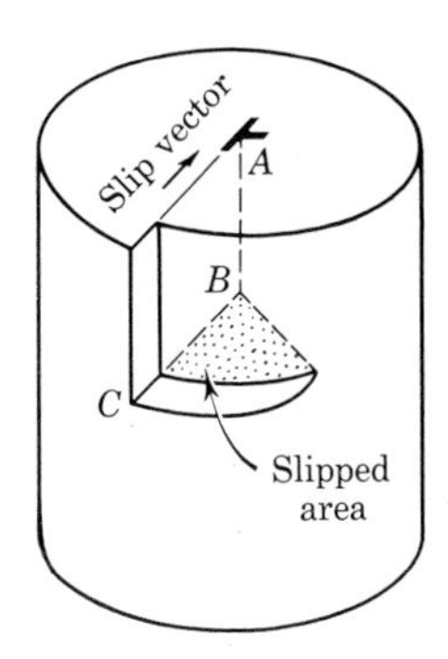

FIG. 5. Slip resulting from the motion of a single dislocation line.

location across the plane. This attaches special importance to the recognition of processes whereby a dislocation can produce a large amount of slip and can multiply.*

We shall first show by purely topological reasoning how an unlimited amount of slip could result from the motion of a single L-shaped dislocation line ABC (Fig. 5). For simplicity, we assume that the horizontal planes are the only active slip planes. The segment AB, therefore, is anchored. A small shear stress applied on the slip plane and in the slip direction will cause the line BC to sweep around like the hand of a clock, producing slip of one atomic spacing per revolution.

Actually the line BC would not remain radial but would form a rotating spiral because of the higher angular velocity of the innermost portion. The quantitative treatment of the problem is

* The multiplication process described here was conceived independently by F. C. Frank and W. T. Read, Jr., and was first presented at the 1950 Carnegie Institute of Technology Conference (reference 2) and published as a joint letter (reference 7).

strictly analogous to the theory of crystal growth[8] except that, when the spiral has many turns, a correction must be made for the mutual repulsion between successive turns. If slip is prevented at the boundary (as could occur in a polycrystal), the spiral would reach an equilibrium state, as illustrated in Fig. 6 for the case of a square boundary.

Another process closely analogous to crystal growth, and leading not only to continued slip but also to the generation of suc-

FIG. 6. Sketch of the equilibrium spiral when slip is prevented at boundary.

cessive closed loops of dislocation line, is illustrated in Fig. 7. The segment BC of a dislocation line lies in the active slip plane, the other parts of the line lying outside the plane so that the points B and C are anchored. A suitable applied shear stress will cause BC to curve as shown and to generate dislocation loops at essentially the same rate as turns of the spiral were generated in the previous case. The minimum stress at which this will occur is determined by the distance BC and is approximately the rigidity modulus divided by the distance BC in lattice spacings. At a smaller stress some thermal activation will be required.

It is necessary for this mechanism that the end points B and C should be held at least in some degree. This locking may be provided in various ways in dislocation networks, the simplest example being that in which BC is one side of a rectangular dislocation loop $ABCD$, the Burgers vector being normal to the plane of the loop. The stress which causes the motion of BC in Fig. 7 pro-

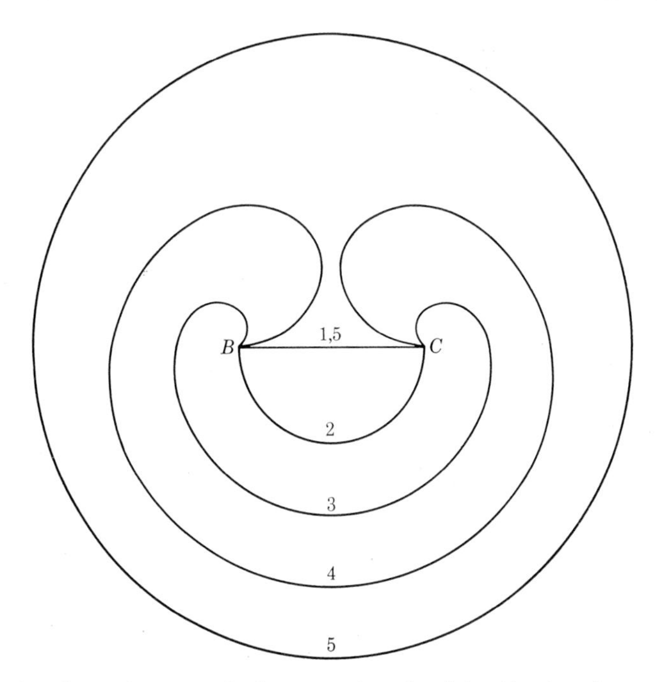

FIG. 7. Successive stages in the generation of a dislocation loop by segment BC of a dislocation line. Process can be repeated indefinitely.

duces an opposite motion of AD, with no net force on AB and CD. In many cases (for example, probably the hexagonal metals) the lower mobility of dislocations in planes of less than closest packing may suffice to anchor the points B and C.

REFERENCES

1. *Report of a Conference on the Strength of Solids*, University of Bristol, England, Physical Society, London, 1948.
2. *Carnegie Institute of Technology Symposium on the Plastic Deformation of Crystalline Solids*, Office of Naval Research, 1950.
3. A. H. Cottrell, *Progress in Metal Physics*, Chapter II, Interscience Publishers, New York, 1949.
4. J. M. Burgers, *Proc. Kon. Ned. Akad. v. Wet., Amsterdam*, **42**, 293 (1939).

5. V. Volterra, "Sur l'équilibre des corps élastiques multiplement connexes" (Paris), *Ann. éc. norm.* (Sec. 3). t, 24 (1907), pp. 401–517. See also A. E. H. Love, *A Treatise on the Mathematical Theory of Elasticity*, 4th ed., p. 221, Cambridge University Press, London, 1926.
6. F. C. Frank, *Proc. Phys. Soc.* (*London*), **62**, 202 (1949). See also discussion of paper by Frank in reference 2.
7. F. C. Frank and W. T. Read. *J. Phys. Rev.*, **79**, 722 (1950).
8. F. C. Frank, *Discussions of the Faraday Society*, **5**, 67 (1949).

II. THE ROLE OF IMPERFECTIONS IN DEFORMATION

3.

Imperfections from Transformation and Deformation*

C. S. BARRETT

Institute for the Study of Metals, University of Chicago

ABSTRACT

Stacking faults (twin faults) can be detected and analyzed by diffraction patterns made with polycrystalline metals oscillating through small angles; line broadening in powder patterns can also be used, though less reliably.

Plastic deformation causes faulting in certain Cu-Si, Au-Cd, Ag-Sn, and Ag-Sb alloys, and perhaps also in Cu-Zn alloys (possibly also in Cu and Ag at low temperatures), but not in Al or Al alloy "24S-T." Faulting can be expected when glide on slip planes can rearrange the structure into a new stable or metastable phase of lower free energy. The faulting that accompanies transformation in Co, Li, and Li-Mg is ascribed to the strains of the martensitic-type transformation.

Other distortions connected with plastic flow are (1) elastically bent glide lamellae; (2) local distortion around slip bands, (3) rotational slip (swivelling), (4) deformation bands (including kink bands), (5) deformation twins, (6) martensitic transformation, (7) grain-boundary and subboundary flow, and (8) strain gradients near grain boundaries.

1. STACKING FAULTS

If an atom layer in a crystal is displaced to a position that destroys the regular stacking sequence of the layers, a stacking fault is produced. The displacement vector for the layer is parallel to the plane of the layer but is not a translation vector of the lattice. A fault in a face-centered cubic crystal is illustrated in Fig. 1.

* This work was supported in part by the ONR (Contract No. N-6ori-IV, NR 019 302).

The close-packed $(1\bar{1}1)$ plane is shown in plan view at the top of the drawing, and in the elevation below it is seen that the (111) planes are offset where the manner of stacking the $(1\bar{1}1)$ planes is altered. Faults may result from imperfect crystal growth, from

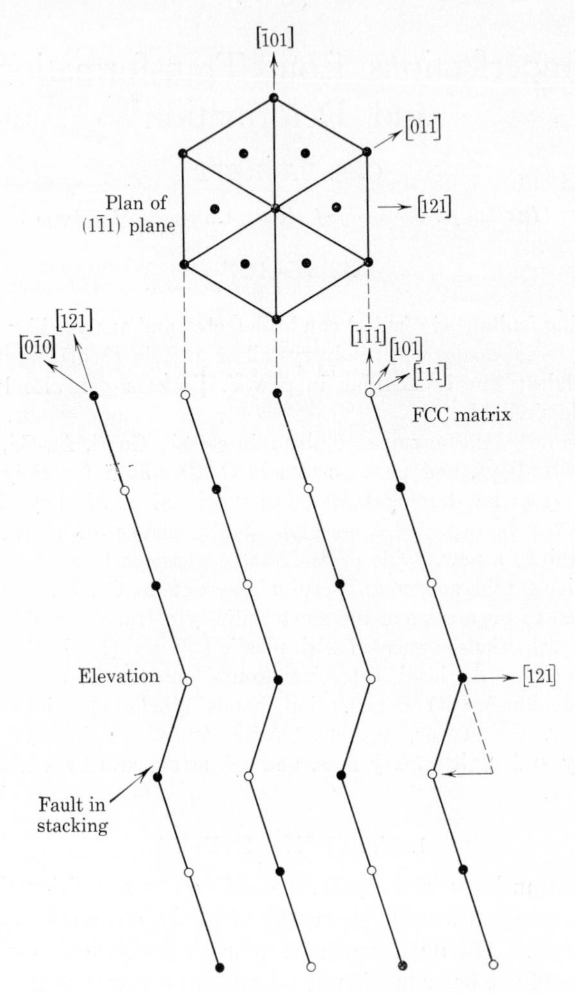

Fig. 1. Fault on $(1\bar{1}1)$ planes of a face-centered cubic crystal. Atoms centered at the filled circles lie in the plane of the drawing in the elevation view, and those at open circles lie in the next layer above; the second layer above repeats the pattern of the filled circles, the third layer that of the open circles, etc. The displacement producing the fault is in the [121] direction.

plastic deformation, or from phase transformation; they are most likely to occur in crystals of the layer-structure type, where interatomic forces between the atoms of a layer are stronger than the forces between layers.

In the close-packed metals the ideal stacking sequence may be destroyed by the shift of a close-packed layer out of its resting place in the hollows of the layer beneath and into any neighboring set of hollows. In the ideal case the direction of movement bisects the angle between two close-packed rows of atoms in the layer, both in the close-packed hexagonal (two-layer) and in the face-centered cubic (three-layer) cell. This displacement is such that in a face-centered cubic crystal it would create a *twin fault*, a twin of minimum thickness on a (111) plane, as in Fig. 1. If every plane shifted in this way with respect to its neighbor underneath, the result would be a homogeneous shear that would produce a twin of the original crystal. Regularly spaced faults of this kind spaced two layers apart would convert the cubic to the hexagonal structure or, conversely, the hexagonal to the cubic, and other structures with unit cells four or more layers high could be created with properly spaced displacements. Stacking disorders with varying degrees of departure from the ideal stacking sequences would be produced if varying numbers of irregularly spaced faults were introduced.

If the twin fault of Fig. 1 were produced during the growth of the crystal by deposition of $(1\bar{1}1)$ layers, J. B. Hess points out that two mistakes in face-centered cubic stacking would be necessary: a single mistake would initiate the growth of a twin and a second would be required to resume the growth of the original. Hess accounts in this way for the excessive twin bands lying parallel to the surface in electrodeposited copper (Fig. 2), and he proposes it as a mechanism that can account for the formation of annealing twins during grain growth.

Layer structures in which the individual layers remain perfect or nearly so, but in which a degree of stacking disorder has been found to exist, include the micas, graphite, cadmium iodide, zinc sulphide, silicon carbide, hexagonal cobalt, and hexagonal lithium.

A stacking fault may not extend over the entire layer of a close-packed plane in a crystal; in such cases it must end at a type of dislocation that involves a displacement vector (Burgers vector) that is not a lattice vector, a dislocation that has been called, by various authors, a twin dislocation, a half dislocation (in face-centered cubic metals, where two nonparallel displacement vectors may be added to produce a lattice vector), or a partial dislocation.

As is true for the complete dislocations (edge dislocations) of Taylor, partial dislocations may be either positive or negative.

FIG. 2. Twins formed during electrodeposition of copper. A cross section through base (at the bottom) and electro-deposit, etched to bring out the twins. (J. B. Hess.)

When two complete dislocations of opposite sign move apart on the same slip plane they leave between them a region that is normal since it has been displaced by the exact amount of a lattice vector. On the other hand, when two partial dislocations do the same they leave a stacking fault. Shockley speaks of such a pair in a face-centered cubic crystal as *extended half-dislocations*, but the term *partial dislocations* is now preferred. Similarly, if a partial dislocation in the form of a ring expands over the surface of a slip plane, the faulted region within it expands. This region is bounded on the forward and back edges by partial dislocations in which the displacement is in the direction of motion, and on the lateral edges by partial dislocations analogous to the screw dislocations of Burgers. If a succession of rings of this type are generated at the same place and expand outward one after the other, the net effect is that of slip within the area; but with the additional feature (not found when slip occurs by expanding rings of complete dislocations) that, if the partial dislocations come to rest within the crystal, they form concentric loops enclosing concentric bands of faulted material. Theoretical computations suggest that the activation energy should be less to generate a succession of partial dislocations (*Shockley dislocations*) than complete dislocations in face-centered cubic metals.[1,2] When partial dislocations are arrested within the crystal by inclusions, grain boundaries, and local stress fields, we may expect ribbons of faulted material. It thus seems likely that a severely cold-worked metal is criss-crossed by great numbers of faults, probably in the form of narrow ribbons on many nonparallel crystal planes. Faults may exist not only between a pair of Shockley half dislocations, but also between a Shockley dislocation and a sessile dislocation, which is a relatively immobile type proposed by Frank.[3]

Burgers,[4] Bragg,[5] Shockley and Read,[6] and others have pointed out the advantages of considering mosaic blocks as regions separated by arrays of dislocations. Blocks may be tilted with respect to each other by having edge dislocations arranged on the common boundary, the disorientation of the blocks increasing with the density of dislocations, and the tilt being about the axis of the dislocations. Similarly, a block may swivel on its neighbor if screw dislocations are arrayed on the boundary, and we may postulate mixtures and irregular distributions that introduce inhomogeneous distortions of various kinds. To picture the imperfections in cold-worked metal we must include these subboundaries with their arrays of dislocations, together with the interlacing network of dislocations of various kinds throughout the interior of the mosaic blocks, a situation of great complexity and irregularity, particularly in polycrystalline metals, where many slip systems are operative.

THE DETECTION AND MEASUREMENT OF FAULTS

The interpretation of x-ray and electron diffraction patterns in terms of faults has been treated at length in recent textbooks and articles. In this review only statements of the general principles are attempted, together with a discussion of the uncertainties and ambiguities that may be encountered.

The presence of faults may be inferred from diffraction patterns by noting the streaks that radiate outward from certain diffraction spots of the faulted crystal, corresponding to rods extending out from certain points in the reciprocal lattice of the crystal. When the faults are confined to a single set of parallel planes in the crystal, all the reciprocal lattice rods are normal to these planes. When faults exist on nonparallel sets of crystal planes, nonparallel systems of rods coexist, several rods extending out from most of the reciprocal lattice points.

An approximate idea of the degree of disorder can be inferred directly from the length of the rods, for slight disorders (widely spaced faults) can cause only short rods, and faults spaced every few atom layers are indicated when rods extend with reasonable intensity much of the distance from one lattice point to the next. Methods have been developed for the analysis of the intensity distribution along the rods in terms of the stacking disorder.[7-12]

There are several causes of rods in a reciprocal lattice that must be considered before we can conclude that stacking faults of the simple type just mentioned are responsible. (1) The presence of thermal vibrations introduces a diffuseness at each of the lattice points, related to the elastic constants of the crystal; but these need not be confused with rods that result from faults if their dependence on temperature is noted. (2) The presence of thin plates of a second phase or planes enriched in one of the elements produces rods. When the structure of the second phase differs sufficiently from the structure of the matrix, the rods will not pass through the reciprocal lattice points of the matrix, and it is consequently easy to avoid confusing these rods with those produced by faults. But in the case of segregation and any precipitation in which the structure of the plane of the precipitate matches the structure of a parallel matrix plane against which it lies, the rods will be accurately aligned with all the reciprocal lattice points of the matrix. There will be points, however, that will be elongated into rods by segregation or by the thinness of plates of precipitate and that will not be elongated by faults; consideration of these points may lead to identification of the cause of the rods. For example, the 11·0 reflection of hexagonal close-packed crystals is not affected by faults on the basal plane that would convert lamellae to the face-centered cubic packing, yet this reflection is widened when the diffracting crystal becomes sufficiently thin.

The ideal data from which to deduce the state of disorder in a crystalline substance would be a complete map of a representative sample of the reciprocal lattice of an undistorted single crystal, made with monochromatized x-rays in a spectrometer, a technique employed by Warren and his co-workers in order-disorder

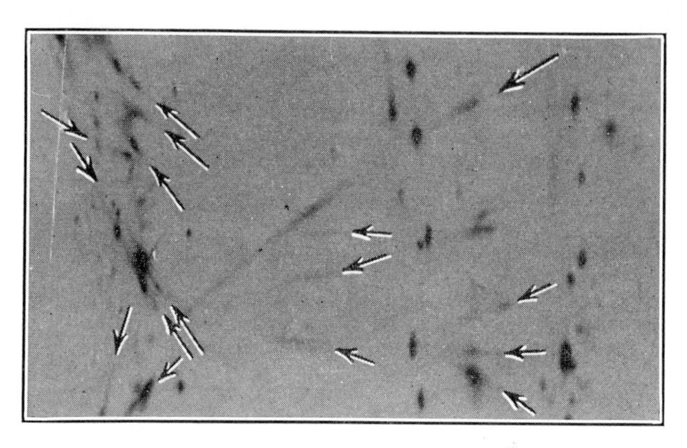

FIG. 3. Oscillating crystal diffraction pattern of a polycrystalline alloy containing faults. Face-centered cubic alloy of copper plus 5.12 per cent silicon, quenched after recrystallization at 820° C. Streaks indicated by arrows indicate faults on {111} planes caused by the deformation induced by the quenching stresses.

studies. Much can be learned, however, by less time-consuming methods, in which there is more latitude in the preparation of the specimen. Polycrystalline samples have been used in which the grain size is such that spotty Debye rings are recorded when the sample is oscillated.[13] A typical example is shown n Fig. 3. Streaks on such films, arising from faults, can be recognized and differentiated from the general radiation streaks by the angles they make with the Debye rings. Similarly, the plane on which faulting occurs can be inferred from the angular position of the longest streaks. Moderate plastic deformation—of the order of 5 per cent—leaves the grains sufficiently undistorted so that streaks can be seen, but severely deformed grains cannot be studied this way. For these we must resort to a powder method and analyze the breadth of the Debye lines, attempting to separate the breadth due to faults from the breadth due to stresses and other causes.

FAULTS FROM PLASTIC DEFORMATION

A number of effects can be interpreted as evidence of faults: strain markings in deformed metals,[14] of the type shown in Fig. 4;

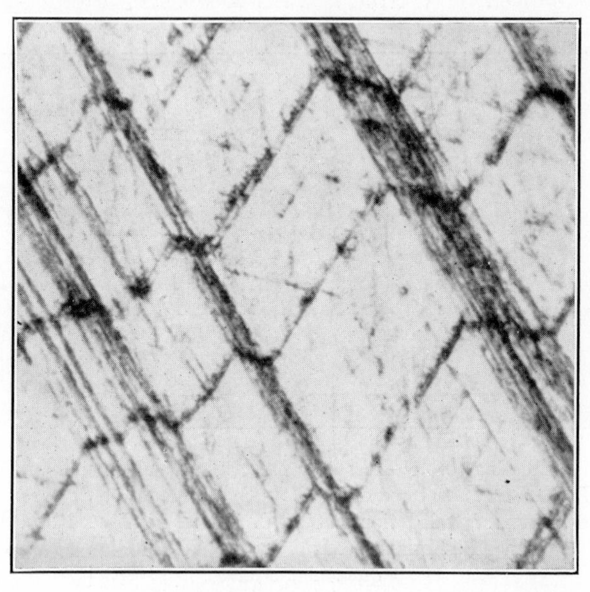

FIG. 4. Strain markings brought out by electropolishing and etching brass (70 per cent copper, 30 per cent zinc) that had been previously deformed. The displacement at the markings, both in direction and amount, corresponds to slip and not twinning (Burke and Barrett[14]), but twin faults (perhaps clustered) may account for the markings.

the increased reflecting power of metal at slip bands that is revealed by x-ray reflection micrographs,[15] illustrated in Fig. 5; the disappearance of Kikuchi lines in electron diffraction patterns during cold work;[1] and the hardening of latent slip planes.[1] But other explanations of these effects are available, and there is no direct proof that they are due to faults or to faults alone.

Conditions that should be favorable to faulting include (1) a low energy interface at the fault and (2) a decrease, or at most a small increase, in free energy in converting a lamella from its ordinary structure to the structure at the fault. The low interface energy requirement is met to some extent in all face-centered cubic metals and alloys since a fault merely produces a thin twin on a (111) plane and since coherent twin boundaries (in annealing twins) are known to be low energy interfaces.[16] Hexagonal close-packed structures must likewise meet this requirement when faulted on the

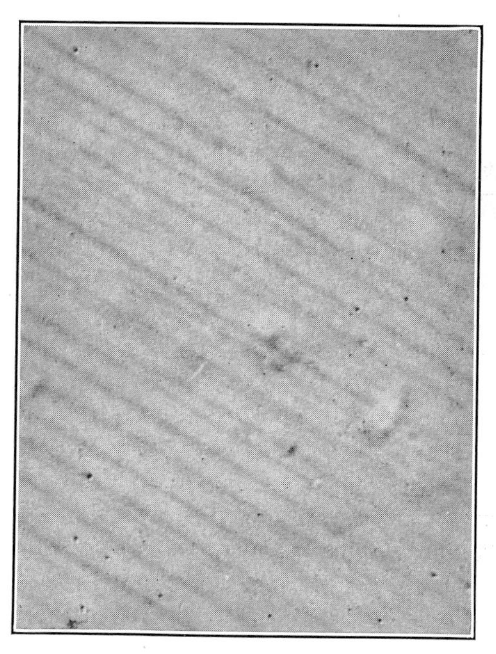

FIG. 5. X-ray reflection micrograph of a ferrite crystal in which slip has occurred. This is an enlargement (×250) of a Bragg reflection caught on a fine-grain emulsion close to the crystal.[15] The disturbed material in a thin layer along a slip plane reflects more strongly than the material between slip planes.

basal plane. The condition that the free energy change be favorable is met when either of these close-packed structures transforms to the other, as in cobalt. It is also met in some alloys. If a phase diagram of an alloy system shows a two-phase field in which the two close-packed structures co-exist, this condition implies that a composition exists for which the free energies of the two are equal; and in the neighborhood of this composition the faulting tendency should be high, especially when the alloy is heat treated so that one phase is supersaturated with respect to the other.

These conditions are met in the copper-silicon system (Fig. 6). The face-centered cubic alpha solid solution of silicon in copper extends to 5.3 per cent silicon at 842°C and is in equilibrium with an hexagonal close-packed kappa phase containing 5.9 per cent silicon. Interatomic distances in the close-packed planes are

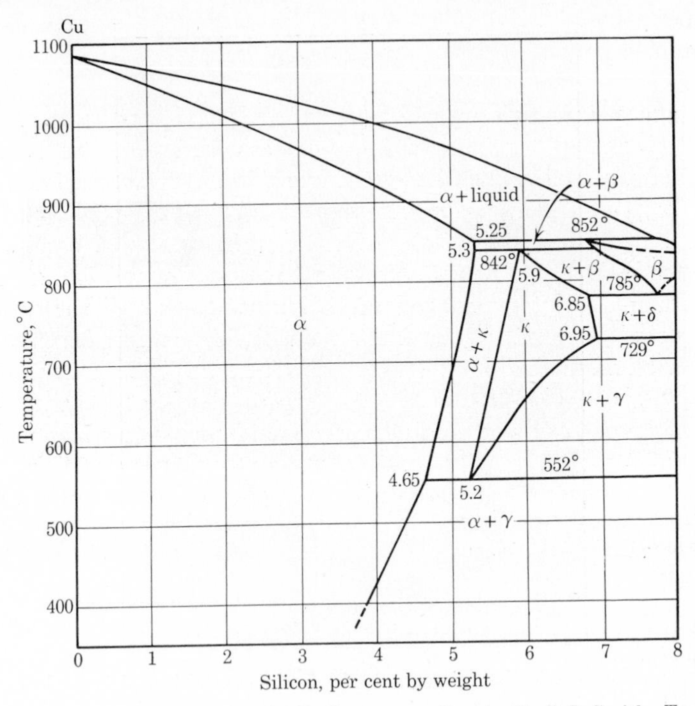

FIG. 6. Phase diagram for Cu-Si alloys, according to Cyril S. Smith, *Trans. AIME*, **137**, 313 (1940).

identical (or nearly so) in the two phases when they co-exist, and interplanar spacings differ by 0.1 per cent. Because the change of solubility of alpha with temperature is considerable, it is possible to cool the alpha phase to a temperature where it must have a higher free energy than the hexagonal structure would have at the same composition. These conditions were found to be favorable to faulting.

OSCILLATING CRYSTAL DATA

An x-ray diffraction study of the Cu-Si alloys indicated many faults when the alloys were deformed under certain conditions.[13]

There were very prominent streaks on photographs made with oscillating polycrystalline samples (Fig. 3), the location of the streaks and their angles indicating faults on the close-packed planes, and the length of the streaks indicating that faults were frequently clustered as close as five or ten atom layers, after 3 to 5 per cent reduction in thickness of the samples. Streaks were obtained only with alloys having compositions in the range 4 to

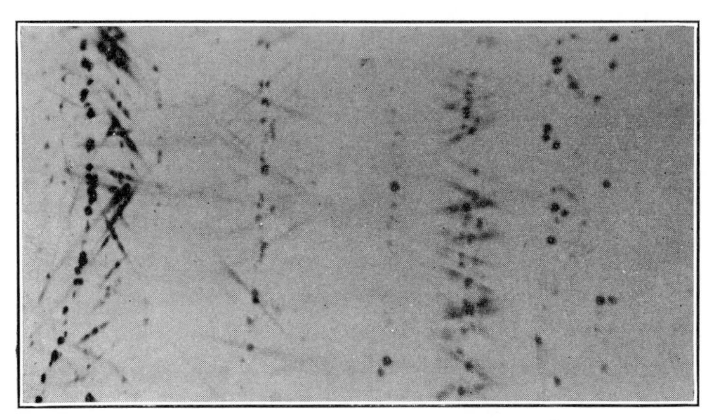

FIG. 7. Oscillating crystal pattern for polycrystalline alloy of copper plus 5.12 per cent silicon, quenched and deformed after recrystallization at 820° C. Streaks from a metastable structure induced by the gliding of close-packed layers.

5.4 per cent silicon. Plastic deformation at temperatures within the stable range of the alpha solid solution failed to produce faults in the same alloys that faulted profusely at lower temperatures where they were supersaturated.

The tendency to faulting was frequently so great that the quenching from temperatures near 600°C was sufficient to introduce large numbers of faults. Since faulting could be almost completely avoided by air-cooling the specimens, it was concluded that plastic deformation accompanying the quenching initiated the faulting.

The streaks produced in 4 to 5 per cent silicon alloys were of the type predicted by theories of the faulting of face-centered cubic structures, consisting of spikes extending out from spots of the cubic structure. Alloys containing 5 to 5.4 per cent silicon, on the other hand, produced a type of streak having intensity maxima well removed from the cubic spots, as in Fig. 7. These streaks could not be accounted for by random faults in the matrix, but led to the conclusion that a metastable phase was produced by the strain, a phase oriented on the matrix (111) plane and coherent with it, which was developed without appreciable diffusion and presumably by the sliding of the close-packed (111) layers over each other into positions having stacking disorder.

In the Cu-Si alloys it was possible to precipitate the hexagonal kappa phase from the cubic alpha phase, or vice versa, by suitable heat treatment, but these spontaneous precipitation processes were found to be ineffective in producing faults. Apparently the gradual movement of the alpha-kappa interface in a thermally activated process provides opportunity for building a perfect structure, as contrasted with the irregularity introduced by strain. When faults were produced by deformation and the faulted specimen was subsequently annealed at a low temperature, the diffraction streaks increased in intensity, indicating either that there was segregation of silicon on the faults, or that additional faults were formed.

No faults were found in alloys containing only the kappa phase when deformed at various temperatures; this may be attributed to the fact that they were not supersaturated with respect to the alpha phase at the working temperatures, so that an increase in free energy would have been required to create a lamella of alpha. Faults were removed by recrystallizing the samples and cooling them slowly from the recrystallization temperature, although faults in alpha plus kappa two-phase alloys were often retained through long annealing treatments in the absence of recrystallization. The immobility of faults is to be expected since twin boundaries are known to be immobile during annealing, and since coherent alpha-kappa boundaries, which are likewise similar to fault planes, resist coalescence during long annealing.

The faulting tendency of the Cu-Si alloys may be responsible for their unusual strain-hardening characteristics. Compared with most copper-base solid solutions (for example, Cu-Zn, Cu-Ni, Cu-Al, and Cu-Mn) the hardening of Cu-Si alloys per atom per cent solute is unusually high. Straight-line strain markings resembling twin boundaries are common in Cu-Si photomicrographs, as in Fig. 8. It is appropriate to ascribe these in some way to faults, since the number of markings increases to a maximum in the composition range where the faulting is most common. The markings could not be individual faults, because of their spacing, but might be clusters of faults separated by relatively perfect crystalline layers. The markings represent intersections of the face-centered cubic (111) planes with the plane of polish—the same planes on which the faults are found.

FIG. 8. Strain markings in a Cu–4.91% Si alloy, electropolished and etched. ×200.

The solid solution of tin in silver should be susceptible to faulting since the phase diagram shows that a phase with hexagonal close packing, with an axial ratio $c/a = 1.61$, is stable at compositions very near the solubility limit of the face-centered cubic phase. We have found clearly defined fault streaks with an 11 per cent Sn alloy after compression of 5 per cent at room temperature.

A phase with pronounced stacking disorders in the hexagonal

close-packed structure has been reported by Byström and Almin[17] in the gold-cadmium system at 25.7 and 29.5 atomic per cent Cd. No study of thermal or mechanical variables was made. The axial ratio at 25.7 per cent is $4.784/2.908 = 1.64$. These alloys are said to transform to a distorted face-centered cubic structure (tetragonal, c/a near 1.005).

We have obtained no evidence for mechanically induced faulting in oscillating crystal patterns of Ag-Sb alloys (7 and 8.5 per cent Sb) in spite of the fact that there is as much reason to expect faulting in these as in the silver-tin system. Similarly, we have been unable to detect faults in silver cold worked at liquid nitrogen temperature or in zirconium buttons (hexagonal close-packed) that were hammered while immersed in a salt bath at 837°, 840°, 850°, and 859°C (near the temperature of transformation to body-centered cubic) and immediately quenched.

DATA FROM FILED POWDERS

The oscillating crystal technique used in the foregoing studies is not suitable for heavily deformed samples, yet it is desirable to use severe deformations in order to produce maximum numbers of faults. Accordingly, the possibility of using a powder technique was explored. Widths were determined on filings mounted in an x-ray spectrometer with Geiger counter recording of the diffraction lines at room temperature. The samples were freshly filed; the radiation was copper K-α, unfiltered. A typical record is reproduced in Fig. 9.

Integral widths were measured, and from these were subtracted the integral widths from the unresolved K-α doublets of annealed powders, a common approximate correction method that is equivalent to fitting the curves with a function of the type $1/(1 + m^2x^2)$. A series of determinations was made with conditions varied that are known to influence the faulting tendency, thus providing an opportunity to correlate the broadening characteristics with faulting tendency. The integral widths of the deformed filings minus the widths of the annealed filings are given in Table 1 as B_{111} and B_{200} for the 111 and 200 lines, respectively. The table gives also the ratio of these corrected widths.

In studying this table in the light of the oscillating crystal data previously mentioned, a correlation is immediately evident. All specimens in which deformation faulting is known to occur have very pronounced widening, with B_{200} exceeding 0.5° (Cu–4.17% Si, Ag–11% Sn). In these, also, the ratio B_{200}/B_{111} is equal to 2.0 or more.

The specimens that would be expected to contain many faults, but in which the oscillating crystal technique has not revealed them, also have wide lines, B_{200} being roughly 0.5° and B_{200}/B_{111} about 2.5. In this class are Ag–7% Sb and Cu–2.94% Si filed at

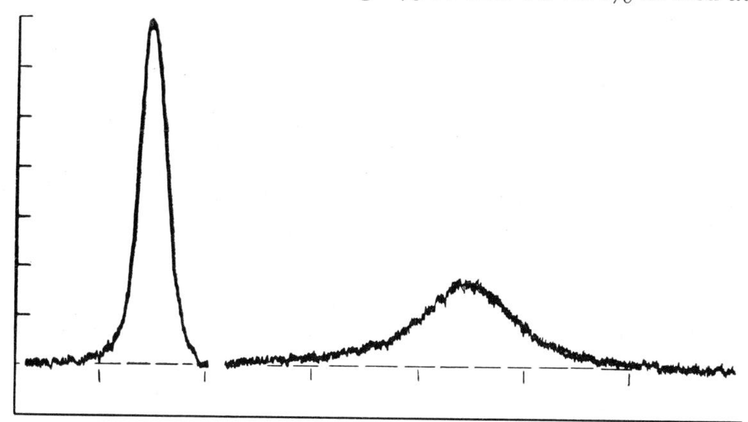

FIG. 9. Spectrometer records of 200 diffraction lines from Cu–2.94% Si alloy. Curve on the left is for annealed state, curve on the right for room-temperature cold work. Scale of intensity (ordinate) is linear; scale of abscissa is marked in intervals of $\theta = \frac{1}{2}°$.

low temperatures (20° to −195°C), where it is supersaturated. The widths of the lines from Cu–30% Zn also suggest that faulting may possibly be common in this alloy.

A high ratio B_{200}/B_{111} would be expected when faults are frequent in face-centered cubic crystals. In any region where there are faults on one set of {111} planes, say the $(\bar{1}11)$, but not on $(1\bar{1}1)$, $(11\bar{1})$, or (111), the reflections from the latter three develop fault streaks, but $(\bar{1}11)$ does not. The Debye ring from such regions therefore contains three components that are widened by faulting and one that is not. The 200 ring, on the other hand, is composed of reflections all of which are widened.

If a major portion of the broadening in these copper and silver alloys is due to the faults, as would seem probable, then the relative sharpness of the lines and the low B_{200}/B_{111} ratio of some of the other specimens implies that they have few faults or none.

In this class is aluminum, aluminum alloy 24S-T, and Cu–2.94% Si deformed at 450°C.

The fact that a variation in line-width ratio with deformation temperature is observed in the copper alloy, where faulting is believed to depend markedly on temperature, and is not observed in copper and aluminum, supports the interpretation proposed

TABLE 1

Specimen	*Filing Temperature*	B_{111}	B_{200}	B_{200}/B_{111}
Cu (electrolytic)	20°C	0.079	0.160	2.0
	−195	0.103	0.213	2.1
Cu–1.89% Si	20	0.159	0.391	2.5
Cu–2.94% Si	450	0.078	0.128	1.6
	350	0.087	0.208	2.4
	20	0.205	0.487	2.4
	−195	0.224	0.626	2.8
Cu–4.17% Si	20	0.339	0.690	2.0
Cu–8.5% Zn	20	0.137	0.221	1.6
Cu–30% Zn	20	0.244	0.456	1.9
Ag (electrolytic)	20	0.067	0.183	2.7
Ag–7% Sb	20	0.197	0.501	2.5
Ag–11% Sn	20	0.244	0.576	2.4
Al (2S)	20	0.020	0.022	1.1
	−195	0.027	0.027	1.0
Al alloy (24S-T)	20	0.104	0.112	1.1

above. The elastic anisotropy and the type of microstress distribution probably remain unaltered by these changes in the deformation temperature, though the magnitude of the stresses must change; therefore the line-width ratio due to stresses would be expected to be invariant with temperature.*

* The elastic anisotropy is known for several of the materials used: Young's modulus ratio E_{111}/E_{100} is 1.2 in Al, 2.6 in Ag, 2.86 in Cu, 3.06 in Cu–8.5% Zn, and 3.68 in Cu–30% Zn. But since B_{200}/B_{111} depends both upon the elastic anisotropy and the nature of the stress distribution, which is unknown, and since the relative magnitudes are also unknown for the components that make up the total broadening (faults, stresses, and perhaps crystallite size), it does not appear possible to draw rigorous conclusions from the observed values of the B_{200}/B_{111} ratio. From Table 1 the value $(B_{200} \cot \theta_{200})/(B_{111} \cot \theta_{111})$ for Cu–30% Zn is 1.61, to be compared with Smith and Stickley's figure[18] 1.63 for Cu–28% Zn. It is possibly significant that this ratio is not

The possible presence of widening from the crystallite-size effect, and how this might affect the ratio at different filing temperatures, are uncertain. Several investigators have concluded that it is unimportant compared with stress widening, though there has not been universal agreement on the point. But if it is an important factor here, it alone would not alter the ratio unless the crystallites effectively differed in *shape* when they were produced by filing at different temperatures. The fact that the ratio is unchanged by filing temperature in copper and aluminum suggests that this factor is either absent or independent of temperature and can be ignored. An even better correlation between these data and the expectations for fault widening that are based on the prior work is found when merely the width of one line is considered, for example, B_{200}. With this criterion the aluminum alloys, silver, copper, and copper with low alloy content all fall in the class of nonfaulting metals, and all alloys known to be susceptible to faulting at a given deformation temperature fall in a class having large widths.

The data and computations summarized in Table 1 are by no means of high precision. But the same trends were found on several duplicate experiments, and also were confirmed by measuring line widths at half-maximum intensity, and correcting by the relation $B^2 = B^2_{\text{filed}} - B^2_{\text{annealed}}$. Control tests showed that recovery at room temperature was not introducing important errors. The filing at elevated temperatures was done in such a way that the filings dropped immediately into water, giving less than one-half second for recovery at temperature; control tests showed that line sharpening began to be detectable only after 15 sec at 350°C. Although some may doubt that the aluminum tests were entirely free from recovery, even though commercial rather than high-purity aluminum was used, there can be little doubt that the 24S-T alloy was recovery-free.

It is concluded that fault widening should not be ignored in studies of line widths of face-centered cubic metals, as it usually has been in the past. In aluminum, however, faulting appears to be negligible, and it is concluded that the energy associated with a fault in aluminum is large; this is in accord with the fact that

---

accounted for by the type of stress distribution that Blackman[19] assumed in order to explain the relative widening of most of the lines from alpha brass; his best-fitted stress system predicted 1.45 for the ratio.

annealing twins are rare or absent in aluminum.* Annealing twins are frequent, on the other hand, in Cu-Si solid solutions of high silicon content.

In dislocations language, the stresses introduced by filing appear to be sufficient to dissociate a Taylor dislocation into two Shockley partial dislocations (or the equivalent), and to separate these so as to introduce a twin fault between them, in some supersaturated copper and silver alloys, but not in aluminum.

It has been pointed out [20,21] that the effective average stress calculated from line widths of cold-worked metals is of the order of the flow stress in the various metals, and roughly proportional to it. This has been considered an indication that stresses are responsible for the widening. It now seems open to question, however, whether this conclusion applies to face-centered cubic structures in general. In cases involving fault-induced widening the density of the faults would be expected to increase as the deformation increases, hence as the stress increases. In these cases line widths could be due largely to faults and yet show a clear correlation with flow stress. To separate adequately the widening from particle size, residual stresses, and faults doubtless requires high precision data on various lines and detailed Fourier analysis.

FAULTS FROM TRANSFORMATIONS IN COBALT AND LITHIUM

Hexagonal cobalt has been shown by Edwards and Lipson[8] to yield diffraction patterns (both powder and single-crystal patterns) that indicate faulting on the basal planes, the faults occurring at random intervals and at spacings that average about ten layers. The transformation on cooling from the face-centered cubic form to the close-packed hexagonal form involves a shifting of layers that can be described as the passage of partial dislocations over planes that are spaced at irregular intervals. The change cannot occur without a change of shape of the transforming material—when viewed on a scale of atomic dimensions—and, since any change of shape in a nucleus is resisted by the surrounding untransformed material, there are strains generated that could account for the heterogeneity of the process. At temperatures

* Recent interface tension data obtained by R. L. Fullman indicate that the tension ratio twin-boundary/grain-boundary is much larger in aluminum than in copper. This would lead us to expect that faults would be much more difficult to produce in aluminum than in copper.

near the transformation point the free energies of the two forms are nearly equal, and it is possible that mechanical faulting can also be made to occur in either phase.

The transformation in lithium and Li-Mg alloys[22,23] that occurs by cooling the body-centered structure is productive of a faulted hexagonal structure. This also is a martensitic type of transformation in that individual crystals of the low-temperature structure form with a click and plastically deform the surrounding material. Permanent scars are left on a polished surface even after reversion to the body-centered cubic structure, as recent experiments of J. S. Bowles have shown. The resistance offered by the matrix to the change of shape of the hexagonal phase could again be responsible for the faulting. On the reverse transformation the body-centered cubic phase that forms is fault-free since no low-energy fault planes can exist in the body-centered cubic structure, and is free from major distortions. However, the retransformed crystals must be traversed by many dislocations, to judge by the permanent scars that are left.

The transformation of hexagonal to face-centered cubic lithium and Li-Mg alloys by cold work, like the transformation in cobalt, which also is aided by cold work,[24] is the result of shifts of atom layers that are very probably irregular enough to leave faults in the face-centered structure.

2. DISTORTION FROM THE MOVEMENT OF DISLOCATIONS

Research on faults, discussed in Section 1, is but a very small portion of the research that has been devoted to the disturbances resulting from plastic deformation. Because numerous detailed summaries of these distortions have appeared, no repetition here is necessary. Instead, the aim here will be to review concisely the more fundamental characteristics of the distortions, with emphasis on their interpretation in terms of dislocations.

ELASTICALLY BENT GLIDE LAMELLAE

Optical and electron microscopic evidence, as well as electron diffraction evidence (Heidenreich and Shockley[1]), seems to support the general belief that plastic flow is confined to slip bands and avoids the interior of the lamellae between the active slip bands. The same may be concluded from x-ray reflection micrographs like Fig. 5. The slip bands may be individual planes or close clusters of planes; bands are spaced at distances apart of the order of microns. The lamellae between these bands, while apparently free from visible plastic distortion, must nevertheless be stressed within the elastic range in many instances. In plastically deformed silver chloride the stresses in the lamellae produce birefringence that can be studied under polarized light (Nye[25]). When the system of applied stresses is such as to cause a glide lamella to be bent, there will be a pattern of dislocations along each of its boundaries, the net effect of which will be equivalent to a system of edge dislocations (Taylor dislocations) parallel to the axis of bending, on the convex and concave boundaries of the lamella. If the lamella is bent into a spherical cap, the dislocations on its boundaries will have the net effect of concentric dislocation rings.

LOCAL DISTORTION AROUND SLIP BANDS

At the edge of a slip band, a series of dislocations pile up behind the leading one, producing a localized elastic stress field extending on into the unslipped material, a stress field which tends to propagate the slip band farther. Distortions are to be expected, also, along the surfaces of glide lamellae, since the surfaces cannot be perfect atomic planes, free of imperfections and inclusions; slip must jump from one atomic plane to another at times. All such irregularities, together with local residual stresses, are potential sources of local disturbances, *local curvatures*.

There has been much discussion of x-ray evidence that appears to support local curvatures of this sort.[26] Clear proof is difficult because the absence of bend gliding from various causes must first be established. When a long single crystal is deformed in a way to eliminate as much as possible the obvious forms of bend gliding and conjugate slip on interfering slip planes, asterism is sometimes found in Laue photographs (for example, Collins and Mathewson[27]); yet in other experiments it is not found (Maddin, Mathewson and Hibbard,[28] Dehlinger,[29] Honeycombe[30]). The question of the sensitivity of the test for asterism must be considered in each case, as well as the uncertainty that bend gliding is absent. Perhaps the most direct evidence that some type of distortion is present is that given by x-ray reflection micrographs,[15] which show that slip bands have a higher reflecting power for x-rays than the lamellae between the bands (Fig. 5). This observation indicates reoriented or distorted material concentrated at the bands, therefore local distortions that are distinguishable from any uniform distortion that extends throughout the lamellae.

ROTATIONAL SLIP

X-ray studies of an aluminum single crystal pulled in tension (Mathewson[31]) and electron diffraction patterns of a strained aluminum crystal (Heidenreich and Shockley[1]) indicate that the displacement of glide lamellae over each other need not be a simple parallel displacement, but may involve also a rotation of the lamellae with respect to each other about their normal. This swiveling is the natural interpretation, also, of the fact that a single crystal rod of zinc can be twisted so that longitudinal scratches form a spiral along the rod, provided that the basal planes are nearly parallel to the cross-section plane. In terms of dislocations, this type of distortion is given by a pattern of screw dislocations on the boundaries of the lamellae. Wilman[32] concludes that rotational slip of this kind is quite common in gypsum, cadmium iodide, graphite, copper, silver, lead sulphide, sodium chloride, magnesium oxide, and potassium ferrocyanide trihydrate.

DEFORMATION BANDS, KINK BANDS

Lamellar regions in which, with increasing deformation, the orientation of the lattice becomes progressively different from that of the surrounding material are known as deformation bands. The bands are crystallographic, as may be seen from their appearance in a compressed single crystal of aluminum in Fig. 10. They occur in most metals, perhaps in all, and in both single crystals and polycrystalline metals. The tendency to form these bands depends upon the orientation of a crystal relative to the applied stress.[26] The bands form early in the deformation process. Honeycombe[30] has recently found deformation bands in aluminum single crystals elongated in tension as little as 1 per cent. (The bands were spaced about 0.05 mm apart and were parallel to (110) planes.)

Slip within a band differs from slip in the adjacent material, as is indicated by the fact that the reorientation of the lattice within a band differs from that in adjacent material and is the direct result of the direction and amount of slipping.[26] As deformation increases, the divergence in orientation between neighboring bands increases, and the crystal axes in each band rotate farther from the

FIG. 10. Single crystal of aluminum in which deformation bands have developed during compressional straining. Deeply etched to bring out orientation differences.

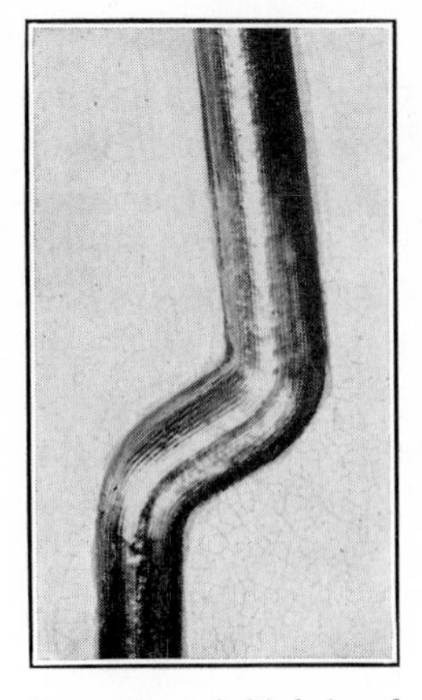

FIG. 11. A kink band in a zinc crystal that had been compressed axially, normal to the hexagonal axis.

original orientation; but the boundaries of the bands that appear in the early stages do not migrate appreciably during the later stages. The orientation within a band is usually not uniform; there is an orientation gradient that is easily seen metallographically. Thus there is frequently severe bend gliding within a band, particularly near the boundaries.

The *kink bands* (Fig. 11) that form in crystals of cadmium and zinc, when suitably compressed along a direction in the basal plane, are particularly simple deformation bands (Orowon,[33] Hess and Barrett[34]) that are easy to study. There is bend gliding at the boundaries of a band, and the bending in ideal cases is symmetrical on the two sides. The reorientation within a band progresses with the deformation and may become as much as 80° or more. The reorientation and bending are initially around an

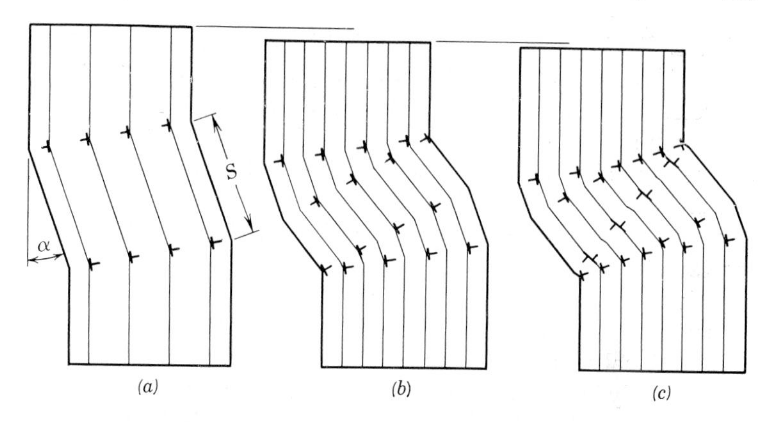

FIG. 12. Successive stages in forming a kink band by generating pairs of dislocations within the length S of a crystal. The slip planes are represented by the lines from top to bottom in each drawing. The process leads to smoothly bent segments, but during polygonalization the dislocations move to planar arrays that radiate out from the grooves, as in sketch *b*.

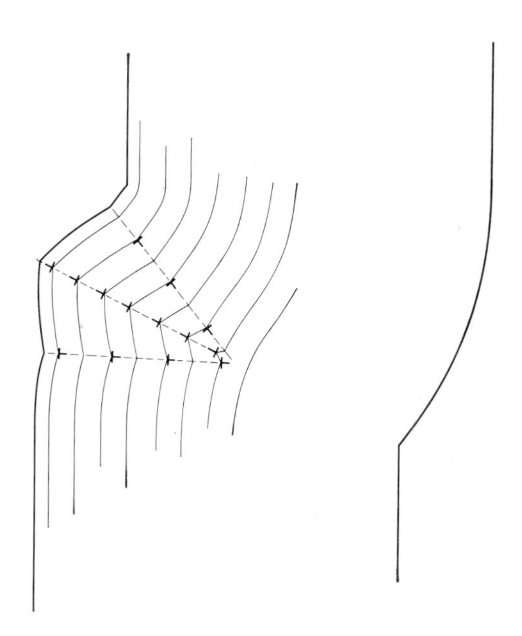

FIG. 13. A ridge formation superimposed on a kink band of more usual form. Dislocation pairs accounting for this manner of deformation in a zinc crystal are indicated.

axis that lies in the slip plane and that is normal to the slip direction. The deformation is confined largely or wholly to the region between the boundaries of the band. The details of kink-band formation are accounted for, as indicated in Fig. 12, by assuming that many pairs of dislocations are generated in the region S between the boundaries. The positive dislocation of each pair moves to one boundary and comes to rest, as in Fig. 12*a*, in a plane array across the crystal (an array of minimum strain energy); the negative dislocation of each pair simultaneously moves to the opposite boundary. Subsequent dislocation pairs similarly build up additional planar arrays next to the first one (Figs. 12*b* and 12*c*), steadily increasing the angle of bend, α, symmetrically on the two sides of the kink band. During annealing, a simple kink band that has smoothly bent glide lamellae undergoes polygonization of a particularly regular type, with subboundaries being very plane, fanning out from a groove, as in Fig. 12*b*. This brings about a splitting up of asterism streaks in Laue photographs into regularly spaced spots. The type of kinking sketched in Fig. 13 is not unusual; this also is readily understood in terms of pairs of positive and negative dislocations that move into the positions indicated.

DEFORMATION TWINS

The mechanism of plastic flow by twinning involves the shearing of atomic layers over each other. The atomic displacements in body-centered cubic crystals produce truly homogeneous shear, since each atom moves a distance proportional to its distance from a plane that is shared with the matrix crystal. In hexagonal close-packed crystals the macroscopic dimension changes are also those for homogeneous shear, but half of the atoms shear homogeneously and the other half move along a path that has the homogeneous twinning shear as one component and a heterogeneous movement, not parallel to the twinning plane, as a second component. Suggested movements are sketched in Fig. 14.[35] The homogeneous component is responsible for the deformation of the surrounding matrix, and coherence is maintained across the boundary of the twin. The second component could not cause distortions of importance in the matrix.

The homogeneous shear in a deformation twin (a shear of 0.131 in magnesium of axial ratio 1.623, zero in crystals of $c/a = 1.732$, and 0.175 in the opposite direction for cadmium, where $c/a = 1.886$)

produces a local stress concentration in the matrix around the edge of the twin, and frequently is known to cause slip and bend gliding in these areas. X-ray reflection micrographs show not only slip

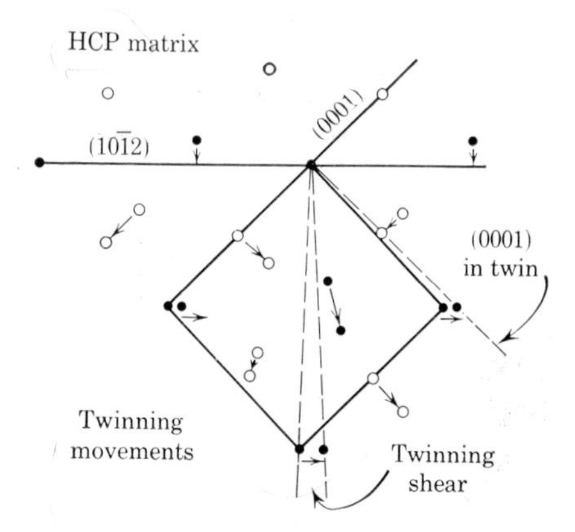

FIG. 14. Atom movements proposed for twinning in a close-packed hexagonal metal like magnesium. Half the atoms in the twin (below the horizontal line indicating the interface) move in homogeneous shear; the others do not. Atoms in the plane of the drawing are shown as dots; those in the layer above as circles.

lines near the rim but also distortion along the boundaries of the twins, where local rotation (doubtless bend gliding) amounts to as much as one degree, in alloyed iron.[15]

MARTENSITIC TRANSFORMATIONS

The characteristics just discussed apply not only to twinning but also to transformations of the martensite (*diffusionless*) type, both spontaneous and strain-induced. Lamellar or lenticular regions transform with a homogeneous component of pure shear, and with the propagation of an interface which retains coherence with the surrounding matrix crystal. The matrix is thereby distorted in the neighborhood of the martensite plate. The matrix distortion is severe enough to be readily seen, and is particularly striking when viewed in an optical interferometer, as in Fig. 15. When there are only a few widely spaced plates the resulting strains nevertheless extend throughout nearly the entire matrix.

The homogeneous component of distortion that occurs in a region that is transforming martensitically may be true shear, as it is in the cobalt transformation from cubic to hexagonal close packing, or shear combined with uniaxial expansion, as it is in carbon steels (Bowles[36]). The homogeneous distortion may be followed by or combined with a heterogeneous shear on a different

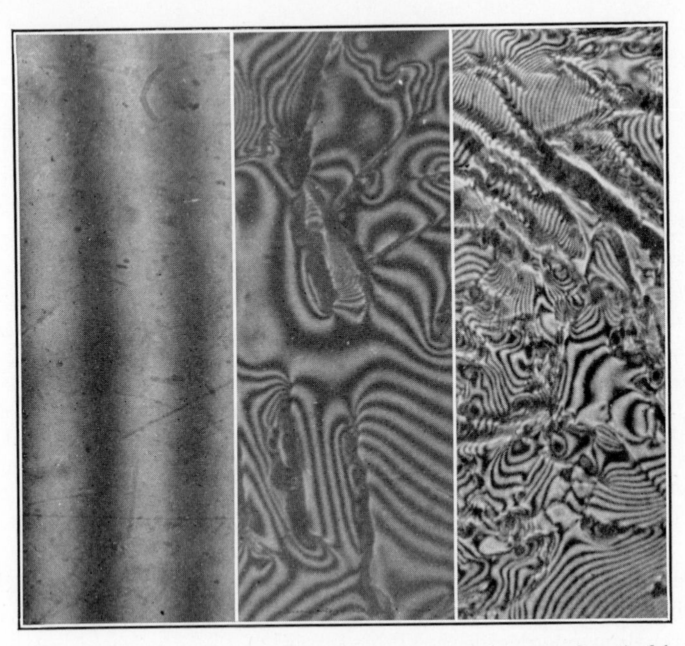

FIG. 15. Strains around martensite plates as shown by curved optical interference fringes. Large-grained Fe-Ni alloy polished optically flat while in face-centered cubic structure and mounted in a Michelson interferometer. (×10.) (*a*) Before transformation. (*b*) Cooled until one burst of martensite crystals formed. Bent fringes show inhomogeneous strain (plastic as well as elastic), extending some distance from each "needle." (*c*) Cooled further; more martensite, steeper strain gradients.

set of planes (as it is in Fe-C martensite), but the latter occurs in layers of submicroscopic thickness and leaves no observable relief effects on polished surfaces. Consequently, this can be neglected as a cause of distortion in the matrix. In some martensitic transformations there is also a change of specific volume that contributes to the matrix distortion.

It is not unlikely that some precipitation processes in supersaturated solid solutions should also be classed as martensitic (at least in the early stages) and that age hardening in these cases results chiefly from the fact that the change of shape of the region that transforms to the precipitate distorts the matrix just as in Fig. 15. This type of distortion would account for the blurring of Laue spots and the strains registered in x-ray reflection micrographs.[15]

GRAIN-BOUNDARY AND SUBBOUNDARY FLOW

Plastic flow at grain boundaries, which is viscous in nature (Zener[37]), becomes an increasingly important mechanism of deformation as the temperature is raised and the time under stress is increased. In creep tests of aluminum it can replace ordinary slip to such an extent that no slip lines are visible (Hanson and Wheeler[38]). There is, nevertheless, distortion in the grains at regions remote from the grain boundaries. That this distortion differs from that observed at room temperature or in short time tests is indicated by the fact that the spots on x-ray diffraction patterns of creep specimens are altered. The spots become subdivided into many smaller sharp spots, which contrast sharply with the smoothly blurred spots (asterism streaks) that normally result from low-temperature deformation (Wilms and Wood,[39] Wood and Rachinger[40]). It has been suggested that the deformation is concentrated at subgrain boundaries, which divide the grains into cells 1 to 10 μ across, and also at the main grain boundaries, with the interior of the cells remaining undeformed. An alternate explanation, that the grains deform in the usual way and polygonalize during the creep experiment, is rejected by Wood and Rachinger on the basis that this mechanism produces much smaller subgrains—when deformation at low temperatures is followed by annealing at the temperature of creep. This criticism, however, presumes that the nature of the distortion in the absence of recovery is independent of the cold-working temperature, which may not be the case if we judge by stress-strain curves, which are clearly different when made at different temperatures.

Read and Shockley[41] have shown how deformation can occur by the movement of boundaries between slightly tilted regions, both by the movement of dislocations along slip planes and by the movement of dislocations normal to slip planes (with the aid of diffusion). Mott[42] and Kê[43] have discussed the possible nature of flow in more disorganized grain boundaries, such as must occur when adjacent grains differ widely in orientation.

STRAIN NEAR GRAIN BOUNDARIES

The individual grains of polycrystalline metals have different effective yield strengths and differently oriented slip systems, and since they must remain fitted together during any deformation of the aggregate they must deform in a nonuniform manner.[26] Boas and Hargreaves[44] found that in large-grained aluminum elongated 5 per cent, portions of individual grains were strained as little as 3 per cent and as much as 14 per cent. Grains with small average extension inhibited the deformation in neighboring grains and were themselves more heavily deformed near their boundaries than if they had been free. In two-phase alloys similar strain gradients were found.[45] Strain gradients are found throughout the interior of grains, but are especially severe near boundaries since slip lines and deformation twins frequently end in these regions.

The author of this paper wishes to thank Drs. M. S. Paterson, Charles S. Smith, and F. Laves, and Mr. J. B. Hess for helpful discussions, and Mr. F. D'Heurle and Miss M. A. Barrett for assistance in the line-width experiments.

REFERENCES

1. R. D. Heidenreich and W. Shockley, *Report of a Conference on the Strength of Solids*, University of Bristol, England, Physical Society, London, 1948.
2. *Carnegie Institute of Technology Symposium on the Plastic Deformation of Crystalline Solids*, Office of Naval Research, 1950.
3. F. C. Frank, *Proc. Phys. Soc. (London)*, **A62**, 202 (1949).
4. W. G. Burgers, *Proc. Phys. Soc. (London)*, **52**, 23 (1940); *Proc. Kon. Ned. Akad. v. Wet. Amsterdam*, **42**, 293 (1939); **50**, 595 (1947).
5. W. L. Bragg, *Proc. Phys. Soc. (London)*, **52**, 54 (1940).
6. W. Shockley and W. T. Read, *Phys. Rev.*, **75**, 692 (1942); also reference 41 below.
7. S. B. Henricks and E. Teller, *J. Chem. Phys.*, **10**, 147 (1942).
8. O. S. Edwards and H. Lipson, *Proc. Roy. Soc. (London)*, **A180**, 268–277 (1942); *J. Inst. Metals*, **69**, 177 (1943).
9. W. H. Zachariasen, *Phys. Rev.*, **71**, 715–717 (1947); *Acta Cryst.*, **1**, 277–281 (1948).
10. A. J. C. Wilson, *Proc. Roy. Soc. (London)*, **A180**, 277–285 (1942); *X-ray Optics*, Methuen D Co., London, 1949.
11. H. Jagodzinski, *Acta Cryst.*, **2**, 201, 208 (1949).

12. J. Mering, *Acta Cryst.*, **2**, 371 (1949).
13. C. S. Barrett, *Trans. AIME*, **188**, 123 (1950).
14. C. H. Mathewson and A. Phillips, *Trans. AIME*, **54**, 608 (1916). C. H. Mathewson, *Trans. Am. Soc. Metals*, **32**, 38–87 (1944). Discussion to J. E. Burke and C. S. Barrett, *Trans. AIME*, **175** (1948).
15. C. S. Barrett, *Trans. AIME*, **161**, 15 (1945).
16. Cyril S. Smith, *Trans. AIME*, **175**, 15 (1948).
17. A. Byström and K. E. Almin, *Acta Chem. Scandinavica*, **1**, 76 (1947).
18. Charles S. Smith and E. E. Stickley, *Phys. Rev.*, **64**, 191 (1943).
19. Nelson W. Blackman, *Phys. Rev.*, **70**, 698 (1946).
20. H. D. Megaw and A. R. Stokes, *J. Inst. Metals*, **71**, 279 (1945).
21. M. S. Paterson and E. Orowan, *Nature*, **162**, 991 (1948).
22. C. S. Barrett and O. R. Trautz, *Trans. AIME*, **175**, 579 (1948).
23. C. S. Barrett, *Phase Transformations in Solids*, National Research Council Committee on Solids, Symposium Held at Cornell University, 1948, John Wiley and Sons, 1951.
24. A. R. Troiano and J. L. Tokich, *Trans. AIME*, **175**, 728 (1948).
25. J. F. Nye, *Nature*, **161**, 367 (1948).
26. C. S. Barrett, *Structure of Metals*, McGraw-Hill Book Co., New York, 1943.
27. J. A. Collins and C. H. Mathewson, *Trans. AIME*, **137**, 150 (1940).
28. R. Maddin, C. H. Mathewson, and W. R. Hibbard, *Trans. AIME*, **185**, 527 (1949).
29. U. Dehlinger, *Carnegie Institute of Technology Symposium on the Plastic Deformation of Crystalline Solids*, Office of Naval Research, 1950.
30. R. W. K. Honeycombe, *Proc. Phys. Soc. (London)*, **A63**, 672, 1950.
31. C. H. Mathewson, Campbell Lecture, *Trans. Am. Soc. Metals*, **32**, 38 (1944).
32. H. Wilman, *Nature*, **165**, 321 (1950).
33. E. Orowan, *Nature*, **149**, 643 (1942).
34. J. B. Hess and C. S. Barrett, *Trans. AIME*, **185**, 599 (1949).
35. C. S. Barrett, *Seminar on Cold Working of Metals*, pp. 65–98, American Society for Metals, Cleveland, 1949.
36. J. S. Bowles, *Acta Cryst.* (in press).
37. C. Zener, *Elasticity and Anelasticity of Metals*, University of Chicago Press, 1948.
38. D. Hanson and M. A. Wheeler, *J. Inst. Metals*, **45**, 229 (1931).
39. W. A. Wilms and W. A. Wood, *J. Inst. Metals*, **75**, 693 (1949).
40. W. A. Wood and W. A. Rachinger, *J. Inst. Metals*, **76**, 237 (1949).
41. W. T. Read and W. Shockley, *Phys. Rev.*, **78**, 275 (1950).
42. N. F. Mott, *Proc. Phys. Soc. (London)*, **60**, 391 (1948).
43. T. S. Kê, *J. App. Phys.*, **20**, 274 (1949); *Phys. Rev.*, **73**, 267 (1948).
44. W. Boas and M. E. Hargreaves, *Proc. Roy. Soc. (London)*, **A193**, 89 (1948).
45. W. Boas, *Helv. Phys. Acta*, **23**, 159 (1950).

DISCUSSION

W. T. Read (Bell Telephone Laboratories):

Was it possible to determine the relative number of stacking faults that cut across the active slip planes? As Heidenreich and Shockley have pointed out,[1] a fault increases the slip resistance of the planes that it intersects; this may be the mechanism of hardening in the Cu-Si alloys.

C. S. Barrett (*in reply*):

Judging by the strain markings in photomicrographs, which presumably indicate how the faults are arranged, there is a distinct tendency for faults to lie in parallel sets and to avoid crossing each other. This tendency may predominate in the very early stages of deformation, but as plastic flow continues they must soon be forced to cross frequently. Figure 8 shows many groups of parallel markings, but even the widely spaced markings shown in this micrograph cross each other frequently in some areas. There has been no statistical study of the amount of crossing versus the hardness or the strain hardening, but I have noticed that the same element — silicon — that confers an unusual amount of strain-hardening property to copper-base alloys also is the element that increases the faulting tendency most markedly.[13] There are certainly grounds for believing that strain hardening is due in part to slip having to cross previous slip planes or twin faults.

W. L. Bragg (Cavendish Laboratory, Cambridge):

In the line-width studies is there no line that is unwidened by faults? It would be useful to compare the width of such a line with the widths of the fault-widened lines.

C. S. Barrett (*in reply*):

No, in these face-centered cubic metals there was no line available that would not be widened by faults on the close-packed planes. With hexagonal close-packed metals, of course, the situation is better, and I hope to continue some studies I have started on these.

B. E. Warren (Massachusetts Institute of Technology):

There should be reflections, even with face-centered cubic structures, that would not be widened by faults. Consider the vectors from a given atom to the two nearest atoms on one side of it in a close-packed plane. One of these vectors is $(\mathbf{a}_1 + \mathbf{a}_3)/2$ and the other is $(\mathbf{a}_2 + \mathbf{a}_3)/2$, where $\mathbf{a}_1$, $\mathbf{a}_2$, and $\mathbf{a}_3$ are the lattice vectors that define the unit cell. The displacement vector for a fault parallel to this plane is one-third the sum of these two vectors, thus is

$$\delta = \frac{\mathbf{a}_1 + \mathbf{a}_2 + 2\mathbf{a}_3}{6}. \tag{D.1}$$

Consider now the reciprocal lattice vector $\mathbf{H} = h\mathbf{b}_1 + k\mathbf{b}_2 + l\mathbf{b}_3$. A reflection will not be widened by faults if the dot product $\delta \cdot \mathbf{H}$ is an integer,

$$\delta \cdot \mathbf{H} = \left(\frac{\mathbf{a}_1 + \mathbf{a}_2 + 2\mathbf{a}_3}{6}\right) \cdot \quad (h\mathbf{b}_1 + k\mathbf{b}_2 + l\mathbf{b}_3) = n, \tag{D.2}$$

where n is an integer. This reduces to

$$\frac{h + k + 2l}{6} = n, \tag{D.3}$$

and so the 600, 060, and 006 reflections, for example, would not be widened with face-centered cubic crystals. Unfortunately the 600 line falls on the 244 line.

C. S. Barrett (*in reply*):

The 600 line would be very difficult, if not impossible, to work with in cold-worked metals. In fact, I doubt that high indices reflections like this could be seen even if a wavelength were chosen that would give them a chance to reflect.

B. E. Warren:

I think it would be well to get the widening for all possible planes, or at least for several, and to compare the results with the variation in Young's modulus for these planes. In brass we find that the relative widening of different planes *does* match the relative values for Young's modulus, as if isotropically distributed normal stresses caused the widening. From this it looks like not more than 10 or 20 per cent of the widening could be due to faults.

C. S. Barrett (*in reply*):

There is some discussion of the elastic anisotropy and the unknown nature of the stress distribution in a footnote of this paper (page 112). I doubt that the measurements reported in Table 1 are precise enough to permit very sound conclusions on this point, and I feel also that there are too many unknowns involved in stress widening to reach rigorous conclusions yet as to whether or not stresses fully account for widening in brass. M. S. Paterson is looking into the possibility of separating stress, particle size, and fault broadenings by Fourier analysis when they occur together in unknown proportions, and I would guess that such an approach might eventually solve the problem. For the present I believe the data presented here on the temperature dependence and composition dependence of the widening in alloys indicate that the possible presence of fault widening must not be ignored in analyzing line widths of cold-worked metallic phases, as has been the custom in the past.

4.

Experimental Information on Slip Lines

W. T. READ, JR.

Bell Telephone Laboratories, Murray Hill, N. J.

ABSTRACT

This paper is a brief review of experimental information on slip lines, no attempt being made at interpretation. For the most part, the results refer only to metal single crystals; the various metals are considered one after another. The experimental investigations reported have been concerned with determining the slip direction and slip plane, the form of the slip lines (straight or wavy, continuous or discontinuous), and the spacing of the various classes of slip lines and the amount of slip per line. The slip direction is always observed to be the line of closest atomic spacing; but the other features of slip (slip plane, form of the lines, and distribution of slip) vary with the metal, temperature, stress, and manner of loading. Techniques for the study of the influence of experimental conditions on slip lines include light and electron microscope observations, multiple-beam interferrometry, and, in case of transparent crystals, photoelasticity. Light microscope results are discussed in relation to the resolving power of the microscope, and the various classes of slip lines are distinguished. Special emphasis is given to the recent electron microscope studies of slip in aluminum in which anodic oxide replicas are used to obtain the highest resolution at present possible in slip studies. Multiple-beam interferrometry is discussed as a powerful technique for the study of slip at small deformation. Recent and current studies of cross slip and deformation bands and the influence of surface treatment on slip lines are reported.

1. SLIP LINES

The term *slip lines* will be used to denote the visible marking, on the surface of a crystal resulting from slip. It is necessary to distinguish various classes of slip lines, depending on (1) the magnification at which the line is observed as a single line and (2) the resolution required to reveal the fine structure of the line. The purpose of this paper is to review the experimental information on slip lines, no attempt being made at interpretation. Because of the great variation in results from metal to metal, the various metals will be considered separately or in small groups. Unless otherwise specified, it will be understood that the experiments were performed on single crystals. The experimental investigations reported here have been concerned mainly with determining:

(1) The slip direction.
(2) The slip plane.
(3) The form of the slip lines, straight or wavy and continuous or discontinuous.
(4) The distribution of slip, that is, the spacing of the various distinguishable classes of lines and the slip per line.

All these, except 1, are found to vary with the metal, temperature, stress and manner of loading; under all conditions the slip direction lies in the line of closest atomic packing, no reliable evidence to the contrary having been reported. We shall review the experimental evidence regarding the variation of the slip plane, form of the slip lines, and the distribution of slip as functions of the experimental conditions. Emphasis will be placed on the importance of the resolving power of the microscope used and the necessity of distinguishing clearly the various classes of slip lines. What appears to the eye as a single line is observed to be a cluster of fine lines when viewed in a light microscope, and these, in turn, may be revealed as clusters of lines by the electron microscope.

With the exception of photoelastic studies of silver chloride no attempt has been made to review the extensive work on non-metallic crystals. Much of this work is covered in books by Friedel[1] and Tertsch[2] and in the review paper by Smekal.[3] Other reviews of experimental information on slip lines include the Schmid and Boas classic,[4] Elam,[5] Kochendorfer,[6] Barrett,[7] and the review article by Miss Kuhlmann.[8] Slip planes and directions are summarized in Table 1.

TABLE 1

Slip in Metals

(By permission from *Structure of Metals*, by C. S. Barrett. Copyright, 1943, McGraw-Hill Book Co., Inc.)

Structure	Metal	Low Temperatures		High Temperatures	
		Plane	Direction	Plane	Direction
F.c.c.	Al	(111)	[$10\bar{1}$]	(100)	[$10\bar{1}$]
	Cu	(111)	[$10\bar{1}$]		
	Ag	(111)	[$10\bar{1}$		
	Au	(111)	[$10\bar{1}$]		
	Ni	(111)	[$10\bar{1}$]		
	Cu-Au	(111)	[$10\bar{1}$]		
	α-Cu-Zn	(111)	[$10\bar{1}$]		
	α-Cu-Al	(111)	[$10\bar{1}$]		
	Al-Cu	(111)	[$10\bar{1}$]		
	Al-Zn	(111)	[$10\bar{1}$]		
	Au-Ag	(111)	[$10\bar{1}$]		
B.c.c.	α-Fe	(110)	[111]		
		(112)	[111]		
		(123)	[111]		
	Mo	(112)	[111]	(110)	[111]
	W	(112)	[111]		
	K	(123)	[111]	(123)	[111]
	Na	(112)	[111]	(110)	[111]
	β-Cu-Zn	(110)	[111]		
		(112)(?)			
	α-Fe-Si; 5% Si	(110)			
H.c.p.	Mg	(0001)	[$2\bar{1}\bar{1}0$]	($10\bar{1}1$)	[$2\bar{1}\bar{1}0$]
				($10\bar{1}2$)	
		($10\bar{1}1$)	[$10\bar{1}0$]		
	Cd	(0001)	[$2\bar{1}\bar{1}0$]		
	Zn	(0001)	[$2\bar{1}\bar{1}0$]		
	Be	(0001)	[$2\bar{1}\bar{1}0$]		
	Zn-Cd	(0001)	[$2\bar{1}\bar{1}0$]		
	Zn-Sn	(0001)	[$2\bar{1}\bar{1}0$]		
	Te	(0001)			
Rhombohedral	Bi	(111)	[$10\bar{1}$]		
	Hg	(100) and complex			
Tetragonal	β-Sn (white)	(110)	[001]	(110)	[111]
		(100)	[001]		
		(100)	[011](?)		
		($10\bar{1}$)	[101]		
		(121)	[101]		

2. HEXAGONAL METALS

In hexagonal metals, at room temperature, slip occurs on the basal plane. The slip lines are straight, regular, and continuous, unless the slip planes themselves are bent, as, for instance, in the bend gliding caused by the constraining flexural moment at the grips in the usual tensile test.

In cadmium, Andrade and Roscoe[9] found that slip lines visible to the eye appear after small extension and become more prominent as the extension proceeds. At ×1000 these coarse lines are resolved into finer lines, several classes of lines from faint to well developed being distinguishable. At higher extensions the differences between classes of lines are accentuated; there are some very well-marked lines, whereas the whole length of the specimen is covered with fine lines.

In cadmium, the distribution of slip is strongly dependent on temperature. At high temperatures most of the glide takes place on a few well-marked and widely spaced planes. The same effect is observed in zinc and other metals (Schmid and Boas.[4])

Bakarian and Mathewson[10] made a study of slip in magnesium as a function of temperature, orientation of the specimen, and method of loading. Their results are summarized in the next three paragraphs.

Compression. Basal slip alone operates from room temperature to 310°C for angles between the compression axis and slip plane pole of 20° to 60°. Larger angles give profuse twinning; smaller angles give either fracture or basal slip, followed by fracture.

Tension. Basal slip alone operates below 225°C. Slip on the pyramidal planes begins to operate at 225°C. However, even well above this temperature, the critical shearing stress for pyramidal slip is about six times that for basal slip. Slip functions on one pyramidal plane until a position of symmetry is reached between two slip systems, and then duplex slip occurs as in face-centered cubic metals.

In contrast to basal slip lines, which are straight and continuous for all temperatures from room to 300°C and for both tension and compression, the pyramidal slip lines are irregular, forked, and discontinuous, resembling those in alpha iron. No characteristic spacing is observed for the basal slip lines.

Parker and co-workers[11] studied the effect of a thin layer of copper plating on the high-temperature creep of zinc single crystals. At the test temperatures the copper layer, which was 10^{-5} in. thick, diffused a short distance into the specimen, creating a thin surface layer of Cu-Zn alloy. In addition to hardening the specimen considerably, the surface layer caused a pronounced change in the slip lines. Instead of a large amount of slip on a few slip planes as observed for unplated specimens at high temperature, the plated specimens showed a much more uniform distribution of slip, with many smaller slip lines covering the length of the specimen and no slip lines growing to extremely large size.*

3. MOLYBDENUM, SODIUM, AND POTASSIUM

Tsien and Chow[12] and Andrade and Chow[13] studied the effect of temperature on slip in molybdenum. At 20° and 300°C slip occurred on the (112) planes, and at 1000° on (110). Andrade[14] suggests that the active slip plane in body-centered cubic metals depends only on the ratio of the test temperature to the melting temperature, and that it is the same in all metals for the same ratio. The following table gives the variation of slip plane in various metals with the ratio of test temperature T to melting temperature T_m:

Metals	T/T_m	*Slip Plane*
W, Mo, Na	0.08–0.24	(112)
β-brass Mo, Na	0.26–0.50	(110)
Na, K	0.80–0.87	(123)

The results on alpha iron, however, do not fit this table.

Andrade and Tsien[15] found that the slip lines in sodium and potassium at room temperature are slightly irregular near the heads (that is, when viewed parallel to the slip vector), indicating that glide can take place for short distances on planes other than the operative plane at the test temperature, in this case (123). Andrade and Chow[13] report that the glide planes in molybdenum, potassium, and sodium are regular and parallel, although again some waviness is seen near the heads.

The distribution of slip in sodium, potassium and molybdenum is markedly affected by temperature. At 2000°C the slip lines

* The author of this paper is indebted to Dr. Parker for a further discussion of the slip lines in private communication.

in molybdenum are broad and well marked, nearly all of the slip taking place on only a few planes spaced at about one centimeter. As the temperature is decreased, the lines become progressively finer and more numerous. The same variation is observed in sodium and potassium; at $-182°C$ the slip lines are exceedingly fine and dense.

4. IRON AND SILICON FERRITE

Barrett, Ansel, and Mehl[16] studied the variation in slip plane in silicon ferrite as a function of the temperature and percentage of silicon. In pure iron, slip takes place on (110), (123), and (112) planes, the mechanism being independent of temperature

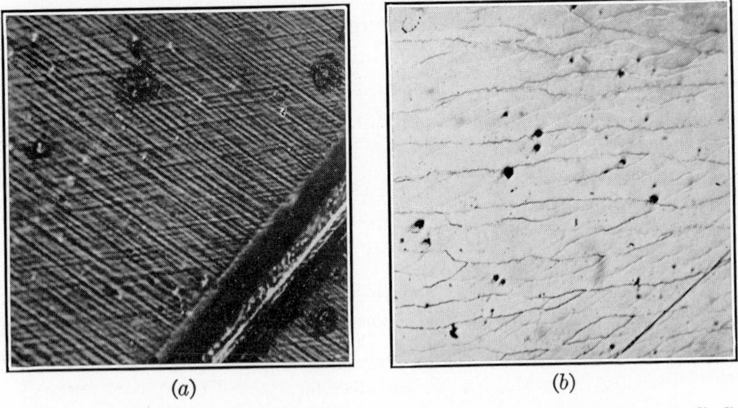

(*a*) (*b*)

FIG. 1. Slip lines in alpha ion: (*a*) straight, (*b*) wavy. (Courtesy of C. S. Barrett, private communication.)

from 20° to $-195°C$. However, in silicon ferrite, at low deformation temperatures or high silicon content (above 4 per cent), slip is confined to (110) planes. When only (110) slip operates, the slip lines are perfectly straight under all conditions of stress. In pure iron or silicon ferrite in the range where three slip planes are effective, the slip lines are very wavy, forked, and irregular. As pointed out by Shockley and Read (Paper 2 of this book), when all three slip systems operate, there are twelve slip planes per slip vector so that slip can shift from one plane to another easily. In contrast, when (110) alone operates there are only three slip planes per slip vector. Micrographs illustrating straight and wavy slip lines in iron are shown in Fig. 1.

Smoluchowski and Opinsky[17] measured the relative values of the critical shearing stresses for (112), (110), and (123) slip at room temperature in a silicon ferrite alloy, where the percentage of silicon was such that the specimens were just within the range where all three slip planes operate. They found that the critical shear stress for the (123) plane was 7 per cent higher than for the (110) plane, and about the same as for (112).

5. SILVER CHLORIDE

Nye[18] observed the slip lines and birefringence patterns in thin transparent sheets of polycrystalline silver chloride. The slip direction was always [110], but the plane was not in general crystallographic and was very wavy in the direction perpendicular to the slip vector. The photoelastic pattern observed in the grains was studied after removal of the load and was found to be independent of the method of loading. In specimens where the slip plane was relatively straight throughout the thickness, clear-cut fringes were obtained in polarized light looking edge-on to the slip plane and at right angles to the slip direction. The photoelastic analysis showed that, in addition to slipping over one another, the glide lamellae were considerably bent, all the lamellae in one grain being bent by the same amount. Thus the stress varied approximately linearly through the thickness of the lamella, with tension on one side and compression on the other and a discontinuity in stress at the boundaries between adjacent lamella.

6. MERCURY

Andrade and Hutchings[19] studied slip in high-purity single crystals of mercury (face-centered rhombohedral) at temperatures from −43°C to −50°C. They found that the slip plane was a rhombohedral face. At a magnification of 22, the slip lines appeared straight and regular. Increasing glide took place on the planes developed in the initial stages; they were spaced about 50 μ. In the later stages of deformation, some much fainter lines appeared between the original lines but never became as prominent as the original lines.

Greenland[20] studied the slip lines in pure single crystals of mercury deformed at −62°C, using a magnification of 16. It was found that, if great care was taken in handling the specimens before stretching in tension, the slip lines were very forked, wavy, and irregular, when viewed parallel to the slip direction. However, when the crystals were slightly bent before stretching, faint but perfect slip lines were observed. When the bent crystals were extended by 1 per cent in tension, these faint lines became more pronounced, indicating slip on the planes developed in bending. Further extensions increased the number of lines. Increasing extension took place by increasing the number of slip lines; each distinguishable glide surface reached a limit of glide of around 5 μ.

Where great care was taken in handling before stretching in tension, the wavy slip planes appear to have a mean orientation coinciding with rhombohedral faces. However, the straight slip planes produced when the crystals were first slightly bent could not be identified as simple crystallographic planes.

The slip lines were not sharp steps at the surface, but rather curved regions 5 to 10 μ in width, indicating either a distribution of small slips or an elastic skin effect.

7. ALPHA BRASS

Treuting and Brick[21] photographed slip lines in alpha brass with a light microscope at room temperature. The slip lines, which are traces of octahedral planes, for the most part are straight and regular, with only occasional discontinuities.

At a magnification at around 800 the lines are observed to occur in clusters which appear as a single line to the naked eye. The number of lines in a cluster as well as the number of clusters increases with the strain.

Maddin, Mathewson, and Hibbard,[22] using a light microscope with a magnification of 1000, observed that slip in alpha brass (approximately 70 to 30 composition) does not follow the classical Taylor and Elam[23] pattern, according to which the slip system with the highest resolved shearing stress operates until a position of symmetry is reached between two equivalent systems. Instead, they found that, in crystals oriented wholly within the range of predicted single slip, cross slip occurred, the cross-slip system having the same slip vector as the primary slip system but a different slip plane (Fig. 2). The cross-slip folds were the order of 10 μ in extent and connected active slip planes of the primary system. Thus slip appeared to have taken place on segmented planes. Increasing elongation produced no marked change in the character of the pattern, the cross-slip lines neither displacing nor being displaced by the primary slip lines. As in Treuting and Brick's observations, the number of lines increased with elongation, the new lines appearing preferentially in areas where earlier markings were present. After a shear of 0.257, the cross-slip lines became longer and more marked and displaced the

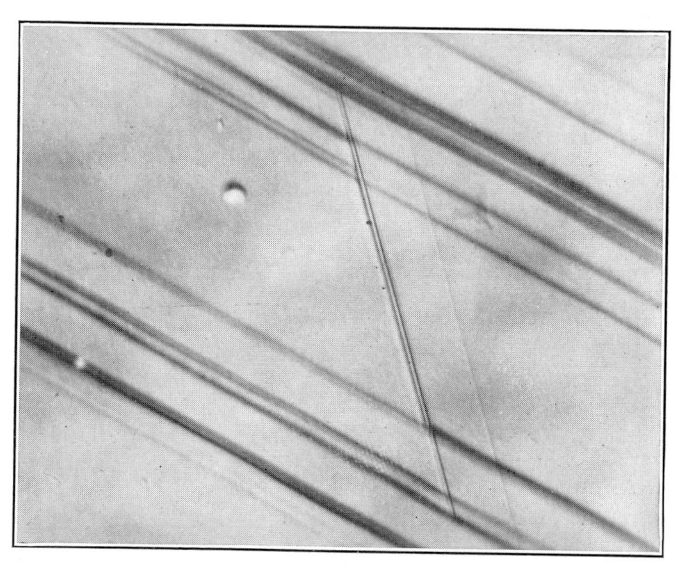

FIG. 2. Prominent cross-slip in alpha brass after shear of 0.09%. ×1000. (From Maddin, Mathewson, and Hibbard, reference 22. Courtesy of A.I.M.E.)

primary slip lines. It was also observed that the Taylor and Elam conjugate slip system began to operate well before the symmetry position was reached.

In general, when a deformed specimen is polished, all evidence of slip lines is removed. However, if deformed alpha brass specimens are polished and etched, fine lines called *strain markings* can be detected on the surface. Burke and Barrett,[24] who made an extensive study of these lines, found that strain markings which can be developed by polishing and etching are visible whenever slip is detected on the unpolished surface. The strain markings followed the direction of the surface slip lines and increased in intensity with increasing deformation. It was concluded that the strain markings were the traces of slip lines which can be etched because of local distortion in the vicinity of a slip line. Essentially the same conclusions were reached by McClean[25] as the result of a similar study.

8. ALUMINUM

At room temperature the slip plane in aluminum is a (111) type plane. Lacombe and Beaujard[26] have observed that, in aluminum single crystals of high purity (99.9 per cent) tested at high temperatures, the slip lines are different from those developed at room temperature. The slip lines at 450°C were no longer straight or parallel. The slip plane appeared to have a mean (100) orientation, in agreement with earlier observations by Schmid and Boas.[4] At deformation temperatures between room temperature and 450°C, slip lines were observed to have an irregular branched appearance.

Lacombe and Beaujard observed that in polycrystalline aluminum the slip lines extended through grain boundaries with a change in orientation, unless there was a large angle of misfit between the adjoining grains, in which case the lines terminated at the boundary.

The early work of Yamaguchi[27] showed that, even at room temperature, the slip lines in aluminum are not perfectly straight, but present an irregular, segmented, wobbly form when viewed along the slip direction.

Crussard[28] observed that slip lines in pure aluminum at room temperature were straight and sharp but discontinuous. He watched the development of slip lines as the specimen was stretched under the microscope at ×100 to ×600. If the elongation was rapid (around 0.1 mm per second), the lines appeared suddenly fully developed and remained unchanged as the load increased. If the stretching was slow and regular, then either a weak line appeared and became progressively stronger, or a segment of a fully formed line appeared and grew at both ends, frequently by jerks. Again a line having developed to a certain extent ceased to grow as the stress was increased. This was proved conclusively by the following experiment. A specimen was stretched 10 per cent, then repolished electrolytically to make the slip lines disappear, with the exception of an area which was protected by varnish. The sample was then stretched an additional 5 per cent so that slip lines were observed on the polished surface. However, many of the lines in the original area did not correspond to any new lines in the polished area, indicating that no further slip had occurred on many of the original slip planes.

Initially, the spacing of the lines seems to be random unless the deformation is very rapid, as in shock tension, in which case the lines occur in bundles.

Cross slip, or slip on planes segmented by folds, has been studied in aluminum single crystals by Cahn[29] and by Rosi and Mathewson,[30] all using light microscopes with magnification around 1000 to 2000. Cahn found that the cross-slip traces were generally not perfectly straight and well defined, and that the plane of cross slip appeared to vary from trace to trace, the most common cross-slip planes being (111), (100), and (212). Mathewson and Rosi have observed that, at least in some cases, apparent cross slip on planes other than the (111) type could be resolved into segmented slips on the primary slip plane and the usual (111) cross-slip plane observed in alpha brass.

Cahn found that cross-slip lines have a fine structure and are actually clusters of fainter lines which, in some cases, are so widely spaced that, at low magnification, the cross slip is not visible and the primary slip lines have the commonly observed appearance of fading out opposite one another. This phenomenon has been called "intimate" cross slip, and is distinguished from "prominent" cross slip where the cross-slip lines have essentially the same structure and appearance as the primary slip lines. Figure 3 from Cahn shows an example of intimate cross slip in aluminum. Figure 2, already discussed for alpha brass, illustrates prominent cross slip. The micrographs of Yamaguchi[27] show clearly the appearance of prominent cross slip at various stages of deformation.

Cahn reports that specimens prepared in the same way showed markedly different amounts of cross slip; when there was less of it, it was predominately intimate. Lower temperatures favored intimate cross slip; the amount of prominent cross slip increased with temperature. At 400°C the cross slip was very prominent and wavy, the cross slip segments connecting the primary lines in an intricate and interlaced pattern. At lower temperatures, the individual lines are less often joined together. The amount of very intimate cross slip increases with increasing deformation at room temperatures, with the result that the slip lines look increasingly wobbly.

Incidentally to these experiments, Cahn observed a strong tendency for slip to be deflected onto the cross-slip plane in the vicinity of an etch pit.

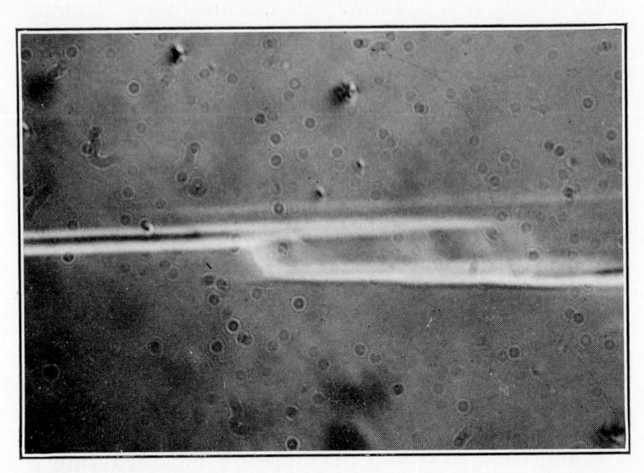

FIG. 3. Intimate cross-slip in aluminum crystal extended 5 per cent. ×2350. (From Cahn, reference 29. Courtesy of the Institute of Metals.)

9. ELECTRON MICROSCOPE STUDIES OF SLIP IN ALUMINUM

Heidenreich and Shockley[31] carried out studies of slip in aluminum single crystals with the electron microscope. Anodic oxide replicas were employed offering a resolution of about 50 Å. What appears in the light microscope as a single line is revealed under the electron microscope to be a cluster of steps, each step being about 200 Å in height (measured normal to the slip plane) with a slip of about 2000 Å per step. That is, a slip cluster is made up of a number of glide lamellae, about 200 Å thick, which slip over one another about 2000 Å in the slip direction. As deformation proceeds, the number of lamellae per cluster was observed to increase, until adjacent clusters ran together, producing one large cluster.

The Kikuchi line electron diffraction pattern was used to investigate the crystal perfection. An aluminum crystal produces a Kikuchi line pattern when annealed, but not when deformed; about 4 per cent deformation is sufficient to extinguish the lines. From observations with various orientations of the electron beam and specimen it was concluded that most of the deformation occurred in the glide lamellae, with practically none in the regions between clusters of active slip planes.

Incidentally to these experiments, it was found that tapping a crystal caused hardening without slip observable in the electron microscope.* In this state no Kikuchi lines are obtained. However, when about 200 μ of material was electrolytically removed, the Kikuchi lines again became visible, showing that the hardening was a surface effect.

Brown[33] continued the electron microscope studies, but used polycrystalline aluminum, deformed by compression or bending at various temperatures. Again it was found that the lines seen optically could be resolved into clusters of elementary lines. Furthermore, Brown discovered that the slip unit is approximately the same at all temperatures, namely, a lamella 200 to 800 Å thick that has slipped about 2000 Å relative to its neighbors. The thickness of the lamella is more variable than the relative displacement and does not appear to be directly related to temperature. The most common thickness is about 200 Å, but values up to 800 Å were found, particularly at high temperature. The slip distance varied between 1500 and 2500 Å. It appeared that the average slip distance at liquid-air temperature is a little less than at higher temperatures.

The grouping of the elementary slip lines into clusters depends on the temperature. For a given amount of deformation, there will be more elementary slip lines per cluster at higher temperatures, and the clusters will be more widely spaced. A typical example of the effect of temperature is the following, taken at a shear of about 40 per cent.

Temperature	*Spacing of Clusters*	*Lines per Cluster*
−180°C	0.5 to 1 μ	1–2
20°C	about 2 μ	3–4
250°C	about 4 μ	5–6
500°C	about 10 μ	~12

At higher deformation more sublines are found per cluster; at very low deformation, the clusters are more widely spaced at all temperatures and contain only one elementary slip line. Thus the progress of deformation is different at different temperatures.

* Hardening of alpha brass specimens by application of a cyclic stress well above the yield point and without visible slip is reported by Wood.[32]

At all temperatures, one-line clusters are found at small deformation. Further deformation increases the number of single lines until a minimum spacing is reached, which varies with temperature as shown above. Thereafter, further deformation takes place primarily by increasing the number of lines per cluster, new clusters rarely being formed.

At higher temperature the slip lines appear to be curved. This is explained by the observation that, if an elementary slip line is followed in the direction of the cluster, it is sometimes found to take a sidewise step corresponding to another possible slip plane having the same slip direction. This phenomenon was observed at room temperature but not at liquid-air temperature.

A slower rate of deformation resulted in less straight slip lines at all temperatures. The slip clusters found in slow deformation at high temperatures were found to consist of a network of interwoven elementary slip lines, with cross slip extending on both sides of the cluster. These results agree with the light microscope observations of Cahn.

10. INTERFERROMETRIC METHODS

Tolansky and Holden[34] report a preliminary study of slip lines, using multiple-beam interference methods. The slip steps on the surface are revealed as discontinuities in the interference fringes. Measurement of the discontinuity in the fringes permits the height of the steps to be measured with an accuracy of a few angstrom units. The high degree of accuracy in measurement of the slip distance, together with the fact that a relatively large surface of the specimen is observed, makes this technique very powerful for studying slip at small deformation, where the spacing between slip lines is easily resolved by the light microscope. It was found that the quality of the fringes, and consequently the accuracy, could be improved by casting the metal against an optical flat. In these preliminary experiments, which clearly indicate the power of the method, no determinations of crystal orientation were made; as a result values of slip distance and spacing were not obtained.

11. SLIP AND DEFORMATION BANDS

The deformation of a metal single crystal in axial tension is generally not a simple relative translation of neighboring parts along a slip plane. Honeycombe[35] studied the lattice distortion in single crystals of aluminum lightly deformed in tension (1 to 10 per cent), using the x-ray technique developed by Berg[36] and applied to metallurgical investigations by Barrett.[37] It was found that the lattice distortion occurred in planar regions around 50 μ in thickness and about 0.05 mm apart. These regions, called deformation bands, appeared after as little as 1 per cent extension,

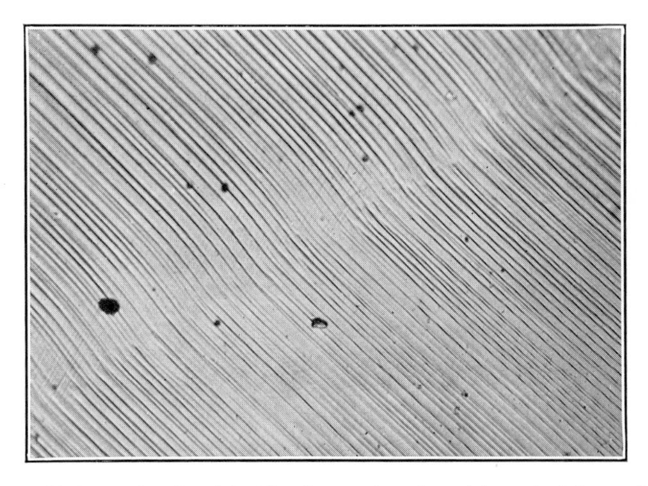

FIG. 4. Deformation band in aluminum viewed at (almost) right angles to slip vector after 24 per cent extension. ×250. (From Cahn, reference 29. Courtesy of the Institute of Metals.)

and usually formed on planes at right angles to the active slip direction [110]. In the light microscope deformation bands are practically invisible up to elongations of about 5 per cent; after greater deformation they are observed as narrow regions in which the lattice is bent (Fig. 4). No deformation bands were found in deformed cadmium crystals and also no x-ray extinction, even after an extension of 100 per cent.

Cahn studied deformation bands in thin aluminum single crystals about 10 by 2 by 50 mm, oriented with the tension axis in the long dimension and the slip vector in the plane of the tension axis and short dimension, so that the flexural moment at the grips was negligible. The tension axis was oriented so that only a single slip system operated over the range of extension. The deformation bands gave the specimen a somewhat crumpled appearance after a few per cent extension. It was found by measuring the deformation of different sections of the specimen that the deformation was inhomogeneous, differences of 5 per cent being found in the same specimen.

The material inside the bands differed in orientation from the rest of the crystal by varying amounts, the rotation about an axis normal to the slip vector and tension axis being much less in the bands than in the main body of the crystal. The plane of the band rotated with respect to the main body of the crystal and remained very nearly normal to the direction of the slip vector in the band. Most of the bands formed at the start, and developed with increasing deformation, the spacing of the bands remaining constant. In weakly extended specimens there was no discontinuity in the slip lines in passing through a band. At higher deformations many lines stopped in the bands and new ones began on the other sides, and some short segments of slip lines corresponding to other slip systems appeared in the bands. Where a line stopped abruptly in a band there was considerable local distortion.

The development and spacing of the bands were found to be independent of the angle between the tension axis and slip direction, the thickness of the specimen, and the temperature from room temperature to 400°C. No experiments in compression were carried out, but it was found that no bands ever appeared in specimens deformed by pure bending even when the curvature was severe, 2 cm^{-1}.

N. K. Chen[38] made a study of deformation bands in aluminum single crystals over a range of orientations. Most of the crystals produced bands, in all cases the plane of the band being perpendicular to the active slip direction. However, when the axis of tension was near a [111] direction, slip occurred without the development of deformation bands, and the slip lines were strongly clustered as in alpha brass, which also does not form bands.

The author of this paper wishes to express his gratitude for helpful discussion and advice to C. S. Barrett, C. H. Mathewson, Robert Fullman, R. D. Heidenreich, and R. G. Treuting and to R. W. Cahn for a copy of his unpublished work on cross-slip and deformation bands in aluminum.

REFERENCES

1. G. Friedel, *Leçons de cristallographie,* Berger Levant, Paris, 1926.
2. H. Tertsch, *Die Festigkeitserscheinungen der Kristalle,* Wein, Springer, Berlin, 1949.
3. A. Smekal, *Handbuch der Physik,* Vol. 24, pt. 2, Springer, Berlin, 1933.
4. E. Schmid and W. Boas, *Kristallplastizität,* Berlin, 1935; English translation, Hughes and Co., London, 1950.
5. C. F. Elam, *Distortion of Metal Crystals,* Clarendon Press, Oxford University, London, 1935.
6. A. Kochendorfer, *Plastische Eigenschaften von Kristallen,* Springer, Berlin, 1941.
7. C. S. Barrett, *Structure of Metals,* McGraw-Hill Book Co., New York, 1943.
8. D. Kuhlmann, *Z. Met.,* **41**, 129 (1950).
9. E. N. da C. Andrade and R. Roscoe, *Proc. Phys. Soc. (London),* **49**, 152 (1937).
10. P. W. Bakarian and C. H. Mathewson, *Trans. AIME,* **152**, 226 (1943).
11. E. R. Parker, M. R. Pickus, L. O. Seaborn, and E. Henderson, *First Technical Report,* University of California Institute of Engineering Research, 1950.
12. L. C. Tsien and Y. S. Chow, *Proc. Roy. Soc. (London),* **A163**, 19 (1937).
13. E. N. da C. Andrade and Y. S. Chow, *Proc. Roy. Soc. (London),* **A175**, 297 (1940).
14. E. N. da C. Andrade, *Proc. Roy. Soc. (London),* **168**, 310 (1938).
15. E. N. da C. Andrade and L. C. Tsien, *Proc. Roy. Soc. (London),* **A163**, 1 (1937).
16. C. S. Barrett, G. Ansel, and R. F. Mehl, *Trans. Am. Soc. Metals,* **25**, 702 (1937).
17. R. Smoluchowski and A. J. Opinsky, *Carnegie Institute of Technology Symposium on the Plastic Deformation of Crystalline Solids,* Office of Naval Research, 1950. A. J. Opinsky, Carnegie Institute of Technology Thesis, 1950.
18. J. F. Nye, *Proc. Roy. Soc. (London),* **200A**, 47 (1949).
19. E. N. da C. Andrade and P. J. Hutchings, *Proc. Roy. Soc. (London),* **148**, 120 (1935).
20. K. M. Greenland, *Proc. Roy. Soc. (London),* **163A**, 28 (1937).
21. R. G. Treuting and R. M. Brick, *Trans. AIME,* **147**, 128 (1942).
22. R. Maddin, G. H. Mathewson, and W. R. Hibbard, Jr., *Trans. AIME,* **185**, 527 (1949).
23. G. I. Taylor and C. F. Elam, *Proc. Roy. Soc. (London),* **A102**, 645 (1923).
24. J. E. Burke and C. S. Barrett, *Trans. AIME,* **175**, 106 (1948).
25. D. McClean, *J. Inst. Metals,* **74**, pt. 2, 95 (1947).
26. P. Lacombe and L. Beaujard, *J. Inst. Metals,* **74**, pt. 1, 1 (1947).
27. K. Yamaguchi, *Sci. Papers, Inst. Phys. Chem. Research* (Tokyo), **8**, 289 (1928); **9**, 277 (1929).
28. C. Crussard, *Rev. de mét.,* **42**, 286 (1945).
29. R. W. Cahn, *J. Inst. Metals,* **79**, pt. 3, 129 (1951). See also *Trans. AIME,* **188**, 1038 (1950).

30. F. D. Rosi and C. H. Mathewson, *Trans. AIME*, **188**, 1159 (1950).
31. R. D. Heidenreich and W. Shockley, *Report of a Conference on the Strength of Solids*, University of Bristol, England, Physical Society, London, 1948.
32. W. A. Wood, *Proc. Phys. Soc. (London)*, **52**, pt. 1, 110 (1940).
33. A. F. Brown, *Metallurgical Applications of the Electron Microscope*, p. 103, Institute of Metals, London, 1950.
34. S. Tolansky and J. Holden, *Nature*, **104**, 754 (1949).
35. R. W. K. Honeycombe, *Proc. Phys. Soc. (London)*, **63A**, pt. 6, 672 (1950).
36. W. Berg, *Z. Krist.*, **89**, 286 (1934).
37. C. S. Barrett, *Trans. AIME*, **161**, 15 (1945).
38. N. K. Chen, Yale University Dissertation, 1950.

DISCUSSION

C. S. Barrett (University of Chicago):

The stopping of slip lines as they approach a boundary of a deformation band is very similar to the behavior of slip lines in a kink band. The orientation of the material within a deformation band is not uniform. There is a rotation of crystal axes as one moves from the center of a band to either boundary, and the same is true of a kink band formed, for example, by the compression of a zinc crystal along a direction lying in the basal plane. In both cases the rotation implies slip lines that come to an end within the bent region near the boundary.[1]

J. Koehler (Carnegie Institute of Technology):

Brown's observations on the increase in the slip zone spacing in aluminum with increasing temperature might be explained in the following way. Let us suppose that there exists in the original crystal a distribution of free lengths of dislocation which can, under sufficient stress, produce glide by the Frank and Read mechanism. As the load is gradually increased, the longest free lengths will produce single-glide lamellae first. After a certain amount of flow has resulted from a given weak spot, further slip on the particular glide plane being used becomes impossible. No good description of the way in which this hardening of the glide plane takes place has yet been given. At any rate we know from the Heidenreich and Shockley electron diffraction experiments that there are large internal stresses in the vicinity of the atomic plane on which glide has occurred. At low temperatures the next stage involves the use of some of the shorter free lengths as sources

[1] Examples are given in C. S. Barrett and L. H. Levenson's *Trans. AIME*, **137**, 112 (1940) (deformation bands in aluminum) and in C. S. Barrett and J. B. Hess's *Trans. AIME*, **185**, 599 (1949) (kink bands in zinc).

for dislocations. These shorter lengths on hitherto unused glide planes require a somewhat larger stress for the production of glide. At high temperatures the thermal fluctuations produce appreciable random stresses which enable the crystal to deform partially by cross slip. In this case the initial weak spot is still utilized, but the dislocations are detoured away from the large internal stresses on the original glide plane via thermally assisted cross slip. Such detouring can take place only over short distances because thermal fluctuations over large volumes are highly improbable. After the dislocations have got far enough away from the original glide plane their motion again turns into a plane parallel to the original glide plane as dictated by the external applied stress.

If the above explanation is correct, one would not expect the same behavior in the case of the hexagonal metals where only one easy slip plane exists.

E. Orowan (Massachusetts Institute of Technology):

There is an essential difference between the pattern on the surface of deformed aluminum, which Cahn and Honeycombe call *deformation bands*, and Barrett's well-known deformation bands, which are now assumed to be kink bands. The latter are regions of plastic deformation within a crystal, bounded by planes that are not parallel and often nearly perpendicular to the operative slip planes. On the other hand, the Cahn-Honeycombe "bands" are layers, nearly perpendicular to a set of visible slip lines, in which there is a discontinuity of the slip line pattern. Some lines terminate here, others join up with lines coming from the other side of the discontinuity layer at the cost of making a more or less pronounced side step. Figure D.1 is a photograph of such a discontinuity layer, at a magnification of about 50. This photograph shows the phenomenon in a crystal of AgCl deformed by a few cycles of extension and compression, but the pattern is practically indistinguishable from that observed by Cahn and Honeycombe on aluminum. The two arrows indicate positions and direction of two (parallel) discontinuity layers.

One cannot escape the impression that the deformation process leading to the formation of the visible slip lines has developed in any single region bounded by two parallel discontinuity layers independently of the other regions; in the boundary layers there is a complex state of drastic distortion, frequently with the operation of another system of slip lines. Cahn finds that the macroscopic deformation in these boundary layers is less than in the regions of undisturbed slip between them; it would be more logical, therefore, to call them no-deformation bands, rather than deformation bands. The latter name should be avoided, because the discontinuity layers are quite different from what

Barrett has called deformation bands. Of course, the regions between the discontinuity layers may well be kink bands which have ultimately extended over most of the volume of the crystal and are separated only by thin layers of slip incoherence.

In the course of the present Conference, Dr. Dunn has shown me micrographs of deformed and annealed iron-silicon crystals (3.3 per

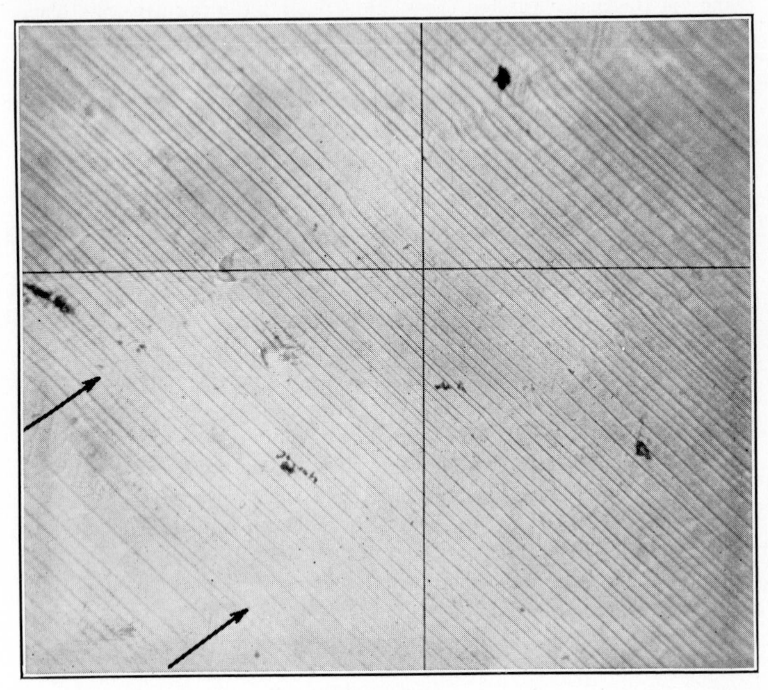

Fig. D.1

cent silicon). One of these photographs shows exactly the same pattern as Fig. D.1; however, this has arisen by annealing after deformation, not by the deformation alone. The deformation has produced slip lines *parallel* to the discontinuity layers formed subsequently by annealing. In the course of annealing, the initial slip lines have gradually disappeared, and a pattern closely resembling Fig. D.1, with the lines nearly perpendicular to the original slip lines and the discontinuity layers parallel to them, has developed. This phenomenon, probably a case of polygonization, may be very significant as a clue to the interpretation of the discontinuity layers.

Perhaps the most important fact about slip lines that has emerged in the course of the last years is that they are by no means a necessary accompaniment of the slip process. In the Lüders bands which appear on mild steel when the upper yield point is exceeded, the slip lines are often completely absent, and appear only when the stress starts to rise from the level of the lower yield point. During the last year, Mr. W. M. Lomer, in the Metal Physics Group of the Cavendish Laboratory, has investigated the formation of Lüders lines by means of a very sensitive microscopical Schlieren-method; with the material (Armco iron) and the heat treatments he has used, slip lines can only rarely be observed in the Lüders bands before the end of the yield. Hanson and Wheeler[2] observed many years ago the absence of slip lines in aluminum crystals

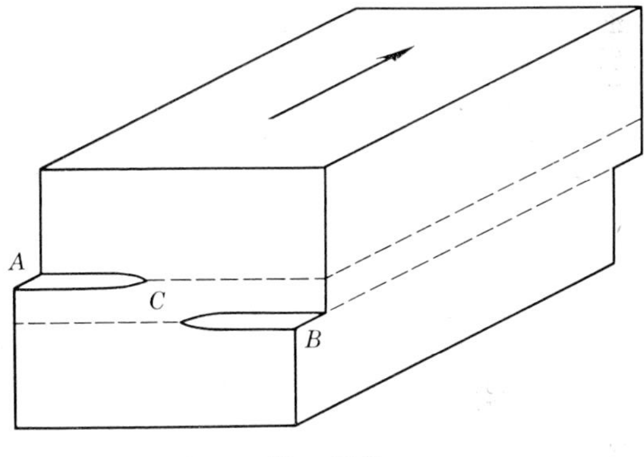

Fig. D.2

deformed slowly at 250°C. In 1949 G. C. Smith and Dewhirst[3] found that there are no slip lines in deformed oxidation-hardened copper containing 0.6 per cent aluminum. If a sheet of this material is heated in air until a surface layer is oxidation hardened, and then bent, the slip lines which are abundant in the nonhardened interior stop abruptly at the boundary of the hardened layer, although the deformation here is at least as strong as in the interior, and it takes place undoubtedly with the same slip mechanism. These phenomena are a reminder that a fundamental problem of slip still awaits solution: why is slip usually concentrated in thin layers, and why does the mechanism of this slip concentration sometimes not work?

The problem of how Mathewson and Hibbard's "unpredicted cross slip" arises may have a trivial solution. Suppose that slip bands start to develop in a crystal at the same time from points A and B (Fig. D.2) in slightly staggered slip planes. Where they meet in the region C, the material is subjected locally to shear stresses that are quite different

[2] D. Hanson and M. A. Wheeler, *J. Inst. Metals*, **45**, 229 (1931).
[3] G. C. Smith and D. W. Dewhirst, *Research* (*London*), **2**, 492 (1949).

from the mean shear stress in the material; obviously, the maximum shear stress here must occur in some plane intersecting the active slip planes at an angle, as indicated in the figure. The ensuing "cross slip" may very well take place in a slip plane of maximum resolved local shear stress, although this is not now the plane of maximum shear stress as calculated macroscopically from the external forces and the orientation of the crystal.

A phenomenon of great importance to the theoretical study of slip is kinking. In kinking, slip propagates at a very high velocity in a direction across the operative slip planes, without extending, as a rule, over more than a fraction of one slip plane. This shows immediately that a dislocation multiplication mechanism such as Frank's reflection mechanism cannot be at work because the slip need not extend to the boundaries of the slip plane. What is much more important, however, is that the operative multiplication mechanism must be one that can spread slip perpendicularly to the slip plane, not only in the slip plane itself. This eliminates, among others, the Frank-Read mechanism, at least in the case of kinking.

I could so far find two multiplication mechanisms that do what is demanded by the phenomenon of kinking, that is, spread slip to neighboring slip planes. First, the plane of maximum shear stress around a sufficiently rapidly moving dislocation is not in the slip plane itself but at an angle to it. This follows already from the circumstance discovered by Frenkel and Kontorova and Frank that a rapidly moving dislocation suffers a quasi-relativistic contraction, with the velocity of the Rayleigh surface waves playing the role of the limiting velocity. For screw dislocations, the contraction is given by the Lorentz transformation formula; for edge dislocations, the conditions are substantially, though not exactly, similar. The high tensile and compressive stresses acting in the slip direction that arise around an edge dislocation as a consequence of the contraction represent high shear stresses in the planes at 45° to the slip plane, and this must have the consequence that the plane of maximum shear stress swings out of the slip plane when the velocity reaches a critical value. Similar conclusions can be reached for screw dislocations. This problem has been treated mathematically (to be published) by Mrs. E. H. Yoffe-Mann, and the results show that the critical velocity is about half of the Rayleigh wave velocity. Quite similar conditions exist for the propagation of a crack in brittle fracture; this is the cause of the tendency of the crack to leave its own plane at a higher velocity, as manifested in the wave part of the surface of fracture which surrounds the "specular" area in fractured glass and other similar brittle materials. A second possible cause for a slip process leaving its own plane is the presence of thermal stresses; this cause is particularly effective with screw dislocations, and its effect combines with that of the velocity. In this way slip can be transferred into a nonparallel plane and, after some propagation in this, again into a plane parallel to the first one which is favored by being that of the maximum resolved shear stress.

Against the possibility of the velocity deflection of edge dislocations speaks the work of Leibfried, who estimates that the maximum velocity of a dislocation at room temperature cannot reach the order of magnitude of 10 per cent of the velocity of sound This upper limit is less than half the critical velocity required for a dislocation to leave its own plane spontaneously. However, there are many uncertain factors in Leibfried's estimate, and, even if his upper limit is correct, the velocity of the dislocation can reach locally much higher values. Finally, the joint effect of the velocity and of thermal stress fluctuations may deflect a screw dislocation at velocities much below half of the Rayleigh velocity.

It may be remarked that, if velocity deflection is the basic multiplication mechanism of dislocations, an explanation of the low but reproducible value of the yield stress of metals appears feasible. The yield stress of a single crystal may be the critical value of the resolved shear stress above which the dislocations can reach the velocity required for deflection-multiplication.

5.

X-Ray Diffraction Studies of Cold Work in Metals*

B. E. WARREN AND B. L. AVERBACH

Massachusetts Institute of Technology

ABSTRACT

The dependence of measured broadening upon λ and θ indicates that cold-work broadening is due primarily to distortion rather than to fragmentation. The integrated intensities of the high-order reflections are not decreased by cold work. The effect is quite different from that of temperature vibration, and the term *frozen heat motion* is an incorrect description of cold-work distortion. Modern techniques allow measuring precisely the shape of a reflection rather than just the width. A new method of Fourier analysis has been developed to get as much information as possible from the x-ray data without making any *a priori* assumptions about the nature of cold-work distortion. For cold-worked (70-30) alpha brass filings the x-ray data indicate that the strains in any direction are inversely as the values of Young's modulus for that direction, and hence that stress is roughly isotropic. Stress distribution functions are obtained using all the powder pattern lines. The root mean square averaged stress decreases with the distance of averaging, indicating the nonuniform nature of the stresses and strains in cold-worked metal. A rough calculation of stored elastic energy for alpha brass gives 1.4 cal/gram.

1. THE INADEQUACY OF LINE BREADTH MEASUREMENTS

Cold work in a polygrained metal produces a broadening of the x-ray powder pattern lines. Most of the earlier discussions have been based upon either the fragmentation theory or the microstress theory. In the former it is assumed that cold work breaks

* Research sponsored by ONR under Contract N5 ori-07832 and by U. S. Atomic Energy Commission under Contract AT-30-1-GEN-368.

the material down into crystals so small that the ordinary particle size broadening appears. In the microstress theory it is assumed that residual strains are left in the material, the strains varying in magnitude from one grain to the next. The different crystals have slightly different planar spacings d, and the reflected beams from the different crystals merge into one broadened reflection. It is possible to distinguish between the two theories by considering the dependence of breadth on λ and θ:

$$\text{Fragmentation theory:} \qquad B = \frac{K\lambda}{L \cos \theta}, \tag{1.1}$$

$$\text{Microstress theory:} \qquad B = f\left(\frac{\Delta d}{d}\right) \tan \theta. \tag{1.2}$$

Comparisons[1,2] between the experimentally measured breadth and either $\lambda/\cos \theta$ or $\tan \theta$ are in much better agreement with the microstress theory, and show that any broadening by the fragmentation theory is of minor importance.

The effect of cold-work distortion on the integrated intensities of powder diffraction lines has been measured in several laboratories, with conflicting results. Brindley[3] and his collaborators concluded that the effect of cold work is to increase the strongest reflections due to reduction in extinction, and to reduce progressively the higher angle reflections in a manner similar to the reduction by temperature vibration. On the basis of this assumed similarity in the effect of either cold work or temperature vibration on the x-ray diffraction pattern, the term *frozen heat motion* has been coined to describe cold-work distortion in a metal.

Recent precision measurements[4] using crystal monochromated radiation and a spectrometer allowed direct comparison between cold-worked and annealed samples. It was found that the effect of cold work is to increase the integrated intensity of the stronger reflections due to reduction in extinction and to give no change in the integrated intensity of the other lines. The spreading out of the high angle reflections from cold-worked filings is so pronounced that, in general, there is considerable overlapping of the tails of neighboring lines. Unless this point is carefully investigated, too high a background level will be assumed, with a resulting peak area which is too low. This is presumably the explanation for Brindley's results, since he used film recording where direct comparison of the cold-worked and annealed patterns is not easy. The effect of cold-work distortion on the integrated intensities is quite different from the effect of temperature vibration, and the use of the term frozen heat motion should be discontinued.

To get the most valuable information from an x-ray study of the nature of cold-work distortion, it is desirable to make accurate measurements which will represent every bit of information available. This means measuring the precise *shape* of the reflection rather than just the breadth, and then using all the additional information contained in the shape of the reflection. It is desirable that the method of analysis be designed to get as much information as possible directly from the x-ray data, without putting in any *a priori* assumptions about the nature of cold-work distortion.

2. FOURIER ANALYSIS OF REFLECTIONS FROM COLD-WORKED METAL

A method[5] is being developed at present for getting as much information as possible from x-ray measurements of cold-worked metals. Precise spectrometer measurements are made of the shape of a reflection from a cold-worked sample, and of the same reflection from an annealed sample. Using Stokes'[6] method, we represent each peak shape by a Fourier series, and, from the two sets of coefficients, we obtain directly the coefficients of a third series, which represents the shape of the reflection due to cold-work distortion only.

We consider a cubic crystal for which it is always possible to adopt a new set of orthogonal axes so as to make any reflection of the form $(00l)$. Consider a general distortion such that the position of cell $m_1m_2m_3$ is given by

$$\mathbf{R}_{m_1m_2m_3} = m_1\mathbf{a}_1 + m_2\mathbf{a}_2 + m_3\mathbf{a}_3 + \boldsymbol{\delta}_{m_1m_2m_3}, \tag{2.1}$$

where the displacement $\boldsymbol{\delta}_{m_1m_2m_3}$ is in general different for every cell. The directions of the primary and diffracted beams are represented by unit vectors $\mathbf{s}_0$ and $\mathbf{s}$, and the combination is represented by a position $h_1h_2h_3$ in reciprocal space:

$$\mathbf{s} - \mathbf{s}_0 = \lambda(h_1\mathbf{b}_1 + h_2\mathbf{b}_2 + h_3\mathbf{b}_3). \tag{2.2}$$

Represent the displacement $\boldsymbol{\delta}_m$ in terms of its components.

$$\boldsymbol{\delta}_m = X_m a_1 + Y_m a_2 + Z_m a_3 \qquad m = m_1, m_2, m_3. \tag{2.3}$$

The distribution in angle of the diffracted power $P_{2\theta}$ is related to the total power in the reflection by

$$P = \int P_{2\theta} d(2\theta). \tag{2.4}$$

Carrying through the integrations involved in getting an integrated intensity,[5] we obtain finally for the distribution of intensity in the reflection

$$P_{2\theta} = K \sum_{n=-\infty}^{+\infty} A_n \cos 2\pi n h_3, \tag{2.5}$$

where

$$h_3 = 2a_3 \frac{\sin\theta}{\lambda}, \qquad A_n = \langle \cos 2\pi l Z_n \rangle_{\text{av.}}. \tag{2.6}$$

$Z_n = Z_{m_3} - Z_{m_3'}$, and the average is over every pair of cells $m_1 m_2 m_3$ and $m_1' m_2' m_3'$, such that $m_1 = m_1' m_2 = m_2'$ and $m_3 - m_3' = n$. The significance of the quantity Z_n is best seen by considering the crystal in terms of columns of cells perpendicular to the reflecting planes $(00l)$. Consider two cells in such a column which are separated by n cell lengths. In the normal crystal the distance between these cells is $L = na_3$. Because of cold-work distortion this length is changed by the amount $\Delta L = Z_n a_3$.

The actual planar spacing d is given by $d = a_3/l$, and the coefficients A_n of equation (2.6) can be represented in terms of distance by

$$A_L = \left\langle \cos 2\pi \frac{\Delta L}{d} \right\rangle_{\text{av.}}. \tag{2.7}$$

In practice the coefficients A_n of equation (2.6) are determined from the experimental curves for $n = 0, 1, \cdots 15$. They are then plotted as the curve A_L vs. L. There is such a curve for each measured reflection. The set of curves for cold-worked alpha brass (70-30) filings is given in Fig. 3.

If the ΔL values are small, or if for a given L the distribution function for the ΔL values is Gaussian, the average of the cosine can be represented by an exponential

$$A_L = \left\langle \cos 2\pi \frac{(\Delta L)}{d} \right\rangle_{\text{av.}} \to \exp\left[-\frac{2\pi^2}{d^2} \overline{(\Delta L)^2} \right]. \tag{2.8}$$

To the extent that the approximation of equation (2.8) is justified, each of the A_L vs. L curves can be converted to a curve of root mean square ΔL vs. L. Figure 1 shows such curves for the (111) and (222) reflections from cold-worked alpha brass filings. The two curves represent the same quantity, and should therefore coincide. Curve A is obtained from the experimentally determined distribu-

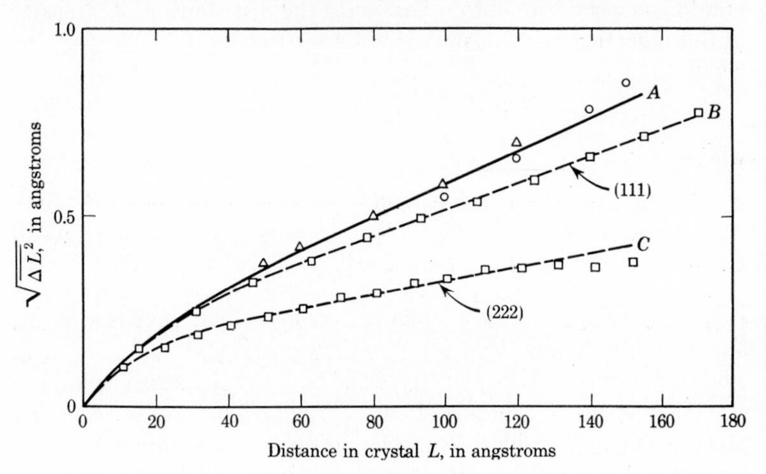

FIG. 1. Root mean square relative displacements in the (111) direction as a function of distance along (111) for cold-worked alpha brass. (A) Obtained from the distribution functions; ○○○ stress distribution function, △△△ strain distribution function. (B) Obtained from the (111) reflection by the approximation of equation (2.8). (C) Obtained from the (222) reflection by the approximation of equation (2.8).

tion functions discussed later, and is independent of the approximation in equation (2.8). The curves (111) and (222) not only do not agree with each other, but they also depart from curve A. Evidently the distribution function for relative displacements ΔL is not well enough represented by a Gaussian function to allow the approximation of equation (2.8).

It is important to recognize clearly the meaning of the quantities represented by curve A. For any point on the curve, the abscissa value represents the length L of a column perpendicular to the (111) planes. Since the component of strain along the direction of the column may not be constant over the column length L, the change in length ΔL due to cold work is given in terms of a strain component averaged over the length L:

$$\Delta L = \langle \epsilon L \rangle_{\text{av.}\,L}. \tag{2.9}$$

The ordinate of curve A is a root mean square average of ΔL quantities for all columns of length L perpendicular to the planes (111). Hence for a given L, the value of $(\overline{\Delta L^2})^{1/2}$ involves a root mean square average of a strain component already averaged over the length L:

$$(\overline{\Delta L^2})^{1/2} = L[\langle(\langle\epsilon\rangle_{\text{av.}\,L})^2\rangle_{\text{av.}}]^{1/2}. \tag{2.10}$$

It is this root mean square of an averaged strain component which is given by the slope of a line from the origin to any point of curve A. If strains were constant over distances large compared to L, the first averaging over the length L would be independent of L, and curve A would be a straight line. The drooping of curve A is to be expected if strains in a cold-worked metal are nonuniform over distances of the order of a few cell lengths. The true root mean square strain component is given by the initial slope of curve A.

3. STRAIN DISTRIBUTION FUNCTION

In principle it is possible to determine the distribution function for ΔL from experiment rather than assuming it to be Gaussian. Introduce a distribution function for the magnitude of ΔL such that

$$\int_0^\infty P_L\,(\Delta L)\,d(\Delta L) = 1. \tag{3.1}$$

The average involved in equation (2.7) can then be expressed by

$$A_L(l') = \int_0^\infty P_L(\Delta L)\cos\left(2\pi\frac{l'}{a}\,\Delta L\right)d(\Delta L), \tag{3.2}$$

where

$$l' = \sqrt{h^2 + k^2 + l^2} = a/d. \tag{3.3}$$

If measurements are made for several orders l' of a set of planes hkl, then, since $P_L\,(\Delta L)$ is the same, we can consider the quantity $A_L(l')$ of equation (3.2) as a function of the variable l'. The distribution function is then given directly as the Fourier transform of the $A_L(l')$ coefficients:

$$P_L\,(\Delta L) = \frac{1}{2}\,\frac{4}{a}\int_0^\infty A_L(l')\cos\left(2\pi\,\frac{l'}{a}\,\Delta L\right)dl'. \qquad (3.4)$$

Quantities such as the root mean square relative displacement can then be computed from the distribution function:

$$\langle(\Delta L)^2\rangle_{\text{av.}} = \int_0^\infty P_L\,(\Delta L)\,(\Delta L)^2\,d(\Delta L). \qquad (3.5)$$

Since L refers to a distance along a given direction in the crystal, it is necessary to measure A_L for various orders of the same set of

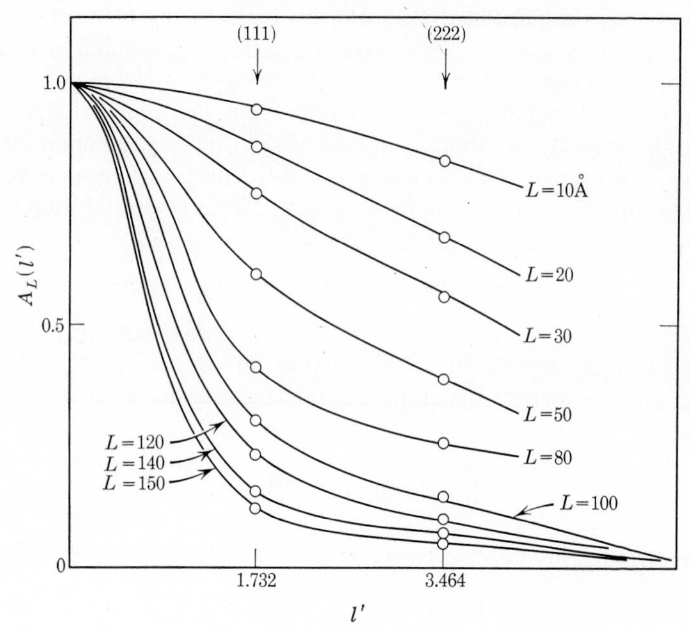

FIG. 2. Fourier coefficients $A_L(\alpha)$ plotted against α for various lengths L. Cold-worked (70-30) alpha brass. See Fig. 3.

planes to determine the values of $P_L\,(\Delta L)$. The plane (hkl) selects a direction in the crystal, the index n selects a distance $L = na_3$ along this direction, and $P_L\,(\Delta L)$ gives the distribution of changes in length ΔL for an original length L. With powder patterns of cubic materials it is possible to measure only the first two orders of a set of planes, since the third order always coincides with some other index combination. For example, measurements can be made for (111) and (222) or for (200) and (400), but (333) coincides with (511) and (600) coincides with (442).

Figure 2 shows the extent to which $A_L(l')$ can be determined as a function of l' for the direction perpendicular to the (111) planes. In addition to the two measured points, we have the added information that at $l' = 0$, $A_L(l') = 1.0$, and the slope is zero, and that $A_L(l')$ approaches zero for large l'. It is evident that the curve $A_L(l')$ vs. l' is not well enough established by the two measured points to give a reliable Fourier transform for $P_L(\Delta L)$.

4. STRESS DISTRIBUTION FUNCTION

Preliminary calculations indicate that the strains in any direction are inversely as the values of Young's modulus for that direction. This would mean that over the distances L for which we measure averaged strains, the stress can be considered to be isotropic. The point can be tested by the available data. Once the relation is established, it is possible to use stress as the variable rather than strain or relative displacements. This makes it possible to use all the powder pattern lines to give a stress distribution function rather than to use just two orders of a reflection to get a strain distribution function.

For a column of length L normal to the planes (hkl) let σ_L be the component of stress along the column averaged over the length L:

$$\sigma_L = E_{hkl} \frac{\Delta L}{L} \cdot \tag{4.1}$$

Equation (2.7) can then be written

$$A_L(\alpha) = \left\langle \cos \left(2\pi \frac{L}{a} \alpha \sigma_L \right) \right\rangle_{\text{av.}}, \tag{4.2}$$

where

$$\alpha = (h^2 + k^2 + l^2)^{1/2}/E_{hkl}. \tag{4.3}$$

Figure 3 shows the curves A_L vs. L for six powder pattern lines from cold-worked alpha brass filings. The value of α which is indicated for each line is taken from Table 1.

It is evident that the curves of Fig. 3 are in the same order as the α-coefficients, as would be expected from equation (4.2) if the

TABLE 1

VALUES OF YOUNG'S MODULUS α AND THE RADIATION USED FOR SIX LINES FROM COLD-WORKED ALPHA BRASS

Line	E_{hkl} *(kilobars)*	$\alpha \times 10^3$	*Radiation*
111	1800	0.96	Cr
222	1800	1.92	Cu, Co
331	1240	3.52	Cu
200	515	3.88	Cr
311	775	4.27	Fe
400	515	7.77	Cu

stresses are isotropic. The crossing of curves (222) and (331) is presumably due to experimental error. A still more exacting test for the assumption that the stresses can be treated as isotropic is given by the curves of Fig. 4. Here the $A_L(\alpha)$ values from Fig. 3

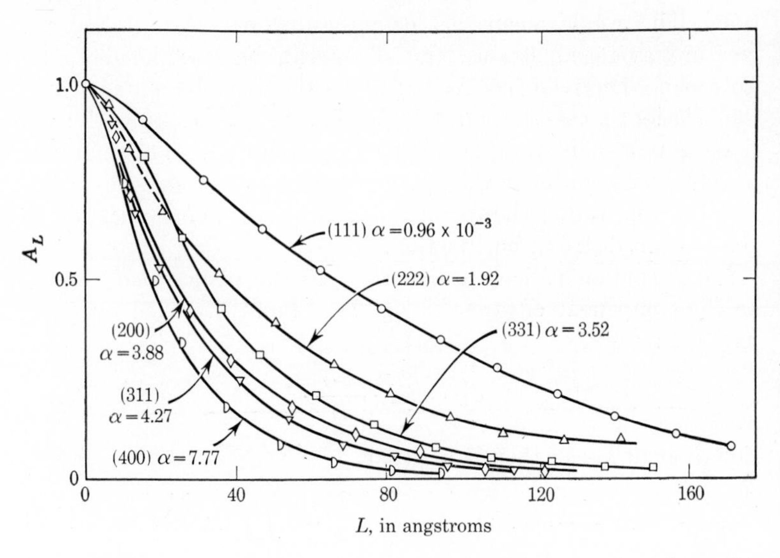

FIG. 3. Fourier coefficients A_L vs. L for six powder pattern lines from cold-worked alpha brass. Each curve is marked with the value of $\alpha \times 10^3$, where $\alpha = (h^2 + k^2 + l^2)^{1/2}/E_{hkl}$.

are plotted as a function of α for various values of L. The test for isotropic stresses is the condition that the points must fall on smooth curves with no appreciable systematic scatter. Since Young's modulus varies from one direction to another by as much as 3.5, and this variation is contained in the abscissa values a, the lack of scatter of the points is a very exacting test for isotropy of stress.

In terms of a stress distribution function $p(\sigma_L)$, where

$$\int_0^\infty p(\sigma_L)\, d\sigma_L = 1.0, \tag{4.4}$$

we can write equation (4.2):

$$A_L(\alpha) = \int_0^\infty p(\sigma_L) \cos\left(2\pi \frac{L}{a} \alpha\sigma_L\right) d\sigma_L, \tag{4.5}$$

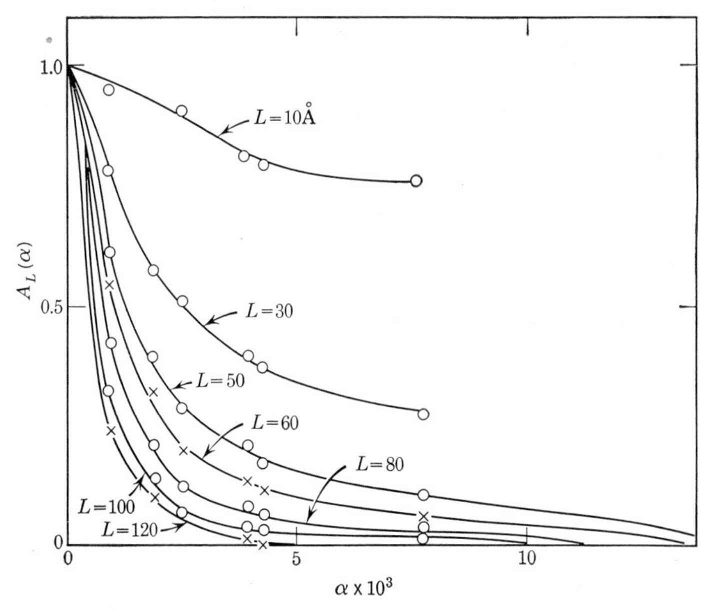

FIG. 4. The coefficient $A_L(l')$ as a function of l' for directions perpendicular to the (111) planes in cold-worked alpha brass. $l' = \sqrt{h^2 + k^2 + l^2}$.

and $p(\sigma_L)$ is given as the Fourier transform of the $A_L(\alpha)$ curves of Fig. 4:

$$p(\sigma_L) = 4\frac{L}{a}\int_0^\infty A_L(\alpha) \cos\left(2\pi \frac{L}{a} \alpha\sigma_L\right) d\alpha. \tag{4.6}$$

For each curve of Fig. 4 there are seven known points, and for L values between 60 and 120 Å the curves are defined well enough to give a reliable Fourier transform.

Figure 5 shows the stress distribution functions obtained from equation (4.6) for distances L between 50 and 120 Å. To appreciate the meaning of the curves of Fig. 5, we consider a column of length L in the crystal. Along this column the stress may vary,

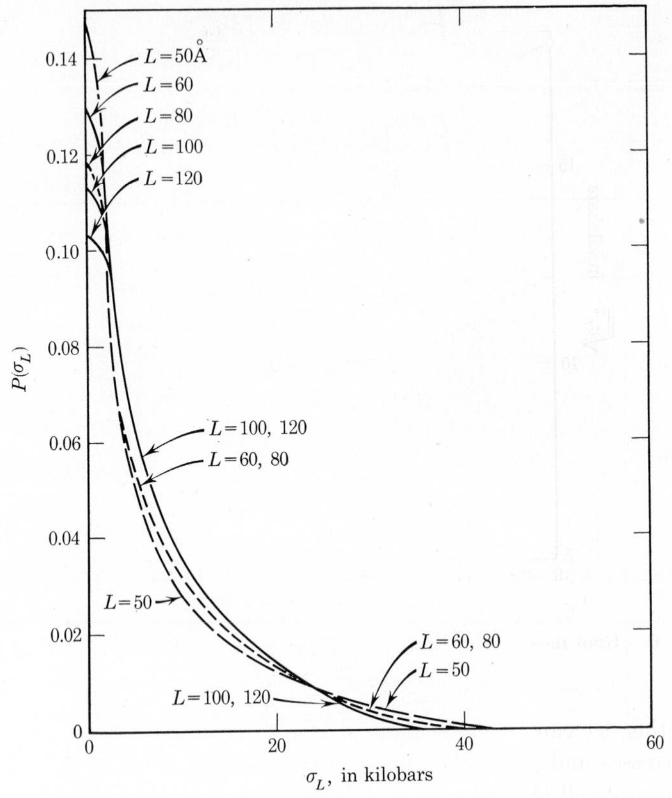

FIG 5. Stress distribution functions for cold-worked (70-30) alpha brass obtained as Fourier transforms of the curves of Fig. 4.

and σ_L is the component in the direction of the column averaged over the column length L. Among all the columns of length L in the sample $p(\sigma_L)\,d\sigma_L$ is the probability of finding columns with averaged stress component between σ_L and $\sigma_L + d\sigma_L$. If stresses and strains in the material were constant over distances large compared to L, the curves of Fig. 5 would coincide.

The root mean square averaged stress $(\overline{\sigma_L{}^2})^{1/2}$ was calculated from each of the curves of Fig. 5, and the values are shown by Fig. 6.

The value at $L = 0$ was obtained from the Young's modulus values, and the initial slopes of the $(\overline{(\Delta L)^2})^{1/2}$ vs. L curves. For the initial slopes the approximation of equation (2.8) is valid. There is some scatter in the values for $L = 0$ obtained by the initial slopes of the different powder pattern lines, and it is not obvious

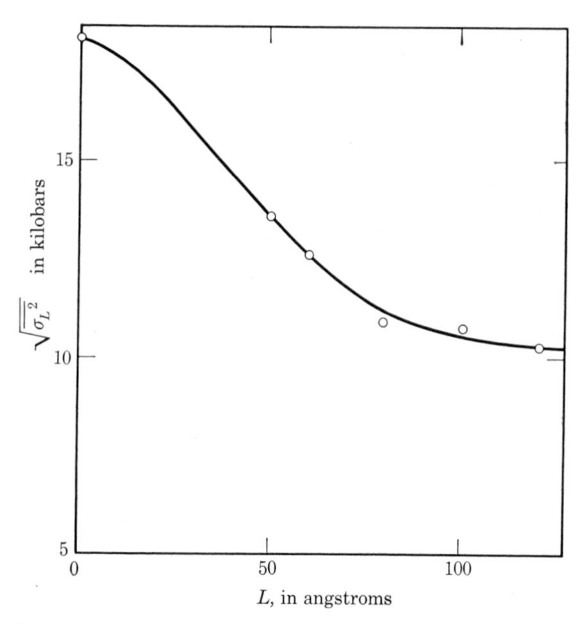

FIG. 6. Root mean square values of stress averaged over distances L for cold-worked (70-30) alpha brass.

whether σ_L can be considered isotropic for very small L values. If stresses and strains are nonuniform over distances of the order of several cell lengths, the initial averaging over L to give σ_L will produce a drooping curve such as Fig. 6. The shape of the curve in Fig. 6 is interpreted to mean that a major fraction of the stresses in cold-worked alpha brass are nonuniform over distances of several cell dimensions.

From the root mean square averaged stress curve of Fig. 6 and the appropriate values of Young's modulus we can now compute the root mean square relative displacements in any direction:

$$(\langle \sigma_L{}^2 \rangle_{\text{av.}})^{1/2} = \frac{E_{hkl}}{L} (\langle (\Delta L)^2 \rangle_{\text{av.}})^{1/2} . \tag{4.7}$$

Figure 7 shows these values for the two directions having the greatest difference in Young's modulus.

The energy per unit volume stored as a result of plastic deformation may be calculated from the approximate relation

$$V = \langle 3\sigma^2/2E\rangle_{av.}. \tag{4.8}$$

A rough evaluation of V can be obtained by using for $\overline{\sigma^2}$ the value for $L = 0$ from Fig. 6, and using the average polycrystalline

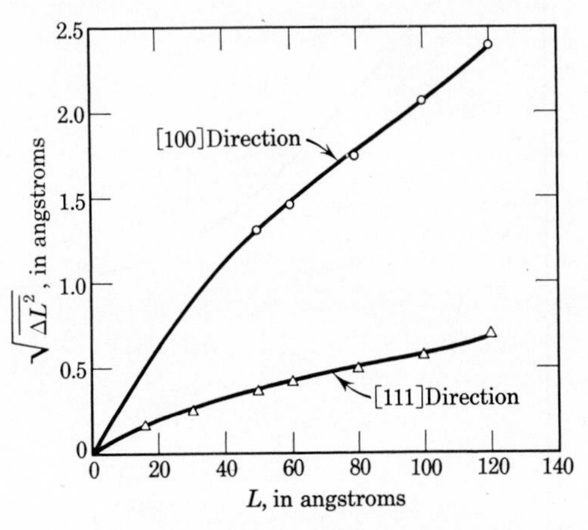

FIG. 7. Root mean square relative displacements $(\langle(\Delta L)^2\rangle_{av.})^{1/2}$ for the directions (100) and (111) in cold-worked alpha brass.

modulus of 1000 kilobars. The value computed is 1.4 cal/gram, and this is of the same order of magnitude as the values usually obtained by calorimetric methods.

5. CONCLUSIONS

The results reported in this paper have been obtained from measurements on cold-worked filings of (70-30) alpha brass. This represents an extremely severe example of cold work, and the results reported here do not necessarily apply to less severe examples of cold-work distortion. The measurements have been interpreted in terms of residual stresses and strains in the material. The most convincing justification for this is the smooth variation of the curves of Figs. 3 and 4 with the parameter α which involves the directional variation of Young's modulus. Because of the systems of slip involved in the distortion, there must be a certain amount of stacking disorder and actual fragmentation into smaller crystals scattering incoherently. Either effect would produce particle size broadening. The results of this study indicate that the major part of the broadening is due to strain-type distortion, but they do not exclude the possibility that a minor part of the broadening may be due to small particle size.

Although the lines are considerably broadened, all the lines of the powder pattern of cold-worked alpha brass filings can still be clearly recognized. Hence the material cannot be considered as amorphous or liquid-like; it is still crystalline, although highly distorted. The results for filings indicate that the mean square strains in any direction are roughly inverse to the value of Young's modulus for the direction, and hence that mean square stresses are roughly isotropic. This may indicate that there are centers of disturbance which exert stresses over appreciable regions of surrounding material. Presumably the x-rays are not measuring the atomic displacements in the centers of disturbance but rather the resulting strains in the surrounding material.

The root mean square averaged stress shown in Fig. 6 decreases with increase in the distance L over which it is first averaged. If this is a real effect, it indicates that the major part of the strained material is close enough to centers of disturbance so that the strain varies appreciably over distances of, say, 50 Å. For example, if stresses were uniform over distances of the order of 1000 Å, an initial averaging over distances of 50 Å would have little effect on the root mean square averaged stress. If it is a real effect, the dependence of averaged quantities on the averaging distance L is one of the most important results of these measurements. It must be emphasized, however, that these results are based upon an analysis which assumes that the broadening is due to distortion only, and that particle size broadening due to stacking disorders and fragmentation can be neglected.

It would be desirable to get a complete picture of the nature of cold-work distortion directly from the x-ray measurements, without putting in any assumptions or preconceived models. We would like to interpret the results directly in terms of dislocation centers, and from the x-ray results deduce the nature of the dislocation centers, the variation of the residual strains about them, and the average distance between dislocation centers. The x-ray measurements reported in this paper give definite quantitative results to be checked against any proposed picture of cold-work distortion, but at the present stage of the analysis we are still forced to postulate a picture and compare with the x-ray measurements rather than to deduce a picture directly from the measurements.

We should like to acknowledge the assistance of Mr. M. McKeehan and Mr. D. Hay in carrying out the experimental measurements and computations reported in this paper.

REFERENCES

1. C. S. Smith and E. E. Stickley, *Phys. Rev.*, **64**, 191 (1943).
2. A. R. Stokes, K. J. Pascoe, and H. Lipson, *Nature*, **151**, 137 (1943).
3. G. W. Brindley and F. W. Spiers, *Phil. Mag.*, **20**, 882, 893 (1935). G. W. Brindley and P. Ridley, *Proc. Phys. Soc. (London)*, **50**, 501 (1938). G. W. Brindley, *Proc. Phys. Soc. (London)*, **52**, 117 (1940).
4. B. L. Averbach and B. E. Warren, *J. Appl. Phys.*, **20**, 1066 (1949).
5. B. E. Warren and B. L. Averbach, *J. Appl. Phys.*, **21**, 595 (1950).
6. A. R. Stokes, *Proc. Phys. Soc. (London)*, **61**, 382 (1948).

DISCUSSION

W. T. READ, JR., AND W. SHOCKLEY (BELL TELEPHONE LABORATORIES):

The results of these investigations are probably the most direct evidence ever presented that the cold-worked state consists of a substantially uniform distribution of dislocations. This conclusion is based on the fact that certain features of Fig. 6 are in significant agreement with dislocation theory.

It is possible to obtain from dislocation theory a rough quantitative prediction of the relation between the root mean square average stress $\langle\sigma_0{}^2\rangle^{1/2}$ at $L = 0$ and the distance over which the stress is substantially uniform. If D is the average spacing between dislocations, the root mean square stress is approximately

$$\langle\sigma_0{}^2\rangle^{1/2} = (Gb/\pi D)(\ln D/2b)^{1/2}, \tag{D.1}$$

where $b \doteq 2.5$ Å is the slip distance and G is the shear modulus. To investigate theoretically the dependence of root mean square stress on orientation in an anisotropic material such as alpha brass, it would be necessary to use anisotropic elasticity and to carry out a much more involved analysis than is attempted here. We shall therefore take $G = c_{44} = 720$ kilobars. From the curve of Fig. 6, $\langle\sigma_0{}^2\rangle^{1/2} = 18$ kilobars. Substituting in the foregoing equation gives $D = 50$ Å.

If the dislocations are spaced 50 Å apart, it would be expected that the stress would be uniform for regions less than 50 Å in extent but would decrease for regions larger than 50 Å, a prediction in agreement with the curve of Fig. 6, which shows an appreciable decay for ordinates larger than 50 Å. Thus the dislocation density calculated from the peak of the curve agrees with the spacing of centers of disturbance as indicated by the rate of decay of the root mean square average stress with distance of averaging.

It should be emphasized that the general agreement between the value of D deduced from $\langle\sigma_0{}^2\rangle^{1/2}$ and the value of L at which $\langle\sigma_L{}^2\rangle^{1/2}$ begins to decrease would not necessarily be obtained for other models of the cold-worked metal. For example, the alloy might be considered to consist of large blocks, perfect except for elastic deformation, fitted together at grain boundaries in such a way as to be alternately under compression and tension. Under these conditions, the strain would be homogeneous over regions whose size was large compared to D deduced above. It should thus be regarded as a gratifying, but not surprising, confirmation of dislocation theory that the values of L and D do turn out to be comparable in magnitude.

Because of the atomic nature of the material studied, it follows that the stress cannot vary appreciably for distances less than one or two atomic diameters. Consequently, $\langle\sigma_L{}^2\rangle^{1/2}$ must have a value independent of L as L approaches zero and must, therefore, have a vanishing derivative at $L = 0$. The curve of Fig. 6 should, accordingly, be drawn with a zero slope at $L = 0$; this is entirely consistent with the experimental points.

P. B. Hirsch (Cavendish Laboratory, Cambridge):

*An X-ray Microbeam Investigation of Cold-Worked Aluminum**

Introduction. The structure of cold-worked metals has been studied by measurements of the breadth of the continuous diffraction rings obtained from these materials (Fig. D.1). The interpretation of the broadening is, however, difficult, as both particle size and strains may be contributing factors. The principle of the microbeam technique is to irradiate such a small volume of material that a spotty ring is obtained. It is found that spotty rings can always be obtained from spectroscopically pure aluminum, even after the heaviest deformation (Fig. D.2). From the number of spots on the diffraction rings the mean particle size can be determined. The spread of the spots along arcs indicates the range of misorientation of the material constituting

* This note, kindly supplied by P. B. Hirsch, describes work which was briefly discussed at the conference by W. L. Bragg. Some of this report was published in *Nature*, **165**, 554–555 (1950), from which the illustrations reproduced in this discussion were borrowed with permission of the editors.

the original grain; the shapes of the spots lead to estimates of the distortion of the particles.

Technique. A high-intensity x-ray tube with a rotating anode and fine focus produces an x-ray beam of intensity per unit area fifty times that obtained from an ordinary sealed-off tube. The x-ray beam is

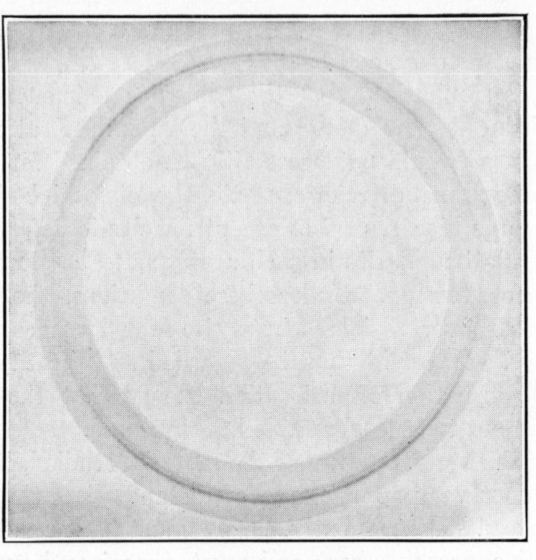

FIG. D.1. Back-reflexion photograph (422-ring) of heavily cold-rolled, spectroscopically pure aluminum, examined with a beam of 1 mm. diameter.

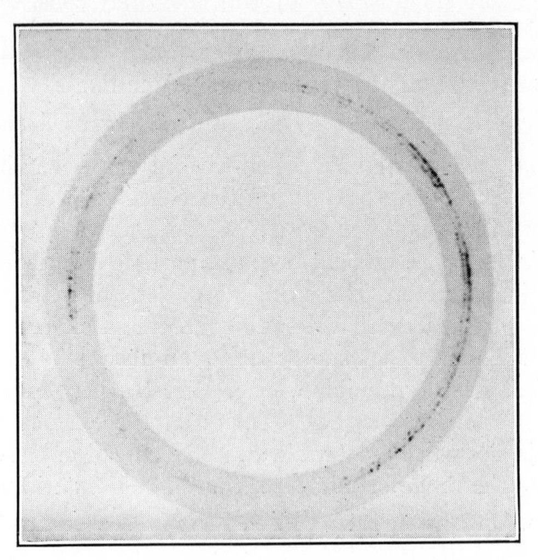

FIG. D.2. Back-reflexion photograph (422-ring) of some specimen, taken with a beam of $\sim 35\ \mu$ diameter.

collimated by means of lead-glass capillaries. A back-reflexion photograph of heavily cold-rolled aluminum taken with a beam of 35 μ diameter requires an exposure of 10 to 20 hours.

Measurement of particle volume. When aluminum is cold-rolled, the original sharp spots on the x-ray photographs spread into arcs (Fig. D.3),

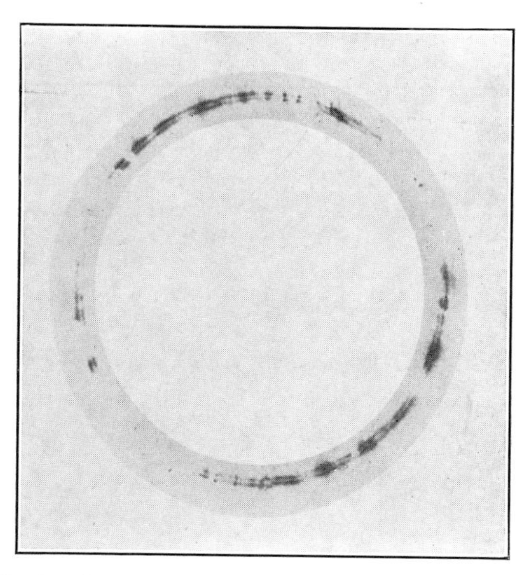

Fig. D.3. Back-reflexion photograph (422-ring) of a slightly deformed specimen of spectroscopically pure aluminum, examined with a beam of $\sim 150\ \mu$ diameter.

consisting of a number of spots (Fig. D.4). This shows that the material breaks up into smaller particles. The number of spots is proportional to the number of particles irradiated, which is equal to

$$\frac{\text{Area of cross section} \times \text{penetration of beam}}{\text{volume of particle}}.$$

Since the penetration of the beam into the specimen is not known, the difference of the number of spots on two photographs of different exposures is counted. This number is due to the particles in the volume equal to the difference between the two volumes irradiated, which is known in terms of the absorption coefficient of the metal, and the relative exposure times.[1]

[1] J. N. Kellar, P. B. Hirsch, and J. S. Thorp, *Nature,* **165**, 554–556 (April 8, 1950).

The results show that spectroscopically pure aluminum reaches a lower limiting particle size of 2 μ after $\sim$ 10 per cent reduction. If the heavily deformed specimen is left to recover for a year, the particle size decreases by 20 per cent. Impure aluminum behaves similarly for small deformations, but for large deformations the break-up into particles is not so distinct. An approximate estimate of the limiting particle size is $\sim$ 1 μ.

FIG. D.4. Enlargement of an arc from a photograph of a slightly deformed specimen showing particles.

Misorientations. The spread of the spots into arcs along the ring (Fig. D.3) indicates that the material inside the deformed grain covers a range of orientations. This total range of misorientations increases with the degree of cold work; for the heavily rolled material, the range of misorientations in one original grain is $\sim$ 20°.

A further feature of the photographs, in particular of those of slightly deformed material, is that the mean radii vary from arc to arc (Fig. D.3). Moreover, the radius varies continuously along each arc. This effect may be due to a variation of the mean strains or positions of the different parts of the material. Whatever may be the cause of this effect, the fact that the variation is continuous along each arc suggests that adjacent spots in the arc are due to neighboring crystals in the grain. The mean angle between particles increases with cold working; an order of magnitude estimate for the heavily cold-rolled material is 1°.

The photographs of heavily rolled impure aluminum are characterized by the bad resolution of the spots. Photographs taken with smaller beam diameters and divergence are similar, and indicate that the poor resolution is due to small angular misorientations (a few minutes) between adjacent particles.

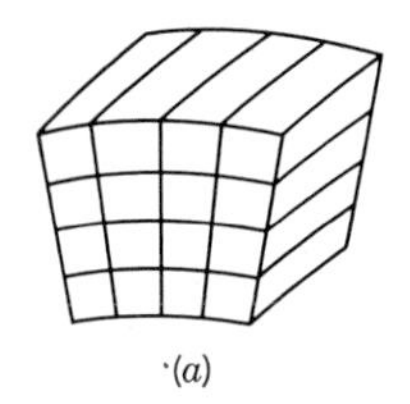

Shapes of spots. The tangential and radial breadths of the spots were measured; they depend on physical factors, such as shape and distortion of the particles, and on experimental factors, such as the divergence of the x-ray beam and the wave-length spread of the characteristic radiation. Since the experimental factors are known, the physical tangential and radial broadenings can usually be estimated.

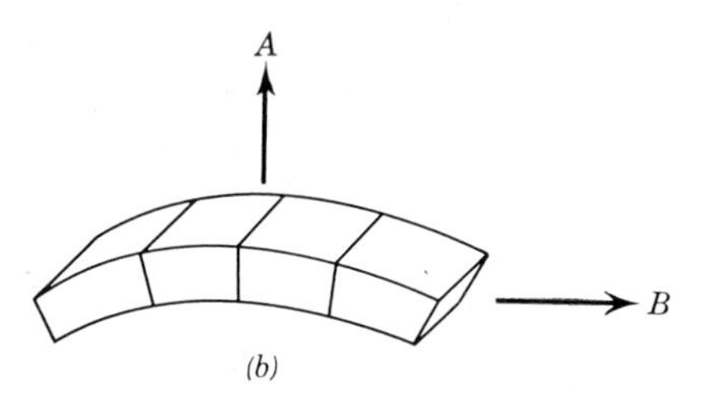

The physical broadenings must then be interpreted in terms of distortion and shape of the particles. The following example shows the type of argument used. Suppose that the broadening is all due to shape. Then the tangential and radial breadths give the dimensions of the particles in two directions at right angles. Since the volume of the particles is known, the third dimension can be calculated. For the heavily rolled material examined immediately after rolling, this length would be several millimeters. As the initial grain size is only $\sim 20\ \mu$, this model can be discarded, and distortion must be present. The three models which can explain the values of the broadenings are shown in Fig. D.5. A common feature

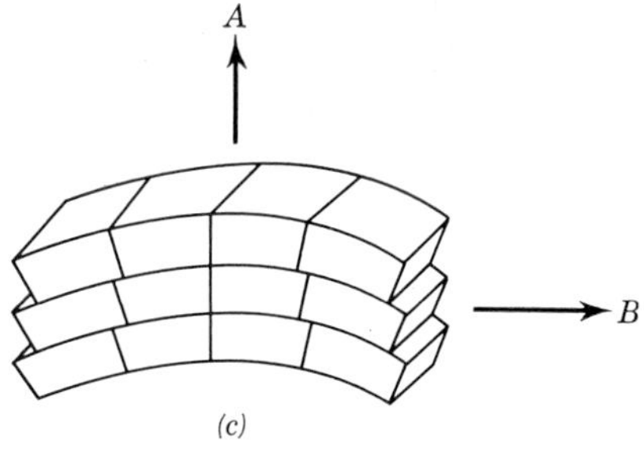

FIG. D.5. Possible models to explain broadenings: (*a*) Equiaxed particle, bent about two axes. All the broadening is due to distortion. (*b*) Bent lamella; broadening is partly due to small particle size and distortion, corresponding to directions *A* and *B* in the particle. (*c*) Bent equiaxed particle with lamellar structure; broadening as in (*b*).

of all three models is that the particles are bent. The range of strains associated with this bending is found to be 1.3×10^{-3} radian; the corresponding range of stresses is of the order of the measured yield stress of the bulk material.

The broadenings decrease with time after rolling, but even a year after rolling some distortion is present in the material.

The background between spots also decreases with time after rolling.

Conclusions. The results show that heavily deformed aluminum consists of particles of mean diameter 2 μ, making mean angles of $\sim 1°$ with each other. The particles are distorted; the range of strains is of the order of the yield strain of the bulk metal. From the angles between particles, the number of dislocations in the boundaries can be calculated, and correspond to an overall density of $\sim 10^9 \rightarrow 10^{10}$ sq cm. This estimate is low compared with that obtained from calorimetric measurements, and it appears likely that dislocations are present inside the particles. It is suggested that the dislocations in the boundaries are excess dislocations of one sign, which segregate spontaneously during deformation due to a recovery process akin to polygonization. The recovery observed in the experiments is thought to be a slow continuation of this process. The further decrease in particle size and of the distortion can be explained by a process of polygonization. The smaller angles between particles of the impure material may be due to interference in the movement of dislocations by impurity atoms.

It is doubtful if the microbeam technique can be applied to materials with particles <1 μ in diameter, but much useful information might be obtained from the study of small deformations, particularly of single crystals.

6.

Mechanical Strength and Creep in Metals

N. F. MOTT

University of Bristol, England

ABSTRACT

In this paper the effects responsible for mechanical strength in metals are summarized. They include dissolved impurities, which may lock dislocations without diffusing to them, as well as impurities after a process of diffusion, as envisaged by Cottrell. Both processes are discussed. Frank's ideas on the strength of pure metals, which depends on the distance between the two locking points of a Frank-Read source, are reviewed. Finally, a theory of exhaustion creep is presented and compared with experiments due to Davis and Thompson.

1. DEFORMATIONS AND DISLOCATIONS

In discussing the mechanical strength and creep of metals, it is necessary to distinguish between temperatures and rates of strain for which grain-boundary slip occurs, and conditions when this is not so. In the former case the reversible flow studied by Kê[1] will set up stress concentrations in particular in the grain boundaries, and plastic deformation will occur preferentially near to them. Much creep of technical importance is of this type, but, apart from a rough estimate of the conditions under which this occurs,[2] no quantitative theory of the phenomenon exists.

Most of this report deals with deformation of single crystals or crystalline grains under conditions such that the grain boundary does not flow. We assume the existence before deformation of dislocations in the crystals or grains, and, in order to explain work hardening and slip bands, we require a mechanism for the multiplication of dislocations. Two are available: the dynamic mechanism of Frank[3] and the spiral mechanism of Frank and Read.[4] In view of criticisms of the former by Leibfried,[5] we adopt the latter. We thus suppose that a pair of locked or anchored dislocations in planes unfavorable for slip, ending on a slip plane in which they are joined by a dislocation of length l, can act as a source of dislocation rings in that plane if the stress applied is greater than about

$$Gb/l. \tag{1.1}$$

Here G is the rigidity modulus and b the magnitude of the Burgers vector. If, therefore, a stress greater than (1.1) is applied to a crystal otherwise perfect, unlimited slip along this plane will occur as dislocation rings are created and move outwards and disappear at the boundary.

We have then to ask what determines the resistance to the motion of dislocations, in other words the mechanical strength. There is first of all the resistance or friction due to lattice imperfections, such as foreign atoms in the lattice or in interstitial positions, incipient precipitates (Preston-Guinier zones), or other dislocations. This, we believe, in most technical materials is the important factor. Second, there is the stress (1.1) required to create dislocations. And, finally, there is the stress required to transmit slip from one grain to another,[6] which in pure materials, especially if fine grained, may be the predominating factor.

Turning now to creep, we may distinguish two extreme cases.

(1) In hard alloys at relatively low temperatures there occurs what we call exhaustion creep. Here the resistance to flow is entirely due to internal stresses (friction). Under an applied stress first those dislocations move which can do so without thermal activation, then those which require only a little activation energy, and so on. Creep slows down when all the easily moved dislocations are exhausted. A theory worked out by Mott and Nabarro[7] in 1947 gives for this type of creep (s = strain)

$$s = C\{\ln(\nu t + 1)\}^{2/3}, \tag{1.2}$$

and experiments by Davis and Thompson[8] on a Cu-Ag alloy give good agreement with this formula. The theory was worked out before Frank and Read's multiplication mechanism was known; but, as shown in Section 4, it is consistent with that mechanism; the elementary act is the spreading of a single dislocation ring, but multiplication does not take place, because the dislocation cannot get back to its original position.

(2) In pure single crystals, creep of the Andrade type

$$s = \alpha t^{1/3} + \beta t \tag{1.3}$$

occurs—or more generally with exponents other than $1/3$.

It has not yet proved possible to make a theory of creep of this kind. Assuming that the average amount of slip on each band does not change during the experiment, we have to show that, if n is the number of slip bands formed at time t,

$$\frac{dn}{dt} = \frac{\text{const}}{n^2} \cdot \tag{1.4}$$

Why the rate of formation should vary as the square of the distance between them is not clear.

A further case of importance that will be considered here is that in which dislocations are locked by foreign atoms which precipitate along their length. This mechanism, first proposed by Cottrell, leads to a sharp elastic limit in single crystals and a yield point (lowering of resistance after yield) in polycrystalline material.

2. THE INFLUENCE OF IMPURITIES ON DISLOCATIONS

In this section we shall discuss the movement of a dislocation in a crystal containing impurities.

Case 1. The impurities consist of Preston-Guinier (P.G.) zones, or other centers of stress some hundreds of atomic spacings apart. We denote this spacing by Λ. Provided the precipitates have not broken away from the matrix, the mean stress σ_i in the matrix, independently of the shape of the P.G. zone, is of the order of

$$\sigma_i = G\epsilon f. \tag{2.1}$$

[G is the shear modulus, $(1 + \epsilon)a$ is the radius of the solute atom, a being that for the matrix; f is the ratio of atoms precipitated to atoms of the matrix.] If Λ is great compared with $T/\sigma_i a$ (T = energy per unit length of dislocation), the dislocation will take up a position determined by the internal stresses, the tension being unimportant. Putting $T = Ga^2/2\pi$, the condition is

$$\Lambda \gg \frac{Ga}{2\pi\sigma_i} \cdot \tag{2.2}$$

This gives

$$\Lambda \sim 20a \tag{2.3}$$

if $\sigma_i \sim 0.01G$. The dislocation may thus be expected to take up a curved form (Fig. 1) in which the average inclination to its mean position is ca. 45°. Under the action of a stress σ, the typical movement forward will be the displacement of a *loop* from a position such as ABC to a new position of equilibrium such as $AB'C$.

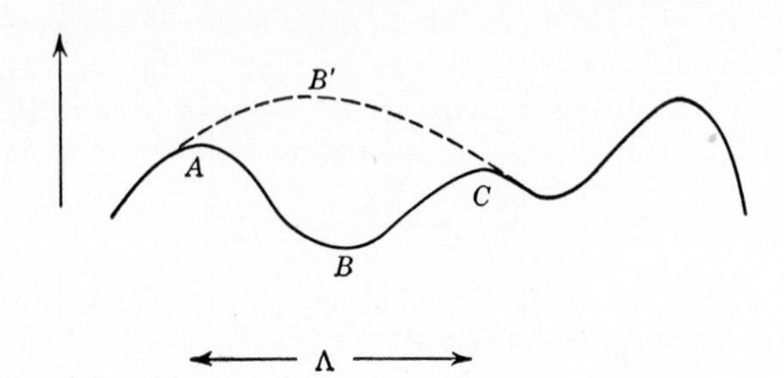

FIG. 1. Curved dislocation in lattice containing strains due to Preston-Guinier zones.

The stress σ_i to make such a loop move will be of the order of (2.1), but will vary from loop to loop. The activation energy for the motion of such a loop in the absence of stress will be of the order of

$$\sigma_i a \Lambda^2, \tag{2.4}$$

which, if $\sigma_i \sim 0.01G$ and $\Lambda > 20a$, is several multiples of Ga^3, and thus too large by several electron volts for such motion to occur through thermal activation alone without the help of an applied stress. In the presence of an applied stress σ which approaches σ_i, Mott and Nabarro[7] give for the activation energy

$$0.15\sigma_i a \Lambda^2 \left(1 - \frac{\sigma}{\sigma_i}\right)^{3/2}. \tag{2.5}$$

To summarize: especially if Λ, the distance between the precipitates, is large ($> 100a$), the dislocation cannot be set in motion, even with the help of temperature, unless the applied stress σ approaches σ_i.

Case 2. Cottrell locking. Cottrell[9] suggests that impurities present either interstitially or substitutionally may diffuse to the neighborhood of dislocations and lock them in position. The condition for this to happen is that the metal shall have been at some time in its history at a temperature high enough for the atoms to diffuse, and that at this temperature free energy is gained if an appreciable concentration of atoms forms at the dislocation.

The most effective agents for locking dislocations are expected to be interstitial atoms in lattices other than face-centered cubic, such as carbon or gases in iron, molybdenum, cadmium, and zinc—metals in which a more or less sharp yield point can be induced by the presence of gases.

For such cases it is probably reasonable to set for the energy of a dislocation displaced a distance x from a locking impurity,

$$-V_0\lambda^2/(x^2 + \lambda^2), \tag{2.6}$$

where λ is of the order of the size of the "center" of a dislocation, say 5 Å, and V_0 a parameter probably of the order of 0.5 to 1 electron volt for carbon in iron. The maximum value of the gradient of this is approximately V_0/λ, so that, if a fraction f of the planes threaded by the dislocation contains a locking atom, the stress required to move the dislocation is about

$$\sigma_i = fV_0/\lambda ab, \tag{2.7}$$

where b is the slip distance (magnitude of the Burgers vector) and a the distance between planes of atoms. If we take this to be the yield point of iron extrapolated to the absolute zero (1.25×10^{10} dynes/cm^2), and assume $a \doteq b \doteq 3 \times 10^{-8}$ cm, $V_0 = \frac{1}{2}$ ev, $f = 1$, then $\lambda \sim 7 \times 10^{-8}$ cm, which is perhaps not unreasonable.

An elementary analysis shows that, if the number N_2 of impurity atoms is greater than the number of sites in dislocations, then practically all sites are occupied at temperatures below T_0, where

$$kT_0 = V_0/\ln (N/N_2). \tag{2.8}$$

Here N is the number of sites in the lattice (available for impurities); above this the proportion occupied decreases as

$$\exp\left\{-\frac{V_0}{kT} + \frac{T_0}{T}\right\}. \tag{2.9}$$

This enables us to set lower limits to V_0. If, as Cottrell states (see Section 3), the phenomenon of the yield point is to be associated with this type of locking of dislocations, and if the phenomenon persists at 400°C for a carbon content of, say, 0.01 per cent, then V_0 must be greater than

$$673°\text{K} \ln 10^4 \sim 0.5 \text{ electron volt}. \tag{2.10}$$

A value much greater than this would give improbably large values of λ in the analysis above.

It is characteristic of Cottrell locking that the stress required to move a dislocation locked in this way is very sensitive to temperature and time. This property contrasts with that of dislocations

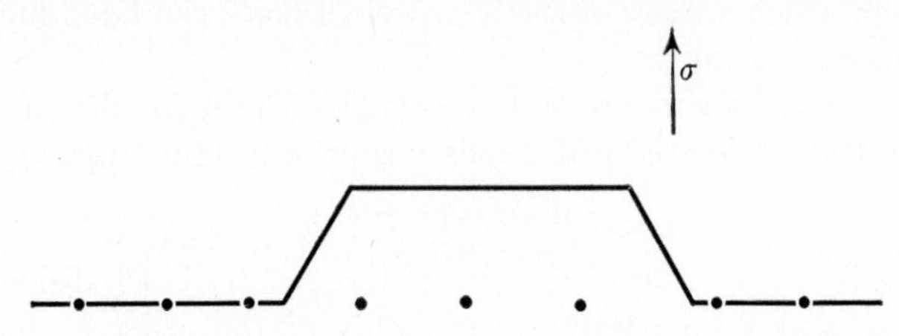

FIG. 2. A locked dislocation breaking away from its row of carbon atoms.

locked by the stresses varying with position comparatively slowly, which exist round P.G. zones. The reason is the short-range nature of the forces around the locking atoms. In the presence of an applied stress only a very short length of loop (Fig. 2) need be de-

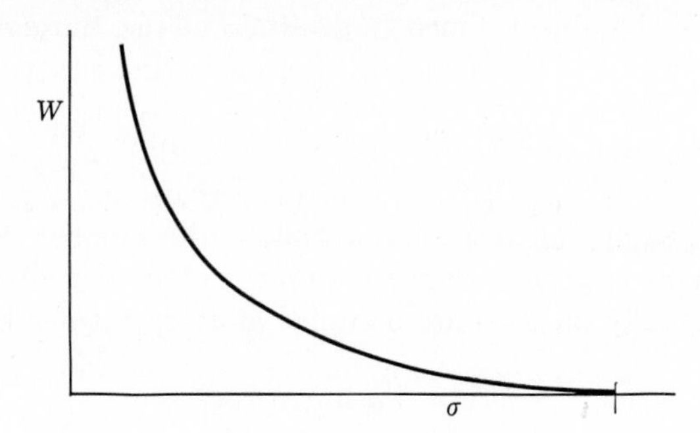

FIG. 3. Activation energy W to break away from a row of carbon atoms as a function of applied stress.

tached from the locking atoms for an unstable situation to develop, and the activation energies are small. A (rather complicated) analysis has been given by Cottrell and Bilby,[10] who find for the activation energy to form an unstable loop a function such as that shown in Fig. 3 is necessary. For σ near to σ_i we can set this in the form (2.5), namely,

$$W(\sigma) = W_0\left(1 - \frac{\sigma}{\sigma_i}\right)^{3/2}, \tag{2.11}$$

where W_0 is now of the order of $a\lambda^2\sigma_i$, and so a fraction of an electron volt.

The chance per unit time that a dislocation breaks away is then

$$\exp\{-W(\sigma)/kT\}. \tag{2.12}$$

The frequency ν, with which the dislocation vibrates is expected to be of the order of 10^{10} to 10^{11} sec^{-1} (see Mott and Nabarro[7]). Thus the stress σ required to move the dislocation in one second at temperature T is, for σ near to σ_i,

$$\sigma = \sigma_i - \left\{\frac{kT}{W_0} \ln \nu t\right\}^{2/3}. \tag{2.13}$$

With $\ln \nu t \sim 25$ and $W_0 < 1$ ev, we see that the effect of temperature may be to halve σ between 0°K and room temperature.

Case 3. Effect of dissolved impurities. As stated in Case 2, impurities can segregate to dislocations. Also, a dislocation which has moved out of the position that it had when the crystal was cooled will take up an equilibrium position such that it

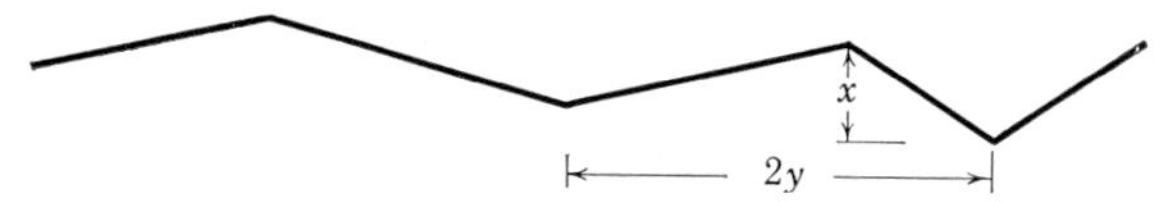

FIG. 4. Dislocation line locked by a few impurity atoms.

tends to pass through as many impurity atoms as possible, without increasing its length too much. The degree of locking may be estimated as follows.

Suppose that there are N impurity atoms per unit volume, and we consider the dislocation (Fig. 4) to lie in a given plane, in which there are Na per unit area. When a dislocation passes through one of these impurity atoms, suppose the energy is lowered by V_0. Then the dislocation will take up a form such as is shown in Fig. 4, being displaced an average distance x from its mean position. The number of impurities at a distance less than x is Nax, so that $y = 1/Nax$. The energy due to locking by impurities is, per unit length,

$$-V_0/y = -V_0Nax, \tag{2.14}$$

and the increase in the line energy, if T is the energy per unit length, is

$$\frac{2T}{y}\{(x^2 + y^2)^{1/2} - y\} \simeq \frac{Tx^2}{y^2} = TN^2a^2x^4. \tag{2.15}$$

To find x, y in the configuration of minimum energy we thus have to minimize

$$Na(-V_0x + NaTx^4), \tag{2.16}$$

giving

$$x = \left(\frac{V_0}{4TNa}\right)^{1/3}, \qquad \frac{1}{y} = Na\left(\frac{V_0}{4TNa}\right)^{1/3}. \tag{2.17}$$

Taking, for instance, $N \sim 10^{20}$, we find $y \sim 200a$. Thus for this concentration of carbon atoms the increase in yield strength will be only 1/200 of the yield strength due to a complete row, and thus of order 10^8 dynes/cm^2.

We doubt, however, whether at room temperature locking of this type will in fact lead to any increase in the strength of materials, because clearly the activation energy required to remove a dislocation from a *single* locking atom (in contrast to a row) is only V_0 in the absence of an applied stress, and less in the presence of a stress. For most locking atoms V_0/kT at room temperature will not be unduly large.

When, however, we have to discuss the movement of a dislocation in an alloy, it seems reasonable to suppose that, if the applied stress is small, it will be considerably slowed down by trapping processes of this type. We shall return to this point in Section 4.

Nabarro[7] has given a different treatment of the effect of impurities, which leads to a term much less dependent on temperature. In this report we give a slightly modified version which leads to a different formula. Nabarro considered the strains around each dissolved atom; they will give, he claims, a random stress of "wavelength,"

$$\Lambda = af^{-1/3} \qquad f = \text{concentration} \tag{2.18}$$

and mean magnitude

$$\sigma_i = \int_a^\Lambda \frac{G\epsilon a^3}{r^3}\, 4\pi r^2\, dr \Big/ \int_0^\Lambda 4\pi r^2\, dr \tag{2.19}$$

giving

$$\sigma_i \sim G\epsilon f \ln(1/f).$$

The equilibrium form of a dislocation in such a field is as in Fig. 5.

The curvature $1/\rho$ in each arc is $a\sigma_i/T = \sigma_i/2\pi aG$, and the angle θ turned is thus $\theta = \Lambda/\rho = \Lambda/\sigma_i/2\pi aG$, which is small. One of these loops cannot move to a new position of equilibrium shown dotted in Fig. 5 without normally moving back before the next loop follows it. Suppose, however, we take n^2 loops; the mean

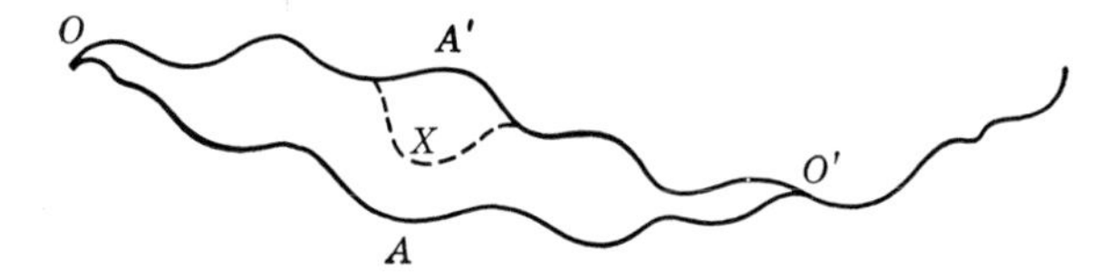

FIG. 5. Showing the motion forwards of a dislocation in an alloy.

angle turned through will be $n\theta$, and the distance AA' will be $n\theta n^2\Lambda$. It seems reasonable to suppose that a new equilibrium position exists, $OA'O'$, if $AA' \sim \Lambda$; thus

$$n^3 \sim 1/\theta. \tag{2.20}$$

The stress resisting the motion of OO' from A to A' is $n\sigma_i$, so the strength σ is given by

$$n^2\sigma = n\sigma_i \tag{2.21}$$

or

$$\sigma = \sigma_i\{\Lambda\sigma_i/2\pi aG\}^{1/3}. \tag{2.22}$$

The review of effect on hardness of dissolved atoms given by G. V. Smith[11] certainly gives an increase in hardness with ϵ, but we doubt if experiments are yet made which would enable the power of ϵ to be estimated. Equation (2.22), when we substitute for σ_i and Λ, gives $\epsilon^{4/3}$.

3. STRENGTH OF METALS AT MODERATE TEMPERATURES AND RATES OF STRAIN

To produce any appreciable nonrecoverable deformation we may assume that some multiplication of dislocations must occur. We therefore assume the presence of a number of sources of the type introduced by Frank and Read. The stress required to produce concentric rings of dislocations will consist of two terms; one term (1.1) of the order of

$$Gb/l, \tag{3.1}$$

and the "frictional" term σ_i, discussed in Section 2, required to drive the dislocation through an imperfect lattice. It is reasonable to suppose that in single crystals of pure metals Gb/l predominates, but in alloys, especially age-hardened ones, σ_i is more important.*

In hard materials the process of forming a dislocation loop is illustrated in Fig. 6. As the applied stress is increased, the sources from which a dislocation will spread first will be, in general, those in which a dislocation, anchored at O, O', lies in a position like

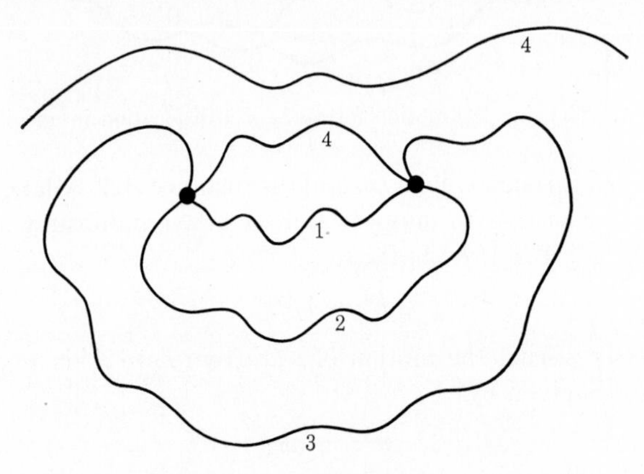

FIG. 6. Action of a Frank-Read source in an alloy.

that marked 1 rather than like that marked 2, for an applied stress forcing the dislocation downwards. When a ring has been formed the loop will return to the position 5; but the stress required to force it through the orifice OO' will, for about half the sources initially present, be greater than that required to start it off. Thus, as the applied stress is increased, about half the sources present will give rise to one loop, which will spread to the boundary of the grain, before any further multiplication occurs. We call the increase of stress which occurs during this process *exhaustion hardening*, the easily moved sources being exhausted one by one. During the region of exhaustion hardening, hardening should be completely absent for reversed stress, and no slip bands should occur. The plastic strain expected in this region should be of the order of

$$Nad^2. \tag{3.2}$$

(N = number of sources per unit volume, d = grain size, or more

* The length l will doubtless be less in alloys than in pure metals, but it is difficult to see how it could be decreased *during* age hardening.

generally the distance a loop expands before it is stopped.) With present information it is difficult to estimate the order of magnitude of N. N should be greater than $1/d^3$. We have to do here, certainly, with strains not much greater than the elastic limit—that is, with regions such as OA in a stress-strain diagram (Fig. 7). For larger strains a number of dislocation loops will pile up and

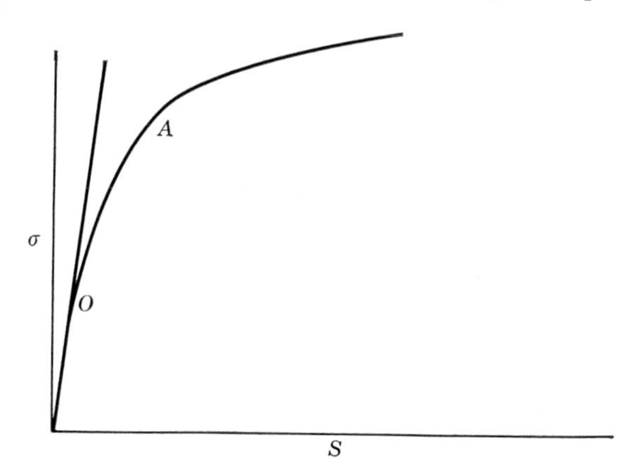

FIG. 7. Stress-strain curve showing exhaustion region.

press against the grain boundary, until the stress there increases to the point where new dislocations are spontaneously created in the next grain. For pure metals (σ_i negligible) this case has been treated by Frank,[6] and may possibly be the most important factor determining the strength of pure metals of small grain size, leading to stresses of the order of (page 8 of Frank's paper)

$$\frac{G}{5}\sqrt{\frac{a}{l}}\,. \tag{3.3}$$

(L = grain size). Such a term is probably smaller than the stress σ_i required to move a single dislocation in a hard alloy, however, so that an applied stress only slightly exceeding σ_i will be great enough to pile up dislocations against the grain boundary and exert the necessary pressure.

The preceding arguments assume that the dislocation in the slip plane is not locked in Cottrell's sense, for example, by a line of carbon atoms. If it is, the phenomenon is rather different. There will be no movement of dislocations until a stress is applied great enough to pull the dislocation away from its atmosphere (the upper yield point), after which the ring will move freely outwards, and the dislocation will come back to its original position anchored by the carbon atoms. There is thus no softening after the yield point is reached; the same stress has to be applied to form a second ring, and so on. The softening after yield probably arises as follows: When dislocations pile up at the grain boundary, and initiate yield in neighboring grains, through *spontaneous* formation of dislocation rings, these can move without any hindrance from carbon atmospheres. Thus on this model, although carbon atmospheres within the grain are responsible for the sharp yield, the softening after yield will occur only in polycrystalline materials.

4. EXHAUSTION CREEP

We give here the theory of exhaustion creep—that is, creep in which the slowing down of the extension is due to the exhaustion of easily moved dislocations. The theory is essentially that given in 1947 by Mott and Nabarro,[7] but reinterpreted in terms of the Frank-Read model of dislocation sources and discussed in the light of the experimental results of Davis and Thompson[8] obtained at Bristol.

The experimental conditions for the realization of exhaustion creep are as follows: The matrix must be such that the dislocations on planes unfavorable for creep which anchor the ends of the loops in the Frank-Read model are securely locked; the internal stresses, and hence the frictional force, are not changed appreciably during the experiment either by work hardening (other than exhaustion) or by softening; and no grain boundary flow shall occur. Neither of the first two conditions is likely to be satisfied for pure single crystals; the theory is more likely to be applicable to age-hardened alloys at comparatively low temperatures.

We suppose, then, that per unit volume of the solid there are $N(\sigma_i)\,d\sigma_i$ sources which will not allow a loop to spread if an external stress σ_i is applied, but which will do so for a stress $\sigma_i + d\sigma_i$. As already explained, we do not expect multiplication of dislocations until a considerably larger stress is applied; we expect slip of amount Aa/Ω, where Ω is the volume of the whole specimen and A the area through which the loop spreads, say, the square of the diameter of a grain or perhaps of a mosaic element.

When a stress σ is applied, all loops for which $\sigma_i < \sigma$ move at once. After time t the number of loops in the range σ_i to $\sigma_i + d\sigma_i$ which have moved is

$$N(\sigma_i)\, d\sigma_i\{1 - e^{-\alpha t}\}, \tag{4.1}$$

where

$$N(\sigma_i) = \nu \exp\{-W(\sigma)/kT\}, \tag{4.2}$$

and

$$W(\sigma) = 0.15a\Lambda^2\left(1 - \frac{\sigma}{\sigma_i}\right)^{3/2}. \tag{4.3}$$

The vibrational frequency ν of a dislocation is a quantity that will be discussed below. The deformation s (excluding the instantaneous deformation) is thus given by

$$S = Aa\int_{\sigma}^{\infty} N(\sigma_i)\,\{1 - e^{-\alpha t}\}\, d\sigma_i. \tag{4.4}$$

A sufficiently accurate estimation of the integral can be given as follows. In Fig. 8 we give a suggested form for $N(\sigma_i)$. Sources

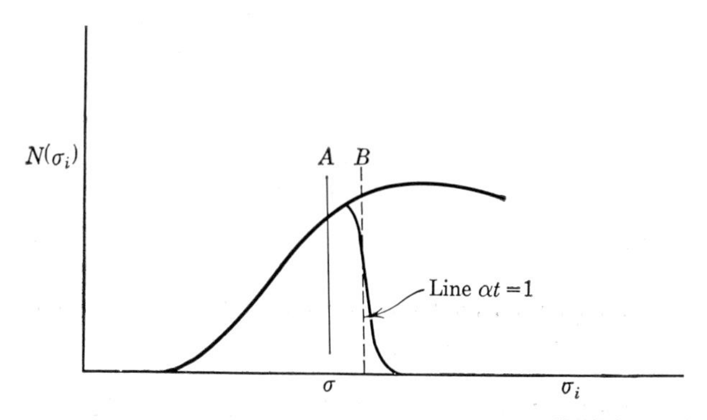

FIG. 8. Density of sources plotted against strain required to make them yield dislocations.

represented by points on the area to the left of A give loops instantaneously when a stress σ is applied; those in the area between A and B after time t. We approximate by saying that all sources for which $\alpha t > 1$ have produced loops at time t and those for which $\alpha t < 1$ have not. In other words, the vertical line $\alpha t = 1$ shown in Fig. 8 moves from left to right and separates sources which have given loops from those which have not. The value of t for which this line must be drawn is given by

$$\nu t \exp\{-W(\sigma)/kT\} = 1, \tag{4.5}$$

whence

$$\sigma_i - \sigma = \sigma \left\{ \frac{kT}{0.15a\Lambda^2} \ln(\nu t) \right\}^{2/3}. \tag{4.6}$$

If it is assumed that between σ_i and σ the quantity $N(\sigma_i)$ is constant, this gives for the strain S (the product of the area to the left of B and Aa)

$$S = B\{\ln(\nu t)\}^{2/3}, \qquad B = AaN(\sigma)\sigma \left\{ \frac{kT}{0.15a\Lambda^2} \right\}^{2/3}. \tag{4.7}$$

Experiments by Davis and Thompson[8] were made on a copper alloy containing 2.75 weight per cent of silver aged for 30 min at

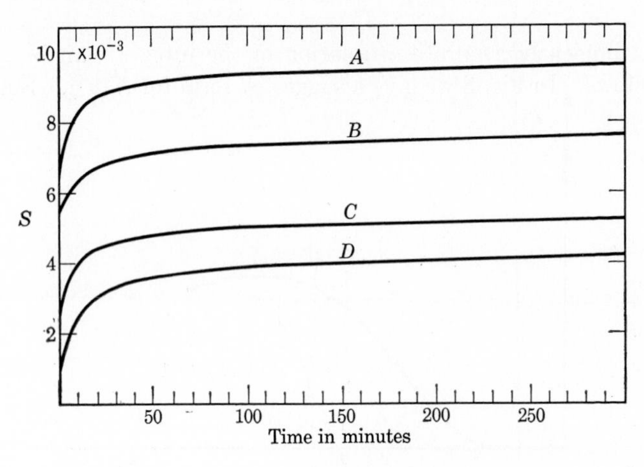

FIG. 9. Extension-time curves of Cu-Ag alloys. Stresses in kg/cm^2: A = 6.55, B = 6.00, C = 5.77, D = 5.60. All measurements at room temperature.

500°C, with a grain size of 10^{-2} cm. Figure 9 shows some experimental results. The first task is to compare with a formula of type (4.7).

If we differentiate a curve of the type

$$S^x = C \ln(\nu t), \tag{4.8}$$

we find

$$xSS^{x-1} = C/t, \tag{4.9}$$

and hence, eliminating S,

$$(\dot{S}t)^{-x/(x-1)} = \text{const. } \{\log t + \log \nu\}. \tag{4.10}$$

With $x = \frac{3}{2}$, $x/(x-1) = 3$. Plotting $(\dot{S}t)^3$ against $\log t$, we obtain the curves of Fig. 10, showing a good agreement with the

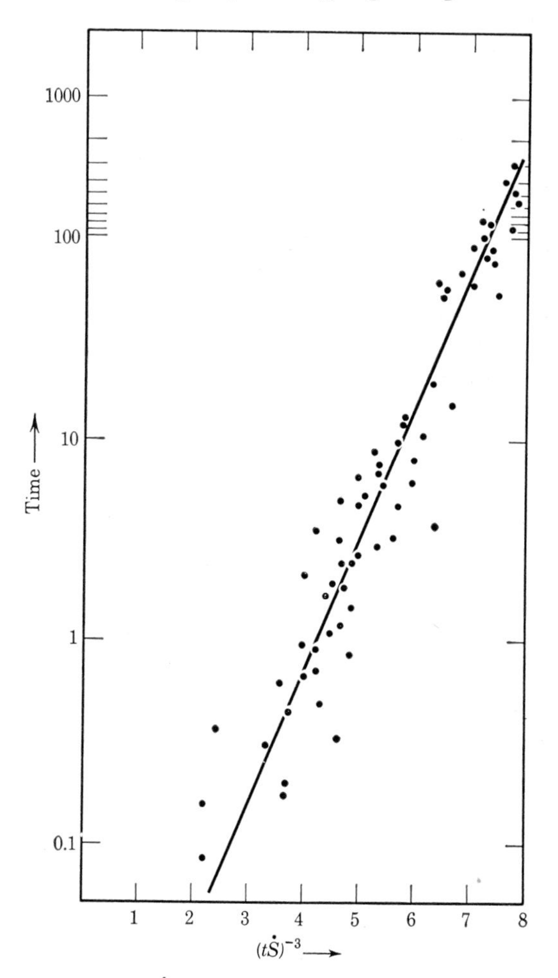

FIG. 10. Plot of $(t\dot{S})^{-3}$ against ln (time), for $\sigma = 6.00$ kg/mm^2.

linear relation expected. The exponent x must certainly be greater than 1. It is hardly possible, however, to distinguish between the value $\frac{3}{2}$ and the value 2 that would be given by the Becker-

Orowan theory. This method of plotting avoids also the necessity of estimating the zero of S.

From the intercept with the axis we obtain for ν the surprisingly small value $\nu \sim 1 \text{ sec}^{-1}$. This may possibly be due to the sticking of the dislocation by dissolved impurities as it vibrates towards the top of the potential barrier.

We can also make an estimate of the parameter that appears as $Aa\sigma N(\sigma)$; this is of the order of 0.01 (an estimate of $kT/0.15a\Lambda^2$ is given below). If we assume that A is the square of the grain size, 10^{-4} cm^2, and $a \sim 10^{-8}$ cm, then

$$\sigma N(\sigma) \sim 10^{10} \text{ cm}^{-3}. \tag{4.11}$$

Moreover $\sigma N(\sigma)$ should be somewhat but not too much less than the total number of sources per unit volume. These are thus rather less than 5×10^{-4} cm apart. If each one of them gave

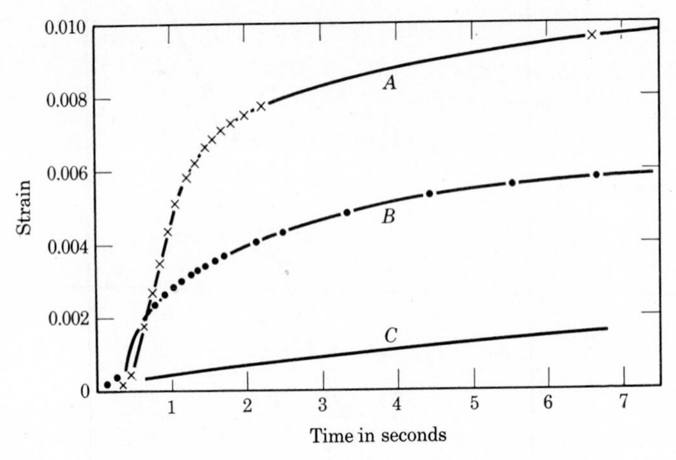

FIG. 11. Extension of specimens of Ag-Cu alloys after application of an increase in load, in kg/mm². $A = 1.86$. $B = 1.60$. $C = 1.20$. The original load was 7.0 kg/mm².

rise to a slip band there would be 10^4 slip bands per grain, and thus at a distance of 10^{-6} cm apart. If slip took place over 100 atoms on each grain, this would correspond to a total deformation unity. Thus we picture slip taking place as follows:

(1) Up to $S \sim 0.01$, through the using up of sources each forming one loop only. In this region we have exhaustion hardening, and thus no hardening for reverse strains.

(2) For strains beyond $S \sim 0.01$, formation of slip bands, at first about 1 μ apart.

Some further experiments were made as follows. A specimen was allowed to creep until its extension had virtually stopped; then the stress was suddenly increased. Figure 11 shows the extension which resulted.

It will be seen that the smaller incremental stresses give no instantaneous extension, and slow initial creep rates, whereas the larger ones give creep curves of the same type as for the initial loading. The explanation is that the smaller stresses are less than the stress represented by the vertical line $\alpha t = 1$ in Fig. 8. Thus all the sources which could instantaneously provide a loop are exhausted. In fact the interval AB after several hours creep must be ca. 1.4 kg/mm² when $t \sim 24$ hours.

These results enable us to estimate Λ. Putting $\nu t \sim 10^4$, $\sigma_i - \sigma = 1.5$ kg/mm², $\sigma = 7$ kg/m², we obtain for equation (4.6)

$$kT/0.15a\Lambda^2\sigma_i = 1.5/7 \ln 10^4 \sim 0.02. \tag{4.12}$$

Thus

$$0.15a\Lambda^2\sigma_i \sim 1 \text{ ev}, \tag{4.13}$$

from which we deduce

$$\Lambda \sim 10^{-6} \text{ cm}, \tag{4.14}$$

a not unreasonable value. It will be realized that the approximations in the theory are not such that this value can be trusted to within a factor 2.

REFERENCES

1. T. S. Kê, *Phys. Rev.*, **71**, 533 (1947).
2. N. F. Mott, *Research*, **2**, 162 (1949).
3. F. C. Frank, *Report of a Conference on the Strength of Solids*, p. 47, University of Bristol, England, Physical Society, London, 1948.
4. F. C. Frank and W. T. Read, *Phys. Rev.*, **79**, 722 (1950).
5. G. Leibfried, *Z. Phys.*, **127**, 344 (1950).
6. F. C. Frank, *Carnegie Institute of Technology Symposium on the Plastic Deformation of Crystalline Solids*, Office of Naval Research, 1950.
7. N. F. Mott and F. R. N. Nabarro, *Report of a Conference on the Strength of Solids*, p. 1, University of Bristol, England, Physical Society, London, 1948.
8. M. Davis and N. Thompson, *Proc. Phys. Soc. (London)*, **B63**, 847 (1950).
9. A. H. Cottrell, *Report of a Conference on the Strength of Solids*, p. 30, University of Bristol, England, Physical Society, London, 1948.

10. A. H. Cottrell and B. A. Bilby, *Proc. Phys. Soc.* (*London*), **62**, 19 (1949).
11. G. V. Smith, *Properties of Metals at Elevated Temperatures*, McGraw-Hill Book Co., New York, 1950.

DISCUSSION

J. KOEHLER (CARNEGIE INSTITUTE OF TECHNOLOGY):

The attractive cork-screw mechanism of Frank and Read for the production of large numbers of dislocations predicts that at temperatures which are low enough so that the number of thoroughly pinned down points on the dislocations does not change with temperature the yield stress of the material should not depend on the temperature. Data on 99.999 per cent copper crystals obtained at the Carnegie Institute of Technology by Dr. P. Neurath indicates that this is the case. Measurements made at 25°C gave a yield stress of 218 ± 17 grams/mm^2; at -190°C the yield stress was 220 ± 25 grams/mm^2. It is not clear why the yield stress of hexagonal crystals depends on temperature.

The cork-screw mechanism also enables us to calculate the length of the free loop which gave rise to yielding. The copper data above imply a free loop length of 5×10^{-4} cm. Neurath's yield data on 99.999 per cent lead crystals at -190°C imply a free loop length of 2×10^{-4} cm.

The foregoing figures for free loop lengths are also of interest in connection with the theory of damping, which attributes the amplitude dependence to the breaking away of dislocations from impurity atoms. In that theory it was decided that such breakaway would continue only until certain very strong obstacles to further lengthening were encountered. The average free length after this process had gone to completion was calculated from decrement measurements to be 1.3×10^{-4} cm. This result agrees well with the yield strength data given above. It should be noted that both the yield and the damping measurements were made on copper crystals grown from the same original copper stock.

Mott in his paper has given a very simple expression which enables us to calculate the average separation distance of dissolved impurities along a dislocation. Using his equation for 99.999 per cent copper crystals and assuming that the potential energy gained by the coagulation of one impurity atom with a dislocation is a quarter of an electron volt, we calculate the average separation distance to be 3×10^{-4} cm. The value obtained from the decrement data is 2×10^{-5} cm. The reason for the discrepancy is clear. Mott's calculation assumes that the impurities are randomly distributed and that only the dislocations can move. Actually during cooling from the melting temperature probably both the dislocations and the impurities move. This will tend to make the locking process somewhat more efficient than Mott's calculation indicates and may remove the discrepancy.

E. OROWAN (MASSACHUSETTS INSTITUTE OF TECHNOLOGY):

Professor Mott has shown that the experiments of Davis and Thompson, evaluated on the basis of the exhaustion hypothesis, led to an extremely low value of the vibration frequency of a dislocation; it is of the order of 1/sec, whereas the theoretical expectation[1] was 10^8 or 10^9 times higher. This increases the suspicion that the exhaustion hypothesis may not represent a useful approximation in the theoretical treatment of transient creep. The following simple consideration indicates that, in fact, the conditions under which transient creep is experimentally observed are quite different from those assumed in the exhaustion hypothesis, and that any resemblance between the creep curves calculated on this basis and the experimental curves is probably accidental.

To make clear what exactly is implied in the exhaustion hypothesis, let the creep specimen be subdivided into cells of equal volume, just large enough to satisfy the requirement that a slip process started by a thermal stress fluctuation within a cell should not reverse spontaneously when the fluctuation has disappeared. The increase of the operative shear stress component needed for starting slip in a cell is called its *activation stress.* In a creep test, the application of the load is followed by a practically sudden deformation, after which the different cells are left with different values of the activation stress. Figure D.1 shows schematically the distribution of the activation stresses over the cells in the specimen; the abscissa values include the applied stress τ_a, so that $\Delta = \tau - \tau_a$ is the additional stress that must be provided by a thermal fluctuation in order to produce stable slip in a cell. A vertical strip of the area below the distribution curve, between the values τ and $\tau + \delta\tau$ of the abscissa, can be regarded as consisting of a number of small rectangles such as R in Fig. D.1, each representing one individual cell in the specimen having an activation stress between $(\tau - \tau_a)$ and $(\tau - \tau_a) + \delta\tau$. The probability of thermal slip activation is considerable only in the cells represented by a small part of the curve nearest to the point τ_a. After the occurrence of slip in the cell represented by the rectangle R, this rectangle is thrown into the high-stress part of the curve, as indicated by the arrow 1. The characteristic assumption of

[1] N. F. Mott and F. R N. Nabarro, *Report of a Conference on the Strength of Solids*, p. 1, University of Bristol, England, Physical Society, 1948.

the exhaustion hypothesis is that this process is the only one that need be considered. The cells with low activation energy are exhausted in the course of creep by being transferred, through the occurrence of slip, to the high-stress part of the curve, where they stay henceforth.

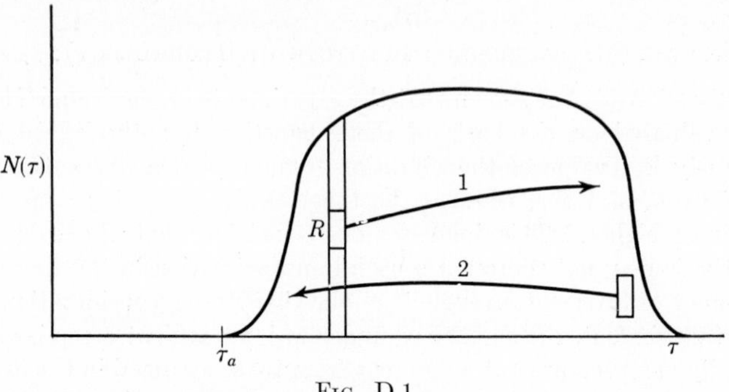

FIG. D.1

That this assumption, in the best case, is a rough approximation can be seen from Fig. D.2, representing a small volume in the specimen, where S_1 and S_2 are the positions of two "soft" (that is, low activation stress) cells whereas H is a "hard" cell. If slip is activated in the cell S_1 and extends over a small area of a slip plane, the side view of which is

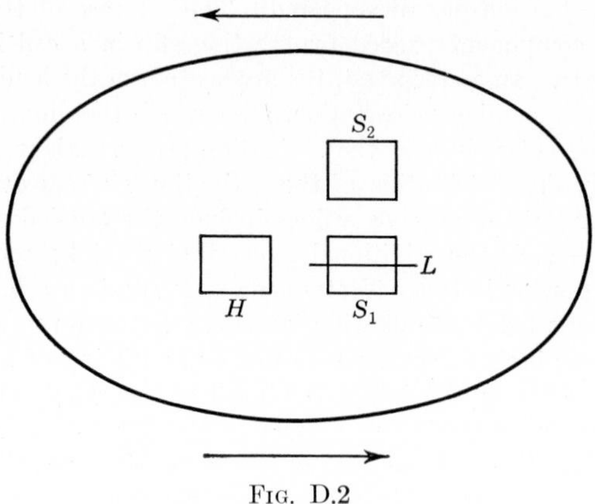

FIG. D.2

indicated by the short line L, the operative shear stress is greatly increased in H and reduced in S_2. As a consequence, the hard cell H becomes soft and the soft cell S_2 hard, without any slip occurring in them. Slip in the soft cell represented by the rectangle R in Fig. D.1, therefore, is accompanied by a mass migration of other rectangles, representing neighboring cells, from the high-stress parts to the low-stress parts of the distribution curve and vice versa, as exemplified by the arrows 1 and 2 in Fig. D.1. The decisive question for the exhaustion hypothesis is: Can this migration, induced by slip in another cell, be neglected? If not, one cannot speak of exhaustion in the above sense, because the supply of the soft cells initially present may be continually replenished from the high-stress part of the curve. The following consideration shows that, in fact, the circulation of cells between the high-stress and low-stress parts of the curve, far from being negligible, is a dominating factor in transient creep.

When slip occurs in a small area of a slip plane, the shear stress in this area falls to a very low value, and the activation stress needed for repeated slip here is very high. As slip continues in other parts of the specimen, however, the initially slipped area comes under increasing shear stress, and its activation energy drops. This effect is neglected in the exhaustion treatment where, consequently, a slipped area is regarded as practically stressless for the duration of the creep experiment, that is, as equivalent to a crack opened up in the slip plane. The process of exhaustion creep is the continued creation of such shear cracks in the specimen. The material between the "cracks" remains entirely elastic, and the mean elastic strain in it is the creep strain; the corresponding increase of the mean stress in the elastic regions can be obtained from Hooke's law. The assumption implied in the exhaustion hypothesis would be acceptable only if this increase of stress, when applied by an external force, did not alter the creep rate substantially; in other words, if it did not affect considerably the activation probabilities of the inactive cells. Now it is well known that an increase of the applied stress by 1 per cent increases the transient creep rate by an amount of its own order of magnitude; the highest rise of stress, compatible with the exhaustion treatment, therefore, cannot exceed 0.1 per cent. In the experiments of Davis and Thompson, the applied stress was of the order of $10^{-3}G$ where G is the shear modulus; the highest permissible increase of the mean stress, therefore, would be less than $10^{-6}G$. However, the maximum creep strain in these experiments was 1 per cent, and so the corresponding rise of the mean stress to which the exhaustion hypothesis would lead would be of the order of $10^{-2}G$, that is, at least 10^4 times higher than the amount compatible with the assumption of this hypothesis.

Obviously, a small fraction of the deformation produced in a typical creep test is sufficient to change even the initially hardest cells into soft ones; the exhaustion process practically does not exist. Strain hardening is not an exhaustion of soft cells but a relatively slow movement of the distribution curve towards higher stresses, accompanied by a rapid circulation of the cells within the area under the distribution curve. It seems, therefore, that the appropriate treatment of transient creep must be based on the method given by the present speaker;[2] in this, the circulation of the cells between the high and low stress parts of the distribution curve, as well as the progressive displacement of the curve towards higher stresses, are implicitly taken into account by making use of experimentally determined stress-strain curves.

Professor Mott has mentioned that the majority of transient creep curves can be represented by Andrade's third-root formula; Davis and Thompson, on the other hand, obtain curves of a logarithmic type in their experiments with an aged Cu-Ag alloy. This was interpreted by assuming that in alloys with considerable microstress fields transient creep was of the exhaustion type, whereas in pure metals some unknown factor led to Andrade curves. It seems that this point has found elucidation in experiments which Mr. O. H. Wyatt and the present speaker have recently completed in the Cavendish Laboratory. The material was H. C. copper; transient creep curves under constant stress were observed in the temperature interval between liquid nitrogen and +170°C. The creep curves were logarithmic up to about −60° or −70°C; at higher temperatures, they became of the Andrade type. The low-temperature curves, by the way, fitted the simple logarithmic formula of Phillips[3] rather than equation (4.7) in Professor Mott's paper. It seems, therefore, that the Andrade formula reflects the operation of some recovery-like process which takes place during creep already at temperatures far below that of ordinary thermal softening, but ceases in copper before the temperature of liquid nitrogen is reached. The results of Davis and Thompson may then be due to the well-known increase of the temperatures of recovery and recrystallization by alloying: unalloyed copper shows the same type of curve as the Cu-Ag alloy if the temperature is lowered by 80 or 90 degrees.

The interpretation of the yield stress of pure metals by means of the Frank-Read model and the two-dimensional bubble-pressure formula Gb/L is interesting but not very hopeful. The reproducibility of the yield stress would demand the existence of a well-defined upper limit for the spacing L of the anchored dislocations; without a reason why such a fairly sharp upper limit should exist, the initial yield stress is not explained.

The hypothesis put forward to explain the yield phenomenon in low-

[2] E. Orowan, *Trans. West of Scotland Iron and Steel Inst.*, 1947, p. 45.

[3] P. Phillips, *Phil. Mag.* (6) **9** (1905), 513. The logarithmic formula of Phillips does not carry the same weight as the third-root formula of Andrade, because Phillips used constant load instead of constant stress, and did not separate the viscous component of creep from the transient one.

carbon steel assumes that the upper yield point was the stress at which a Frank-Read mobile dislocation was torn away from locking impurity atoms, whereas the stress drop itself was due to the spontaneous formation of dislocation loops in neighboring grains under the high stress produced by the Frank-Read loops pressing against the boundary. If this were so, single crystals would yield, without stress drop, at the stress level of the *upper* yield point of polycrystalline material; in reality, they yield at stresses below the *lower* yield point. In addition, it is difficult to see why the neighboring grains do not develop their own dislocation loops, rather than having to wait for slip nucleation by stress concentration originating from outside. Finally, the model contains only elements common to many metals, whereas the yield phenomenon is observed only in a few.

At this point, some cautionary remarks about the locking of dislocations by impurity atoms seem appropriate. It is widely assumed, particularly by theoretical physicists, that the various yield phenomena provide conclusive evidence for the impurity locking of dislocations, the theoretical aspects of which have been so thoroughly explored by Cottrell, Nabarro, and their collaborators in Birmingham. Such a view, however, is an optimistic anticipation of experiments yet to be carried out. It has been proved recently by Cottrell and Gibbons, Low and Schwarzbarth, and Hollomon and Holden that single crystals of iron do not show the characteristic yield phenomenon of polycrystalline iron, even if they contain the necessary amount of carbon. They show certain less conspicuous yield phenomena, which, however, are clearly of a different nature. Since impurity locking would produce at least as marked yield phenomena in single crystals as are observed in fine-grained polycrystals, it cannot account for the sharp yield point in iron. Although this seems to be fairly generally recognized among workers in this field, there is an equally widespread view that the yield phenomenon that was observed by the present writer in zinc and cadmium crystals[4] and studied by C. L. Smith[5] is due to impurity locking. In fact, Wain and Cottrell[6] showed that the sharp yield in these crystals does not occur without the presence of some impurity (probably nitrogen) taken up from commercial nitrogen and even from high-purity argon. This fact, however, is not a conclusive proof for impurity locking being the cause of the sharp yield point. An alternative hypothesis was put forward by Edwards, Phillips, and Liu,[7] who assumed that the

[4] E. Orowan, *Z. Physik,* **89**, 634 (1934).

[5] C. L. Smith, *Nature,* **160**, 466 (1947).

[6] H. L. Wain and A. H. Cottrell, *Proc. Phys. Soc. (London)*, **B63**, 339 (1950).

[7] C. A. Edwards, D. L. Phillips, and Y. H. Liu, *J. Iron Steel Inst.,* **147** (1943).

yield point was due to submicroscopic precipitation along the active slip planes (that is, precipitation nucleated by dislocations). Superficially, this may seem nearly identical with impurity locking; in reality, there is a profound difference between the two. Locking removes nuclei for slip without hindering their movement considerably once they have started; precipitation, on the other hand, creates obstacles to the movement of dislocations in and near the affected slip planes. An undistorted crystal, containing only few dislocations, ought to show the yield phenomenon at least as intensely as a slightly distorted crystal if it is due to impurity locking, because a few dislocations are more completely locked than many by a given amount of impurity atoms. On the other hand, if the yield phenomenon is due to the blocking of operative slip planes by particles precipitated at dislocations, it cannot arise without a certain minimum amount of deformation followed by heat treatment. Neither the present writer nor C. L. Smith has ever observed the phenomenon without preliminary straining; Wain and Cottrell state that usually two strain-aging treatments were necessary for the yield point to become pronounced. Unless some additional factor must be taken into account, therefore, this looks like a crucial experiment for the slip plane precipitation hypothesis and against impurity locking. Further experimental work would be highly desirable; at the moment, impurity locking seems to be an attractive theoretical possibility that has not yet received experimental confirmation. There is no such doubt about the adsorption of impurities by dislocations which has been strikingly illustrated by Wert (damping of carbon steel). From the mere fact that adsorption occurs, however, it does not follow that the corresponding locking force is large enough to produce easily observable mechanical effects.

It may be added that the necessity of a preliminary straining and heating for producing the yield phenomenon in cadmium or zinc crystals cannot be attributed to the nonuniformity of stress distribution arising from irregularities of gripping in the testing machine. The nonuniformity is highest in the elastic region, before yielding begins, and here it depends only on the geometry of the specimen and of the grips, so that it cannot differ substantially from that present before yielding in mild steel tensile specimens. However, the upper yield point in mild steel is known to be fairly insensitive to slightly inaccurate gripping, and the lower yield point is hardly sensitive at all; besides, the probability of an accidentally very accurate gripping is quite high. Consequently, the absence of both upper and lower yield points in cadmium and zinc before strain annealing cannot be attributed to this trivial cause.

7.

The Influence of Dislocations and Impurities on the Damping and the Elastic Constants of Metal Single Crystals*

J. S. KOEHLER†

Department of Physics, Carnegie Institute of Technology

ABSTRACT

The motion of edge-type dislocations which are "pinned down" by impurity atoms is treated for the case of a periodic external stress. An expression for the distribution of free lengths of dislocation is obtained. The zero amplitude decrement and plastic contribution to the elastic constants are calculated. The amplitude dependence is discussed by supposing that some of the dislocations break away from the impurities. The results obtained are in agreement with experiment if the damping force on a dislocation is about a hundred times previously suggested values.

1. DAMPING PHENOMENA IN METAL SINGLE CRYSTALS

Experimentally, sound waves in a metal single crystal are subject to a damping which depends sensitively on the amount of previous cold work and on the purity of the metal.[1] The elastic constants are also found to decrease by a few per cent during cold work.[2]

This paper is a survey of the research done thus far in an effort to understand these effects. It is assumed from the start that these phenomena result from the motion of dislocations which are "pinned down" by impurities, by precipitates, and by other dislocations.

* *Technical Report* 5, Contract N6ori-47, Task Order 1, NR 019 301, U. S. Navy Department, Office of Naval Research, Washington, D. C.

† Present address: Physics Department, University of Illinois.

2. THE EXPERIMENTAL FACTS

We shall consider measurements made at frequencies of oscillation in the kilocycle range. Let us first consider the experimental information available on the damping. Given a metal single crystal in oscillation, the decrement (Δ) is:

$$\Delta = \frac{w}{2W}, \tag{2.1}$$

where w is the energy loss per cycle and W is the total vibrational energy of the specimen.

1. *Order of Magnitude*

The order of magnitude of the decrement is as follows:

(*a*) Annealed 99.99 per cent copper crystal, $\Delta = 2 \times 10^{-5}$, S.A. = 3×10^{-7}.[3] S.A. means strain amplitude.

(*b*) Vacuum annealed 99.999 per cent copper crystal, $\Delta = 2$ to 5×10^{-3}, S.A. $= 3 \times 10^{-7}$.[4]

2. *Impurities Decrease* Δ

(*a*) 99.999 per cent copper crystal after 42 hours at 1000°C in vacuum, $\Delta = 1.7 \times 10^{-3}$, S.A. $= 2.8 \times 10^{-7}$. Then this specimen had 20 hours at 1000°C in hydrogen at atmospheric pressure. The result was $\Delta = 1.0 \times 10^{-4}$, S.A. $= 2.8 \times 10^{-7}$.[4]

(*b*) 0.21 per cent by weight of iron was added to 99.999 per cent copper during melting. The vacuum-annealed crystal had $\Delta = 8 \times 10^{-5}$, S.A. $= 3 \times 10^{-7}$.[4]

3. *Increasing S.A. Increases* Δ

For small strain amplitudes, we find:[3]

$$\Delta = \Delta_0 + B(\text{S.A.})^2.$$

For strain amplitudes larger than about 5×10^{-7} the decrement increases less rapidly with strain amplitude (see Fig. 1).[4]

4. Δ_0 *and* B *Vary Together*

(*a*) Annealing decreases both Δ_0 and B. A 99.99? per cent copper had various vacuum anneals at 500°C.[4]

No anneal	$\Delta_0 = 4.05 \times 10^{-3}$	$B = 1.8 \times 10^{10}$
4 hours	$\Delta_0 = 2.05 \times 10^{-3}$	$B = 5 \times 10^{9}$
8 hours	$\Delta_0 = 0.95 \times 10^{-3}$	$B = 4 \times 10^{8}$
15 hours	$\Delta_0 = 0.60 \times 10^{-3}$	$B = 5 \times 10^{7}$

(*b*) Impurities decrease both Δ_0 and B.

42 hours in vacuum at 1000°C	$\Delta_0 = 5 \times 10^{-4}$	$B = 1.5 \times 10^{10}$ [4]
42 hours plus 20 hours in H_2 at 1000°C	$\Delta_0 = 8 \times 10^{-5}$	$B = 1.1 \times 10^8$

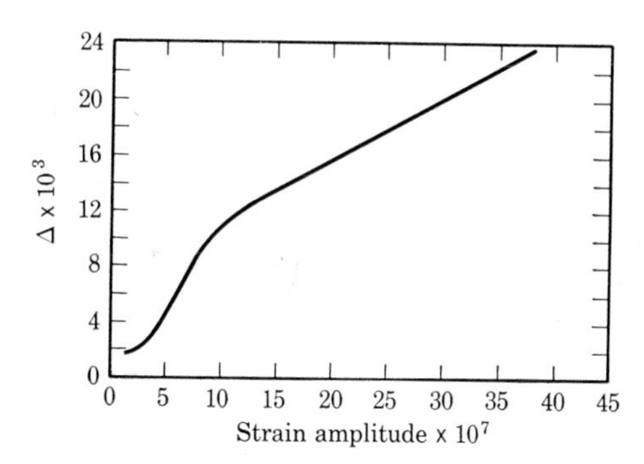

FIG. 1. Reversible decrement changes in copper. (J. Marx and J. S. Koehler.[4])

(*c*) Permanent deformation raises both Δ_0 and B. 99.998 per cent copper crystals were loaded statically in compression.[3]

No load	$\Delta_0 = 1.0 \times 10^{-4}$	$B = 3.7 \times 10^7$
120 lb/in.^{2}	$\Delta_0 = 1.2 \times 10^{-4}$	$B = 1.2 \times 10^8$
150 lb/in.^{2}	$\Delta_0 = 1.9 \times 10^{-4}$	$B = 3.2 \times 10^8$

5. *Specimens Having Large Δ_0 Are Permanently Affected by Small Stresses*
For 99.999 per cent copper crystals:[4]

$\Delta_0 = 6.95 \times 10^{-3}$	$\sigma_r = 25$ grams/mm^2	specimen 7C-3
$\Delta_0 = 3.3 \times 10^{-3}$	$\sigma_r = 33$ grams/mm^2	specimen 7B-1
$\Delta_0 = 1.4 \times 10^{-3}$	$\sigma_r = 56$ grams/mm^2	specimen 9A-1 (contaminated?)

σ_r is the smallest oscillating resolved shearing stress which produces a permanent increase in Δ.

6. *Data on Frequency and Temperature Dependence Is Not Complete*[3,5,6,7]
Let us next consider the data available on the changes produced in Young's modulus.

7. *Decreases in Δ Are Associated with Increases in Young's Modulus*
(*a*) The changes in Δ and the Young's modulus γ produced by varying the strain amplitude are proportional to one another.

99.99 per cent copper $\frac{\Delta - \Delta_0}{\delta\gamma/\gamma} = 3.55 \pm 0.06$ (ref. 3)

99.998 per cent copper $\frac{\Delta - \Delta_0}{\delta\gamma/\gamma} = 4.36 \pm 0.09$ (ref. 5)

99.99? per cent copper $\frac{\Delta - \Delta_0}{\delta\gamma/\gamma} = 29.0 \pm 0.6$ (ref. 4)

The change in γ is 0.0135 per cent of its initial value.

99.999 per cent copper (7B-1) $\frac{\Delta - \Delta_0}{\delta\gamma/\gamma} = 31.8 \pm 3.0$ (ref. 4)

99.999 per cent copper (7C-3) $\frac{\Delta - \Delta_0}{\delta\gamma/\gamma} = 49.5 \pm 2.5$ (ref. 4)

where $\delta\gamma$ is the change in γ produced by varying the strain amplitude. Note that the ratio is largest for the specimen of highest purity.

(*b*) Annealing and impurities produce much larger changes in γ than the ratios in *a* predict:

7A-1, 15-hour vacuum anneal 500°C $\frac{d(\Delta)}{\delta\gamma/\gamma} = 0.165$ (ref. 4)

where $d(\Delta)$ is the change produced in Δ. The change in γ is 5.9 per cent of its final value.

7A-1, additional 27-hour hydrogen anneal 500°C $\frac{d(\Delta)}{\delta\gamma/\gamma} = 0.115$ (ref. 4)

The change in γ is 3.4 per cent of its final value.

Note: The curve $d(\Delta)$ versus $\delta\gamma/\gamma$ is not a straight line during these annealing experiments; instead the ratio $\frac{d(\Delta)}{\delta\gamma/\gamma}$ increases with time. The values quoted are the average values.

3. THEORY

THE MOTION OF A PINNED-DOWN, DAMPED, EDGE DISLOCATION

Suppose that a rapidly oscillating external shearing stress is applied to a crystal. If the frequency of the applied stress is in the kilocycle range, the impurity atoms are completely unable to follow the alternating stress, since diffusion is an extremely slow process at room temperature. The dislocations are therefore anchored by the Cottrell force[8] to the impurity atoms, and the portion of the line dislocation between two impurity atoms oscillates back and forth on its slip plane like a stretched string. This situation is illustrated in Fig. 2, where the plane of the figure is the slip plane.

Let us assume that the interactions of the dislocations with one another are negligible. Let x be the displacement of an element of

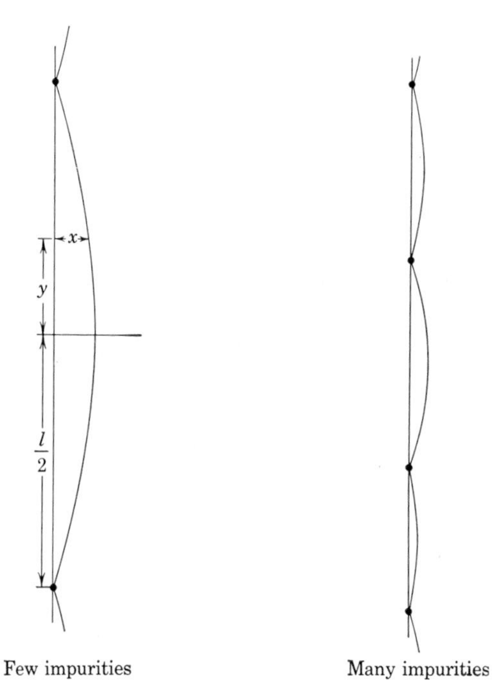

FIG. 2. The oscillations of anchored dislocations.

the dislocation loop from its equilibrium position, and let y be the distance of the element from the center of the loop (see Fig. 2). If the applied shearing stress tending to move the dislocation along its slip plane is $\sigma_0 \cos \omega t$, the equation of motion of the pinned-down dislocation loop is

$$A \frac{\partial^2 x}{\partial t^2} + B \frac{\partial x}{\partial t} - C \frac{\partial^2 x}{\partial y^2} = \sigma_0 a \cos \omega t, \tag{3.1}$$

where a is the interatomic distance, and the term on the right gives the force per unit length produced on the dislocation by the external shearing stress. The term in A on the left gives the inertial force acting on the dislocation; in fact, A is the effective mass per unit length. Eshelby and Frank[9] have shown that

$$A = \pi\rho a^2, \tag{3.2}$$

where ρ is the density of the material. The term in B gives the damping force per unit length acting on the dislocation; we shall discuss the physical nature of this force later in the paper. The term in C arises because the length, and therefore the self-energy, of a bowed-out dislocation are greater than the length and the self-energy of a straight dislocation. Hence, as Mott and Nabarro[10] have shown, there exists a tension πC which tends to decrease the length of the dislocation. Their calculations give

$$C = \frac{2Ga^2}{\pi(1 - \nu)}, \tag{3.3}$$

where G is the modulus of rigidity and ν is Poisson's ratio. The equation of motion of a loop of screw-type dislocation would be expected to look somewhat similar to equation (3.1), although the numerical values of the coefficients might differ from ours by a factor of 3 or so. It should be noted that impurity atoms will not pin down a pure screw-type dislocation. The splitting of the whole dislocations into Shockley partials[11] occurs in the face-centered cubic metals in such a way that it is impossible to obtain a pure screw-type dislocation in such crystals. If this were not the case, the influence of impurities on the mechanical behavior of the face-centered cubic crystals would be much less marked. The same statements about splitting and the influence of impurities can be made for the hexagonal metals.

Equation (3.1) must be solved subject to the condition that x is zero at the ends of the loop. An examination of orders of magnitude reveals that the terms of largest order in (3.1) are those resulting from the tension and from the external shearing stress; the term arising from the damping is next in importance; the smallest term arises from inertia. Since x is an even function of y, we try the following zeroth-order solution:

$$x_0 = \{a_0 + a_2 y^2 + a_4 y^4 + \cdots\} \cos \omega t. \tag{3.4}$$

Upon substituting into (3.1), under the assumption that the A and B terms can be neglected, we find that the zeroth-order solution obeying the boundary conditions is

$$x_0 = \frac{\sigma_0 a}{2C}\left(\frac{l^2}{4} - y^2\right) \cos \omega t, \tag{3.5}$$

where l is the loop length. We next suppose that $x = x_0 + x_1(yt)$, where x_1 is small compared with x_0. The trial solution for x_1 is

$$x_1 = \{b_0 + b_2 y^2 + b_4 y^4 + \cdots\} \sin \omega t. \tag{3.6}$$

Inserting x into (3.1), we obtain first-order terms, using x_0 in the expression giving the damping force and using x_1 in the expression giving the force produced by tension. The inertial force is neglected in first order. The resulting solution for x_1 which satisfies the boundary conditions is

$$x_1 = \frac{\sigma_0 a \omega B}{8C^2}\left(\frac{5l^4}{48} - \frac{y^2 l^2}{2} + \frac{y^4}{3}\right) \sin \omega t. \tag{3.7}$$

Continuing in this fashion, we obtain the second- and third-order corrections to our solution. They are

$$x_2 = \frac{\sigma_0 a \omega^2}{8C^2}\left[A\left(\frac{5l^4}{48} - \frac{l^2 y^2}{2} + \frac{y^4}{3}\right) - \frac{B^2}{24C}\left(\frac{49l^6}{192} - \frac{5l^4 y^2}{4} + l^2 y^4 - \frac{y^6}{3}\right)\right] \cos \omega t, \tag{3.8}$$

$$x_3 = \frac{\sigma_0 a \omega^3 B}{8C^3}\left[A\left(\frac{61l^6}{2880} - \frac{5l^4 y^2}{48} + \frac{l^2 y^4}{12} - \frac{y^6}{45}\right) + \frac{B^2}{144C}\left(\frac{6687l^8}{35{,}840} - \frac{49l^6 y^2}{64} + \frac{5l^4 y^4}{8} - \frac{l^2 y^6}{5} + \frac{y^8}{28}\right)\right] \sin \omega t. \tag{3.9}$$

If only the zeroth approximation is used, the maximum displacement at the center of the loop is

$$x_m = \frac{\sigma_0 a l^2}{8C}\cdot \tag{3.10}$$

For copper at a fairly large strain, amplitude of 10^{-6} and with a loop length of 10^{-4} cm, the maximum displacement is only 3.7×10^{-8} cm.

THE EFFECTIVE MODULUS OF RIGIDITY AND THE DISTRIBUTION OF LOOP LENGTHS

Eshelby[9] noted that the presence of dislocations would lower the apparent elastic moduli and hence the resonant frequency of a single crystal. This phenomenon occurs because of a limited motion of the dislocations under the influence of the applied stress. The total strain is therefore made up of the elastic strain and the reversible plastic strain. The average displacement of a dislocation of length l can be obtained as follows:

$$\bar{x} = \int_0^{l/2} \frac{x\,dy}{l/2} = \frac{\sigma_0 a l^2 \cos \omega t}{12C} + \frac{\sigma_0 a \omega B l^4 \sin \omega t}{120C^2}, \quad (3.11)$$

where zeroth- and first-order terms have been included. The plastic shearing strain produced by this single loop in a cube of material of edge L is

$$\epsilon_1 = \frac{\bar{x} l a}{L^3} = \frac{\sigma_0 a^2 l^3 \cos \omega t}{12CL^3} + \frac{\sigma_0 a^2 \omega B l^5 \sin \omega t}{120C^2L^3}. \quad (3.12)$$

Equation (3.12) shows that for a given total length of line dislocation the amount of plastic strain will depend in a sensitive way upon the distribution of loop lengths in the solid. The number of long loops will be important in determining the plastic strain. The distribution function can be determined as follows. Suppose that there are N atomic lengths of dislocation line and that somewhere along the dislocation line there are n impurity atoms. We shall assume that the solvent and solute atoms are arranged at random along the dislocation line. The probability of finding two impurities separated by s solvent atoms is approximately

$$P(s) = \frac{n}{N}\left(1 - \frac{n}{N}\right)^s = c(1 - c)^{l/a} \cong ce^{-cl/a}, \quad (3.13)$$

where c is the concentration of impurities along the dislocation line ($c = n/N$). Thus the number of loops having lengths between l and l plus dl is

$$N(l)\,dl = \frac{Nc^2}{a} e^{-cl/a}\,dl. \quad (3.14)$$

The numerical factor in (3.14) has been chosen to give the correct total length of dislocation line, that is, Na. The exponential can be used provided c is much less than one.

The total reversible plastic strain ϵ_p is

$$\epsilon_p = \int_0^\infty \epsilon_1 N(l)\, dl = \frac{\sigma_0 a^5 N \cos \omega t}{2CL^3c^2} + \frac{\sigma_0 a^7 N\omega B \sin \omega t}{C^2L^3c^4}. \tag{3.15}$$

If G' is the effective modulus of rigidity and G is the true elastic modulus of rigidity, the total strain can be written

$$\epsilon_e + \epsilon_p = \frac{\sigma_0 \cos \omega t}{G'}$$

$$= \sigma_0 \cos \omega t \left[\frac{1}{G} + \frac{Na^5}{2CL^3c^2} + \frac{Na^7\omega B \tan \omega t}{C^2L^3c^4}\right]. \tag{3.16}$$

If $dG = G' - G$, then

$$\frac{dG}{G} = \frac{NGa^5}{2CL^3c^2} + \frac{NGa^7\omega B \tan \omega t}{C^2L^3c^4}, \tag{3.17}$$

where dG has been assumed small compared with G. We shall wait until later to compare this with experiment.

THE DECREMENT

To calculate Δ, the energy loss w_1 per cycle for a single loop must first be evaluated. We find that

$$w_1 = 2\int_0^{l/2} dy \int_0^{2\pi/\omega} (\sigma_0 a \cos \omega t) \frac{\partial x}{\partial t}\, dt. \tag{3.18}$$

Inserting x and carrying out the integrations, we have

$$w_1 = \frac{\pi\sigma_0 a^2 B\omega l^5}{120C^2} + \frac{\pi\sigma_0 a^2\omega^3 B}{10{,}080C^3}\left[17Al^7 + \frac{41}{9}\frac{B^2l^9}{C}\right]. \tag{3.19}$$

The total energy loss per cycle is

$$w = \int_0^\infty w_1 N(l)\, dl$$

$$= \frac{\pi N\sigma_0{}^2 B\omega a^7}{C^2c^4}\left[1 + \frac{17Aa^2\omega^2}{2Cc^2} + \frac{164B^2a^4\omega^2}{C^2c^4}\right]. \tag{3.20}$$

The vibrational energy in a cube of edge L is $W = \sigma_0{}^2L^3/4G$, and hence the decrement according to (2.1) is

$$\Delta = \frac{2\pi NGB\omega a^7}{C^2L^3c^4}\left[1 + \frac{17Aa^2\omega^2}{2Cc^2} + \frac{164Ba^2\omega^2}{C^2c^4}\right]. \tag{3.21}$$

Before we compare this with experiment it will be necessary to discuss the dependence of Δ and dG/G on strain amplitude.

DEPENDENCE OF STRAIN AMPLITUDE, USING BREAKAWAY

It will be supposed that the amplitude dependence observed occurs because an increasing portion of the dislocation line breaks away from the impurity atoms at large strain amplitudes.

The maximum force exerted on an impurity atom by an anchored dislocation during a cycle is

$$F = \pi C(\phi_1 - \phi_2) = \frac{\pi \sigma_0 a}{2} (l_1 + l_2), \tag{3.22}$$

where πC is the loop tension and ϕ_1 and ϕ_2 are the angles made by the loops of length l_1 and l_2 at the impurity when maximum displacement occurs; these angles are measured to the unstressed position of the dislocation. Only the zeroth-order displacement was used in evaluating the angles to obtain the right side of (3.22).

The attractive force between an impurity and a dislocation is of the order of:[8]

$$f = \frac{4G\epsilon a^3 \lambda}{R^2}, \tag{3.23}$$

where ϵ is the difference in atomic radii divided by the atomic radius of the solvent atom, R is the distance of the impurity from the dislocation axis, and λ is the edge-type component of the Burgers vector of the dislocation. The maximum value f^* of this force occurs when the impurity is two or three atomic distances from the dislocation and equation (3.23) is of course not valid for smaller separation. f^* is 3.8×10^{-7} dyne for a Shockley partial dislocation, using an impurity that is readily soluble in copper (that is, having $\epsilon = 0.05$).

Breakaway will occur in all cases where F exceeds f^*. Physically this should not mean that a catastrophic tearing loose will then occur because, for a given dislocation, there will be only a finite length lying in the active slip plane which can be pulled loose. The remainder of the closed dislocation line may occupy inactive slip planes. In addition, there may exist points at which a very large obstacle to breakaway exists, such as a precipitate. We shall therefore assume that the distribution of free lengths after breakaway has cleared the dislocation of small obstacles such as impurity atoms is

$$M(l)\,dl = \frac{Nr^2}{a}\,e^{-rl/a}\,dl, \tag{3.24}$$

where r is of course less than c. Hence our distribution changes from $N(l)\,dl$ to $M(l)\,dl$ as breakaway occurs. At low strain amplitudes most of the change in the distribution occurs at large loop lengths, but as the strain amplitude is increased the effect becomes noticeable over the entire distribution. Let us attempt to calculate the distribution function appropriate for any strain amplitude.

The number of times a loop of length l_1 is found next to a loop of length l_2 is

$$\nu\,dl_1\,dl_2 = \frac{Nc^3}{a^2}\,e^{-(c/a)(l_1+l_2)}\,dl_1\,dl_2. \tag{3.25}$$

If $(l_1 + l_2)$ is greater than $\mathfrak{L}$, breakaway occurs. According to equation (3.22), $\mathfrak{L}$ is given by

$$\mathfrak{L} = \frac{2f^*}{\pi\sigma_0 a}\cdot \tag{3.26}$$

The total decrease at l_1 resulting from this initial breakaway is

$$\begin{aligned} dN(l_1) &= -N(l_1)\,dl_1 && \text{if} \quad l_1 > \mathfrak{L}, \\ dN(l_1) &= dl_1\int_{\mathfrak{L}-l_1}^{\infty}\nu\,dl_2 = -\frac{Nc^2}{a}\,e^{-c\mathfrak{L}/a} && \text{if} \quad l_1 < \mathfrak{L}. \end{aligned} \tag{3.27}$$

The increase in the distribution occurs for values of l larger than $\mathfrak{L}$. This increase is obtained by integrating equation (3.25) over those values of l_1 and l_2 having a given sum l. Thus

$$dN(l) = +\frac{Nc^3}{a^2}\,le^{-cl/a} \qquad l > \mathfrak{L}. \tag{3.28}$$

The resulting distribution is

$$\begin{aligned} N^1(l)\,dl &= \frac{Nc^2}{a}\,(e^{-cl/a} - e^{-c\mathfrak{L}/a})\,dl && l < \mathfrak{L}, \\ N^1(l)\,dl &= \frac{Nc^3}{a^2}\,le^{-cl/a}\,dl && l > \mathfrak{L}. \end{aligned} \tag{3.29}$$

We should, of course, carry the calculation through further

stages of breakaway, but the calculation rapidly becomes cumbersome. Instead we shall use equation (3.29) to guide us in making a judicious guess at the result. We shall assume that the final distribution is

$$\left.\begin{aligned} N^*(l)\,dl &= \frac{Nc^2}{a}\,(e^{-cl/a} - e^{-cT/a})\,dl && l < T, \\ N^*(l)\,dl &= 0 && T < l < \mathfrak{L}, \\ N^*(l)\,dl &= \frac{Nr^2}{a}\,e^{-rl/a}\,dl && l > \mathfrak{L}, \end{aligned}\right\} \tag{3.30}$$

where T must be chosen so that the total length of dislocation is Na. Upon integration of $lN^*(l)\,dl$ we find the condition for T to be

$$\frac{cT}{a} - \log\left\{\frac{1}{2}\left(\frac{cT}{a}\right)^2 + \left(\frac{cT}{a}\right) + 1\right\} = \frac{r\mathfrak{L}}{a} - \log\left\{\left(\frac{r\mathfrak{L}}{a}\right) + 1\right\}. \tag{3.31}$$

This gives approximately

$$T \simeq \frac{r\mathfrak{L}}{c}. \tag{3.32}$$

The distribution given by equations (3.30) and (3.32) can now be used to calculate the dependence of the modulus of rigidity and the decrement on strain amplitude. Proceeding in the same fashion as before, we find:

$$\frac{dG}{G} = \frac{NGa^5}{2GL^3c^2}\left[1+\frac{c^2}{r^2}\,e^{-z}\left\{\frac{z^3}{3!}+\frac{z^2}{2!}+z+1\right\}+\frac{2a^2\omega B\tan\omega t}{Cc^2} \times\left(1+\frac{c^4}{r^4}\,e^{-z}\left\{\frac{z^5}{5!}+\frac{z^4}{4!}+\frac{z^3}{3!}+\frac{z^2}{2!}+z+1\right\}\right)\right] \tag{3.33}$$

and

$$\begin{aligned}\Delta = \frac{2\pi NGB\omega a^7}{C^2L^3c^4}&\left[1+\frac{c^4}{r^4}\,e^{-z}\left\{\frac{z^5}{5!}+\frac{z^4}{4!}+\frac{z^3}{3!}+\frac{z^2}{2!}+z+1\right\}\right. \\ &+\frac{17A\,a^2\omega^2}{2Cc^2}\left(1+\frac{c^6}{r^6}\,e^{-z}\left\{\frac{z^7}{7!}+\frac{z^6}{6!}+\frac{z^5}{5!}+\frac{z^4}{4!}+\frac{z^3}{3!}+\frac{z^2}{2!}+z+1\right\}\right) \\ &\left.+\frac{164B^2a^4\omega^2}{C^2c^4}\left(1+\frac{c^8}{r^8}\,e^{-z}\left\{\frac{z^9}{9!}+\frac{z^8}{8!}+\cdots+z+1\right\}\right)\right]\end{aligned} \tag{3.34}$$

where

$$z = \frac{r\mathfrak{L}}{a} = \frac{2rf^*}{\pi\sigma_0 a^2}. \tag{3.35}$$

The foregoing equations are of course only the first few terms of a development. The equations given are only valid if c^2/r^2 is much greater than one. The dependence on strain amplitude is mainly determined by the exponential terms.

4. COMPARISON WITH EXPERIMENT

ORDER OF MAGNITUDE AT ZERO AMPLITUDE

The constants used are appropriate for copper; they are:

$\rho = 8.93$ grams/cm^3
$a = 2.55$ Å
$G = 4.53 \times 10^{11}$ dynes/cm^2
$\nu = 0.340$

A and C can then be calculated, using equations (3.2) and (3.3). We find:

$$A = 2.51 \times 10^{-14} \text{ gram/cm}, \tag{4.1}$$

$$C = 3.90 \times 10^{-4} \text{ gram cm/sec}^2. \tag{4.2}$$

For the measurements at 37 kc, ω is 2.3×10^5 cycles/sec.

The terms in equations (3.33) and (3.34) which appear at zero amplitude contain three quantities not thus far determined. They are N, B, and c. We have some ideas regarding the value of N from information about the mosaic structure. Seitz[12] estimates that the total length of dislocation line in a well-annealed metal single crystal is of the order of 10^8 or 10^9 cm/cm^3. If we assume that this length is 3.5×10^8 cm/cm^3, N is 1.4×10^{16} atomic distances/cm^3.

The quantities B and c can then be calculated from the values of dG/G and Δ at zero amplitude. If we consider a well-annealed 99.999 per cent pure copper single crystal, the experiments indicate that $dG/G \cong 0.06$ and $\Delta \cong 10^{-3}$. The value of dG/G is obtained by supposing that a long anneal in hydrogen produces a specimen in which the anchoring is so nearly complete that the modulus then obtained is very nearly the true elastic value. Using these figures in equations (3.33) and (3.34), we find that $c = 1.2 \times 10^{-3}$ and $B = 4.8 \times 10^{-3}$ gram sec^{-1} cm^{-1}. The average separation distance between impurities on the dislocation line is a/c, which has the value 2.1×10^{-5} cm. If there is one impurity atom at each pinned point, then the total number which take part in pinning is $1.7 \times 10^{13}/\text{cm}^3$ of specimen. If these were the only impurity atoms present, there would be only two impurity atoms for each 10^{10} solvent atoms. Actually there is one impurity for every 10^5 solvent atoms. There are two possible explanations for the discrepancy. First, the samples may be cooled through the temperature range in which an atmosphere is formed with sufficient rapidity that the association of dislocations and impurities is not complete. Second, some of the impurities may be present as precipitates.

The value of B is much larger than the values thus far suggested by theory. Eshelby[9] and Leibfried[13] have discussed possible mechanisms for the damping force. Eshelby associated it with the irreversible heat flow which occurs in the neighborhood of an oscillating dislocation. Leibfried connects it with the scattering of thermally excited sound waves. Both theories give a value of B which is about 5×10^{-5} gram sec^{-1} cm^{-1} in copper.

This increase in B does not conflict with known data on the speed effect. If a polycrystalline cube of copper which is one centimeter on an edge is sheared and acquires a strain of one-third in 3×10^{-4} sec, the stress required is about 25 per cent higher than if the deformation were done statically.[14] If we suppose that there are 4×10^8 dislocation lines/cm^2 which move (and this is probably an underestimate since they are generated during deformation), then each must move a distance of 0.1 cm during the 3×10^{-4} sec. The average velocity is therefore 100 cm/sec. The dissipative force per unit length is thus $Bv = 0.5$ dyne/cm, where the large value of B has been used. The static stress required to obtain a strain of one-third is about 2.8×10^9 dynes/cm^2.[14] The static force per unit length on a dislocation is therefore $\sigma_0 a = 70$ dynes/cm. Since the dissipative force obtained using the large value of B is small in comparison with this static force, the calculation indicates that we have not used too large a value for B. The speed effect is very large in single crystals of naphthalene;[15] if the correlation suggested here between speed effect and damping is valid, the decrement of a naphthalene crystal should also be large.

A check on the magnitude of the higher order terms in both dG/G and in Δ reveals that they can be neglected at zero amplitude.

THE DEPENDENCE ON STRAIN AMPLITUDE

Experimentally, the $d\gamma/\gamma$ change during an increase of the strain amplitude through the reversible range is about 1×10^{-3} for 99.999 per cent pure copper crystals. The stress amplitude at which deviations from a smooth concave upward curve begin to occur is at $\sigma_0 = 3 \times 10^5$ dynes/cm^2 (that is, $\epsilon_0 = 6.6 \times 10^{-7}$). Simultaneously, the decrement increases from 1×10^{-3} to perhaps 5×10^{-3}.

There are two parameters left at our disposal, r and f^*, although f^* is fairly well known. Unfortunately the developments given do not converge for the large strain amplitude mentioned above. A numerical calculation indicates that convergence does occur at a strain amplitude of 1×10^{-7} ($\sigma_0 = 4.53 \times 10^4$). For such a strain amplitude the increase in the decrement above the zero amplitude value is small, and amounts to perhaps 5 per cent of the zero amplitude result. The numerical calculation of r can, therefore, be carried through, since a preliminary investigation discloses that z is much greater than one. The equation giving r is

$$\frac{c^4}{r^4} e^{-z} \frac{z^5}{5!} = 0.05. \tag{4.3}$$

Using $f^* = 4 \times 10^{-6}$, we find $r = 2 \times 10^{-4}$. Thus the average length of dislocation when pulled free is $a/r = 1.3 \times 10^{-4}$ cm, which does not sound unreasonable. The maximum force f necessary for breakaway is ten times the value given by theory. This may mean that more than one impurity atom occupies a pinned point on the average, or it may indicate that atomic size is not the important source of binding between impurities and dislocations.

The developments given in equations (3.33) and (3.34) predict that the amplitude dependence should change with frequency. This should be investigated experimentally.

In conclusion, the present theory indicates that much information can be obtained on the dislocation and impurity structure in a solid from decrement and elastic constant measurements. It is clear that the theory is not yet complete.

REFERENCES

1. F. Seitz, *Physics of Metals*, Chapter X, McGraw-Hill Book Co., New York, 1943.
2. E. Schmid and W. Boas, *Kristallplastizität*, p. 212, Springer, 1935.

3. A. S. Nowick, *Carnegie Institute of Technology Symposium on the Plastic Deformation of Crystalline Solids*, Office of Naval Research, 1950.
4. J. Marx and J. S. Koehler, *Carnegie Institute of Technology Symposium on the Plastic Deformation of Crystalline Solids*, Office of Naval Research, 1950.
5. T. A. Read, *Trans. AIME*, **143**, 30 (1941).
6. P. G. Bordoni, *La Ricerca Scientifica*, p. 851 (August, 1949).
7. J. Marx, Thesis, Carnegie Institute of Technology (1951).
8. A. H. Cottrell, *Report of a Conference on the Strength of Solids*, p. 30, University of Bristol, England, Physical Society, London, 1948.
9. J. D. Eshelby, *Proc. Roy. Soc. (London)*, **A197**, 396 (1949).
Note. F. C. Frank discusses the question of assigning an equivalent mass to a moving dislocation and indicates that care must be used. See F. C. Frank, *Report of a Conference on the Strength of Solids*, p. 47, University of Bristol, England, Physical Society, London, 1948.
10. N. F. Mott and F. R. N. Nabarro, *Report of a Conference on the Strength of Solids*, p. 8, University of Bristol, Physical Society, London, 1948.
11. R. D. Heidenreich and W. Shockley, *Report of a Conference on the Strength of Solids*, p. 71, University of Bristol, England, Physical Society, London, 1948.
12. J. S. Koehler and F. Seitz, *J. Appl. Mech.*, p. A-220 (September, 1947). See also A. H. Cottrell, *Progress in Metal Physics*, Vol. I, p. 104, Interscience Publishers, New York, 1949.
13. G. Leibfried, *Z. Physik*, **127**, 344 (1950).
14. M. Manjoine and A. Nadai, *Proc. ASTM*, **40**, 822 (1941).
15. A. Kochendörfer, *Z. Krist.*, **97**, 263 (1937).

DISCUSSION

THOMAS A. READ (COLUMBIA UNIVERSITY):

One of the predictions derived by Koehler is that the internal friction associated with the oscillatory motion of dislocations should be proportional to the frequency of oscillation. Nowick,[1] E. P. T. Tyndall,[2] and I agree that no systematic dependence of the internal friction of copper single crystals on frequency can be found. Measurements of this kind are difficult to carry out with precision. Even though measurements are made on the same crystal specimen at different frequencies, it has been found that the crystals used are sufficiently inhomogeneous that the difference in vibration amplitude distribution in the specimen in the two cases has a significant effect on the results obtained. Nevertheless, it appears that the scatter in results in these measurements is not great enough to hide a proportionality of the internal friction to the first power of the frequency.

[1] A. S. Nowick, *Phys. Rev.*, **80**, 249 (1950).
[2] Private communication.

An alternative mechanism for the dissipation of energy through the oscillatory motion of dislocations is sketched in the accompanying figure (Fig. D.1). This mechanism is of interest because it provides for a rate of energy dissipation per cycle of vibration which is independent of the frequency of vibration. In the figure are shown two lengths of edge dislocation AB and CD, joined by a length BC of screw dislocation. Let us suppose the edge dislocations are pinned by impurity atoms at points E and F. Application of an appropriate shearing stress will cause the screw dislocation to move upwards until stopped by the impurity atom at E. Motion of the dislocation downwards will not occur, however, until a shearing stress of the opposite sign is applied. Elaboration of this mechanism by considering a series of pinning atoms along the edge dislocations and the stress-induced motion of the screw dislocation past some of them will be necessary, for example, to account for the amplitude dependence of the internal friction. But a mechanism of this general character will give rise to frequency independent internal friction, so long as a damping term proportional to the velocity of the screw dislocation does not constitute the major resistance to its motion.

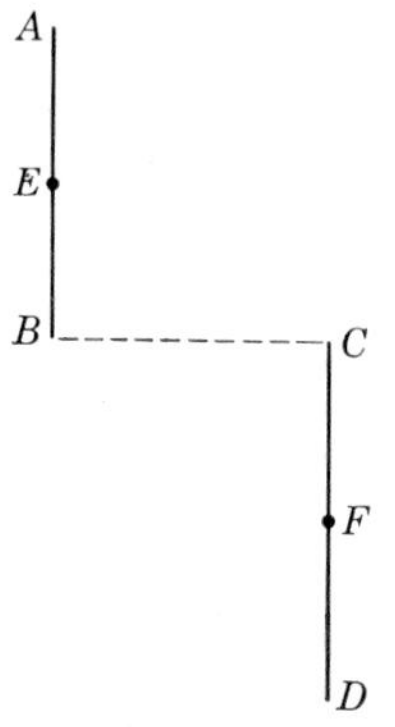

FIG. D.1. A dislocation configuration proposed to account for frequency-independent internal friction.

J. S. KOEHLER (*in reply*):

The suggestion made by Dr. Read concerning the use of screw-type dislocations may be a valuable idea since it allows a large amount of motion of the dislocations under alternating stress. In the case of the edge-type dislocations, as we have seen, the amount of motion is very limited. Let us, therefore, calculate the damping produced by screw dislocations.

Consider the motion of a screw-type dislocation through the distance l separating two impurity atoms. The applied stress is $\sigma_0 \sin \omega t$. At time zero the dislocation will start from rest at one impurity and will move with increasing velocity until it strikes the other impurity. Let us calculate the velocity v, assuming that a damping force of Bv exists per centimeter length of dislocation and assuming that the dislocation moves through the distance l in a time τ. Since the velocity of motion will be determined by equating the applied force on the dislocation to the dissipative force, we find

$$\sigma_0 a \sin \omega t = Bv$$

or

$$v = \frac{\sigma_0 a \sin \omega t}{B}. \tag{D.1}$$

The transit time τ is obtained by integrating equation (D.1) (where we have neglected the time required to stop the dislocation at the impurity). Thus:

$$l = \int_0^\tau v\,dt = \frac{\sigma_0 a}{\omega B}(1 - \cos\omega\tau),$$

$$\cos\omega\tau = 1 - \frac{\omega l B}{\sigma_0 a}\cdot \tag{D.2}$$

If $\omega lB/\sigma_0 a$ is greater than 2, the dislocation never reaches the second impurity. Let us next calculate w, the energy loss per cycle per centimeter of dislocation. If F is the force on the dislocation,

$$w = 2\int_0^\tau Fv\,dt = 2\int_0^\tau Bv^2\,dt = \frac{2\sigma_0^2 a^2}{B}\int_0^\tau \sin^2\omega t\,dt. \tag{D.3}$$

The factor 2 enters because there are two movements of the screw dislocation per cycle. Thus:

$$w = \frac{\sigma_0^2 a^2}{B}\left\{\tau - \frac{1}{2\omega}\sin 2\omega\tau\right\}\cdot \tag{D.4}$$

There are thus two types of behavior. At low frequencies, where $\omega\tau \ll 1$, we can expand the trigonometric functions. We find:

$$w = \frac{2\sigma_0^2 a^2 \omega^2 \tau^3}{3B} = \frac{1}{3}\sqrt{2^5 \sigma_0 a \omega B l^3} \qquad \omega\tau \ll 1, \tag{D.5}$$

where we have substituted from equation (D.2) for τ in the right-hand expression.

At very high frequencies the screw dislocation never reaches the second impurity and we have

$$w = \frac{\sigma_0^2 a^2}{B}\int_0^{2\pi/\omega} \sin^2\omega t\,dt = \frac{\sigma_0^2 a^2 \pi}{B\omega} \qquad \frac{\omega l B}{\sigma_0 a} \gg 2. \tag{D.6}$$

The decrement is:

$$\Delta = \frac{Nw}{2W}, \tag{D.7}$$

where N is the length of dislocation line per cubic centimeter and $W = \sigma_0^2/4G$ is the total vibrational energy per cubic centimeter. The resulting expressions for the decrement in two limiting cases are

$$\Delta = \frac{8NG}{3}\sqrt{\frac{2a\omega B l^3}{\sigma_0^3}} \qquad \frac{\omega l B}{\sigma_0 a} \ll 1, \tag{D.8}$$

$$\Delta = \frac{2\pi N G a^2}{B\omega} \qquad \frac{\omega l B}{\sigma_0 a} \gg 2. \tag{D.9}$$

Thus the decrement increases slowly with frequency, goes through a maximum, and then decreases. The largest decrement occurs at

$$\omega_M \simeq \frac{\sigma_0 a}{lB}. \tag{D.10}$$

If we consider matters at a strain amplitude of 6.6×10^{-7}, then $\sigma_0 = 3 \times 10^5$. We try $l = 2 \times 10^{-5}$ cm, $B = 5 \times 10^{-5}$ gram sec^{-1} cm^{-1} (that is, Leibfried's or Eshelby's value), $a = 2.5 \times 10^{-8}$ cm. Then $\omega_M = 7.5 \times 10^6$ sec^{-1} so that the maximum decrement occurs at a frequency of 1200 kc.

This indicates that equation (D.8) should be used at 37 kc. Equation (D.8) predicts that the decrement decreases with increasing strain amplitude. This prediction is not in accord with the data at low strain amplitudes, where breakaway should probably be unimportant.

Let us also calculate the order of magnitude of Δ at 37 kc, using equation (D.8). We use the values of the constants given above in evaluating ω_M. In addition, we take $N = 3.5 \times 10^3$ cm/cc, $G = 4.53 \times 10^{11}$ dyne cm^{-2}. We find $\Delta = 4 \times 10^{-3}$. This is a very large decrement, considering the small length of dislocation used. It indicates that there is merit in Read's suggestion since it yields a large decrement easily.

We can also calculate the reversible plastic contribution to the elastic constants.

$$\epsilon = \epsilon_e + \epsilon_p = \frac{\sigma_0 \sin \omega t}{G} \pm lNa = \frac{\sigma_0 \sin \omega t}{G'}, \tag{D.11}$$

where we have assumed that we are in the low-frequency region. The plus sign is used when $\sin \omega t$ is positive; the minus sign when $\sin \omega t$ is negative. Thus:

$$\frac{dG}{G} = \frac{G - G'}{G} = \frac{\pm lNaG}{\sigma_0 \sin \omega t}. \tag{D.12}$$

In order of magnitude we get:

$$\frac{dG}{G} = \frac{lNaG}{\sigma_0}. \tag{D.13}$$

Thus again the dependence on strain amplitude looks queer. Let us calculate the value of the change in G which would occur on changing the strain amplitude from 10^{-7} to 10^{-6}. Using the numbers previously given, we find:

$$\frac{dG(10^{-7}) - dG(10^{-6})}{G} = 1.6 \times 10^{-2}. \tag{D.14}$$

Experimentally, we find a value of about 5×10^{-3} so that the calculated value is somewhat too large.

It is probable that if we improve the calculation by using dislocations which zigzag from one impurity to the next, as Mott has suggested in Paper 6 of this book, the magnitude of the changes will be reduced, and the difficulties regarding the dependence on strain amplitude will be reduced or eliminated.

Regarding experimental data on the frequency dependence of the decrement, John Marx, of the laboratory at the Carnegie Institute of Technology, has obtained data on two 99.999 per cent copper single crystals, which indicates that in some cases at least the decrement increases with increasing frequency. He found:

Strain Amplitude	Specimen 11-A1		Specimen 11-A2	
	$\Delta_{37\ \mathrm{kc}}$	$\Delta_{111\ \mathrm{kc}}$	$\Delta_{37\ \mathrm{kc}}$	$\Delta_{111\ \mathrm{kc}}$
5×10^{-8}	1.3×10^{-3}	10×10^{-3}		
1×10^{-7}	1.7×10^{-3}	10.7×10^{-3}		
2×10^{-7}	3.3×10^{-3}	14.3×10^{-3}		
2.6×10^{-7}	5.1×10^{-3}	18.3×10^{-3}		
4×10^{-7}				4.2×10^{-3}
6×10^{-7}			0.75×10^{-3}	5.5×10^{-3}
7.8×10^{-7}				8.3×10^{-3}

Mr. Marx found that the impedance of the apparatus and leads in parallel with the quartz and specimen changes appreciably with frequency. If the bridge method of measurement is used, care must be taken to correct for this apparatus effect. Measurements can be made using a quartz gage method which requires no correction. The final results of the two methods agree in giving the values quoted above.

III. DIFFUSION AND RELATED PHENOMENA

8.

Relaxation Effects in Ionic Crystals

R. G. BRECKENRIDGE

National Bureau of Standards

ABSTRACT

Studies have been made of relaxation effects in the dielectric and mechanical properties of several alkali halides, silver chloride, and thallium halides, both pure and containing added impurities. These relaxation effects are attributed to lattice defects present in the crystals. Values of the activation energies for the motion of lattice defects are obtained from the observed temperature and frequency for maximum loss. The number of lattice defects present is found from the magnitude of the maximum loss. Calculations have been made of the degree of association of vacancy pairs and of foreign ion-vacancy pairs. The results of these experiments are compared with those obtained by other methods. It is found that the values for the activation energy for conductivity in sodium chloride is in good agreement with other results. Similarly, the degree of association found for pairs of defects is in reasonable agreement with existing information.

1. DIELECTRIC LOSSES AND MECHANICAL LOSSES

The methods for the investigation of lattice imperfections in crystals have recently been supplemented by the discovery of relaxation effects in the dielectric and elastic properties of the crystals and the interpretation of these effects in terms of lattice defects. The first observation of such behavior was in the dielectric constant and loss of the alkali halides and silver chloride.[1] Subsequently, measurements of the low-frequency dispersion in the dielectric loss have been made on alkali halides and silver chloride containing impurity ions[2] and on thallium chloride, thallium bromide, and sodium bromide, the latter results to be reported later in this paper. The results of the dielectric loss measurements suggested a study of the analogous mechanical loss in these crystals to see if relaxation effects were present in this case as well. Such effects were observed in three alkali halide crystals. Only a preliminary announcement of these results has been made.[3] The work thus far has been largely of an exploratory nature; hence at this time it is desired to present a discussion of the methods and results particularly in relation to the knowledge of lattice imperfections gained by other methods of study.

2. DIELECTRIC RELAXATION EFFECTS

Since the dielectric effects have been studied in greater detail than the elastic effects, these will be considered first. It is well known that an assembly of charged particles, each having two equilibrium positions separated by a potential barrier available to it, becomes polarized in an external alternating electric field and shows a dielectric response completely analogous to that found by Debye for an assembly of permanent dipoles with two possible positions.[4] This situation has been discussed in some detail[5] so that it will suffice here to give only a brief outline of the calculations.

The applicability of this model to crystal defects must be established first, however. It is accepted that the imperfections present in the alkali halides are Schottky defects, so that we have positive and negative ion vacancies present in equal numbers. A certain fraction of these vacancies will be associated to form pairs and possibly larger complexes because of the coulomb forces between them. The fraction of the vacancies associated in this manner will be discussed later. It seems clear that single ion vacancies do not satisfy the model's requirements in that the vacancy is not constrained to a given pair of possible sites, but is free to continue moving in the field direction. This is, of course, the process giving rise to the normal conductivity of the crystal. On the other hand, a pair of vacancies satisfies the model's picture quite well. Although a crystal in three dimensions is more complicated, it is evident that the pair of vacancies can be represented in either of two orientations in the field direction. This is illustrated schematically in Fig. 1. It is anticipated that a more detailed calculation will modify the results slightly but not in their essentials. For example, the presence of the middle position which has zero moment in the field direction reduces the average polarizability proportionately to its population. In three dimensions some of the possible jumps have slightly different barrier energies; this would be expected to manifest itself in a somewhat broadened distribution of relaxation times. It is evident also that, in addition to the indicated jump via the positive ions, the pair can be reoriented by a similar jump of the negative ion.[6] Because of the larger size of the negative ions in most cases, the process has a greater activation energy than required for the positive ion jump.

For Frenkel defects the situation is more complicated since it would seem that pair formation between a vacant site and an interstitial ion is unlikely, the ion being attracted to the site to

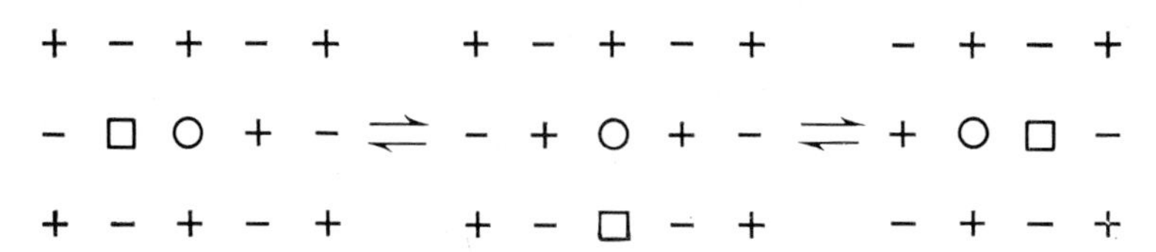

FIG. 1. Reorientation of lattice defect pair.

cause the disappearance of the Frenkel defect. It would be expected that a finite number of pairs is normally present in an equilibrium state, since a pair is certainly present in the first step in forming and in the final state before the disappearance of a Frenkel defect. With Frenkel defects we also would anticipate two methods of reorienting the pair since both the interstitial ion and the vacant site should be mobile and, in fact, should have rather comparable activation energies.

There may be other possible mechanisms that effectively restrict the motion of the charged particles, for example, dislocations, foreign ions, and grain boundaries, and so produce a polarization. This means that a certain ambiguity may be present as to the exact unit giving rise to the polarization. This vagueness may be resolved if supplementary information is available, for example, the dependence on nature and the concentration of foreign ions where they have been added deliberately, but for "pure" crystals there is not much information available. Our best test is a reasonable consistency of results with the accepted picture of the defects, but it must be admitted that the interpretation given is still not proved in the sense that other possible mechanisms have not been entirely eliminated.

We wish now to derive a relation between the number of lattice defects and the observed values of the dielectric loss. In the application of the model to the crystal case, we consider the change in the relative populations of the two potential wells brought about by the electric field, assuming a Boltzmann distribution between wells. Then, following the method of solution indicated in references 4 and 5, we find for the average polarizability per particle

$$\alpha_j = \frac{1}{1 + j\omega\tau} \frac{(zed)^2}{kT}, \tag{2.1}$$

where d is the distance between the two wells, e is the electronic charge, z is the ion valence, and τ is the relaxation time for the jumping process. Using the Clausius-Mosotti equation to relate the polarizability and complex dielectric constant, $\kappa^* = \kappa' - j\kappa''$, we have

$$\frac{\kappa^* - 1}{\kappa^* + 2} = \frac{N}{3\epsilon_0}\left(\alpha_e + \alpha_a + \frac{n}{N}\alpha_j\right), \tag{2.2}$$

where n is the number of ion pairs per m^3 and α_e and α_a are the electronic and atomic polarizabilities respectively, N is the number of ions per m^3, and ϵ_0 is 8.865×10^{-12} farad/m. It is convenient to use the Debye equations in the usual form involving the value of the dielectric constant at frequencies far above the relaxation frequency, κ_∞', and that for frequencies far below the relaxation frequency, κ_s', that is,

$$\begin{aligned} \kappa' &= \kappa_\infty' + \frac{\kappa_s' - \kappa_\infty'}{1 + (\omega\tau)^2} \\ \kappa'' &= \frac{(\kappa_s' - \kappa_\infty')\omega\tau}{1 + (\omega\tau)^2}, \end{aligned} \tag{2.3}$$

and, more directly for our purpose,

$$\tan\delta = \frac{\kappa''}{\kappa'} \cong \frac{\kappa_s' - \kappa_\infty'}{\kappa_\infty'} \frac{\omega\tau}{1 + (\omega\tau)^2}. \tag{2.4}$$

It may be shown[1] that in terms of the polarizability in equation (2.1)

$$\kappa_s' - \kappa_\infty' \cong \frac{n(zea)^2(\kappa_\infty' + 2)^2}{9\epsilon_0 kT}, \tag{2.5}$$

where a is the lattice constant, so that the maximum value for

$\tan \delta$ at $\omega\tau = 1$ is

$$\tan \delta_{\max} = \frac{n(zea)^2(\kappa_\infty' + 2)^2}{18\epsilon_0 kT_j\kappa_\infty'}\,. \tag{2.6}$$

The temperature dependence of the time constant τ is given by

$$\tau = \tau_0 e^{U/kT}, \tag{2.7}$$

where U is the height of the potential barrier separating the equivalent positions and τ_0 is the time constant of natural lattice vibrations. The condition for maximum loss, $\omega\tau = 1$, gives the relation

$$2\pi\nu_m\tau_0 = e^{-U/kT_j}\,. \tag{2.8}$$

By making measurements at two frequencies as a function of temperature, τ_0 may be eliminated from equation (2.8). This has been done only in a few cases for reasons to be given later. In general, the quantity is determined from "reststrahlen" frequencies.

Measurements of the dielectric constant and loss with either constant temperature and varying frequency, or vice versa, yield the value of $\tan \delta$ at $\omega\tau = 1$ and provide the necessary information to determine the height of the potential barrier and the number of defect pairs.

If there were no other source of loss, this would complete the description of the phenomenon. However, as we have already mentioned, the single defects contribute to the conductivity in a normal fashion and give a conductivity varying exponentially with temperature. Then $\tan \delta$ may be written as

$$\tan \delta \cong \frac{\kappa''}{\kappa_\infty'} = \frac{1}{\omega\kappa_\infty'}\,[\sigma_{\text{d.c.}} + \sum_r \sigma_r], \tag{2.9}$$

where $\sigma_{\text{d.c.}}$ represents the ordinary conductivity, and the summation is over the possible relaxation terms. Now

$$\sigma_{\text{d.c.}} = \sigma_0 e^{-U/kT} = n_v{}^f e u_0 e^{-U/kT}, \tag{2.10}$$

where $n_v{}^f$ is the number of free vacancies per m^3 and u_0 is their mobility. The activation energy U is that for diffusion and conductivity in the given temperature range. The relaxation terms resemble equation (2.4), so that

$$\tan \delta = \frac{\sigma_0 e^{-U/kT}}{\omega\kappa_\infty'} + \sum_r \frac{n_r(zea)_r{}^2(\kappa_\infty' + 2)^2}{18\epsilon_0 kT\kappa_\infty'}\,\frac{\omega\tau_r}{1 + (\omega\tau_r)^2}\,\cdot \tag{2.11}$$

The presence of several terms hampers a precise determination of the maximum value of tan δ for a relaxation process. The simplest method is a graphical subtraction of a smooth curve for the d-c conductivity from the observed total curve on a linear temperature scale. In many cases, in spite of obvious drawbacks, this is a reasonably satisfactory method. A more instructive approach is obtained from equation (2.11). At fixed frequency and for a single relaxation process, we have

$$\tan \delta = c_1 e^{-U/kT} + \frac{c_2 \omega \tau_0 e^{U_2/kT}}{1 + (\omega\tau_0)^2 e^{2U_2/kT}} \cdot \tag{2.12}$$

Now, for $T \ll T_j$, that is, $\omega\tau \gg 1$:

$$\tan \delta \cong c_1 e^{-U/kT} + \frac{c_2}{\omega\tau_0} e^{-U_2/kT}. \tag{2.12a}$$

For $T = T_j$, that is, $\omega\tau = 1$:

$$\tan \delta = c_1 e^{-U/kT_j} + \frac{c_2}{2} \cdot \tag{2.12b}$$

And for $T \gg T_j$, that is, $\omega\tau \to \omega\tau_0$:

$$\tan \delta \cong c_1 e^{-U/kT} + c_2 \omega\tau_0 e^{U_2/kT} \to c_1 e^{-U/kT}. \tag{2.12c}$$

For $T \ll T_j$ the dominant term may be either of the two terms. Hence a plot of log tan δ vs. $1/T$ at temperatures quite far from T_j gives straight lines with slopes determined by the U's.

If, as happens in more complicated cases to be discussed later, there are several contributing relaxation processes, the analysis of the logarithmic plot becomes quite difficult. An important advantage of this method of handling the data is that the constant c_1 may be determined; and then, if the mobility u_0 of equation (2.10) is known, the number of free vacancies may be found as well. The independent determination of U by this method is also of interest. In general, we shall use both methods, choosing the one more appropriate for a particular case.

Before considering actual results, we may use equation (2.7) to get some indication of the anticipated behavior. We know that for alkali halides τ_0 is about 2×10^{-13} sec; kT at room temperature is about 1/40 ev and available estimates indicate U is about 0.5 to 0.9 ev. These values indicate τ about 10^{-3} sec, that is, in the kilocycle range of measuring frequencies. The bridge measurements in this frequency range can detect changes in κ' of about 0.02 for a typical sample capacitance. The dielectric constant of the alkali halides is about 5, so that tan δ_{max} must be 0.002 to give a detectable change in κ', as indicated by equation (2.4). The loss measurements are considerably more sensitive than this, indicating changes in loss of 0.00005 in favorable circumstances; thus we can anticipate that relaxation processes may be observed in the dielectric loss without being observed in the dielectric constant.

Experimental coverage of a very wide energy range is desirable, but practical limitations must be considered. Since the effects are small, great sensitivity in the bridge measurements is essential, and some modifications of the conventional bridge are desirable. These are described elsewhere.[7] In general, loss measurements to the desired sensitivity, ± 0.5 per cent, are obtainable only for tan $\delta \leq 0.10$ so that the peak temperature is limited in this respect. Similarly, measurements to this sensitivity are convenient at only one frequency, 10^3 cps, since the bridge sensitivity falls off rapidly either at higher or lower frequencies. Thus we are usually restricted to values of energy $0.1 \leq U \leq 0.8$, and commonly $0.4 \leq U \leq 0.8$.

EXPERIMENTAL

The results of measurements of the dielectric constant and loss at 85°C on a sodium chloride crystal obtained from the Harshaw Chemical Company of Cleveland, Ohio, are shown in Fig. 2.[1] The frequency range covered corresponds to values of U from 0.1 to 0.74 ev according to equation (2.8), and we observe only a single loss maximum. The loss maximum in this case has a value of 0.024 so that we are well above the detectable change in κ', and a portion of the typical relaxation behavior is observed here as well.

A convenient test for the agreement of the results with the Debye equations is given by a Cole-Cole[8] plot of κ' vs. κ''. If the behavior satisfies equation (2.3) completely, a semicircular plot with its center on the axis should be obtained. If, however, there is a distribution of relaxation times, the center of the circle is displaced below the axis. Such a plot is shown in Fig. 3. It is observed that the figure does indicate a distribution of relaxation times as anticipated from the discussion of our model. The numerical value for α, the angle between the axis and the circle radius, is 32.5°, which, however, indicates a rather modest spread.

Similar measurements have been made on KBr and LiF,[1] with indications for a single loss maximum in the range of energies 0.1

to 0.7 ev. In these cases no effect was observed in κ', the loss peak being of the order of 0.001, thus below the detectable limit for changes in κ'.

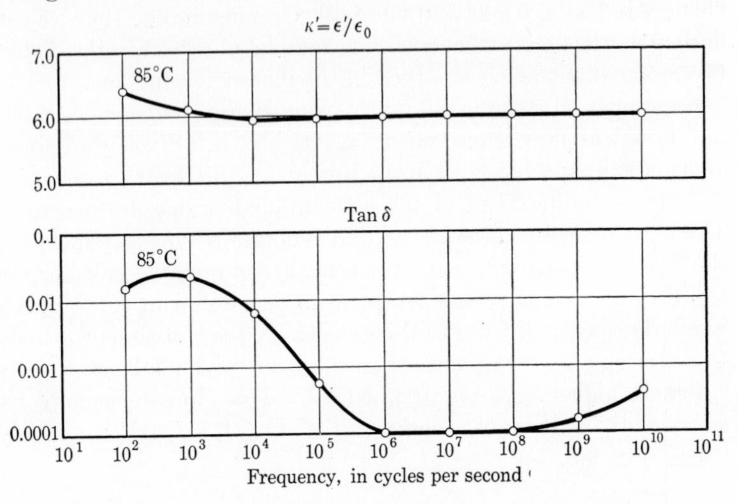

FIG. 2. Dielectric properties of NaCl. $K' = \epsilon'/\epsilon_0$.

As an example of the measurements of the loss as a function of temperature at fixed frequency, in general 10^3 cps, we may use data obtained on crystals of TlCl (Fig. 4) and TlBr (Fig. 5),

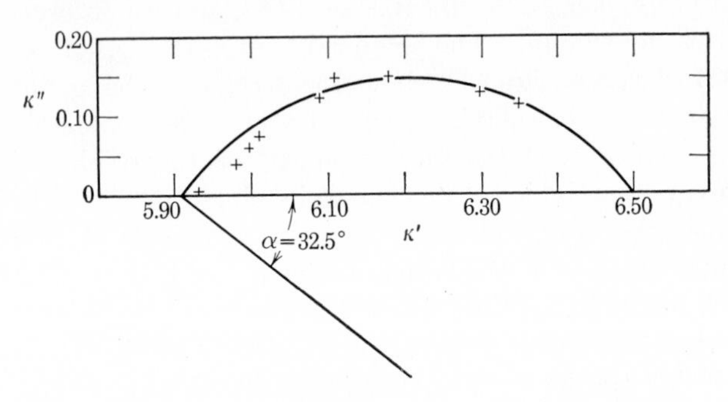

FIG. 3. Cole-Cole plot for NaCl crystal. $T = 85°C$.

obtained through the courtesy of the Crystal Section at the Naval Research Laboratory. The measurements were made at the Laboratory for Insulation Research at the Massachusetts Institute of

Technology* by the method indicated in reference 1 without heat treatment.

In the case of TlCl two loss maxima with a rather small difference in energy are observed in a range of energies from 0.15 to 0.51 ev, in contrast with the single maximum found in a wider range of energies in NaCl. The situation is similar, however, to

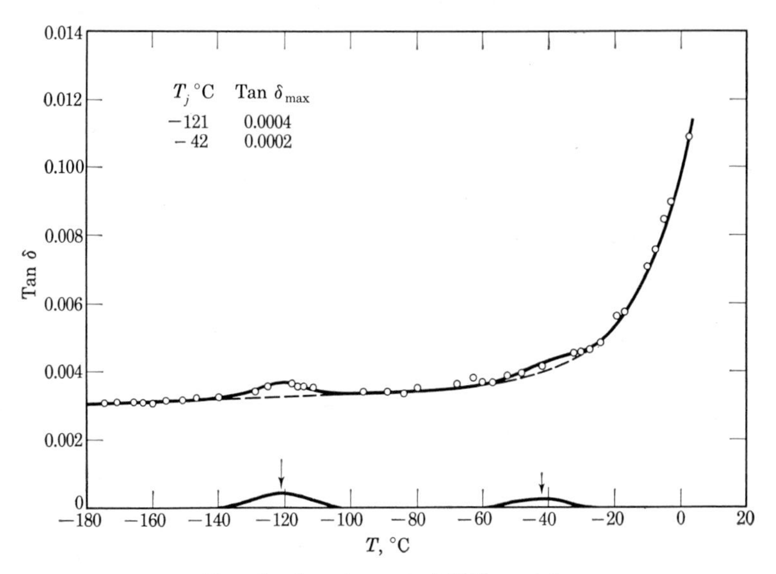

FIG. 4. Loss tangent of TlCl crystal.

that previously found for AgCl.[1] For TlBr evidence was found for two peaks when measured at 10^3 cps, the lower of the two not being completely traversed. This sample was remeasured at 10^4 cps to bring the lower peak into the available temperature range. The loss is considerably lower, and the accuracy of measurement at this frequency is not as great, so that there is more scattering of the experimental points; but both loss maxima in the range of energies from 0.15 to 0.44 ev are clearly indicated. The value of U corresponding to each maximum was computed, using equation (2.8), the values of τ_0 being calculated from data of Rubens,[9] using Försterling's formula[10] to find the natural fre-

* Sponsored by the Navy Department (Office of Naval Research), the Army Signal Corps, and the Air Force (Air Matériel Command) under ONR Contract N5 ori-07801, NR 074-041.

quency from the observed reststrahl frequency. The same value of τ_0 was used for both maxima in the same crystal. These results, with a brief summary of previous results, are given in Table 1.

In the case of TlBr it is possible to calculate U without information about τ_0, since values of T_j for two frequencies are available and τ_0 then may be eliminated from equation (2.8). Unfortunately, it becomes necessary to know the difference in peak temper-

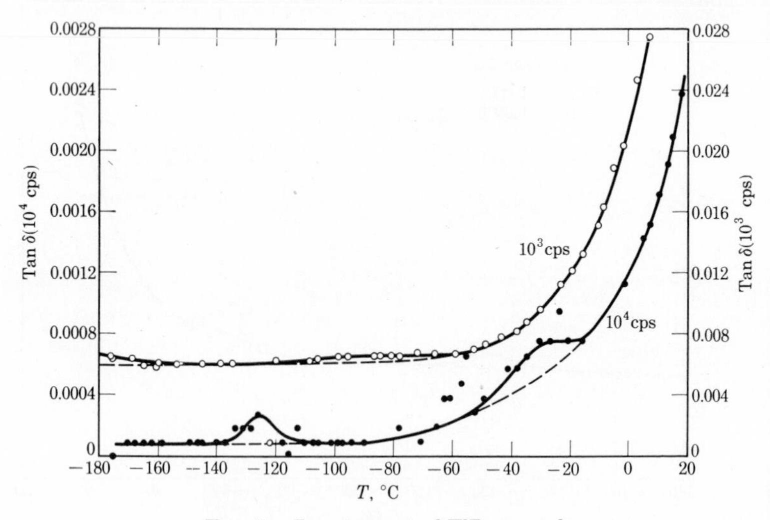

FIG. 5. Loss tangent of TlBr crystal.

ature quite precisely, and, with the data on hand, the result is not very significant. However, if T_j is taken as $-34°C$ at 10^4 cps and at $-64°C$ at 10^3 cps (as is also indicated on a log tan δ vs. $1/T$ plot), a value of $U = 0.33$ ev in reasonable agreement with that given in Table 1 is obtained. The logarithmic plot of the data gives a value for $U = 0.44$ ev, and $\sigma_0 = 1.27\Omega^{-1}\,m^{-1}$ for TlCl; whereas for TlBr, 0.34 ev and $4.52 \times 10^{-2}\Omega^{-1}\,m^{-1}$ are found in the region above the relaxation losses.

As an illustration of the method of plotting the logarithm of the dielectric loss as a function of the reciprocal of the absolute temperature, we may use data on a crystal of NaBr also obtained from the Crystal Section of the Naval Research Laboratory and measured at the Laboratory for Insulation Research at the Massachusetts Institute of Technology under the previously noted contract. The crystal was heated at 625°C for one-half hour, cooled rapidly to room temperature, and then measured as indicated in reference 1. The plot of the data is given in Fig. 6.

The solid curve in Fig. 6 is the sum of the contributions of a high-temperature linear term, with activation energy of 1.13 ev and σ_0 of $3.21 \times 10^4 \Omega^{-1}\,m^{-1}$, a relaxation contribution centered at $1/T = 2.32 \times 10^{-3}$, giving a calculated activation energy of 0.76 ev and of height $\tan \delta_{max} = 0.0017$, and a low-temperature

TABLE 1

Salt	T_j, °C	ν_m cps	$\tau_0 \times 10^{12}$ sec	U_{pair} ev	$U_{cond.}$ ev	$\sigma_0 \Omega^{-1}\,m^{-1}$
LiF	80	10^4	0.109	0.58		
NaF	137	10^3	0.135	0.74		
NaCl	85	6×10^2	0.204	0.65		
	114	10^3	0.204	0.68	0.84	71.5
NaBr	158	10^3	0.249	0.76	1.13	3.21×10^4
KCl	174	10^3	0.236	0.78		
KBr	85	2×10^4	0.294	0.53		
KI	ca. −200	10^4	0.340	ca. 0.1		
RbCl	155	10^3	0.281	0.75		
RbBr	57	10^3	0.380	0.58		
RbI	−135	10^4	0.430	0.21		
AgCl	−153	10^3	0.31	0.21		
	−124	10^3	0.31	0.26		
TlCl	−121	10^3	0.31	0.26	0.44	1.27
	−42	10^3	0.31	0.40		
TlBr	−127	10^4	0.42	0.22	0.34	4.52×10^{-2}
	−34	10^4	0.42	0.36		

conductivity with a very low activation energy, 0.041 ev, from an unexplained source. This residual conductivity may very likely be a surface conductivity effect. The value of $\tan \delta_{max}$ gives $6.8 \times 10^{22}/m^3$ for the number of defect pairs computed using equation (2.6).

A similar analysis has been made of the data on NaCl at 10^3 cps as a function of temperature mentioned in reference 1. This work indicates a high-temperature slope with an activation energy of 0.84 ev and $\sigma_0 = 71.5 \Omega^{-1}\,m^{-1}$, the relaxation loss peak being at 114°C and with $\tan \delta_{max} = 0.0008$. This corresponds to a number of pairs of $5.7 \times 10^{22}/m^3$. As mentioned previously, if the mobility of the vacancies is known from other methods of measurement, the number of free cation vacancies may be calculated from the value of σ_0. Using the mobility data of Etzel and

Maurer,[11] we find $n_v{}^f = 1.1 \times 10^{23}/\text{m}^3$. This information may be used to investigate the degree of association of the lattice defects.

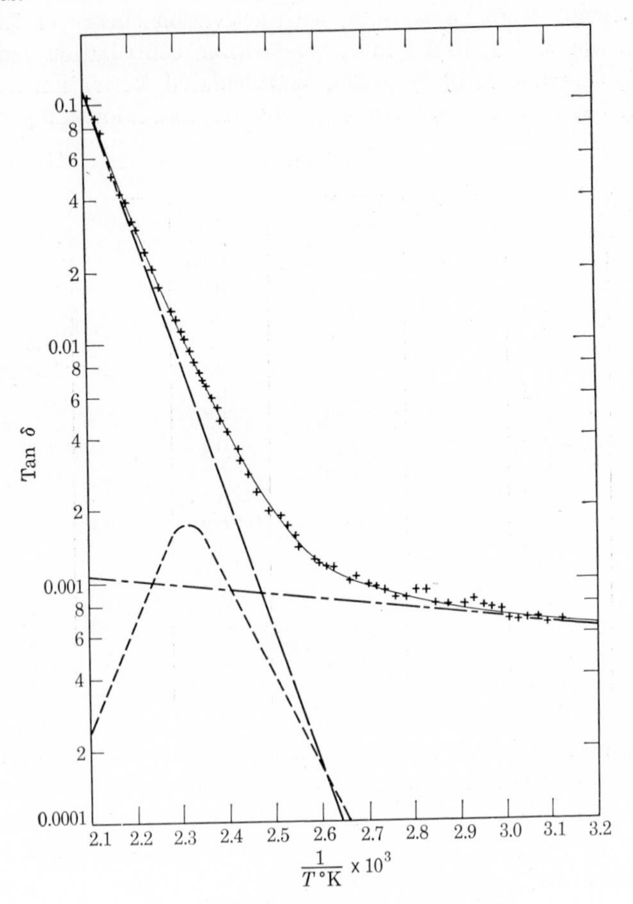

FIG. 6. Dielectric loss of NaBr crystal.

3. RELAXATION EFFECTS IN CRYSTALS CONTAINING FOREIGN IONS

In addition to pairs formed between vacant sites, pairs between other lattice imperfections are possible. For example, if divalent foreign cations are present in a crystal, an equal number of cation vacancies are introduced to preserve electrical neutrality.[12] We may anticipate that a fraction of these foreign ions and vacancies will be present as pairs on adjacent sites because of the coulomb forces between them. Similarly, since elastic stresses in the lattice near a foreign ion may be partially relieved if the foreign ion is adjacent to a vacancy, we may anticipate that pairs may be formed between vacancies and univalent foreign ions in the absence of coulomb forces; or complexes may be formed between foreign ions and vacancy pairs. These various possibilities also should

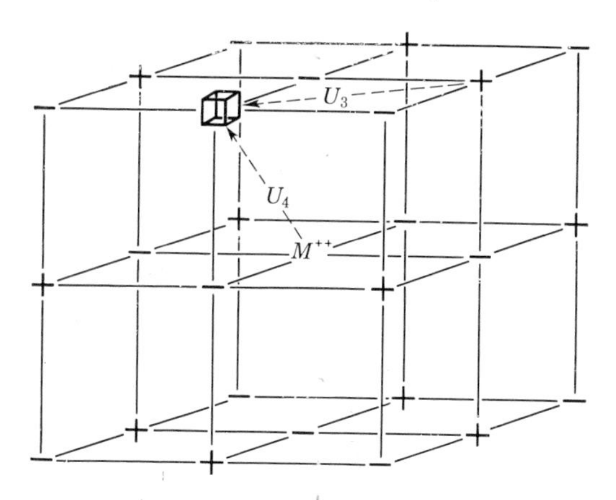

FIG. 7. Mechanisms for pair orientation.

be satisfactorily described by our model. Thus, if we investigate the properties of crystals containing known amounts of foreign ions, we should find new relaxation loss maxima whose height is a function of the concentration of the foreign ion.

It is apparent that, instead of introducing a single relaxation loss peak for each type of foreign ion, the situation in the pure crystal is modified so that several new processes are possible. For example, as seen in Fig. 7, the foreign ion vacancy pair may be reoriented in the field direction either by a place interchange of the foreign ion and vacancy with activation energy, U_4, or by a series of jumps of normal cations. This latter process resembles self-diffusion, except that the activation energy, U_3, may be expected to be modified somewhat by the presence of the foreign ion. Since we anticipate also that foreign ions will be present on sites adjacent to an existing pair of vacancies, as shown in Fig. 8, several other possibilities exist. In this case the pair reorientation energy, U_2, in the pure crystal will be somewhat modified. A new energy, U_2'', due to the reorientation via the motion of the foreign ion, is possible; and, because a slightly different configuration of the complex is produced, the indicated U_2' should also be somewhat different than U_2. These loss maxima would be expected to be much smaller than those from foreign ion vacancy pairs, since there are relatively few vacancy pairs present to form complexes.

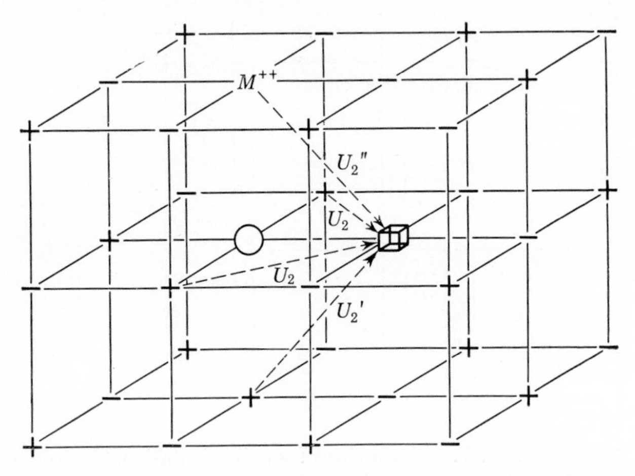

FIG. 8. Reorientation of foreign ion–vacancy pair complexes.

All these characteristics have been observed[2] both for divalent and for univalent foreign ions. This stresses the fact that we are observing the polarization produced by moving charges whose motion is restricted to several available sites rather than a true dipole reorientation. The fact that large loss peaks were found for univalent ions indicates also that the foreign ions are accommodated adjacent to vacant sites, possibly as much because of the elastic forces as because of the coulomb attraction between charges. Calculations have been made of the various activation energies in this way, with the results shown in Fig. 9 for foreign ions in NaCl. The U_5's found in the Tl^+ and Ag^+ have been tentatively identified[2] as U_2'' in Fig. 8. As pointed out in reference 2, the observed broadening of the lowest temperature peak is reasonable evidence for the presence of U_2, U_2', and U_2'' in those cases where the peaks are not resolved.

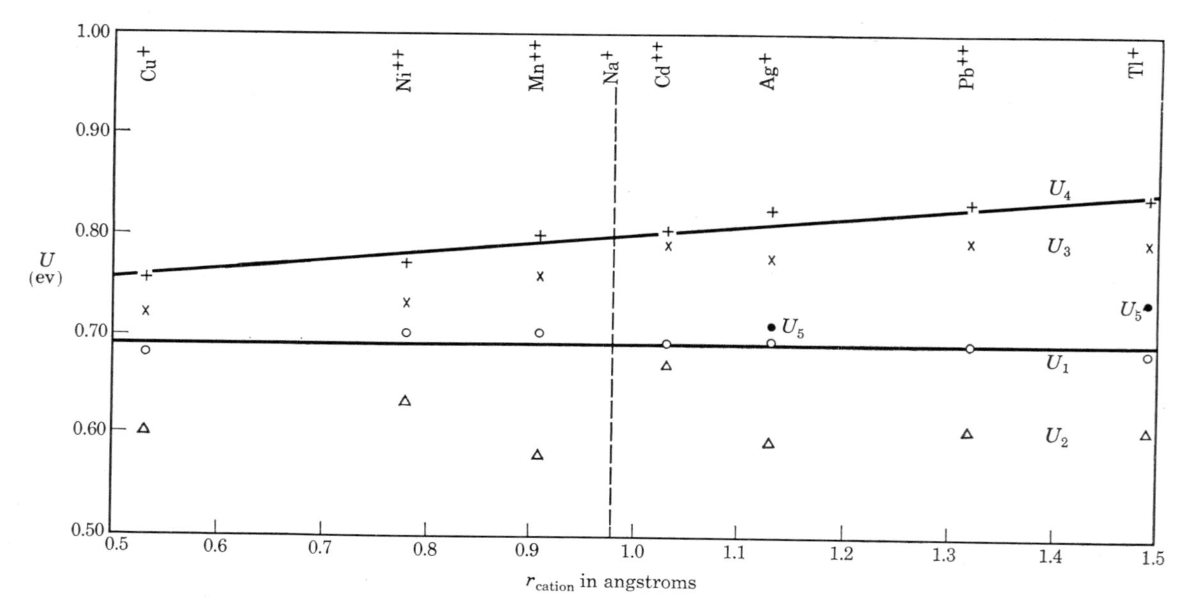

FIG. 9. Activation energies for foreign ions in NaCl.

Calculations were also made of the numbers of pairs of each type present, using equation (2.6). Analysis of the data from the logarithmic plots is possible, but it is complicated by the multiplicity of relaxation processes; however, some useful additional information regarding the number of free vacancies is obtained from the behavior at high temperatures. This information is instructive in a discussion of the degree of association of the lattice defects to be considered later. The number of free cation vacancies has been found from the high-temperature slopes

TABLE 2

Defects and Pairs in NaCl Containing Foreign Ions

Ion	$y \times 10^4$	$x_1 \times 10^6$	$x_2 \times 10^6$	$x_4 \times 10^6$	$x_v^f \times 10^6$
Mn^{++}	0.6	0.1	0.1	0.3	1.7
Mn^{++}	1.2	0.31	0.33	0.7	2.3
Mn^{++}	2.6	0.35	0.93	1.2	11
Cd^{++}	18	0.44	0.21	4	29
Ni^{++}	4.2	0.01	0.01	0.05	1.6
Pb^{++}	1	0.07	0.04	1.3	3.7
Cu^{+}	2.9	0.1	0.1	4.4	3.8
Tl^{+}	5.6	0.2	0.33	33	1.8
Ag^{+}	50	0.2	0.1	16	2.5

for the samples of NaCl containing foreign ions, described in reference 2. The values of x_1 = (the mole fraction of vacancy pairs), x_2 = (the mole fraction of foreign ion vacancy pair complexes), x_4 = (the mole-fraction of foreign ion vacancy pairs), x_v^f = (the mole fraction of free cation vacancies), and y = (the analytically determined foreign ion concentrations) are given in Table 2.

4. ANELASTICITY IN IONIC CRYSTALS

It is well known that stress relaxation in crystals can occur through a variety of mechanisms. Theories have been developed for relaxation by thermal diffusion, atomic diffusion, magnetic diffusion, and others.[13] Numerous studies have been made, particularly on metallic crystals, for many of the various mechanisms; but atomic diffusion has not been explored because the anticipated effects were small. The source of this stress relaxation lies in the nonequivalence of lattice points brought about by the strains in the lattice produced by the applied stress. These strains may be relaxed by a shift in position of the lattice imperfections, for example, solute atoms and lattice vacancies. If an increased concentration of defects expands the lattice, a stress-induced lattice dilation will, at equilibrium, result in an increase in the concentration of defects. A vibrational wave in the crystal will then be damped with a maximum damping when the vibrational frequency is the same as the jump frequency of the defects.

The formal theory of this effect given in reference 13 indicates a behavior analogous to the dielectric relaxation effects. The mechanical loss, the energy absorbed per cycle, is given as

$$\tan \delta = Q^{-1} = \frac{M_U - M_R}{\overline{M}} \frac{\omega\tau}{1 + (\omega\tau)^2} = \Delta \frac{\omega\tau}{1 + (\omega\tau)^2}, \qquad (4.1)$$

where $\overline{M} = \sqrt{M_U M_R}$, M_U and M_R are the unrelaxed and relaxed elastic moduli, respectively, ω is 2π times the measuring frequency, and τ is the time constant for the relaxation process. Obviously, the condition for maximum loss is $\omega\tau = 1$, giving $\tan \delta_{\max} = \Delta/2$. The time constants $\tau = \tau_0 e^{U/kT}$ in this case should include that for the jumping of single vacancies, with a U corresponding to that found from self-diffusion measurements as well as values for the motion of pairs, etc., such as were found in the dielectric measurements. In addition, the relative magnitudes of Δ should provide information about the relative numbers of single and paired vacancies in the crystal.

Again it is instructive to consider the magnitudes of the anticipated effects. In metallic crystals typical values of U are 1.0 to 4.0 ev so that a very slow process is involved. As we have already seen, however, in ionic crystals our U's are 0.1 to 0.9 ev, and with typical values of τ_0 we should again observe effects in the kilocycle range at readily accessible temperatures. The elastic moduli of NaCl have been carefully measured by several workers[14,15,16] over a wide range of temperatures, with no reports of relaxation effects. A marked change of the bulk modulus was noted, however, by Hunter and Siegel,[16] centering at about 575°K when measured at 3.77×10^4 cps. In this case, as in the dielectric studies, the loss measurements are considerably more sensitive than the measurements of the real part of the complex quantity. Thus, if we anticipate a value of $\tan \delta_{\max}$ equal to that found dielectrically in NaCl, that is, $\cong 0.025$, a value of $(M_U - M_R)/\overline{M} =$ 5 per cent should be observed. While this value is large enough to be noted, it is somewhat masked by the normal temperature variation of M. The tan δ or $1/Q$ measurements, on the other hand, are sensitive to ca. 10^{-6}, and so a value of $\tan \delta_{max} = 0.025$ should be conspicuous. Unfortunately, this increased sensitivity and the advantage of observing both single and multiple defects cannot be fully exploited, since the theoretical relation between the number of lattice defects and the observed loss is much less readily derived than in the dielectric cases. A more detailed analysis of the problem will be presented elsewhere, and in this paper we shall confine our attention to the activation energies and relative numbers of defects whose values can be obtained directly.

The experimental investigation of this effect, which will also be described in detail elsewhere, is carried out through a study of the Q as a function of temperature of a composite mechanical resonator consisting of a quartz bar $0.500 \times 0.500 \times 5.00$ cm, cut with its length along the Y-axis, and the crystal to be studied cemented to one end. The crystal is cut to $0.50 \times 0.50 \times$ ca. 0.3 cm. The bar is mounted on knife edge supports in a vacuum chamber, and provision is made for cooling to liquid air temperatures or heating to ca. 400°C. The bar whose natural frequency is 37×10^3 cps is driven in torsional oscillation by means of a Hewlett Packard No. 650-A oscillator. When the bar is in oscillation, it is cut off from the oscillator and its output impressed on the plates of a Dumont 250 oscillograph. A sweep time of 5 to 0.5 sec is normally used, and a timing z signal of 20 to 1000 cps is superposed. The resulting trace on the oscillograph is photographed, and the decay curve measured, using a microscope with a mechanical stage and vernier. The Q of the resonator is calculated from the measured logarithmic decrement. The temperature is measured by a thermocouple in close proximity to the crystal.

The Q of the quartz bar and the composite resonator are both measured for a wide range of temperatures. Data with the present instrument have thus far been taken only on NaCl. Some very preliminary results have been obtained on KBr and LiF, using a less sensitive instrumental setup.

From the observed Q's, the known masses of quartz and the crystal being studied, and the observed resonant frequencies of the quartz bar and the composite resonator, it is possible to calculate the Q of the salt, as may be shown from the circuit equivalents of the inertially loaded crystal.[17]

The results of such measurements at 36.3×10^3 cps, which may be subject to considerable revision, on a crystal of NaCl obtained from the Harshaw Chemical Company are shown in Fig. 10. It will be observed that the loss is a pronounced function of T showing

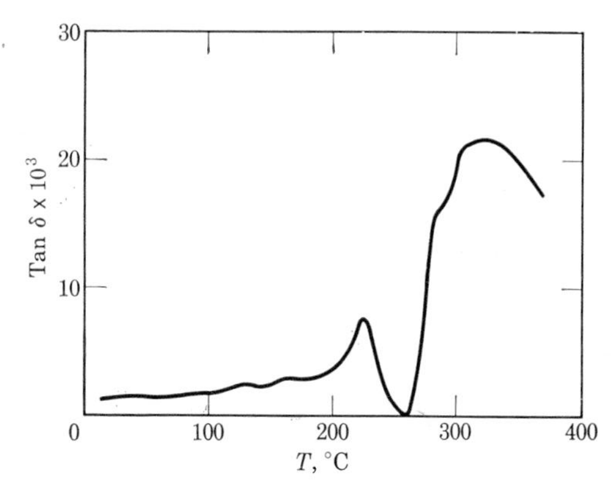

FIG. 10. Anelastic loss in NaCl.

two small peaks, one of moderate size, and one prominent loss maximum which is apparently composed of a major and a minor component. It is of interest that the temperature of the large loss maximum corresponds to that of the anomaly in the elastic modulus found by Hunter and Siegel[16] for a similar frequency.

TABLE 3

ANELASTIC RELAXATION IN IONIC CRYSTALS

Salt	U_2	U_1	U_3	U_4	U	U_x
NaCl	0.59	0.64	0.73	0.82	0.87	
KBr		0.54			0.65	0.69
LiF		0.58			0.70	0.77

The activation energies corresponding to these loss maxima for NaCl have been calculated as well as some tentative values for similar maxima observed in the loss of KBr and LiF, also obtained from Harshaw Chemical Company. In these cases evidence was found for only three maxima. These are given in Table 3 with tentative assignments.

Although we have as yet no direct evidence identifying each peak with a relaxation mechanism, the activation energies found are at least strongly suggestive. It will be noted that the activation energy of the second lowest peak for NaCl, 0.64 ev, is in agreement with that found in the dielectric measurements on the pure crystal which was attributed to pairs of defects. The major peak value of 0.87 ev seems in very good agreement with that obtained for the motion of single vacancies from conductivity studies of Etzel and Maurer[11] and diffusion studies of Maurer, Mapother, and Crookes,[18] so that a discussion on this basis is not unreasonable. The small auxiliary peak at 0.59 ev is not readily explained on the basis of a pure crystal, but this is typical of values of U_2 found dielectrically, if impurities are present. The inherent sensitivity of this method of measurement may detect impurities in amounts of about 1×10^{-5}, which are presumed present in the purest specimens available. It is possible that the moderate peak arises from impurities as well, the activation energy 0.73 corresponding to a value of U_3 in accord with an ion size giving 0.59 ev for U_2.

These assignments were made on the assumption that in these relatively pure crystals the largest loss peak is due to the single lattice defects. The lower maxima agree closely in energy with the value for pairs found dielectrically. The high energy peak U_x is still unexplained, although possibly it may be due to the reorientation of pairs via the anion. Any final picture of these mechanical losses must await the results of a more detailed investigation of these and other crystals, which is at present under way.

5. ASSOCIATION OF LATTICE DEFECTS

We should next like to consider the question of the degree of association of lattice defects to form pairs of various sorts. This matter has been discussed by several authors, with varying conclusions. Seitz[19] has indicated that a considerable fraction of Schottky defects in the pure alkali halides should be present in the form of pairs at low temperatures, whereas Mott and Gurney[20] have concluded that the fraction was probably small. The failure of the Einstein relation between diffusion constant and conductivity at low temperatures has been studied by Maurer, Mapother, and Crookes,[18] with the conclusion that this failure is due to pairs formed between divalent impurity ions and vacancies rather than to pairs of vacancies, although free and associated vacancies were apparently present in comparable amounts. The experimental studies of relaxation effects[1,2] have indicated that in crystals that had been subjected to a strong heating and rapid quench, the mole fraction of pairs is of the order of 10^{-5} to 10^{-7}; in crystals with deliberately added impurities, pairs between vacancies as well as impurity-vacancy pairs were present in amounts of the order of 10^{-6} or larger. The indicated degree of association of the impurities in this case was, however, much smaller than that observed by Etzel and Maurer.[11]

Some further information on this subject is obtained from the more detailed analysis of the dielectric relaxation data given previously, particularly that on NaCl. In the case of pure NaCl the number of free vacancies and pairs correspond to mole fractions of 5.0×10^{-6} and 2.5×10^{-6}, respectively. Then, considering the simple equilibrium

$$\square + \bigcirc \overset{K_1}{\rightleftharpoons} \bigcirc \cdot \square$$

we have

$$K_1 = \frac{x_1}{x_v{}^{f2}} = \frac{2.5 \times 10^{-6}}{(5.0 \times 10^{-6})^2} = 1.0 \times 10^5, \tag{5.1}$$

and for α, the degree of association, we find 0.33. This value of K_1 is much larger than that calculated for the NaCl with Mn^{++} additions in reference 2. These results had also disagreed with the work of Etzel and Maurer,[11] as we have mentioned, so that a reinvestigation of the association is indicated. Since we now have determined the mole fraction of free vacancies from the high-temperature conductivity data and have an independent value for K_1, it is possible to calculate the association in the foreign ion case without the use of the mole fraction of foreign ions determined analytically. Reformulating the expressions for the equilibrium present in the impure crystal

$$M + \square \overset{K_2}{\rightleftharpoons} M \cdot \square$$

$$\bigcirc + \square \underset{K_1}{\rightleftharpoons} \square \cdot \bigcirc$$

$$+$$

$$M$$

$$\downarrow\uparrow K_3$$

$$M \cdot \bigcirc \cdot \square$$

we have

$$x_1 = K_1(x_n - x_1 - x_2)x_v{}^f, \tag{5.2}$$

$$x_4 = K_2 x_v{}^f(x_v{}^f - x_n + x_1), \tag{5.3}$$

$$x_2 = K_3 x_1(x_v{}^f - x_n + x_1), \tag{5.4}$$

where x_n is the mole fraction of anion vacancies and also the mole fraction of cation vacancies produced thermally. This quantity is unknown, and was assumed constant in the previous work. It may now be calculated from equation (5.2), and then used in equations (5.3) and (5.4) to find the values for K_2 and K_3 and an effective value of y^*, that is, the fraction of foreign ions actually contributing a cation vacancy, since

$$y^* = x_v{}^f - x_n + x_1 + x_2 + x_4. \tag{5.5}$$

The results of these calculations, using data from reference 2, are given in Table 4.

TABLE 4

ASSOCIATION OF FOREIGN IONS IN NACL

Impurities	$y \times 10^4$	$y^* \times 10^6$	$x_n \times 10^6$	$K_2 \times 10^{-5}$	$K_3 \times 10^{-5}$
Mn^{++}	0.6	1.4	0.79	1.7	9.6
Mn^{++}	1.2	1.6	2.0	5.0	17
Mn^{++}	2.6	12	1.6	0.11	3.2
			av.	2.3	10.
Cd^{++}	18	33	0.8	0.048	0.17
Ni^{++}	4.2	1.6	0.08	19	6.3
Pb^{++}	1	4.8	0.3	1.0	1.7
Cu^{+}	2.9	7.9	0.46	3.3	2.9
Tl^{+}	5.6	38	1.6	440	40
Ag^{+}	50	17.8	1.1	4.1	0.32

It will be observed that the values of K_2 and K_3 are considerably larger than those given in reference 2. On the other hand, K_2 for Cd^{++} is in good agreement with the value found by Etzel and Maurer for Cd^{++} in NaCl, 4.9×10^3 being the value calculated for the same temperature as the measurements given. This close agreement is obviously fortuitous, as indicated by the scattering in the three Mn^{++} samples, but it is apparent that the original discrepancy has been resolved. It is clear that the overall situation of large association of foreign ions whose size differs markedly from Na^+ in NaCl is still true, and to a much greater degree than previously noted.

This unexpected disagreement of the fraction of free vacancies with the analytical determination of the fraction of foreign ions is at first surprising. However, a study of the luminescence of NaCl phosphors activated with Pb or Cu at the Crystal Branch of the Naval Research Laboratory has shown a marked quenching of fluorescence on standing at room temperatures. The quenching was accelerated by heating to ca. 150°C. This has been attributed to an agglomeration of the foreign ions into invisible precipitates.[21] This would accord well with the dielectric observations.

In the acoustic measurements on NaCl we have observed $\tan \delta_{max} = 0.0216$ for the peak assigned to single vacancies, and $\tan \delta_{max} \simeq 0.0029$ for that assigned to pairs. Neglecting the difference in temperature, we may assume that the peak height is directly proportional to the number of defects, giving for the degree of association 0.12, a value in general agreement with the results of Etzel and Maurer[11] and the dielectric studies.

6. CONCLUSIONS

The results of the relaxation studies are instructive in regard to a number of problems in ionic crystals. Although the occurrence of two loss maxima of similar energy cannot be regarded as conclusive proof of the presence of Frenkel defects, it is strongly suggestive. Obviously, in a crystal with Schottky defects, if the cation and anion have reasonably similar sizes and masses, two peaks of similar energy should be found; such indeed may be true in KCl. In the thallium halides and the silver chloride studied previously the sizes and masses are quite dissimilar; thus two peaks from Schottky defects would be very unlikely. There has been considerable discussion about the nature of the lattice defects in the silver halides. The evidence indicates that both kinds are present but that the Frenkel defects are dominant in the bulk of the crystal.[22] This is substantiated by the information at hand from the dielectric studies on pure AgCl and $AgCl + CdCl_2$, which shows that the defects behave in a fashion quite different from the alkali halides but consistent with a picture of Frenkel defects. The situation in the thallium halides probably is similar; however, the fact that these crystals have the CsCl structure prevents a direct comparison. The lattice defects in this structure have not been considered in detail in the literature, but no essential differences would be expected.

A question of greater importance is in the correlation of the activation energies found from the relaxation studies and those obtained from other techniques. As we have seen, the activation energy for the diffusion of a single vacancy can be found in several ways. The measurements of d-c conductivity of a crystal at low temperatures, where the number of defects is constant, provides the most widely used method. In a few cases, conductivity studies have been made by the technique of Koch and Wagner in which the number of vacancies is made independent of temperature by the introduction of divalent foreign ions. For NaCl and NaBr, direct diffusion measurements have been made, using radioactive sodium. The measurement of the dielectric loss at temperatures above the relaxation peaks provides a value of the activation energy that should be identical with that from d-c conduction studies. The study of dielectric relaxation in crystals with various impurities can be used to get an indication of the activation energy for an ion of the size of the matrix cation. This obviously cannot be a very precise value. The acoustic relaxation provides an independent value that is reasonably accurate.

The most information regarding the activation energy U is available about NaCl. Diffusion measurements[18] gave 0.77 ev $\pm$ 10 per cent; conductivity studies in crystals containing $CdCl_2$[11] gave 0.85 ev $\pm$ 5 per cent; Lehfeldt's d-c conductivity studies[23] indicated 0.78 ev for an artificial crystal and 1.09 ev for a natural crystal. The dielectric conductivity observed above the relaxation peaks in the crystal with Cd^{++} gave 0.83 ev $\pm$ 10 per cent, and dielectric studies on pure NaCl gave 0.84 ev $\pm$ 10 per cent. The acoustic loss that we have identified with the motion of single vacancies suggests a value of 0.86 ev $\pm$ 5 per cent. A weighted average for these figures is 0.84 ev. When this value of U is combined with the activation energy for conductivity at high temperatures, $W/2 + U$, found by Lehfeldt, where W is the energy for forming a defect, a value of $W/2 = 1.06$ ev is obtained. This is in reasonable agreement with the calculated value 0.93 ev found by Mott and Littleton.[24]

For NaBr, Maurer, Mapother, and Crookes[18] found a value of U of 0.84 ev from conductivity studies, whereas Lehfeldt's[23] results gave 1.018 ev. The dielectric data of Fig. 6 indicates a value of 1.13 ev. The agreement between the various methods is much less satisfactory than for the other crystal, but the hygroscopic nature of this crystal makes low-temperature measurements difficult.

As indicated in Table 3, the preliminary acoustic damping measurements are in agreement with the dielectric relaxation measurements for the loss maximum identified with pairs of vacancies and are consistent with values expected for the migration of single defects for the major loss peaks. A detailed comparison, however, must await further measurements on these crystals.

In general, it will be observed that the results of the relaxation studies are in excellent agreement with values of the activation energies found by other techniques and they provide a convenient method for obtaining the information.

The information obtained about the numbers of defects and pairs is also in general accord with the results of other methods of investigation when comparisons are possible. Etzel and Maurer[11] had found a mole fraction of vacancies of about 4×10^{-6} in pure NaCl at low temperatures, ca. 250°C. Wagner and Hantelmann[25] have reported a value of 8×10^{-6} in KCl at 600°C, near the "knee" in the conductivity curve, where the number of vacancies is presumed to become frozen. These may be compared with the value of 5×10^{-6} found dielectrically in the pure crystal of NaCl and with the values of x_n; 8×10^{-7}, 2×10^{-6}, 1.6×10^{-6} found in the crystal containing Mn^{++}, for example. This constancy of the number of thermally produced vacancies strongly suggests that the picture of a frozen equilibrium existing for temperatures below the knee in the conductivity curve is correct, and indicates also that the differing conductivities found in this temperature range are due to the presence of multivalent ion impurities. Similarly, the degree of association found by both the dielectric and acoustic relaxation measurements is in general agreement with that obtained elsewhere, Etzel and Maurer[11] having found ca. 0.50 at 250°C, whereas the diffusion studies of Maurer, Mapother, and Crookes[18] require that the number of free and associated vacancies are of the same order of magnitude. The dielectric studies reported here give 0.33 for vacancy pairs and comparable values for foreign ion-vacancy pairs; whereas the acoustic measurements give 0.12 for vacancy pairs.

It seems, then, that a reasonably consistent fund of information about lattice defects in the simple ionic crystals is being accumulated. It may be anticipated that the existence of this backlog of data will stimulate further detailed theoretical studies of these crystals.

The author of this paper is deeply indebted to W. Westphal and E. McCarty of the Measurements Group of the Laboratory for Insulation Research, Massachusetts Institute of Technology, who carried out the dielectric measurements, and to J. Upham and E. Seitz of the Physical Electronics Section, Atomic and Radiation Physics Division of the National Bureau of Standards, who have assisted in the acoustic relaxation measurements described here.

REFERENCES

1. R. G. Breckenridge, *J. Chem. Phys.*, **16**, 959 (1948).
2. R. G. Breckenridge, *J. Chem. Phys.*, **18**, 913 (1950).
3. R. G. Breckenridge and A. L. Ward, *Phys. Rev.*, **78**, 315 (1950).
4. P. Debye, *Polar Molecules*, p. 105, Chemical Catalog Co., New York, 1929.
5. H. Fröhlich, *Theory of Dielectrics*, pp. 17, 66, Oxford University Press, London, 1949.
6. G. J. Dienes, *J. Chem. Phys.*, **16**, 620 (1948).
7. W. B. Westphal, *Technical Report* XXXVI, Laboratory for Insulation Research, M.I.T., 1950.
8. K. S. Cole and R. H. Cole, *J. Chem. Phys.*, **9**, 341 (1941).
9. H. Rubens, *Sitzber. preuss. Akad. Wiss.*, 513 (1913).
10. K. Försterling, *Ann. Physik*, **61**, 577 (1920).
11. H. W. Etzel and R. J. Maurer, *J. Chem. Phys.*, **18**, 1003 (1950).
12. E. Koch and C. Wagner, *Z. physik. Chem.* (B), **38**, 295 (1937).
13. C. Zener, *Elasticity and Anelasticity of Metals*, University of Chicago Press, Chicago, 1942.
14. F. Rose, *Phys. Rev.*, **49**, 50 (1936).
15. M. A. Durand, *Phys. Rev.*, **50**, 449 (1936).
16. L. Hunter and S. Siegel, *Phys., Rev.*, **61**, 84 (1942).
17. W. P. Mason, *Electromechanical Transducers and Wave Filters*, D. Van Nostrand, New York, 1949.
18. R. J. Maurer, D. Mapother, and H. N. Crookes, *J. Chem. Phys.*, **18**, 1231 (1950).
19. F. Seitz, *Revs. Mod. Phys.*, **18**, 384 (1946).
20. N. F. Mott and R. W. Gurney, *Electronic Processes in Ionic Crystals*, Oxford University Press, London, 1940.
21. J. H. Schulman, R. J. Ginther, and C. C. Klick, *J. Opt. Soc. Am.*, **40**, 854 (1950).
22. *Fundamental Mechanisms of Photographic Sensitivity*, Butterworth Scientific Publications, London, 1951.

23. W. Lehfeldt, *Z. Physik*, **85**, 717 (1933).
24. N. F. Mott and M. J. Littleton, *Trans. Faraday Soc.*, **34**, 485 (1938).
25. C. Wagner and P. Hantelmann, *J. Chem. Phys.*, **18**, 72 (1950).

DISCUSSION

R. SMOLUCHOWSKI (CARNEGIE INSTITUTE OF TECHNOLOGY):

It is interesting to note from Fig. 9 that doubling the ionic radius from 0.5 to 1 Å hardly influences the various activation energies at all. The U_3 and U_4 increase by about 5 per cent, whereas the other U's are practically constant. This is difficult to reconcile with the large difference in temperatures at which the various peaks occur, if the suggested indentification of the individual peaks is correct. Perhaps a closer analysis of an interaction between the various imperfections (stable and metastable associations) may clear up this point.

R. G. BRECKENRIDGE (*in reply*):

In regard to Smoluchowski's observations, it should be pointed out that the activation energies are proportional to the absolute temperatures at which the dielectric loss maxima occur, and are calculated from these temperatures, using equation (2.8) of the paper. Although the original data for Fig. 9 are not included, it was found that the loss maximum tentatively attributed to a place interchange of a vacancy and a foreign ion occurred at 160°C for Ni^{++} and at 197°C for Tl^{+}. These temperatures correspond to activation energies of 0.77 ev and 0.83 ev, respectively. A similar small difference in the activation energy for diffusion in NaCl has been reported for $Au^{+}(r = 1.37$ Å$)$ and $Ni^{++}(r = 0.70$ Å$)$, as determined by another method[1] so that the results of the relaxation studies may not be unexpected.

[1] See N. F. Mott and R. W. Gurney, *Electronic Processes in Ionic Crystals*, p. 56, Oxford University Press, 1940.

9.

Studies of Alkali Halides by Photoelectric Methods

L. APKER AND E. TAFT

General Electric Research Laboratory, Schenectady, N. Y.

ABSTRACT

This paper outlines qualitatively some recent photoelectric investigations of alkali halides. When these crystals are pure, they exhibit no external photoelectric effect in the visible or near ultraviolet. If they contain halogen vacancies, however, F-centers may be formed, and external photoelectrons may then be ejected. The following are some examples of phenomena that may be studied conveniently in this way: direct ionization of F-centers by photons (Section 2); energy distributions of external photoelectrons from directly ionized F-centers (Section 3); production of F-centers by excitons (Section 4); exciton-induced photoelectric emission (Section 5); spatial distribution of centers and destruction of excitons at free surfaces (Section 6); and energy distribution of exciton-induced photoelectrons (Section 7). In Section 8 there are concluding remarks.

1. EXPERIMENTAL PROCEDURE

The external photoelectric effect has a well-known history that began with the work of Hertz in 1887. In the early 1900's, it had an important influence on the evolution of quantum theory. Again, in the 1930's, it furnished some of the most direct evidence for the validity of quantum statistics as applied to the electrons in metals.[1] It is now developing in another direction, and is becoming a useful tool for studying the behavior of electrons in nonmetals. Since electrons interact strongly with imperfections in

[1] See, for example, L. A. DuBridge, *Actualités scientifiques et industrielles*, No. 268 (Hermann et Cie, Paris, 1935).

ionic crystals, information about these imperfections and their interactions may be obtained by photoelectric methods. It is the purpose of this paper to outline some recent progress made in this way on certain alkali halides. We shall be concerned primarily with four of the entities discussed in this book by Seitz,* namely electrons, vacancies, excitons, and phonons.

In this type of work, the alkali halide of interest must be prepared in the form of a photoelectric emitter. Its surface must be reasonably uniform over the emitting area, or the interpretation of the results becomes unduly complicated. The simplest way of preparing a suitable sample is to evaporate a thin layer of the material on a conducting substrate in the evacuated phototube. This layer may then be investigated as it is, or it may be subjected to further treatment, such as sintering, for example. A controlled low pressure of alkali metal or halogen may be admitted temporarily to change the crystal composition and the number of vacancies.

Several different types of photoelectric measurement may be made. (1) We may determine how the photoelectric yield (in electrons per incident quantum) depends on the frequency and hence on the photon energy $h\nu$ of the incident radiation. (2) The energy distribution of the photoelectrons emitted at any particular photon energy may be found by retarding-potential techniques. If the alkali-halide photoemitters are arranged to be interchangeable with clean metallic ones, contact potential differences may be evaluated. (3) At a particular photon energy, the photoelectric yield may be measured as a function of the time during which excitons and vacancies interact.

The temperature of the emitter is an important parameter, and it may be held at various values during these measurements.

The phototubes used in this work are designed in different ways according to the particular measurement to be made. If only the frequency dependence of the photoelectric yield is of interest, the geometry of the tube electrodes may have a variety of forms. In most cases, the emitter surface is enclosed in a metal collecting cylinder in which there is a hole to admit the radiation. Figure 1 shows such a tube, in which the emitter can be held at the temperature of liquid nitrogen, for example. Similarly, introduction of

* See Paper 1, by F. Seitz, in this book. We are very much indebted to Professor Seitz for many discussions of exciton behavior.

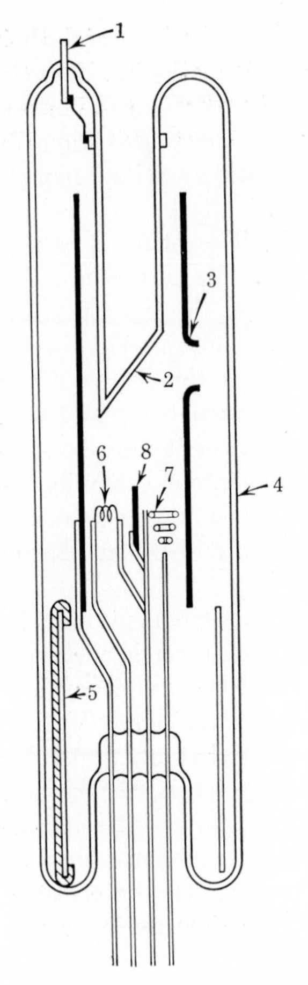

FIG. 1. Cross-section sketch of typical photocell. (1) Lead-in to platinized glass emitter (2), which can be filled with liquid nitrogen or air. (3) Stainless steel collector. (4) Corning 9741 glass envelope. (5) 9741 glass shield with nickel armature. (6) Tungsten filament electron source. (7) Platinum spiral for evaporation of RbI. (8) Shield between (6) and (7) to prevent contamination. [*Phys. Rev.*, **81**, 698 (1951).]

hot oil permits operation above room temperature. A small filament allows the alkali halide to be bombarded externally with electrons to generate F-centers.

For energy distribution measurements, more intricate tubes have been used. The electrode geometry, however, is fundamentally more simple than in the case above. Figure 2 shows an example. The symmetry of the electric field approximates rather closely the radial field between two concentric spheres, the emitter being small and inside a large spherical collector. (If it is small enough, the emitter may even depart widely from a spherical shape without disturbing the results.) Thus the photoelectrons essentially follow radial lines of force whatever their direction of emission from the alkali halide surface. Their kinetic energies may then be measured readily by retarding-potential techniques. The other types of measurement mentioned above may also be made. The complicated tube construction, however, makes low-temperature measurements relatively difficult. It is most convenient, therefore, to hold the emitter only at room temperature or above.

The practical difficulty of making these fundamentally simple spherical phototubes arises with the obvious but annoying necessity of supporting the central emitter. This must be done without disturbing the spherical symmetry of the electric field in the important major fraction of the collector space. Furthermore about ten interchangeable emitters actually are used in the same collector, and the changes must be made conveniently and rapidly. Introduction of heating currents to raise the emitter temperature

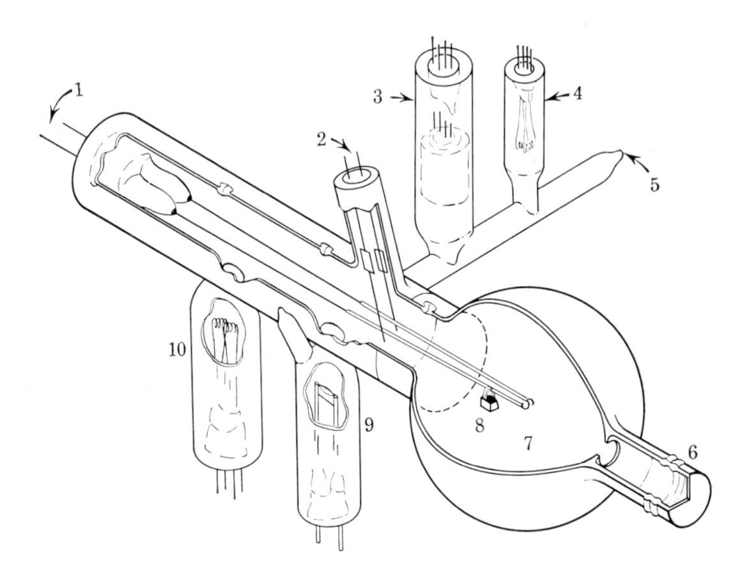

FIG. 2. Cutaway sketch of phototube. (1) Lead-in wires to central conductor of hairpin assembly; these two leads are connected by the bucket support (7). Inside the collecting sphere they are sheathed by metal tubing supported on insulators. (2) Lead-in wires with spring contacts actuated by armatures; these wires supply current to the sheaths and through them to a small heater filament inside the bucket support (7). (3) Ionization gauge. (4) Getter. (5) Seal-off tip. (6) Quartz window. (8) Typical bucket-shaped emitter; there were eight to ten in each tube. (9) KI evaporator. (10) Evaporator for Ag or Pb [see Taft and Dickey, *Phys. Rev.*, **78**, 625 (1950)]. [*Phys. Rev.*, **79**, 964 (1950).]

and the correction of stray fields due to uncontrolled contact potentials present additional problems. Detailed descriptions of these procedures have been given elsewhere.[2] In this paper, we shall have occasion only to draw upon pertinent results as they are needed.

[2] Apker and Taft, *Phys. Rev.*, **79**, 864 (1950) and foregoing papers cited there. For a review, see J. A. Becker, *Elec. Eng.*, **68**, 937 (1950).

2. DIRECT IONIZATION OF *F*-CENTERS IN KI

When photons of energy less than about 5 ev strike a surface of pure KI, no photoelectric emission is observed. This is not surprising, of course. The most loosely bound electrons in this stable salt are those in the filled zone associated with the 5p shell of the I^- ions. It requires at least 7 ev to set them free inside the crystal. An energy of the order of 1 ev more is necessary to eject them entirely from the salt and thus produce photoemission.

If I^- lattice sites in the crystal are vacant, however, electrons may be bound rather loosely in these positions to form the well-known *F*-centers so thoroughly studied in the past.* Electrons in these centers may be set free inside the crystal by photons having energies as low as 1.7 ev. At this photon energy, the *F*-center is first raised to an excited state. Under the influence of lattice vibrations, it then dissociates to release an electron within the crystal. At somewhat higher photon energies, the ionization takes place in the primary process.

At about 2.5 ev, photoelectrons begin to appear outside the crystal. The yield at first is very low, of the order of 10^{-8} electron per quantum. It rises rapidly, however, and at $h\nu \sim 4$ ev reaches a plateau value near 10^{-4} electron per quantum. Figure 3 shows the behavior of the photoelectric emission from a KI sample containing roughly 10^{19} *F*-centers per cm^3 (these were produced by electron bombardment[3]). We may guess that excited electrons escape from depths of the order of 10^{-6} cm. Then the observed photoelectric yield at $h\nu \sim 4$ ev is consistent with a reasonable cross section, in order of magnitude 10^{-18} cm^2, for ionization of *F*-centers at this frequency.

The photoelectric excitation process is fundamentally different for *F*-centers than for the electrons in a metal. When a photoelectron is ejected from a Fermi band of free electrons, only the negligibly small energy associated with the recoil momentum is communicated directly to the crystal lattice. (Something akin to a Peltier heat may be released, because a hole remains in the

* See Paper 1, by F. Seitz, in this book, and papers cited there.

[3] F. Seitz, *Revs. Modern Phys.*, **18**, 384 (1946); *Phys. Rev.*, **79**, 529 (1950); *Carnegie Institute of Technology Symposium on the Plastic Deformation of Crystalline Solids*, Office of Naval Research, 1950.

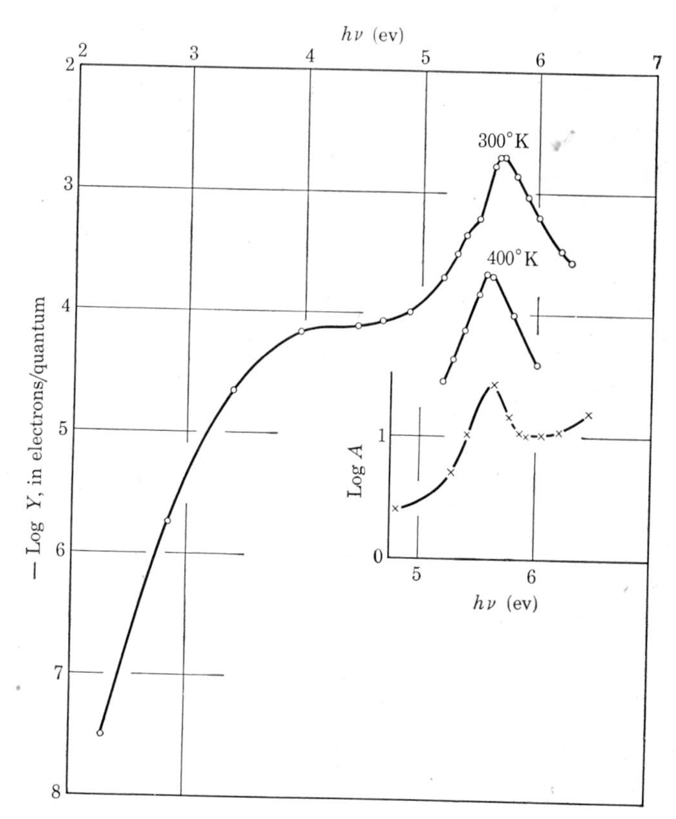

FIG. 3. Spectral distribution of the photoelectric yield Y in electrons/quantum for KI with F-centers. The small inflection just to the left of the peak on the curve for 300°K is reproducible and apparently real. Fesefeldt's values of the optical absorption constant A (in arbitrary units) for KI at 293°K are given on a logarithmic scale below the photoelectric data. [*Phys. Rev.* **79**, 964 (1950).]

Fermi band and the electrons are thus left in an excited state.[4] In a sense, however, this energy is imparted to the lattice only by secondary processes.) Thus, we are not being very inaccurate if we say that only photons and electrons are vitally concerned in

[4] It is of interest to note, in passing, that the lifetime of these states may be so short that the energy levels may be broadened appreciably, as they are in soft x-ray emission experiments; see Jean Dickey, *Phys. Rev.*, **81**, 612 (1951) and references given there.

the primary photoelectric process and that phonons play no very important part.

For an *F*-center in KI, this is not even approximately true. The emission must be treated by entirely different methods, discussed by C. Herring.[5] Because the *F*-center constitutes an imperfection, the surrounding lattice is in a state of strain. According to the Franck-Condon principle, the ionic configuration relaxes to new equilibrium position after the *F*-center is ionized. In a typical case, the phonons thus released carry away more than 1 ev of the energy imparted to the *F*-center by a 5-ev photon. Because of this large coupling between the lattice and the *F*-center, temperature has a much larger effect on the behavior of the yield in Fig. 3 than it would have in the case of a metal. Thus, in the absence of thermal and zero-point vibrations, the *F*-centers would behave like electrons in a sharply defined energy level. At 300°K, fluctuations in the number of phonons released after the ionization process effectively broaden this level into a band roughly one ev wide. This width may be correlated by Herring's methods with the shape of the yield curve in Fig. 3.

3. ENERGY DISTRIBUTION OF PHOTOELECTRONS DUE TO DIRECT IONIZATION

Effects of the general type just considered are common, of course, in crystal luminescence and in optical absorption by solids.* In particular, the optical absorption band of *F*-centers in KI is thermally broadened to a width of several tenths of an electron volt at 300°K. Now the initial state of an *F*-center participating in this absorption is obviously the same as that of a center contributing to the photoelectric emission. The final state of course, is different. The optical absorption leads to an excited state, whereas the photoemission ionizes the *F*-center and leaves a vacancy.

This suggests the following experiment. We may measure the energy distribution of the photoelectrons ejected by photons of some appropriate energy, say, 5 ev. In the case of RbI at 300°K, for example, this distribution is roughly a Gaussian band with an

* See Paper 1, by F. Seitz, in this book, and papers cited there.

[5] C. Herring, *Phys. Rev.*, **73**, 1238 (T) (1948).

rms width near 1 ev, and with its center at 1.6 ev.[6] We may now compare this result with the optical absorption band mentioned above. The latter has roughly one-third the above width and is centered at a photon energy of 1.6 ev. This optical bandwidth indicates the extent to which thermal fluctuations affect the stored energy in the distorted lattice around an *F*-center that has just been excited. The width of the photoelectron energy distribution measures a similar effect for the vacancy left behind immediately after ionization of an *F*-center. It is evident that this second effect is considerably greater than the first. A little consideration shows that this is a reasonable result, for which we have thus obtained direct experimental verification.

We still have unused information on this same system. We know, for example, that the activation energy for thermal ionization of *F*-centers in RbI is roughly 1.3 ev,[7] that the excited state of an *F*-center immediately dissociates into an electron and a vacancy, that the band of photoelectron energies has its center at 1.6 ev, and that the optical absorption peaks at $h\nu = 1.6$ ev. Appropriately combined, this information permits us to make the following rough estimates: (1) The bottom of the conduction band lies less than 1 ev below the potential energy of an electron in the vacuum outside the RbI crystal. (2) When the lattice is held in the equilibrium position appropriate to the ground state of the *F*-center, it may require as much as 1 ev more energy to ionize the center than merely to excite it. (3) When the lattice relaxes after *F*-center excitation, the surrounding ions move in the same general way as they do around the vacancy after *F*-center ionization.

This situation is similar to one considered previously by Mott and Gurney.[7] The latter involved both excitation of *F*-centers and also ionization leading to photoconduction. The experimental data then available were more restricted, however, since the energy distribution of the free electrons naturally could not be measured and the crystal surface was not involved.

[6] Apker and Taft, *Phys. Rev.*, **82,** 814 (1951.) It is interesting to compare the results of this section with the calculations of J. H. Simpson, *Proc. Roy. Soc.* (*London*), **A197**, 269 (1949), on the wave functions and energies of *F*-centers in KCl.

[7] N. F. Mott and R. W. Gurney, *Electronic Processes in Ionic Crystals*, pp. 135 ff, Oxford University Press, London, 1940.

4. PRODUCTION OF *F*-CENTERS BY EXCITONS

In the foregoing discussion, we have merely assumed that *F*-centers were present in the alkali halide crystal. We did not consider how they were formed. *F*-center production has usually been studied by measuring the optical absorption to which the centers give rise. The maximum attainable concentration of centers is of the order of 10^{19} cm^{-3}. Thus they must be produced throughout a rather thick layer of the crystal, if the absorption is to be conveniently measurable. Methods of production that satisfy this requirement involve irradiating the crystal with x-rays, energetic electrons, or the deeply penetrating photons lying in the low-energy tail of the first fundamental ultraviolet absorption band.

Seitz[3,*] has considered in detail the mechanisms by which these treatments produce *F*-centers from groups of vacancies in the crystal. The point of particular interest here is that ultraviolet irradiation produces excitons from which electrons may be captured by vacant I^- lattice sites. *F*-centers are thus formed. Superfluous vacancies left over from the several in an original cluster may diffuse away or may trap holes to form *V*-centers, which are not of direct interest at this point. The quantum yield of *F*-centers is practically unity in the initial stages of this process. Thus we conclude that the interaction of excitons and vacancies is very strong under these conditions. Since the excitons are formed by the weak optical absorption in the low-energy tail of the fundamental band, however, we are not sure that they are representative of the perfect crystal. It is probable that they are formed in the distorted lattice near imperfections. Thus they may be trapped near their point of origin.[3] Subsequent interaction with vacancies might then be more probable than if the excitons were free.

Photoelectric measurements can throw some light on this problem. Radiation lying in the main part of the fundamental absorption band is absorbed in a very thin layer ($\sim 10^{-6}$ cm) at the crystal surface. Since the maximum concentration of *F*-centers does not exceed $\sim 10^{19}$ cm^{-3}, as mentioned before, only $\sim 10^{13}$ of them can be generated per cm^2 of surface area in this thin layer, and this is too small to produce appreciable optical absorption.

* See Paper 1, by F. Seitz, in this book.

However, the centers may be directly ionized at $h\nu \sim 4$ ev, for example. They give rise to an easily measurable photoelectric yield of 10^{-4} electron/quantum, as we have already seen in Fig. 3. Thus, by irradiation in the main part of the absorption band, we may produce excitons that we know to be typical of the perfect crystal. We may follow the consequent production of *F*-centers by observing the photoelectric emission at $h\nu \sim 4$ ev. Work of this type shows that these excitons also interact strongly with vacancies, and that the quantum yield is high in the initial stages of the process.[2]

Direct photon ionization may also be used to measure the rate at which *F*-centers are ionized by thermal vibrations or by irradiation with the frequencies that they absorb. For some purposes, photoelectric techniques are faster, more sensitive, and more convenient than other available methods of approaching these problems.

5. EXCITON-INDUCED IONIZATION OF *F*-CENTERS

The cross section of an *F*-center for direct photon ionization should change only slowly as the photon energy increases from, say, 4 ev to 7 ev. Now the first fundamental ultraviolet absorption band of KI, for instance, has its peak at $h\nu = 5.66$ ev when the temperature is 300°K. Suppose that we make measurements at very low intensities. Then the few excitons produced in the absorption band will not change the number of *F*-centers as they did in the discussion of Section 4. Thus we may measure the photoelectric yield in the range 4 ev $< h\nu <$ 7 ev for a constant number of *F*-centers. We should expect the emission either to change only slowly as a function of $h\nu$ or to decrease as we enter the absorption band of the crystal. Figure 3 shows, however, that it rises rapidly to a peak which has the same shape and location as the optical absorption maximum and varies in the same way with temperature. The photoelectric emission at $h\nu \sim 5.66$ ev is about twenty times higher than that on the plateau. We conclude that the excitons must be migrating to the *F*-centers and ionizing them. Thus the incident energy is more effectively concentrated on the centers, and the photoelectric yield is much higher than could be obtained by direct ionization alone.

This exciton-induced photoelectric emission, while more complex than direct photon ionization, may also be used to indicate the concentration of F-centers present in the alkali halide. Figure 4 shows the behavior of the photoelectric emission from KI as a function of time during irradiation with about 2×10^{11} quanta $\text{cm}^{-2}\ \text{sec}^{-1}$ at $h\nu \sim 5.66$ ev. The F-center concentration in this sample initially was zero. Thus the photocurrent rose rapidly from zero, and in the course of a few minutes reached a value which increased only very slowly with further irradiation. Here the excitons are interacting with vacancies to form F-centers; at

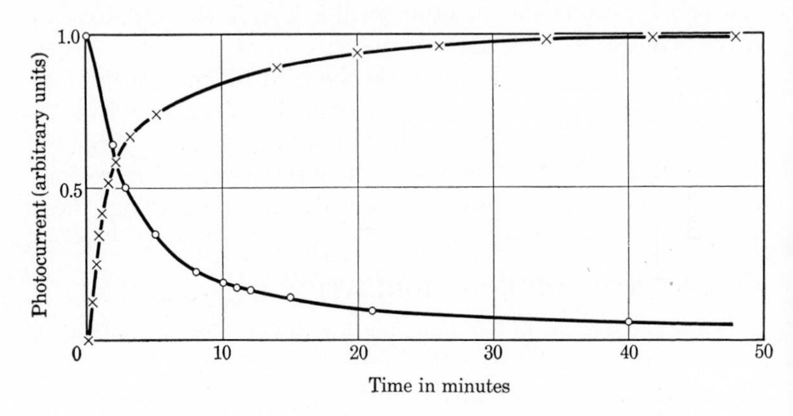

FIG. 4. Increase of photocurrent at $h\nu = 5.66$ ev as F-centers form in emitter (crosses). Decrease of current at approximately 400°K as centers are destroyed thermally (circles). [*Phys. Rev.*, **79**, 964 (1950).]

the same time they are dissociating the resultant centers into vacancies and free electrons, some of which escape through the crystal surface. This situation constitutes a steady state that is simpler than those produced by electron or x-ray bombardment. The method may thus be of value in studying the diffusion processes that accompany F-center production.[3]

In a similar way, thermal ionization of the F-centers may be followed by cutting off the incident radiation except during the negligible periods required to measure yields (see Fig. 4).

6. SPATIAL DISTRIBUTION OF F-CENTERS; DESTRUCTION OF EXCITONS AT FREE SURFACES

The dotted curve in Fig. 5 shows the photoelectric yield at 300°K from an RbI emitter containing F-centers produced by ultraviolet irradiation at $h\nu \sim 5.56$ ev. A radiation intensity of roughly 4×10^{11} quanta $\sec^{-1}$ cm^{-2} was allowed to strike the emitter until the F-center density approached its limiting value. The yield shows the same general behavior as that for KI in Fig. 3, except that the peak in the exciton-induced emission is flattened at the top.

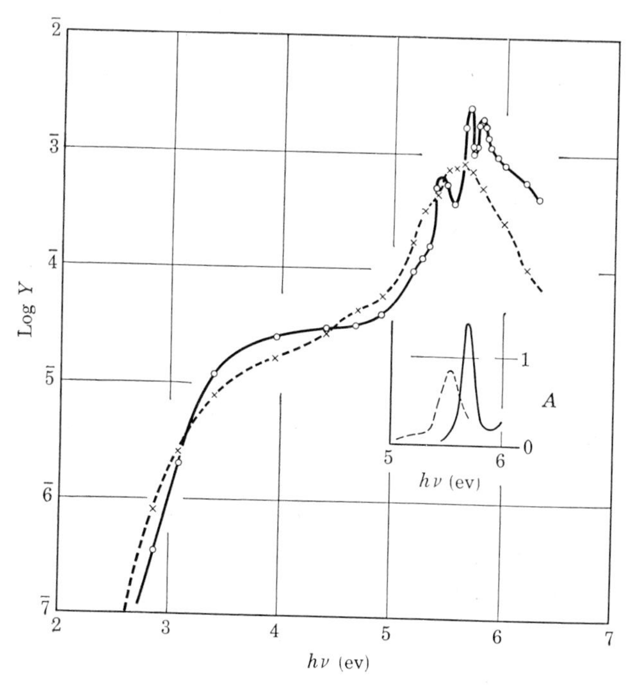

FIG. 5. Spectral distribution of the photoelectric yield Y from F-centers in RbI at 300°K (dotted curve) and at 85°K (solid curve). Y is given in electrons/quantum (note that the characteristics of the logarithms are negative). Below the photoelectric data is the optical absorption coefficient in arbitrary units on the same abscissa scale and on a linear ordinate scale. [*Phys. Rev.*, **81**, 698 (1951).]

When the emitter is cooled to ~85°K, a striking effect is observed. The peak splits into two distinct maxima, separated by a minimum that is essentially coincident with the shifted and intensified optical absorption peak. (A third clearly defined peak also emerges on the low-energy side of this structure, where there was merely an inflection at 300°K; this is an effect of no direct interest here.) The exciton-induced emission appears to increase with increasing optical absorption constant at the edge of the absorption band. It reaches a maximum near an absorption constant of 10^6 cm^{-1}, and then decreases as the absorption increases further. Thus the exciton-induced photoelectric emission seems to decrease when the incident photons are absorbed very close to the crystal surface and when they therefore produce excitons in a surface layer that is very thin.

Two effects which may be responsible for this behavior are the following. (1) The concentration of *F*-centers may be smaller near the surface than deeper in the crystal. (2) Excitons may migrate to the surface and may be destroyed there; thus they would no longer be available for *F*-center ionization. Fano,[8] in a discussion of certain luminescence phenomena, has suggested that this second mechanism may be important in other crystals.

Hebb[9] has given a quantitative treatment of the results in Fig. 5. He first assumed that the density of *F*-centers was spatially uniform, that excitons merely diffused to the surface, and that they were destroyed there. The decrease in yield at $h\nu \sim 5.72$ ev turned out to be five times smaller than that observed. He then took a drastically different point of view and assumed a "dead layer" in which no exciton-induced emission could arise. By taking the thickness of this layer to be ~140 Å, he obtained satisfactory agreement with experiment. Although the dead layer was an idealization that could represent a combination of physical effects, its large thickness suggested that the surface layers of the crystal were somehow different than the interior.

This result agreed with other experiments designed to evaluate mechanism (1) above. When RbI is evaporated in a vacuum, a very small amount of free I is released. The corresponding amount of Rb remains in the RbI source material (probably in the form of permanent *F*-centers). This transient free I reacts with the surface layers of the deposited RbI film and tends to suppress the I^- vacancies at which *F*-centers may be produced. Thus, the density of *F*-centers remains smaller near the surface than deeper in the crystal. This situation is largely responsible for the very pronounced effect shown in Fig. 5. (The phenomenon is somewhat analogous to the extreme self-reversal exhibited by the resonance lines emitted from the usual type of sodium lamp, for

[8] U. Fano, *Phys. Rev.*, **58**, 544 (1940).
[9] Malcolm H. Hebb, *Phys. Rev.*, **81**, 702 (1951).

example, in which the density of excited atoms falls off rapidly toward the tube wall.)

By maintaining a low vapor pressure of Rb in the tube during evaporation, we may increase the attainable density of F-centers near the surface. Then the "self-reversal" effect of Fig. 5 becomes much smaller; it may even be eliminated entirely if enough Rb is used. It is probable, in the latter case, that the density of F-centers actually increases near the surface.

Photoconduction is not observed in KCl when F-centers are irradiated at $\sim$85°K in the main part of their optical absorption band. Mott and Gurney[7] have concluded that the excited state of the F-center no longer dissociates at this low temperature, and thus no free electrons are produced. They have pointed out that photoconduction should not disappear, however, when the radiation lies in the region of continuous absorption on the high energy side of the main F-band peak, since ionization is then produced directly. The persistence of an external photoelectric effect at $\sim$85°K in KCl supports this conclusion.

7. ENERGY DISTRIBUTION OF EXCITON-INDUCED EXTERNAL PHOTOELECTRONS

At 300°K, an energy near 5.56 ev is required to form an exciton at the first fundamental absorption peak of RbI. We have seen that this exciton can deliver enough energy to an F-center to eject the electron from the crystal. This tells us only that the exciton can deliver an energy greater than 2.5 ev. It is interesting, therefore, to measure the energy distribution of the exciton-induced photoelectrons. Preliminary results show that this distribution is quite unlike the one that would be obtained if the electrons were ejected directly by photons of energy 5.56 ev. As indicated in Section 3, the latter should be roughly a Gaussian distribution peaked at an energy near 2 ev. In contrast, the exciton-induced distribution is peaked at the very low value of 0.3 ev. It falls off very rapidly toward higher energies, and at 2 ev has less than one-tenth its peak value.

Of the 5.56 ev in the incident photon, therefore, more than one ev appears in most cases to be dissipated at some point in the triple process of exciton formation, F-center stimulation, and photoelectron migration. Although it is not yet clear just where this loss occurs, two effects may be important. (1) Surface destruction of excitons may force the main source of exciton-induced emission so deep into the crystal that excited electrons are seriously degraded in energy before escape. (This degradation was not important for the direct ionization of Section 3, and was ignored there.) Hebb[9] has shown that electrons would have to migrate ~ 150 Å to lose enough energy to account for the observations.* (2) Phonons may be released during the formation, migration, or annihilation of the excitons.† Seitz has pointed out that energy loss during migration follows naturally if the optically permitted transition occurs to the top of the exciton band rather than the bottom.

The relative importance of these effects may be evaluated more definitely where measurements are made with more carefully controlled spatial distributions of F-centers. Even at this stage, however, they furnish unusually direct information on exciton behavior.

8. CONCLUDING REMARKS

In the preceding sections, we have tried to outline several types of problems which may be attacked conveniently by photoelectric methods. Only two iodides, those of K and Rb, were mentioned specifically. The same approach may be used, of course, to investigate other alkali halides. KCl is of particular interest, since it has been subjected to the most thorough study by other methods. The stable trapping of two electrons at a halogen vacancy to form an F'-center is also conveniently accomplished with this salt. Divalent ionic crystals like BaO and salts like BaI_2, less thoroughly understood than alkali halides, may also be studied by the methods described here.

We are indebted to F. Seitz, W. Shockley, and R. C. Gibbs for suggesting the preparation of this paper.

* This calculation was limited to scattering by the lattice alone, and it might give a different result if scattering by impurities or F-centers were included. We are indebted to Dr. Hebb for discussions of his work.

† See Paper 1, by F. Seitz, in this book.

10.

Diffusion in Alloys and the Kirkendall Effect*

J. BARDEEN AND C. HERRING

Bell Telephone Laboratories, Murray Hill, N. J.

ABSTRACT

The phenomenological theory of diffusion in a two-component system is formulated more rigorously than heretofore, and it is shown that the diffusion currents due to a composition gradient can always be described in terms of two effective diffusion constants, one for each component, provided lattice defects remain everywhere in equilibrium. The detailed atomic mechanism of transport is considered for the special case of diffusion by lattice vacancies, and it is shown that the errors in previous treatments of the relation between radioactive and chemical diffusion coefficients are of the order $1/Z$, where Z is the number of nearest neighbors of a lattice site. The effectiveness of dislocations in holding the vacancy concentration at its equilibrium value is discussed, and some suggestions are made regarding the atomic nature of the plastic flow which takes place in the Kirkendall effect.

1. THE KIRKENDALL EFFECT

Some years ago Kirkendall[1] observed a mass flow relative to the initial interface of a brass-copper diffusion couple. The direction of the mass flow is such as might be expected if zinc diffuses out of the brass more rapidly then copper diffuses in. The mass flow was

* This paper was presented not only at the National Research Council Conference on "Imperfections in Nearly Perfect Crystals" but also at a meeting of the American Society for Metals. It was published in the book *Atom Movements* (American Society for Metals, Cleveland, 1951) and is republished here by permission of the Society.

[1] E. O. Kirkendall, *Trans. AIME*, **147**, 104 (1942).

later verified by Smigelskas and Kirkendall[2] by placing inert markers at the two interfaces in a Cu-brass-Cu couple. It was found that the markers moved toward each other as diffusion progressed and that the displacement was proportional to the square root of time. It thus appeared that the motion of the markers was intimately associated with diffusion.

The Kirkendall effect has since been verified in a series of carefully controlled experiments by da Silva and Mehl.[3] They studied over thirty couples and found that the markers shifted in all systems studied: Cu-Zn, Cu-Sn, Cu-Ni, Cu-Au, Ag-Au. Many different types of markers were used, and the shift was found to be independent of the material used for the marker wires or foils.

A phenomenological explanation of the marker shift has been given by Darken.[4] He pointed out that, if the markers are used as a reference point, two diffusion coefficients should be used, one for each constituent of the alloy. If there is a difference in these diffusion coefficients, there will be a mass flow relative to the markers. He suggested that the coefficient for each constituent is related to that for diffusion of a radioactive tracer of the same constituent in an alloy of similar chemical composition. Darken has recently extended the phenomenological equations to cover multicomponent systems.[5] The markers are taken as a reference system for general diffusion equations of the type used by Onsager and Fuoss for electrolytes.

In an atomistic description of the Kirkendall effect, it is most reasonable to suppose that the markers are fixed relative to the crystal lattice and that there is a mass flow with respect to the lattice. Such a flow is not to be expected if diffusion takes place solely by simple interchange of neighboring atoms or by the "ring" mechanism recently proposed[6] by Zener. In the case of vacancy diffusion, a mass flow of atoms in one direction can be balanced by an equal flow of vacancies in the opposite direction. A mass flow can also occur by interstitial diffusion or by diffusion along grain

[2] A. D. Smigelskas and E. O. Kirkendall, *Trans. AIME*, **171**, 130 (1947).

[3] Unpublished work of L. C. Correa da Silva and R. F. Mehl. The authors are indebted to Dr. Mehl for an opportunity to read da Silva's thesis, *Atomic Flow in Diffusion Phenomena*.

[4] L. S. Darken, *Trans. AIME*, **175**, 184 (1948).

[5] L. S. Darken, "Formal Bases of Diffusion Theory." Presented at the seminar on Atom Movements, National Metal Congress, October, 1950.

[6] C. Zener, *Acta Cryst.*, **3**, 346 (1950).

boundaries or other lattice defects. Of these, vacancy diffusion appears to be the most reasonable explanation of the Kirkendall effect in substitutional alloys. Grain boundary diffusion is not a likely explanation because the diffusion coefficients are not structure sensitive in da Silva's experiments.

Phenomenological equations for vacancy diffusion can be obtained by treating the vacancies as one of the constituents of the alloy. It will be shown that these equations lead to the most general phenomenological equations for diffusion of the various constituents, with no requirement on mass flow relative to the lattice if it is assumed that the concentration of vacancies is maintained in local thermal equilibrium. The relationship between radioactive and chemical diffusion coefficients used by Darken follows only if it is assumed that cross-terms of the type which give a contribution to the current of one constituent proportional to the gradient of the chemical potential of another constituent are negligible. An exact calculation of the relation between diffusion coefficients for mass transport and for self-diffusion of a radioactive tracer in a pure metal by the vacancy mechanism, given in Appendix A of this paper, shows that the cross-term does not vanish even for this simple case. The contribution of the cross-term is of the order of $1/Z$, where Z is the number of neighbors of a given atom, to the diffusion coefficient of the tracer.

Vacancy diffusion in alloys has been considered from the standpoint of kinetic theory by Fisher, Hollomon, and Turnbull[7] and by Seitz.[8] Seitz showed that vacancy diffusion could lead to a mass flow of the type required to explain the Kirkendall effect and that the theory could also lead to a difference between tracer and chemical diffusion coefficients as observed by Johnson.[9] The connection between the kinetic theory approach and the phenomenological equations of Darken was pointed out by Bardeen.[10] By making certain simplifying assumptions and approximations, it was shown that Darken's equations for a binary alloy follow if it

[7] J. C. Fisher, J. H. Hollomon, and D. Turnbull, *Trans. AIME*, **175**, 202 (1948). The calculation is based on absolute reaction rate theory.

[8] F. Seitz, *Phys. Rev.*, **74**, 1513 (1948).

[9] W. A. Johnson, *Trans. AIME*, **147**, 331 (1943).

[10] J. Bardeen, *Phys. Rev.*, **76**, 1403 (1949). Similar equations were obtained by Fisher, Hollomon, and Turnbull (footnote 7), but they did not point out the simplifications which result when it is assumed that the vacancies are in equilibrium.

is assumed that the vacancies are maintained in local thermal equilibrium. It was pointed out that grain boundaries and dislocations could act as sources or sinks for vacancies to help maintain equilibrium.

In a second paper Seitz[11] showed that all that is really required is to have the local concentration of vacancies a unique function of local composition. Diffusion in a binary alloy can then be expressed by using different diffusion coefficients for the two constituents with the lattice as a reference frame. He also showed that interstitial diffusion leads to similar equations if the elementary diffusion step is motion from an interstitial to a normal lattice position, and if the concentration of interstitial atoms is in local equilibrium. Darken's relation between the tracer and chemical diffusion coefficients did not follow from this more general approach. As suggested above, from the phenomenological approach this relation is to be considered approximate rather than exact. We shall discuss this problem from a more general standpoint and show more explicitly the nature of the approximations required to get Darken's relation. We believe the errors involved in using the relation should generally be of the order of $1/Z$, as in self-diffusion in a pure metal, provided that diffusion takes place by the vacancy mechanism.

In Section 2 we give a brief review of the relevant thermodynamic relations for later reference. Section 3 is concerned with the phenomenological equations for vacancy diffusion and the application of the equations to self-diffusion of a tracer in a pure metal and to chemical and tracer diffusion in a binary alloy. Section 4 is concerned with the derivation of the diffusion equations from kinetic theory. The nature of the approximations required to get equations without the cross-terms is discussed. In Section 5 we show that dislocations are probably sufficient to maintain the concentration of vacancies in equilibrium during the diffusion process and show under what conditions the concentration in equilibrium with the dislocations will differ only inappreciably from that in equilibrium with an outside surface.

2. THERMODYNAMICS

The thermodynamics of an alloy with vacant sites can be treated by usual methods if the vacancies are treated as one of the con-

[11] F. Seitz, *Acta Cryst.*, **3**, 355 (1950).

stituents of the alloy. We shall give a brief review of the basic equations for later reference. Let us consider an alloy with N sites, assumed to be equivalent lattice positions, of which N_V are vacant and the remainder are occupied by atoms of n different species, labeled by $i = 1, 2 \cdots n$, with N_i atoms of species i. Then

$$N = N_V + \sum_{i=1}^{n} N_i. \tag{2.1}$$

The Gibbs free energy for the system relative to some standard state may be expressed in the form

$$G = W(N_i, N_V, p, T) - kT(N \log N - N_V \log N_V - \sum N_i \log N_i). \tag{2.2}$$

The second term comes from the entropy of mixing and the first from all other causes. The chemical potentials are defined by

$$\mu_i = \partial G/\partial N_i = \partial W/\partial N_i + kT \log (N_i/N), \quad i = 1, 2 \cdots n, \tag{2.3a}$$

$$\mu_V = \partial G/\partial N_V = \partial W/\partial N_V + kT \log (N_V/N). \tag{2.3b}$$

The free energy μ_i is that required to take an atom of species i from the standard state and place it in the alloy. The free energy μ_V is that required to take an atom from the interior to the surface, forming an additional vacant site and increasing the total number of sites by one. When the vacancies are in thermal equilibrium, $\mu_V = 0$, and the equilibrium concentration of vacancies, $N_V^{(e)}$, is given by

$$N_V^{(e)} = N \exp(-W_V/kT). \tag{2.4}$$

We shall assume that the energy

$$W_V = \partial W/\partial N_V \tag{2.5}$$

is independent of N_V, as will be the case for small concentrations. If N_V differs from the equilibrium value, $N_V^{(e)}$,

$$\mu_V = kT \log (N_V/N_V^{(e)}). \tag{2.6}$$

The free energy may be expressed in terms of the chemical potentials:

$$G = \sum \mu_i N_i + \mu_V N_V. \tag{2.7}$$

The Gibbs-Duhem relation is

$$\sum N_i \, d\mu_i + N_V \, d\mu_V = 0. \tag{2.8}$$

If the vacancies are maintained in their equilibrium concentrations, $\mu_V = 0$, and the equation reduces to

$$\sum N_i \, d\mu_i = 0. \tag{2.9}$$

This equation will apply approximately in any case because N_V is small compared with the concentrations of the other constituents. For a binary system with components A and B, $dN_A = -dN_B$, and the relation may be written in the form

$$d\mu_A/d \log N_A = d\mu_B/d \log N_B. \tag{2.10}$$

3. PHENOMENOLOGICAL EQUATIONS FOR VACANCY DIFFUSION

It is now generally recognized that gradients in chemical potentials rather than concentration gradients are the fundamental motivating forces in diffusion. The most general equations for diffusion in a multicomponent alloy system are analogous to the Onsager-Fuoss equations[12] for diffusion in an electrolyte. Let J_i represent the current, in atoms per square centimeter per second, of species i relative to the crystal lattice. The currents are linearly related to the gradients of the chemical potentials:

$$J_i = -\sum_{j=1}^{n} M_{ij} \, \partial\mu_j/\partial x - M_{iV} \, \partial\mu_V/\partial x \qquad i = 1, 2, \cdots n, \tag{3.1a}$$

$$J_V = -\sum_{j=1}^{n} M_{Vj} \, \partial\mu_j/\partial x - M_{VV} \, \partial\mu_V/\partial x. \tag{3.1b}$$

The coefficients M_{ij} shall be called mobilities. The Onsager relations,[13] based on the concept of microscopic reversibility, apply to diffusion in an alloy as well as to diffusion in an electrolyte. They state that the mobilities must form a symmetric matrix, or

$$M_{ij} = M_{ji} \qquad \text{all } i, j, \tag{3.2a}$$

$$M_{iV} = M_{Vi} \qquad \text{all } i. \tag{3.2b}$$

If the diffusion process is such that the total number of lattice sites is conserved, the equations can be simplified to some extent.

[12] L. Onsager and R. M. Fuoss, *J. Phys. Chem.*, **36**, 2689 (1932).
[13] L. Onsager, *Phys. Rev.*, **37**, 405 (1931); 38, 2265 (1932).

This will be the case for diffusion via vacant lattice positions, as well as for simple exchange of neighboring atoms. The net current of sites must then vanish, or

$$J_V + \sum J_i = 0. \tag{3.3}$$

If this is to be satisfied regardless of the gradients, we must have

$$M_{Vj} = -\sum_i M_{ij}, \tag{3.4a}$$

$$M_{VV} = -\sum_i M_{iV}. \tag{3.4b}$$

Equation (3.1*b*) is superfluous and equation (3.1*a*) reduces to[14]

$$J_i = -\sum_{j=1}^{n} M_{ij}\, \partial(\mu_j - \mu_V)/\partial x. \tag{3.5}$$

The equations can be simplified further if it is assumed that the concentration of vacancies is somehow maintained in local equilibrium so that $\mu_V = 0$ everywhere. Then

$$J_i = -\sum_{j=1}^{n} M_{ij}\, \partial\mu_j/\partial x. \tag{3.6}$$

Equations of this form could be written from a phenomenological point of view without regard to the mechanism of diffusion.[5]

If there were no vacancies and atoms were constrained to lattice positions, diffusion could take place by interchange of atoms on neighboring positions or by the ring mechanism proposed by Zener.[6] Diffusion would be described by equations of the form (3.6), but there would be the additional restriction that there could be no net flow of matter relative to the lattice:

$$\sum J_i = 0. \tag{3.7}$$

On the other hand, diffusion via vacant lattice sites, with the vacancies maintained in local thermal equilibrium, leads to phenomenological equations of the most general types (3.6), in which there are no restrictions on matter flow. There could, of course, be interchange or ring mechanisms of diffusion operating in addition to the vacancy mechanism without affecting the form of the equations. The net flow of matter relative to the lattice is equal to

[14] Equations for vacancy diffusion have been given in this form by C. Herring in *The Physics of Powder Metallurgy* (W. E. Kingston, Editor), Chapter 8, McGraw-Hill Book Co., New York, 1950. See also *J. Appl. Phys.*, **21**, 437 (1950).

the negative of the vacancy current:

$$\sum_{i=1}^{n} J_i = -J_V. \tag{3.8}$$

The vacancy current will give rise to a Kirkendall effect if it is assumed, as seems reasonable, that the markers move with the lattice. The nature of the plastic flow required to maintain the vacancies in their equilibrium concentration will be discussed later (Section 5).

Equations for diffusion currents in alloys have usually been written with omission of the off-diagonal terms. In place of (3.5), we would then have

$$J_i = -M_i\,\partial(\mu_i - \mu_V)/\partial x, \tag{3.9}$$

and there would be a corresponding equation (3.6), with $\mu_V = 0$. It has been shown[7,10] that an equation of the form (3.9) can be obtained from a kinetic theory of diffusion via vacant lattice sites if certain simplifying assumptions are made. A somewhat more general derivation of this sort is given in Section 4, in which it is shown that the errors involved in the derivation which leads to (3.9) usually should be of the order of $1/Z$, where Z is the number of near neighbors of a given atom.

If the simplified equations of the form (3.9) may be used, there is a relationship, pointed out by Darken,[4] between the mobility, M_i, and the diffusion coefficient D_T, of a radioactive tracer of species i in an otherwise homogeneous alloy. The tracer, T, is considered to be one of the constituents of the alloy, and equations (3.9) reduce to the two:

$$J_i = -M_i\,\partial\mu_i/\partial x, \tag{3.10a}$$

$$J_T = -M_T\,\partial\mu_T/\partial x. \tag{3.10b}$$

Since diffusion of a radioactive tracer depends only on the concentration gradient, we may take:

$$\mu_i = kT\log(N_i/N), \tag{3.11a}$$

$$\mu_T = kT\log(N_T/N). \tag{3.11b}$$

We shall suppose that $N_T \ll N_i$. From the fact that there can be no net flow of i-type atoms, it follows that

$$J_i = -J_T, \tag{3.12}$$

and that therefore

$$M_i = (N_i/N_T)M_T. \tag{3.13}$$

The diffusion coefficient for tracer atoms, defined by the equation,

$$J_T = -D_T\,\partial N_T/\partial x, \tag{3.14}$$

is equal to

$$D_T = kTM_T/N_T. \tag{3.15}$$

It then follows from (3.13) and (3.15) that

$$M_i = N_i D_T/kT. \tag{3.16}$$

It should be emphasized that (3.16) applies only when the off-diagonal terms in (3.5) or (3.6) are sufficiently small so that the simplified equations (3.9) may be used.

While we believe that the off-diagonal terms are generally small compared to the diagonal terms,* they are not negligible even for the simplest case of self-diffusion of a radioactive tracer in a pure metal, as will be discussed below. The off-diagonal terms do not lead to a different form for the phenomenological equations for chemical diffusion in a binary alloy, but they do modify the relation between the radioactive and chemical diffusion coefficients. As examples of the use of the general equations (3.5) and (3.6), we shall first discuss self-diffusion of a radioactive tracer in a monatomic substance and then discuss chemical and radioactive diffusion in a binary alloy.

If T represents the tracer, assumed present in a very small concentration $N_T \ll N$, and A the normal atom of the lattice, equation (3.6) may be written:

$$J_A = -M_{AA}\,\partial\mu_A/\partial x - M_{AT}\,\partial\mu_T/\partial x, \tag{3.17a}$$

$$J_T = -M_{AT}\,\partial\mu_A/\partial x - M_{TT}\,\partial\mu_T/\partial x. \tag{3.17b}$$

With the introduction of the diffusion coefficients

$$D_{AA} = kTM_{AA}/N, \tag{3.18a}$$

$$D_{TT} = kTM_{TT}/N_T, \tag{3.18b}$$

$$D_{AT} = kTM_{AT}/N_T, \tag{3.18c}$$

* The off-diagonal terms may be large if diffusion occurs by interchange of neighboring atoms. If interchange of i and j type atoms contributes to diffusion, M_{ij} will be large.

and with

$$\mu_T = kT \log (N_T/N), \tag{3.19a}$$

$$\mu_A = kT \log (N - N_T)/N, \tag{3.19b}$$

equations (3.17) become

$$J_A = + (D_{AA} - D_{AT})\, \partial N_T/\partial x, \tag{3.20a}$$

$$J_T = -\left(\frac{N_T}{N} D_{AT} + D_{TT}\right) \frac{\partial N_T}{\partial x}. \tag{3.20b}$$

The term $(N_T/N)D_{AT}$ is very small, since $N_T \ll N$, and may be neglected. Since we must have $J_T = -J_A$ for diffusion of a tracer in an otherwise homogeneous substance,

$$D_T = D_{TT} = D_A - D_{AT}. \tag{3.21}$$

The coefficient D_{AA} is related to the mass diffusion coefficient for a vacancy gradient. From equations (3.5) and (3.6) it can be seen that the diffusion coefficient for vacancies is

$$D_V = kTM_{AA}/N_V \tag{3.22}$$

so that

$$D_{AA} = (N_V/N)D_V. \tag{3.23}$$

It is often assumed that D_T is equal to $(N_V/N)D_V$, but this is not a consequence of the phenomenological equations unless the cross-term D_{AT} vanishes. The usual argument runs as follows. The frequency with which a given tracer jumps to a given neighboring site is equal to the frequency with which a vacancy jumps times the probability, N_V/N, that the given neighboring site is vacant. If the successive jumps which the tracer makes were uncorrelated, as are those of the vacancies, D_T would be equal to $(N_V/N)D_V$. We show in Appendix A of this paper that successive jumps of the tracer are correlated so that this assumption is not valid. If the tracer has just made a jump to a neighboring site, leaving the original site vacant, the probability that it will make the reverse jump to the original site is more likely than that it will make jumps to other positions. In order to calculate D_T it is necessary to take the correlations into account. Calculations in Appendix A for a square planar lattice and for both body-centered and face-centered cubic lattices give:

$$D_T = 0.744 D_{AA} \quad \text{square planar}, \tag{3.24a}$$

$$D_T = 0.89 D_{AA} \quad \text{b.c. cubic}, \tag{3.24b}$$

$$D_T = 0.90 D_{AA} \quad \text{f.c. cubic}. \tag{3.24c}$$

From a phenomenological standpoint, this means that

$$D_{AT} = 0.256 D_{AA} \qquad \text{square planar,} \tag{3.25a}$$

$$D_{AT} = 0.11 D_{AA} \qquad \text{b.c. cubic,} \tag{3.25b}$$

$$D_{AT} = 0.10 D_{AA} \qquad \text{f.c. cubic.} \tag{3.25c}$$

As we would expect, the errors involved in neglecting the correlations between jumps, or in neglecting D_{AT}, are of the order of $1/Z$. Although the difference is probably of no practical consequence, it is interesting to note that neglect of the cross-terms in equation (3.6) is not strictly justified even for the simplest case.*

We next consider chemical diffusion in a binary alloy with constituents A and B. Equations (3.6) are then

$$J_A = -M_{AA}\,(\partial\mu_A/\partial x) - M_{AB}\,(\partial\mu_B/\partial x), \tag{3.26a}$$

$$J_B = -M_{AB}\,(\partial\mu_A/\partial x) - M_{BB}\,(\partial\mu_B/\partial x). \tag{3.26b}$$

With use of equation (2.10), the expressions for J_A and J_B can be written:

$$J_A = -D_A\,\partial N_A/\partial x, \tag{3.27a}$$

$$J_B = -D_B\,\partial N_B/\partial x, \tag{3.27b}$$

where the diffusion coefficients D_A and D_B are

$$D_A = \frac{d\mu_A}{d\log N_A}\left(\frac{M_{AA}}{N_A} - \frac{M_{AB}}{N_B}\right), \tag{3.28a}$$

$$D_B = \frac{d\mu_A}{d\log N_A}\left(\frac{M_{BB}}{N_B} - \frac{M_{AB}}{N_A}\right). \tag{3.28b}$$

Equations (3.27) are of the form assumed by Darken to account for the Kirkendall effect. There is no need to have $D_A = D_B$ if, as assumed, vacancies are present in local thermal equilibrium. If there are more than two components, equations (3.6) do not simplify to give a single coefficient for each component.

If a small concentration of a radioactive tracer T of atom A is present in an otherwise homogeneous alloy, we find as above that

$$D_T = kT\left(\frac{M_{AA}}{N_A} - \frac{M_{AT}}{N_T}\right). \tag{3.29}$$

* It should be noted that a cross-term of the type D_{AT} would not appear in tracer diffusion of an interstitial atom such as carbon in iron.

The relation

$$D_A = \frac{d(\mu_A/kT)}{d \log N_A} D_T \tag{3.30}$$

used by Darken follows if the cross-terms M_{AB} and M_{AT} are sufficiently small so that they can be neglected. It should be regarded as an approximate rather than an exact relation.

4. KINETIC THEORY OF DIFFUSION VIA VACANT SITES

By making certain simplifying assumptions it has been shown[15] that equations without the cross-terms of the form of equation (3.9) hold approximately for diffusion in a binary alloy. The model used implies that differences between the interaction energies of AA, AB, and BB pairs are less than the order of kT at temperatures at which the diffusion is taking place so that the A and B atoms are distributed at random. This assumption is valid for Cu-Zn and probably also for the other alloys in which the Kirkendall effect has been observed.[3] The remaining approximations made are then similar to those usually made in the calculations of self-diffusion in a monatomic substance which lead to the expression $D_T = (N_V/N)D_V$. As we have seen, a rigorous calculation shows that the errors involved amount to about 10 per cent in a cubic substance, and we believe that the errors in the calculation of the chemical diffusion coefficient are of the same order. For the case of vacancy diffusion, large differences between the radioactive and chemical diffusion coefficients in a binary alloy come from the factor $d(\mu_A/kT)/d \log N_A$ of equation (3.30) rather than from the cross-terms M_{AB} and M_{AT} which do not appear in the approximate treatment.

We shall give here a derivation which makes less restrictive assumptions about the interaction energies of neighboring pairs than the earlier derivation and which also leads to equations of the form (3.9) when appropriate approximations are made. The approximations are such that the errors should usually be no larger than the order of $1/Z$, as indicated by the rigorous calcula-

[15] See footnote 10. These assumptions have been criticized by Seitz, footnote 11, as being exceedingly restrictive. While the model used implies a random alloy with no large amount of local order, we do not believe that it is as restrictive as implied by Seitz.

tion of self-diffusion. The derivation given below for a binary alloy can be extended easily to more components.

As in the earlier paper,[10] we consider a binary alloy with constituents A and B and assume that the concentration gradient is along the x-axis. We shall determine the frequency with which A atoms jump between two neighboring crystal planes, 1 and 2, which are normal to the x-axis. We assume that an atom can jump to a neighboring site if it is vacant. Thus we must first estimate the number of A atoms on plane 1 which are adjacent to vacancies on plane 2, and the number of A atoms on plane 2 which are adjacent to vacancies on plane 1.

The probability that a particular site is occupied by an A atom, B atom, or vacancy depends on the types of atoms on neighboring sites. In Appendix B of this paper we show that the probability, p_{sA}, that a particular type of site, s, is occupied by an A atom is

$$p_{sA} = \exp\,(\mu_A + \mu_s - \epsilon_{sA})/kT, \tag{4.1}$$

with corresponding expressions for p_{sB} and p_{sV}. In these expressions, μ_A, μ_B, and μ_V are the usual chemical potentials. The value of μ_s is chosen in such a way that

$$p_{As} + p_{Bs} + p_{Vs} = 1. \tag{4.2}$$

Only differences between the ϵ's are significant. Thus $\epsilon_{sV} - \epsilon_{sA}$ represents the change in free energy when an A atom is taken from a particular s-type site, leaving a vacancy.

Let us consider an s-type site on plane 1 adjacent to a t-type site on plane 2. If the sites could be treated independently, the probability that there is an A atom on site s and a vacancy on site t would be

$$p_{sA}p_{tV} = \exp\,[(\mu_{A1} + \mu_s - \epsilon_{sA} + \mu_{V2} + \mu_t - \epsilon_{tV})/kT]. \tag{4.3}$$

Similarly, the probability of a vacancy on site s and an A atom on site t would be:

$$p_{sV}p_{tA} = \exp\,[(\mu_{V1} + \mu_s - \epsilon_{sV} + \mu_{A2} + \mu_t - \epsilon_{tA})/kT]. \tag{4.4}$$

The subscripts 1 and 2 indicate that the μ's are to be evaluated on the planes 1 and 2.

If N_{stAV} is the number of situations in which there is an A atom on an s-type site on plane 1 adjacent to a vacancy on a t-type site on plane 2, and N_{stVA} is the number of situations in which the A atom and the vacancy have changed positions, we have from the above

$$N_{stAV} = N_{stVA} \exp [(\Delta\mu_{12} - \Delta\epsilon_{st})/kT], \tag{4.5}$$

where $\Delta\mu$ is the difference in chemical potentials

$$\Delta\mu_{12} = \mu_{A1} - \mu_{V1} + \mu_{V2} - \mu_{A2} \tag{4.6}$$

and $\Delta\epsilon_{st}$ is the difference in free energy

$$\Delta\epsilon_{st} = \epsilon_{sV} - \epsilon_{tV} + \epsilon_{tA} - \epsilon_{sA}. \tag{4.7}$$

Diffusion equations of the form (3.9) rather than the more general (3.5) or (3.6) follow if (4.5) is used. Equation (4.5) is not an exact relation because the sites are not independent. First, when A and V change positions, one of the neighbors of each site is changed in addition to the change on each site itself. However, this fact alone would not make equation (4.5) invalid if $\Delta\epsilon_{st}$ is taken to be the correct change in free energy which occurs when the A atom moves from s to t. In equilibrium, with $\Delta\mu_{12} = 0$, the exact relation is

$$N_{stAV}^{(e)} = N_{stVA}^{(e)} \exp(-\Delta\epsilon_{st}/kT), \tag{4.8}$$

which is in accord with (4.5). Second, the use of $\Delta\mu_{12}$ to give the departures in numbers from equilibrium is not strictly correct even for the simplest case of self-diffusion, as the calculation in Appendix A shows. The errors involved in the use of (4.5) for an alloy would be expected to be of just the same sort as those involved in the corresponding calculation of self-diffusion in a pure metal and should be of the same order. Equation (4.5) implies that each plane normal to the diffusion direction is in equilibrium, and that equilibrium is effectively established after each jump so that the probabilities are not significantly altered by the possibility of an immediate return jump. The errors involved are of the order of the probability of the return jump compared with other possible jumps and are probably of the order of $1/Z$ in most cases, but they may be larger if the frequency of jumps of the atom present in the smaller concentration[16] is abnormally large (as may be the case for brass-copper diffusion couples).

[16] We are not concerned here with such small concentrations of a solute atom that the probability that a given vacancy has more than one solute atom as a neighbor is small. Vacancy diffusion of a solute present in small concentration has been discussed by C. Wagner, *Z. Phys. Chem.*, **B38**, 325 (1938); R. P. Johnson, *Phys. Rev.*, **56**, 814 (1939) and G. Wyllie, *Proc. Phys. Soc. (London)*, **59**, 694 (1947).

The rate of forward jumps of the A atom from an s site to a t site, as compared with reverse jumps, is given by

$$K_{s\to t} = K_{t\to s} \exp(\Delta\epsilon_{st}/kT). \tag{4.9}$$

In equilibrium, there is a balance in the flow of A atoms:

$$N_{stAV}{}^{(e)}K_{s\to t} = N_{stVA}{}^{(e)}K_{t\to s}. \tag{4.10}$$

The net rate of forward jumps of the A atom from s to t when there is a gradient in chemical potential is

$$\begin{aligned} N_{stAV}K_{s\to t} - N_{stVA}K_{t\to s} &= N_{stVA}K_{t\to s}[\exp(\Delta\mu_{12}/kT)-1] \\ &= N_{stVA}K_{t\to s}\Delta\mu_{12}/kT. \end{aligned} \tag{4.11}$$

The last follows because $\Delta\mu_{12}$ is small compared with kT. The total flow of A atoms in the forward direction is obtained by summing (4.11) over all the various types of sites on planes 1 and 2. The result is

$$J_A = -M_A\,\partial(\mu_A - \mu_V)/\partial x, \tag{4.12}$$

where

$$M_A = \lambda\sum_{s,t} N_{stVA}K_{t\to s} \tag{4.13}$$

and λ is the separation between the neighboring planes.

We have thus shown that diffusion via vacant sites leads to equations of the form (3.9) rather than the more general (3.5) or (3.6) if the approximation is made that the concentration of atoms on a particular type of site is that appropriate to the equilibrium concentration on the plane normal to the diffusion direction on which it lies.

5. SOURCES AND SINKS FOR VACANCIES

In this section we shall discuss the nature of the plastic flow required to maintain the concentration of vacancies close to the equilibrium value. A diffusion couple formed from brass and copper may be used to illustrate the nature of the problem. The flow of zinc atoms from the brass to the copper is much larger than the flow of copper atoms into the brass. According to the vacancy mechanism, there is a net flow of vacancies from the copper to the brass which balances the flow of atoms in the opposite direction [equation (3.8)]. Additional lattice sites are created on the copper side, and sites are destroyed on the brass side of the couple. According to measurements of da Silva and Mehl,[3] the increase in volume on the copper side and the decrease on the brass side of the couple take place mostly in the direction of diffusion.

A vacancy is created when an additional site is formed into which an atom moves. The site from which the atom came is then vacant, and the vacancy can wander through the crystal by adjacent atoms moving successively to the vacant site until the site finally moves to a position which corresponds to destruction of a lattice site. Sites which can act as sources or sinks for vacancies are at the surface, at grain boundaries, at pores, and at dislocations. We shall be concerned mainly with the last. When a dislocation line moves out of its slip plane, sites are created or destroyed.

In order to have grain boundaries maintain the vacancies in substantial equilibrium it would be necessary to have the grain size smaller than the distances over which diffusion takes place. It is not certain whether or not this has been the case in the experiments which have been performed. We shall show below that dislocations are probably sufficient so that we would expect a Kirkendall effect in single crystals.

A vacancy will exist an average lifetime τ before it is destroyed, and in equilibrium the number created per second, $N_V^{(e)}/\tau$, is equal to the number which disappear. The concentration of vacancies will be near an equilibrium value during diffusion if the average distance, l_V, a vacancy diffuses during its lifetime is short compared with the distance over which diffusion is taking place in the alloy. Let ν be the number of elementary jumps of distance λ a vacancy makes during its lifetime so that

$$l_V = \nu^{1/2}\lambda.$$

With $\lambda \sim 3 \times 10^{-8}$ cm, we must have $\nu < 10^9$ in order to have $l_V < 10^{-3}$ cm. It is estimated that there are of the order of 10^8 dislocation lines per cm^2 in a well-annealed specimen, which means that about one site in 10^7 lies on a dislocation line. All that we require, then, is that a vacancy disappear about once in a hundred times it meets a dislocation line. Even if only special sites, such as steps in a dislocation line, can act as sources and sinks, it appears that there is ample opportunity for dislocations to maintain the vacancies in equilibrium. We shall see below that the concentration of vacancies which is in equilibrium with the dislocations often, and perhaps usually, does not differ appreciably from that which would be in equilibrium with the outer surface.

The situation is probably even more favorable than is indicated by the foregoing because there is undoubtedly an attractive force between dislocations and vacancies which makes the concentration of vacancies in the vicinity of dislocation lines higher than normal. A higher concentration would enhance vacancy diffusion in a cold-worked alloy with a high density of dislocation lines.

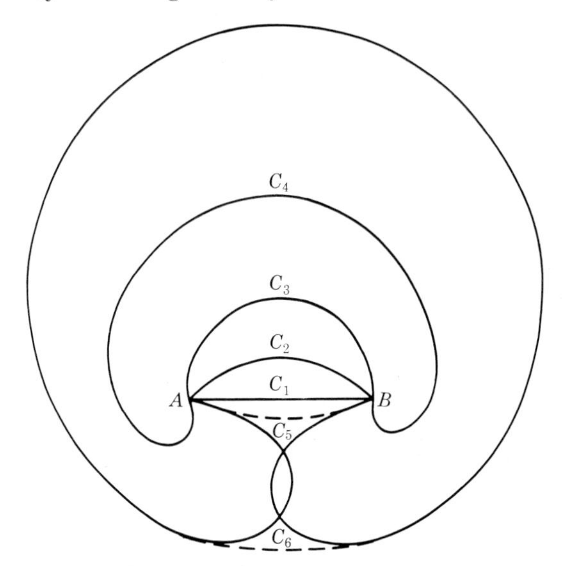

FIG. 1. Creation of a dislocation ring from an edge type dislocation which is relatively fixed at points A and B and which has a slip plane normal to the sheet. There is an extra plane of atoms below the line AC_1B, and this extra plane grows, by creation of vacancies in neighboring planes, by the successive steps AC_1B, AC_2B, ... When the loops meet near C_5 and C_6 they rejoin to form the outer dislocation ring at C_6 and the line AC_5B. The line AC_5B then moves upward to create another dislocation ring.

In order to have a large amount of plastic flow take place, it is necessary to have some mechanism whereby dislocations can be generated. It has been suggested[17] that the mechanism is analogous to those proposed by Frank[18] for crystal growth and by Frank and Read[19] for the generation of dislocations in a slip plane. Let A and B of Fig. 1 represent points at which the dislocation

[17] W. Shockley, private communication; F. Seitz, *Phys. Rev.*, **79**, 1002 (1950).

[18] F. C. Frank, *Discussions of the Faraday Society*, **5**, 67 (1949).

[19] F. C. Frank and W. T. Read, Jr., *Phys. Rev.*, **79**, 722 (1950).

line AB is relatively fixed. It is supposed that the slip plane is normal to the plane shown so that motion in the plane requires creation or destruction of lattice sites. To be specific, let us suppose that there is one more plane of atoms below the line AB in the figure than above. Creation of vacancies by adding additional sites would then move the line AB upward to AC_1B, AC_2B, etc. Similarly, loss of vacancies would move the dislocation line down. Successive steps in the growth of the extra plane are shown. When the loops cross near C_5 and C_6 the lines break and rejoin as shown by the dotted lines. The line AC_5B returns to AC_1B, and there is an extra plane of atoms outlined by the dislocation ring which joins at C_6. As long as it remains in a region in which there is a deficiency of vacancies, this ring will grow indefinitely and add a plane of atoms to the crystals. A single line of the type AB can catalyze the growth of an indefinite number of planes. In a similar way, if there is an excess of vacancies, the line AB will move down and out, and eventually form a ring dislocation which represents a missing plane of atoms. Growth of the ring will remove a plane of atoms from the crystal.

In order to have a dislocation line continue to move, it is necessary to have the gain in free energy from the creation (or loss) of vacancies numerically larger than the increase in energy of the dislocation line. In the analogous problem of slip, a dislocation line of length L can act as a source of dislocation rings if the applied stress, S, is greater than about*

$$Gb/L,$$

where G is shear modulus and b is the Burgers vector. A motion of a dislocation line a distance δX in response to a stress S gives a gain in free energy of $S\delta X$ per unit length of line.[20] The corresponding energy when vacancies are created is the chemical potential, μ_V, multiplied by the number of vacancies per unit length, $\delta Xb/\Omega_0$, in which Ω_0 is the atomic volume. Comparing these two expressions, we see that a chemical potential μ_V is equivalent to an isotropic stress,

$$S = \mu_V/\Omega_0.$$

* See, for example, Paper 6 of this book, by N. F. Mott.

[20] M. Peach and J. S. Koehler, *Phys. Rev.*, **80**, 436 (1950).

The criterion for the creation of dislocation rings in our case is, therefore,

$$|\mu_V| > Gb\Omega_0/L,$$

or, using (2.6),

$$|\log (N_V/N_V{}^{(e)})| > Gb\Omega_0/kTL.$$

Reasonable values for the quantities on the right are

$$G \sim 5 \times 10^{11} \qquad b \sim 2 \times 10^{-8} \qquad \Omega_0 \sim 10^{-23},$$
$$kT \sim 10^{-13}, \qquad L \sim 10^{-4},$$

which give

$$|\log (N_V/N_V{}^{(e)})| > 10^{-2}.$$

Thus a departure from the normal equilibrium concentration of the order of one part in a hundred is sufficient to have a dislocation line of length 10^{-4} cm act as a source of dislocation rings. A departure of this order corresponds to a value of μ_V of the order of $10^{-2}kT$, and this is negligible compared with the driving force of the diffusion process, which is the change in μ_A or μ_B across the diffusion region.[21]

In close-packed metals it is likely that most of the dislocations present form pairs of partial dislocations, in the manner described by Heidenreich and Shockley.[22] These partial dislocations cannot move out of their slip plane without creating a sizable surface energy of misfit. If the number of other more suitable types is sufficiently small, μ_V may become much larger than the estimate we have given above. The formation of pores in dezincification of brass suggests that μ_V may become large under suitable conditions. Da Silva and Mehl[3] have observed that some pores are formed in the diffusion couples used in the study of the Kirkendall effect, but that their volume is a small fraction of that of the material transported. We may therefore conclude that in their

[21] Although this argument indicates that μ_V can be assumed to have the equilibrium value zero in the Kirkendall experiment, its departure from zero cannot be ignored in sintering processes, where chemical potentials of the order of 10^{-4} kT may be important. In fact, it has been suggested in footnote 14 that dislocations may have almost no effect on μ_V in most sintering experiments.

[22] R. D. Heidenreich and W. Shockley, *Report of a Conference on the Strength of Solids*, University of Bristol, England, Physical Society, London, 1948.

case most of the vacancies transported were taken up by some sort of dislocations.

An experiment of da Silva and Mehl[3] with markers placed parallel to the diffusion direction showed that there was little or no lateral change in dimension in a brass-copper couple. This indicates a preferential growth of planes oriented normal to the diffusion direction. A possible explanation based on the model

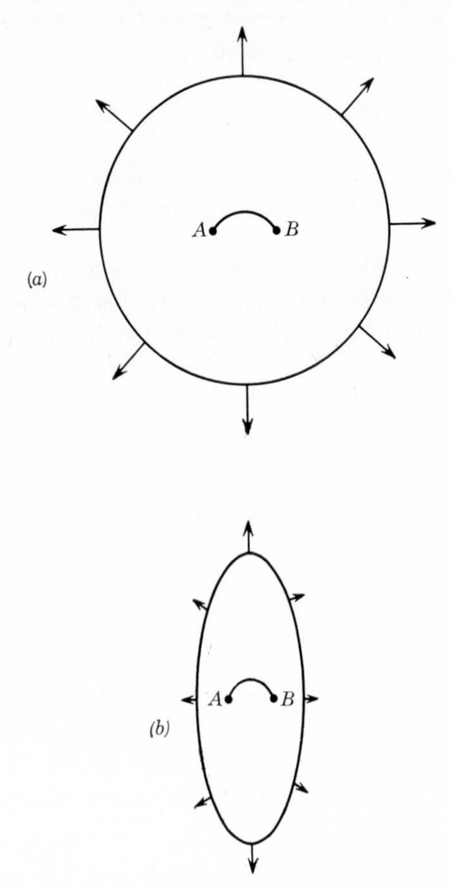

Fig. 2. Possible explanation for more rapid growth of planes normal to the diffusion direction, as in (*a*), than in the parallel direction, as in (*b*). In (*a*) the dislocation ring can grow in all directions without leaving the region of rapid diffusion, where there is an unbalance of vacancies. In (*b*) the ring can grow indefinitely in the lateral direction, but growth is limited in the parallel direction to the region of rapid diffusion.

proposed above is illustrated by Fig. 2. A dislocation ring in a plane normal to the diffusion direction, as in Fig. 2*a*, can grow in all directions without running out of the region of rapid diffusion where there is an unbalance of vacancies. A plane oriented parallel to the diffusion direction, as in Fig. 2*b*, can grow in the lateral direction, but will soon grow out of the region of vacancy unbalance in the parallel direction and will take on an elongated shape. We would expect the growth of such a ring to be much slower than the growth of one which can grow in all directions.

APPENDIX A

Relation of the Diffusion Coefficients for a Tracer and for Mass Transport

We wish to compute the amount by which the diffusion coefficient D_T for a tracer isotope in a single-component substance differs from the value D_{AA} given by equation (3.23). Their ratio can be calculated by comparing the mean-square distances traversed in Brownian motion by a vacancy and a tracer atom, respectively. Explicitly,

$$f \equiv D_T/D_{AA} = \lim_{\nu \to \infty} \left[\left| \sum_1^\nu \mathbf{t}_j \right|^2_{\text{av.}} / \nu t^2 \right], \tag{A.1}$$

where $\mathbf{t}_j$ is the vector, assumed always of length t, describing the jth jump of a particular tracer atom, and where in the average each possible sequence of jumps is to be weighted with its correct probability. Now for vacancy diffusion the tracer atom will jump only when there is a vacancy next to it; if this vacancy is the same vacancy that has been instrumental in some previous jump, the new jump and the previous jump will be statistically correlated, otherwise not. If the density of vacancies is low we can assume that the return influence of each vacancy has degenerated to a random one before the position of the tracer has been appreciably affected by other vacancies, and so write

$$\left| \sum_1^\nu \mathbf{t}_j \right|^2_{\text{av.}} = \nu t^2 + \sum_{j \neq k} (\mathbf{t}_j \cdot \mathbf{t}_k)_{\text{av.}}$$

$$\begin{aligned} f &= 1 + (2/t^2) \sum_{j=2}^{\infty} (\mathbf{t}_1 \cdot \mathbf{t}_j)_{\text{av.}} \\ &= 1 + \theta_1 P_r + \theta_2 P_r^2 + \cdots, \end{aligned} \tag{A.2}$$

where P_r is the probability that a vacancy which starts from a particular lattice site s will at some future time return to that site; θ_1 is the mean cosine of the angle between the first-jump vector $\mathbf{t}_1$ of the tracer atom and the second-jump vector $\mathbf{t}_2$, for those cases where the second jump is caused by the same vacancy as the first jump; θ_2 is the mean cosine of the angle between $\mathbf{t}_1$ and the third-jump vector $\mathbf{t}_2$, for those cases where $\mathbf{t}_1$, $\mathbf{t}_2$, and $\mathbf{t}_3$ are all due to the same vacancy, etc.

Although our principal interest is in cubic crystals, it is instructive at this point to examine these equations briefly for the one- and two-dimensional cases, cases which might be approximated by noncubic crystals in which vacancy diffusion occurs primarily along strings of atoms in the lattice, or along layers in a layer lattice. It is easy to see that in both these cases $P_r = 1$, since as the time $\tau \rightarrow \infty$ the probability of finding the vacancy on a given lattice site near the starting point goes as $\tau^{\frac{1}{2}}$ or as τ^{-1}, respectively, so that its time integral diverges. In the one-dimensional case $\theta_1 = -1$, $\theta_2 = +1$, $\theta_3 = -1$, etc., and equation (A.2) fails to converge; for this case the approximations in (A.2) are not valid, but it is easy to see that as $\nu \rightarrow \infty$, $\Sigma\, \mathbf{t}_j/\nu \rightarrow 0$, since successive $\mathbf{t}_j$'s are equal and opposite. Thus $f = 0$ for this case; vacancy diffusion can cause transport of matter but cannot contribute appreciably to mixing of a tracer isotope. The two-dimensional case, on the other hand, illustrates most of the features encountered in three dimensions, and requires detailed calculations.

It is easy to see that $\theta_1, \theta_2, \cdots$ can be computed if for each of the nearest neighbors s of the starting point in the migration of a particular vacancy the probability p_s of return from that direction is known. For the simple case of a plane quadratic lattice, illustrated in Fig. 3a, we have, if the first jump was to neighbor 1,

$$\theta_1 = p_3 - p_1, \tag{A.3}$$

$$\theta_2 = p_3^{(2)} - p_1^{(2)} = p_1^2 - 2p_1p_3 + p_3^2 = \theta_1^2, \tag{A.4}$$

$$\theta_3 = p_3^{(3)} = p_1^{(3)} = p_3^3 + 3p_1^2p_3 + 6p_1p_2^2 + 2p_3p_2^2 + 4p_1p_2p_3, \tag{A.5}$$

etc.,

where $p_s^{(2)}$ is the probability that the third jump of the tracer atom is in the direction of the vector from s to the origin, given that the first was from the direction 1 to the origin, and $p_s^{(3)}$ is similarly defined for the fourth jump.

The quantities p_s can in principle be calculated by following up all possible trajectories of a migrating vacancy; however, this involves summing an infinite series which does not converge very

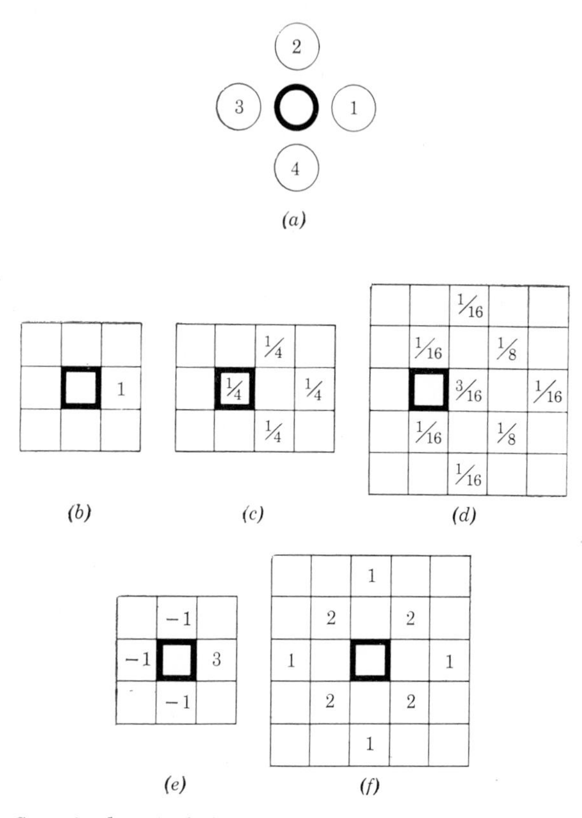

FIG. 3. Steps in the calculation of the relative probabilities for the various directions from which a migrating vacancy can return to its starting point, for the plane quadratic lattice. (*a*) Labeling of positions neighboring the starting point. (*b*), (*c*), (*d*). Successive probability distributions for position of vacancy. (*e*) Probability distribution obtained by subtracting a symmetrical distribution from 4 times (*b*). (*f*) The matrix $T(\mathbf{j} - 1)$ of equation (A.7).

rapidly. The following device, suggested by J. W. Tukey, makes it possible to deal with a more rapidly convergent series, and, if desired, we may apply the Markoff method to the present problem. We note that the problem can be formulated as one of diffusion of probability, as in Fig. 3*b*, *c*, and *d*. If we start counting jumps after the vacancy has jumped from the origin to position 1, its starting probability distribution will be as shown in Fig. 3*b*. After the next jump its probability distribution will be as shown in Fig. 3*c*. The 1/4 at the origin is a contribution 1/4 to p_1, 0 to p_2, p_3, and p_4, since it has come from position 1. Since for θ_1 we are interested only in the *first* return of the vacancy to the origin, we must exclude this 1/4 of the cases in computing the probabilities of later jumps to the origin; we therefore replace this 1/4 at the origin position by 0 and compute the probability distribution after the next jump, which looks as shown in Fig. 3*d*. Continuation of this procedure gives

$$p_s = (1/4) \sum_{\nu=0}^{\infty} (\text{probability site } s \text{ is occupied after } \nu\text{-th jump}),$$

all probabilities at the origin being replaced by 0 after each jump. Now the quantity in parentheses is a linear function of the initial probability distribution. We know by symmetry that, if the initial distribution had had 1/4 on each of the positions 1, 2, 3, 4, instead of on 1 above, each p_s would be 1/4. By subtraction, therefore,

$$p_s = 1/4 + (1/16) \sum_{\nu=0}^{\infty} w_s^{(\nu)}, \tag{A.6}$$

where $w_s^{(\nu)}$ is the probability of occupation of site s after ν jumps, starting from the initial distribution shown in Fig. 3*e*. We can now drop the proviso that the probability at the origin be replaced by 0 after each jump, since the probability at the origin will always be 0 anyway. Equation (A.6) can now be evaluated by the Markoff method, or by direct computation of the $w_s^{(\nu)}$. The latter quantities will decrease rapidly with increasing ν because of the presence of both negative and positive probabilities in the initial distribution.

Several further devices, also suggested by J. W. Tukey, simplify the problem further. It is easily seen by referring to Fig. 3 that, when ν is odd, $w_s^{(\nu)}$ vanishes for the positions $s = 1, 2, 3, 4$ in which we are interested; moreover, for any lattice point j

$$w_j^{(2k+2)} = \sum_l [(1/16)\, T_{jl} + (1/4)\delta_{jl}] w_l^{(2k)}, \tag{A.7}$$

where T_{jl} is a function of the difference $(\mathbf{j} - \mathbf{l})$ between the lattice vectors of points j and l, whose values are shown in Fig. 3*f*.

Thus, symbolically,

$$p_s = 1/4 + (1/16) \sum_{k=0}^{\infty} \left(\frac{T+4}{16}\right)^k w^{(0)} \qquad \text{(evaluated at point } s\text{)},$$

$$\sum_{k=0}^{\infty} \left(\frac{T+4}{16}\right)^k = \frac{1}{1 - \dfrac{(T+4)}{16}} = \frac{16}{12 - T} = \frac{4}{3} \sum_{k=0}^{\infty} \left(\frac{T}{12}\right)^k,$$

whence

$$p_s = 1/4 + (1/12) \sum_{k=0}^{\infty} \left(\frac{T}{12}\right)^k w^{(0)} \quad \text{(evaluated at point } s\text{)}. \qquad \text{(A.8)}$$

The results of calculations with equation (A.8) are shown in the following table:

s	$w_s^{(0)}$	$\left(\frac{T}{12}\right) w_s^{(0)}$	$\left(\frac{T}{12}\right)^2 w_s^{(0)}$	$\left(\frac{T}{12}\right)^3 w_s^{(0)}$	$\left(\frac{T}{12}\right)^4 w_s^{(0)}$	$\left(\frac{T}{12}\right)^5 w_s^{(0)}$	p_s
1	3	−0.416	+0.250	−0.0052	+0.0445	+0.0153	0.490
2 or 4	−1	+0.250	−0.083	+0.0226	−0.0087	+0.0019	0.182
3	−1	−0.083	−0.083	−0.0399	−0.0272	−0.0187	0.146

The third figure in the p_s values is somewhat uncertain. Using these in equations (A.3), (A.4), and (A.5), we have

$$\theta_1 = -0.342,$$

$$\theta_2 = +0.118 = \theta_1^2,$$

$$\theta_3 = -.041.$$

Note that θ_3, though not identically equal to θ_1^3, is equal to it to within 1 or 2 per cent. It seems reasonable to assume that $\theta_m = \theta_1^m$ in this and future cases, whence by equation (A.2)

$$f \approx \frac{1}{1 - \theta_1 P_r} \qquad \text{(A.9)}$$

$$f_{\text{sq}} = \frac{1}{1 - \theta_1} = 0.744, \text{ in the present example.} \qquad \text{(A.10)}$$

Consider next the cubic lattices. We shall assume equation (A.9) to be valid and compute only the quantity $\theta_1 P_r$. We have, for any crystal structure in which all positions are equivalent,

$$P_r \theta_1 = \sum_s p(s,1) \cos \theta(s,1),$$

where $p(s,j)$ is the probability that a vacancy starting from position j, neighboring the origin, returns to the origin for the first time from the direction of the sth neighboring site, and where $\theta(s,j)$ is the angle between the vector (origin $\rightarrow j$) and the vector ($s \rightarrow$ origin). Now $p(s,j)$ and $\theta(s,j)$ are symmetrical in s and j, so that, if Z is the number of nearest neighbors of any given lattice site,

$$P_r\theta_1 = \sum_s p(1,s) \cos \theta(s,1) = \frac{1}{Z} \sum_{\nu=0}^{\infty} W_1^{(\nu)}, \qquad \text{(A.11)}$$

where $W_s^{(\nu)}$ is the occupation probability of the sth lattice site after ν jumps, given that the initial probabilities were $W_s^{(0)} = \cos \theta(s,1)$ on the sites neighboring the origin; zero elsewhere. The requirement that the probability at the origin site be erased after each jump, so that only *first* returns are counted, can be dropped here for the same reason as in the preceding example, since $W_0^{(\nu)} = 0$ identically.

For the body-centered cubic lattice $W_1^{(\nu)}$ vanishes for odd values of ν, and remembering that $Z = 8$, we have the matrix equation

$$W^{(2k)} = \frac{T}{64} W^{(2k-2)} = \left(\frac{T}{64}\right)^k W^{(0)}, \qquad \text{(A.12)}$$

where T_{ij} is a function of the vector displacement $(\mathbf{i} - \mathbf{j})$ from lattice site i to site j, given by

$(\mathbf{i} - \mathbf{j})/a$	T_{ij}
(000)	8
(100), etc.	4
(110), etc.	2
(111), etc.	1
other values	0

The matrices T^k for values of k up to 5 were evaluated by lattice summations, and applied to $W^{(0)}$. With neglect of the contributions to (A.11) from $k \geq 6$ ($\nu \geq 12$), the result is

$$P_r\theta_1 = -0.124, \qquad \text{(A.13)}$$

the error being probably of the order of one or two units in the third decimal place. Inserting this into (A.9) gives finally

$$f_{\text{bcc}} = 0.889. \qquad \text{(A.14)}$$

For the face-centered cubic lattice both odd and even values of ν

contribute to (A.11), and with $Z = 12$, we have

$$W^{(\nu)} = \left(\frac{T}{12}\right)^{\nu} W^{(0)}, \tag{A.15}$$

with T given by

$(\mathbf{i} - \mathbf{j})/a$	T_{ij}
(000)	0
$(\frac{1}{2}\ \frac{1}{2}\ 0)$, etc.	1
other values	0

The matrices T^{ν} were evaluated by direct summation for ν up to 6, and applied to $W^{(0)}$. Neglecting contributions to (A.11) from $\nu \geq 7$, we have

$$P_r\theta_1 = -0.109, \tag{A.16}$$

the error being again of the order of one or two units in the last place. Insertion into equation (A.9) gives

$$f_{\text{fcc}} = 0.902. \tag{A.17}$$

APPENDIX B

Distribution of Atoms in Multicomponent Systems

The probability that a given site in a multicomponent system is occupied by a given type of atom or is vacant depends on the types of atoms on neighboring sites. We may classify different types of sites according to the distribution of neighbors and designate a typical class of sites by the subscript s. We suppose that there are N_s sites of type s, of which N_{si} are occupied by atoms of type i. One of the types of atoms may be a vacancy.

In thermal equilibrium the free energy must be invariant for small changes in the distribution of atoms among the different types of sites. The change in free energy resulting from such a redistribution may be expressed in the form

$$\Delta G = \sum_{s,i} \mu_{si}\, \Delta N_{si}, \tag{B.1}$$

where ΔN_{si} is the change in number of i atoms on sites of type s. The chemical potentials for sites of type s are defined by

$$\mu_{si} = \epsilon_{si} + kT \log p_{si}, \tag{B.2}$$

where

$$p_{si} = N_{si}/N_s$$

is the probability that an s-type site is occupied by an i-type atom. Only differences between the ϵ's are significant. Thus $\epsilon_{si} - \epsilon_{sj}$ represents the change in free energy when a j atom is taken from a particular s site and is replaced by an i atom. The second terms on the right of equation (B.2) represent entropy changes from the changes in numbers of i atoms on s sites.

The ΔN_{si} are subject to the conditions

$$\sum_s \Delta N_{si} = \Delta N_i \qquad \text{all } i, \tag{B.3a}$$

$$\sum_i \Delta N_{si} = 0 \qquad \text{all } s. \tag{B.3b}$$

The first equation gives the total change, ΔN_i in i atoms as the sum of changes over different types of sites, and the second equation implies that s sites are either occupied or vacant.

The auxiliary conditions may be taken into account in the usual way by multiplying (B.3a) and (B.3b) by the Lagrangian multipliers μ_i and μ_s and adding the resulting equations to (B.1). When the coefficients of the ΔN's are set equal to zero, we find

$$\mu_{si} = \mu_i + \mu_s, \tag{B.4a}$$

$$\Delta G = \sum \mu_i \, \Delta N_i. \tag{B.4b}$$

Equation (B.4b) shows that μ_i is the usual chemical potential for component i.

From (B.2) and (B.4a), we find the following expression for the probability that an s-type site is occupied by an i-type atom:

$$p_{si} = \exp\left[(\mu_i + \mu_s - \epsilon_{si})/kT\right]. \tag{B.5}$$

The value of μ_s is obtained from the requirement that

$$\sum_i p_{si} = 1. \tag{B.6}$$

11.

Theory of Diffusion*

CLARENCE ZENER†

Institute for the Study of Metals, University of Chicago

ABSTRACT

It is herein demonstrated that the magnitude of D_0 for chemical diffusion indicates whether the elementary act of diffusion occurs homogeneously throughout the matrix or is confined to short-circuiting paths arising from imperfections. This demonstration is based upon the essential positive sign of the entropy of activation. The frequently found abnormally low D_0 in chemical diffusion is attributed to short-circuiting diffusion paths either along grain boundaries or along a continuous network of the solute atoms. Conditions are described under which D_0 should have a normal order of magnitude.

1. THE FUNDAMENTAL DIFFUSION EQUATION

Atomic diffusion in solids usually refers to a net flux of atoms of one species induced by a concentration gradient of this particular species. This net flux is directly proportional to the concentration gradient, at least for those concentration gradients of the order of magnitude encountered in the laboratory. The mathematical representation of this proportionality,

$$J = D \text{ gradient } n, \tag{1.1}$$

(J = flux of atoms in $\text{cm}^{-2}\ \text{sec}^{-1}$, n = number of atoms per cm^3) is known as Fick's law. The constant proportionality D is known as the diffusion coefficient.

* This research was supported in part by the Office of Naval Research under Contract 6-ori-20-IV, NR 019 302. Portions of this report were published in the April, 1951, issue of the *Journal of Applied Physics* and are reproduced here by permission of the editor.

† Present address: Research Laboratory, Westinghouse Electric Corp., East Pittsburgh.

The purpose of most of the experimental work upon diffusion has been the determination of the diffusion coefficient D and its dependence upon temperature and other variables. Aside from a few exceptions, the diffusion coefficient is found to vary with temperature in the manner

$$D(T) = D_0 e^{-H/RT} \tag{1.2}$$

throughout the temperature range of the experiments. Here R is the gas constant (1.96 calories mole^{-1} degree^{-1}), and H is the enthalpy of activation, commonly called the *heat of activation* or the *energy of activation*. The diffusion coefficient of a single atomic species in a solid of a given composition is thus completely specified throughout a wide temperature range by the two parameters H and D_0. An exhaustive review of the experimental data has been given by Smithels.[1]

The original Fick's law (1.1) may be generalized along several directions. The diffusion coefficient D is a scalar only in isotropic materials or in crystals with cubic symmetry. In crystals with noncubic symmetry, such as zinc, D must be a tensor.

If a solid contains more than one type of solute atom, a flux of atomic species No. 1 may be induced by a gradient in the concentration of atomic species No. 2. The law (1.1) must thus be generalized to

$$J_i = \sum_j D_{ij} \operatorname{grad} n_j. \tag{1.3}$$

The relations which must exist between the components D_{ij} have been discussed by Onsager.[2]

The fundamental diffusion equation as written in (1.1) carries the connotation that the driving force for diffusion is furnished by a gradient in concentration. This connotation is of course not strictly correct. The actual driving force is the gradient of the chemical potential μ. This chemical potential may be constant even though the concentration gradient is nonvanishing. Equation (1.1) may thus be generalized to

$$J = K \operatorname{grad} \mu. \tag{1.4}$$

It is through this generalization of Fick's law that we obtain a relationship between the diffusion coefficients of ions and their mobility coefficients.[3]

A flux of a particular atomic species may be produced not only by a gradient in chemical potential, but also by a gradient in temperature. Such thermally induced diffusion is known as thermal diffusion, or as the Soret effect. A review of this effect has recently been presented by De Groot.[4]

In view of the recent extensive review of diffusion given by le Claire,[5] the foregoing generalizations will not be discussed in this paper. Rather, we shall be concerned exclusively with the atomic mechanism of diffusion. It is upon this particular aspect of diffusion that there have been the greatest differences of opinion. The passage from a particular atomic model to the diffusion coefficient D involves a certain amount of statistical mechanics. Fortunately, the general statistical mechanical reasoning is essentially independent of the assumed mechanism. For this reason the statistical mechanics is discussed in Section 2, before particular atomic mechanisms are taken up.

2. STATISTICAL MECHANICS

The interpretation of diffusion as an example of a random walk phenomenon was given many years ago. An elegant method of demonstrating this correlation was given by Rayleigh.[6] We adopt the crystalline model, where the atomic planes are fixed. For simplicity we shall consider that the concentration gradient is along one of the principal axes of the crystal, and shall take this axis as parallel to the x coordinate axis. We further assume that each elementary act of diffusion consists in a jump forward or backward along the x-axis by an amount Δx, a forward or backward jump having equal probability. The mean time between jumps will be denoted by τ. Following Rayleigh, we then denote by $f(t,x)$ the number of diffusing atoms at time t on a plane of unit area passing through x. The model above then gives for the increment of $f(t,x)$ in the time interval δt, where $\delta t \ll \tau$,

$$f(t + \delta t,x) - f(t,x) = (\delta t/2\tau)\{f(t,x - \Delta x) - 2f(t,x) + f(t,x + \Delta x)\}. \quad (2.1)$$

If we now specify that f change only very slowly over a distance Δx, the foregoing difference equation reduces to

$$\frac{\partial f}{\partial t} = D\frac{\partial^2 f}{\partial x^2}, \quad (2.2)$$

with

$$D = (\Delta x)^2/2\tau. \quad (2.3)$$

This is the standard differential equation for diffusion when D is a constant. Thus, by applying the equation of continuity to equation (1.1), we obtain

$$\frac{\partial n}{\partial t} = Div \quad (D \text{ gradient } n). \tag{2.4}$$

This treatment may be readily generalized to the case where different jump lengths are possible.[7] Thus let Γ_i be the rate at which

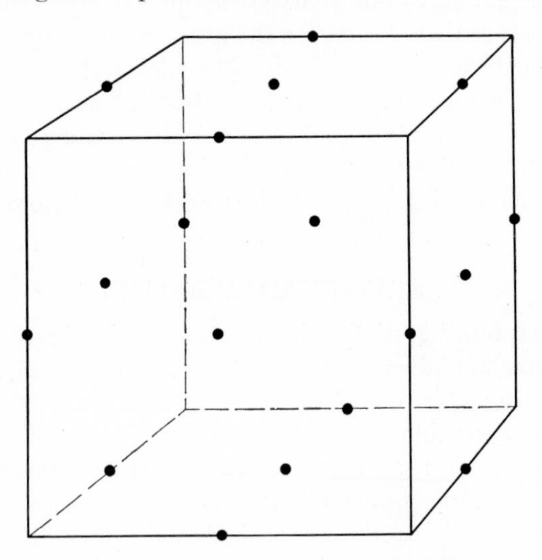

Fig. 1. Interstitial positions in a body-centered cubic lattice.

an atom makes a particular jump i associated with the change Δx_i in the x coordinate. If we then assume that for each Δx_i a second jump type is possible associated with the change $-\Delta x_i$, we obtain

$$D = \tfrac{1}{2}\sum_i \Gamma_i \, \Delta x_i^2. \tag{2.5}$$

One type of solid diffusion in which we may be quite certain that the crystalline model is strictly applicable is the diffusion of solute atoms which dissolve interstitially, a well-studied example of which is carbon in the body-centered cubic (b.c.c.) phase of iron. As shown in Fig. 1, the interstitial positions are at the centers of the faces and edges of the unit cubes. Each interstitial position is coplanar with its four nearest neighboring interstitial positions. We observe that in a given plane normal to the x-axis only two-thirds of the carbon atoms can jump forward or backward along the x-axis. Of these atoms, the probability of a forward jump is 1/4, of a backward jump 1/4, and the probability that a jump leaves the x coordinate unchanged is 1/2. The difference equation analogous to (2.1) is, therefore,

$$f(t + \delta t,x) - f(t,x) =$$
$$(2/3)(1/4)\left\{f\left(t,x+\frac{a}{2}\right)-2f(t,x)+f\left(t,x-\frac{a}{2}\right)\right\}(\delta t/\tau), \quad (2.6)$$

and we are led to

$$D = a^2/(24\tau). \quad (2.7)$$

The computation of the mean time-of-stay τ is a simple exercise in the application of statistical mechanics to rate processes. The

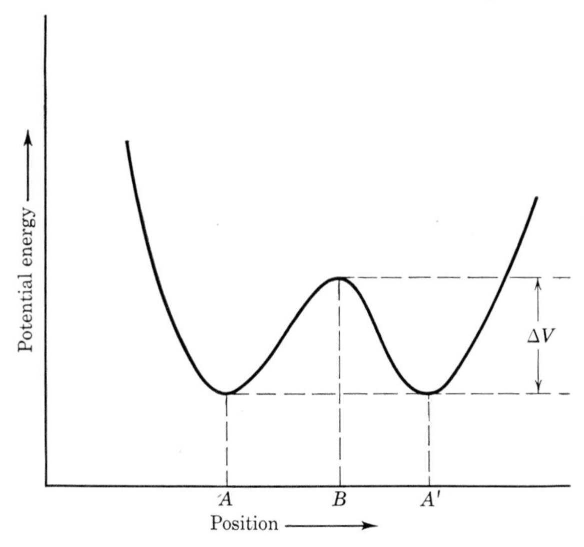

FIG. 2. Illustration of potential energy barrier in diffusion.

wide diversity[5] of formulae which have been proposed for the diffusion coefficient is, however, evidence of a widespread lack of appreciation of the fundamental factors which enter into rate processes. For this reason it appears proper to discuss these factors in some detail.

We shall start this discussion with the simplest possible example, that of a particle in a fixed potential energy field with two identical minima, as in Fig. 2, the particle being in thermal equilibrium with a temperature bath, and being constrained to move in one dimension. We shall seek the rate R at which the particle passes over the potential energy barrier at B from left to right. Quantum effects will at first be neglected. Then

$$R = \bar{v}_x P_B, \tag{2.8}$$

where $P_B\, \delta x$ is the probability that the particle be in the interval δx at B, and where $\bar{v}_x$ is the "positive" velocity average

$$\bar{v}_x = \int_0^\infty v_x f(v_x)\, dv_x \Big/ \int_{-\infty}^\infty f(v_x)\, dv_x, \tag{2.9}$$

$f(v_x)$ being the distribution function for v_x. In the particular case where the height of the barrier, ΔV, is so large compared with kT that during only a very small fraction of the time is the particle outside the essentially quadratic potential near one of the two minima, P_B assumes the form

$$P_B = (2\pi m/kT)^{1/2} P_A \nu e^{-\Delta V/kT}. \tag{2.10}$$

Here ν is the frequency of vibration at a minimum, P_A is the probability that the particle be in the trough A, namely 1/2. We find further that

$$\bar{v}_x = (kT/2\pi m)^{1/2}. \tag{2.11}$$

Substitution of these expressions for P_B and $\bar{v}_x$ into (2.8) gives

$$R = P_A \nu e^{-\Delta V/kT}. \tag{2.12}$$

This expression may be given a very simple interpretation. It is the product of the probability that the particle be in the A trough times the number of times per second that the particle attempts to surmount the barrier times the chance of success of each attempt.

Two modifications are introduced by quantum mechanics. First, equation (2.8) cannot be strictly valid since both velocity and position are specified to some extent. Wigner[8] has shown that the first-order quantum effect is given by the factor $1 + (h\nu'/kT)^2/12$, where ν' would be the frequency of vibration of the particle in a potential energy trough having a curvature of the same magnitude but of opposite sign to that of the potential barrier at B. Second, the first-order quantum correction to the partition function at the potential energy trough introduces a factor $1 - (h\nu/kT)^2/24$. For those temperatures at which the rate R is appreciable, these quantum factors are negligible except possibly for the diffusion of hydrogen.

Under certain conditions the coefficient of P_A in (2.12) is the rate Γ at which the particle leaves the trough A. These conditions are that the interaction of the particle with the temperature bath is so weak that the chance is only very small that such interaction will reverse the velocity of the particle while it is on the potential energy barrier. The theory of the opposite extreme case, where the velocity is reversed many times, has been developed by Chandrasekhar.[9] In the absence of positive evidence to the contrary, it appears best to assume the simpler of the two extreme cases, and so obtain

$$\Gamma = \nu e^{-\Delta V/kT}. \tag{2.13}$$

We shall now investigate the changes which are introduced by a relaxation of our original assumptions regarding a fixed potential energy and a constraint imposing one dimensional motion. In computing the probability $P_B\,\delta x$ we must now consider the partition functions associated with the motion of the particle in a plane transverse to its path over the potential energy barrier, as well as the partition function of the surrounding lattice. The same equations are then obtained as before,[10,11] except that our previous ΔV, representing an increment in potential energy, now becomes replaced by ΔG, representing an increment in the Gibbs free energy. The precise definition of ΔG is obtained as follows. We consider that the particle is constrained to move in a plane normal to the path over the potential energy barrier, as illustrated in Fig. 3. If we now slowly move the position of this plane, so slowly that the surrounding lattice is always in equilibrium with a temperature bath, then the work done in moving the plane is the increment in the Gibbs free energy of the system. In particular, ΔG is the work done in moving the plane from the position of minimum G to the position of maximum G. In most cases there will be more than one path along which the particle can escape from a given equilibrium position, all having the same ΔG. The rate Γ_i refers to one particular path. Equation (2.13) must thus be replaced by

$$\Gamma_i = \nu e^{-\Delta G/kT}. \tag{2.14}$$

The *heat of activation* for diffusion is defined as

$$H = -kd \ln D/d(1/T). \tag{2.15}$$

Since the primary temperature dependence of D will come through τ,

$$H = d(\Delta G/T)/d(1/T). \tag{2.16}$$

Since

$$d(\Delta G/T)/d(1/T) = \Delta H, \tag{2.17}$$

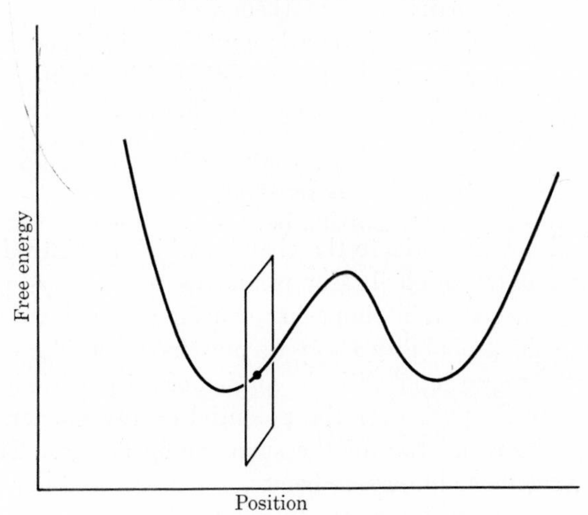

FIG. 3. Illustration of free energy barrier in diffusion.

where ΔH is the increment in enthalpy, the empirically measured heat of activation H may be identified with ΔH. Upon writing

$$\Delta G = \Delta H - T\,\Delta S, \tag{2.18}$$

we thereby obtain

$$\Gamma_i = \nu e^{\Delta S/k} \cdot e^{-H/kT}. \tag{2.19}$$

In discussions of equations of the type (2.19), the statement is frequently made in the literature that H is to be identified as the heat of activation only if it is independent of temperature. It is argued that if, say,

$$H = H_0(1 - \alpha T), \tag{2.20}$$

the H_0 is the measured heat of activation, and the right member of (2.19) contains the additional temperature independent factor $\exp(H_0\alpha/k)$. Since the constancy of H is nowhere assumed in our derivation of equation (2.19), this argument must be incorrect. Its fallacy lies in its neglect of the temperature variation of

ΔS which must accompany a temperature variation of ΔH, namely,

$$T\frac{d\Delta S}{dT} = \frac{d\Delta H}{dT}. \tag{2.21}$$

Thus, substituting (2.20) into (2.19), we obtain

$$\begin{aligned} -kd \ln \Gamma_i - 1/d(1/T) &= H_0 + T^2 d\Delta S/dT \\ &= H_0 + TdH/dT \\ &= H. \end{aligned} \tag{2.22}$$

Since in the current literature on reaction rate more complex formulae than (2.13, 2.14, and 2.19) are consistently being used, it is desirable that a comparison be made between them and these supposedly more correct formulae. In the expressions for the rate of crossing fixed potential energy barriers by a one-dimensional particle, equation (2.13) is written as

$$\Gamma = (kT/h)F_A{}^{-1}e^{-\Delta V/kT}, \tag{2.13a}$$

where F_A is the partition function of the particle in the trough A. If we now make the same assumption as led to equation (2.13), namely, that F_A may be replaced by the partition function for a linear oscillator, we obtain as the coefficient of $\exp(-\Delta V/kT)$

$$(2kT/h) \sinh (h\nu/2kT) = \nu\{1 + (1/24)(h\nu/kT)^2 + \cdots\}. \tag{2.23}$$

As has previously been mentioned, the coefficient of ν in the right member differs appreciably from unity only in the case of the diffusion of hydrogen. Equations (2.13) and (2.13a) are therefore essentially identical. In equations of the type (2.13a) it is usual to replace ΔV by that difference of potential energy ΔV_0 between the first vibrational level and the top of the barrier. These two potential differences are related by

$$\Delta V = \Delta V_0 + (1/2)h\nu. \tag{2.24}$$

In this case we must take

$$F_A = (1 - e^{-h\nu/kT})^{-1}. \tag{2.25}$$

When we now approach the classical limit where $h\nu/kT$ is equal to or is less than unity, a much better approximation is obtained by expanding $F_A{}^{-1} \exp(h\nu/2kT)$ than by expanding $F_A{}^{-1}$ alone. Thus in equation (2.13) ΔV should refer to the total difference in potential without any quantum corrections.

In the more realistic model of a many dimensional system, in place of equation (2.14) one commonly writes

$$\Gamma = (kT/h)e^{-\Delta G^*/kT}. \tag{2.14a}$$

Here the second factor is defined as the ratio of the partition function of the activated state, the coordinate leading across the barrier being excluded, to the partition function of the initial configuration. We may pass directly from (2.14*a*) to (2.14) by separating out of the partition function for the initial configuration that factor which arises from the coordinate which leads across the barrier, and then by applying the expansion (2.23) to this factor. The ratio of the two partition functions is then $\exp(-\Delta G/kT)$, where, as in equation (2.14), ΔG is the work done in isothermally moving the system from the potential trough to the top of the barrier. Throughout this motion we place constraints upon the coordinate leading across the barrier, but otherwise impose no restrictions. Whereas the ΔG^* in (2.14*a*) is commonly called the free energy of activation, it is not strictly a free energy, since it refers to a ratio of partition functions having a different number of degrees of freedom. ΔG^* cannot, therefore, be interpreted as the work done in any thought experiment. This lack of a physical interpretation for ΔG^* places equation (2.14*a*) at a decided disadvantage with respect to (2.14) whenever we wish to estimate from physical considerations such quantities as the entropy of activation.

The entropy of activation ΔS in (2.19) is related to ΔG by

$$\Delta S = -d\Delta G/dT. \tag{2.26}$$

We anticipate that the work ΔG to move the particle from a potential energy minimum to the top of the potential barrier will decrease with an increase in temperature, which increase is necessarily associated with a general loosening up of the lattice. But a negative temperature coefficient for ΔG implies, through equation (2.26), a positive value of ΔS. A more quantitative estimate of ΔS is obtained as follows. We rewrite (2.26) as

$$\Delta S = -\Delta G_0 d(\Delta G/\Delta G_0)/dT, \tag{2.27}$$

where ΔG_0 is the value of ΔG at $T = 0$. Outside the differential ΔG_0 may be replaced by H to a good approximation. Since we anticipate that a major part of ΔG is expended in straining the lattice, the temperature coefficient of $\Delta G/\Delta G_0$ will not differ greatly from the temperature coefficient of μ/μ_0, where μ is the shear or tensile modulus. We thereby obtain the estimate

$$\Delta S \simeq -\{d(\mu/\mu_0)/dT\}H. \tag{2.28}$$

Whereas the shear or tensile moduli of polycrystalline specimens decrease rapidly at elevated temperatures, Kê has shown in extensive measurements[12–15] that this rapid decrease arises from the relaxation of shear stress by the viscous grain boundaries, that in the absence of this relaxation the elastic moduli decrease in a linear manner with a rise in temperature. We may therefore consider the coefficient of H in (2.28) to have a constant value, namely, the value observed at temperatures below that at which grain boundary relaxation is appreciable. Upon defining

$$\beta = -d(\mu/\mu_0)/d(T/T_m), \tag{2.29}$$

we obtain

$$\Delta S \simeq \beta(H/T_m), \tag{2.30}$$

where T_m is the melting temperature. The constant β lies between 0.25 and 0.45 for most metals, as may be seen in Table 1. This table has been constructed from the data of Köster[16] on the temperature variation of the elastic moduli.

TABLE 1

VALUES OF $\beta = -d(\mu/\mu_0)/d(T/T_m)$*

Metal	β	*Metal*	β
Ti	1.1	Au	0.31
Th	0.9	Mg	0.31
Pb	0.50	Zn	0.31
Ag	0.45	Cd	0.27
α-Fe	0.43	Ca	0.25
Ta	0.40	La	0.25
Ba	0.39	Pt	0.25
Mo	0.36	Be	0.22
Al	0.35	Pd	0.18
Cu	0.35		
W	0.35		

* μ = Young's modulus.

It is this relative constancy of β for various metals that explains why D_0 is observed to vary in different systems in an exponential manner with H/T_m.[17]

3. INTERSTITIAL DIFFUSION OF SOLUTE ATOMS

The simplest example of crystalline diffusion is the diffusion of interstitial solute atoms. Here there can be no doubt as to the nature of the elementary diffusion process; the solute atoms simply

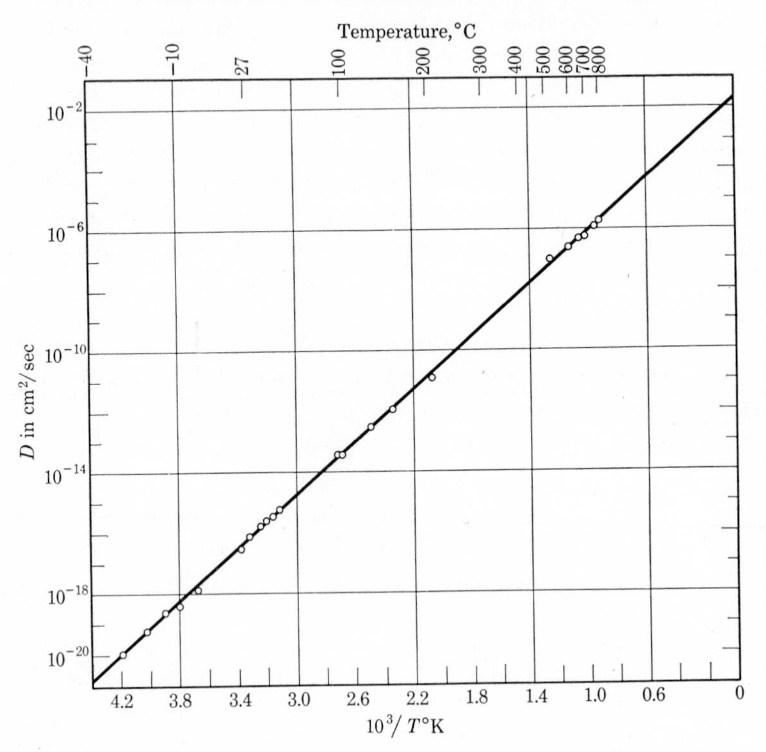

FIG. 4. Diffusion coefficient of carbon in alpha iron. (After Wert.[11])

jump from interstitial sites into neighboring interstitial sites. Extremely precise measurements may be carried out on the diffusion of interstitial solute atoms in body-centered-cubic (b.c.c.) metals. This extreme precision is possible because the high-temperature measurements utilizing standard techniques may be supplemented by low-temperature anelastic measurements in which one measures directly the mean time of stay, τ. The experimental data of Wert[11] for the diffusion of carbon in alpha (body-centered cubic) iron is presented in Fig. 4. Here the experimental data cover 14 cycles of ten. At the lowest temperature of measurement, $-35°C$, the mean time of stay was several hours. At the highest temperature of measurement, 800°C, the mean time of stay was 10^{-10} sec. Throughout this wide range, the data are represented by equation (1.2) with

$$H = 20{,}100 \text{ cal/mole}, \tag{3.1}$$

$$D_0 = 0.020 \text{ cm}^2/\text{sec}. \tag{3.2}$$

The extreme accuracy of these data, combined with the simplicity of the elementary diffusion act, renders it of interest to attempt a quantitative correlation between the empirical and theoretical value of D_0. Upon combining equations (2.7) and (2.19), and upon setting

$$\tau^{-1} = 4\Gamma_i \tag{3.3}$$

corresponding to there being four nearest neighbors of each interstitial site, we obtain

$$D_0 = (1/6)a^2\nu e^{\Delta S/k}. \tag{3.4}$$

If we now estimate ν by assuming that the shape of the free energy barrier is sinusoidal, and that ΔS is given by (2.26), we obtain

$$D_0 = 0.026. \tag{3.5}$$

The close agreement between this theoretical value of 0.026 and the empirical value of 0.020 is especially striking in view of the fact that when this theoretical value was first obtained the experimental value was 0.0005,[18] that this empirical value was then raised to 0.008[10] by more precise measurements undertaken for the purpose of checking the theoretical value, and that the final empirical value of 0.020 was obtained only by the extremely precise measurements covering 14 cycles of ten. The important role of the entropy factor exp $(\Delta S/k)$ may be seen from the fact that, in this particular case, it contributes a factor of 12.

Figure 5 (taken from Wert[19]) is presented to illustrate how in all cases of interstitial solutions in body-centered cubic lattices so far investigated the theoretical and experimental values of ΔS approach one another as the precision of the experiments increases.

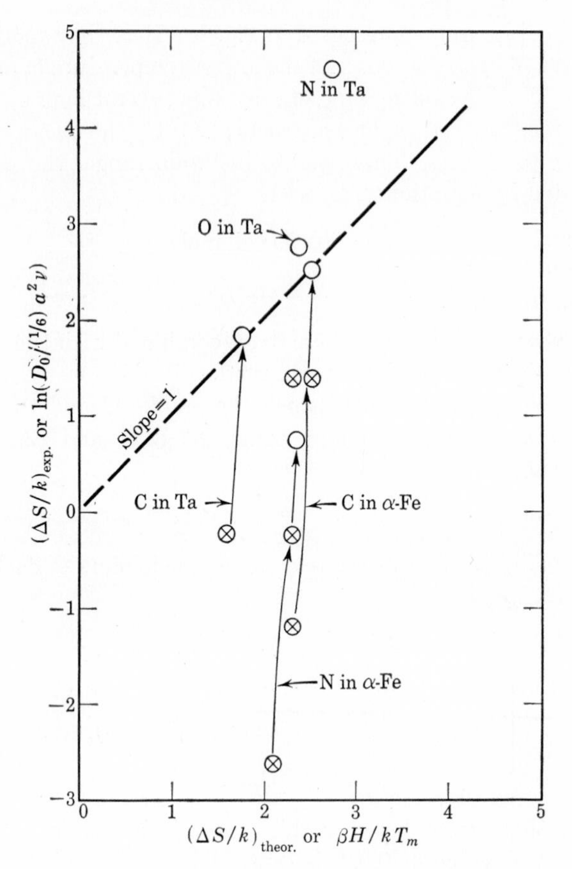

FIG. 5. Comparison of experimental and theoretical values of $\Delta S/k$ for interstitial diffusion in body-centered cubic lattices (after Wert[19]). Successive experimental values are taken from the following references:

C in α-Fe: Snoek[20] (1939, 1941), Stanley[21] (1949), Wert[10] (1949), Wert[19] (1950).
N in α-Fe: Snoek[20] (1939, 1941), Wert[10] (1949), Wert[19] (1950).
C in Ta: Kê[22] (1948), Wert[19] (1950).
N in Ta: Kê[23] (1948).
O in Ta: Kê[22] (1948).

4. SELF-DIFFUSION

A second simple example of diffusion occurs in self-diffusion, that is, the interdiffusion of two isotopes of the same metal. Various mechanisms have been proposed for self-diffusion. It is not to be expected that the same mechanism operates in all types of metals. That mechanism will dominate which has the largest D, and hence, in general, the smallest heat of activation H.

The most direct mechanism of self-diffusion is by the simple interchange of nearest neighbors. This mechanism has been studied in detail by Huntington and Seitz[24] for the particular case of copper. The elementary act for diffusion by simple interchange is illustrated in Fig. 6. The heat of activation is given by the work required to move the two interchanging atoms into the saddle configuration, the atoms in the surrounding lattice being allowed to adjust themselves so as to minimize this work. This work is to be calculated at 0°K, since, as we have previously seen,

$$H = \Delta G_0. \tag{4.1}$$

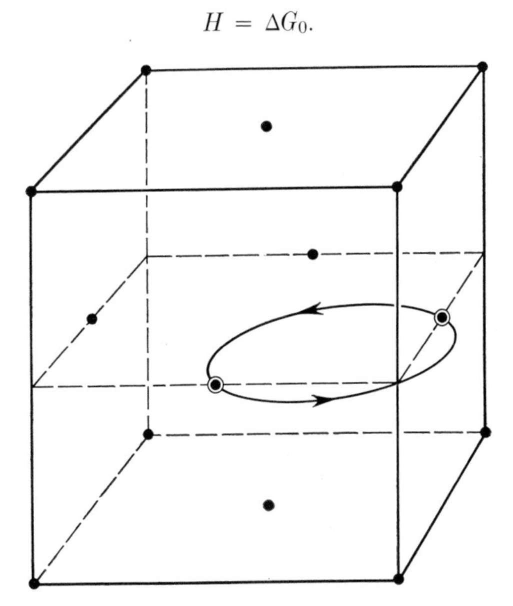

FIG. 6. Illustration of the interchange mechanism of self-diffusion. (After Huntington and Seitz.[24])

The computed H for the simple interchange mechanisms is four times as high as the observed H. We can, therefore, concur with Huntington and Seitz's conclusion that the simple interchange mechanism is of negligible importance in copper, and perhaps in all metallic systems. A study of the simple interchange mechanism is, however, of value because of the insight which it gives into the statistical mechanics of diffusion. The idea is prevalent that the more atoms which must participate in the elementary diffusion process the less frequently will the elementary diffusion process occur. In the simple interchange mechanism not only must the two interchanging atoms participate in the elementary diffusion act, but also the eight nearest neighboring atoms in the surrounding lattice. Without their relaxation the heat of activation would be much higher. The number of participating atoms does not, however, enter explicitly into the theoretical expression for the diffusion coefficient. Thus when we consider that a particular atom may move forward along a particular principal axis by the amount $(a/2)$ through simple interchanges with four nearest neighbors and that each simple interchange may take place through two saddle configurations corresponding to the two directions of rotation of the ring depicted in Fig. 5, we obtain

$$D = 2a^2 \nu e^{\Delta S/k} e^{-H/kT}. \tag{4.2}$$

Here ν is the frequency of vibration of the ring in its equilibrium position, and is essentially the frequency of vibration of a single atom. $-\Delta S$ is the temperature coefficient of the work necessary to rotate the ring to its saddle configuration.

Now that we have lost our inhibitions over letting a large number of atoms participate in the elementary diffusion act, we are led to consider elementary diffusion acts consisting of the rotation of rings containing a larger number of atoms. Zener[25] has shown that in copper the work required to rotate the four-atom ring illustrated in Fig. 7 to its saddle configuration is only 40 per cent of that required to rotate the two-atom ring of Fig. 6 to its saddle configuration. This preference of the four-atom ring over that of the two-atom ring may be traced to the greater symmetry of the four-atom ring, resulting in a smaller interaction between the ring and lattice at the saddle configuration. It is anticipated that this preference of the four-atom ring over that of the two-atom ring will not be confined to copper, but will occur in all types of metals. The diffusion coefficient for the four atom ring mechanism is given by equation (4.2) for face-centered cubic lattices, the coefficient of 2 representing the two distinct rings which may effect the same displacement of a given atom. In body-centered cubic lattices this coefficient is replaced by 3, corresponding to the three distinct rings which may effect the same displacement.

A second possible mechanism for self-diffusion is through the migration of lattice vacancies. In this mechanism an atom at a site A can jump to an adjacent site B only if the site B is initially unoccupied. The probability that this site is unoccupied is just the atomic concentration c of lattice vacancies. The diffusion coefficient by this mechanism is, therefore, for face-centered cubic and body-centered cubic lattices,

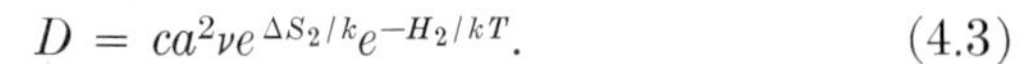

$$D = ca^2\nu e^{\Delta S_2/k}e^{-H_2/kT}. \tag{4.3}$$

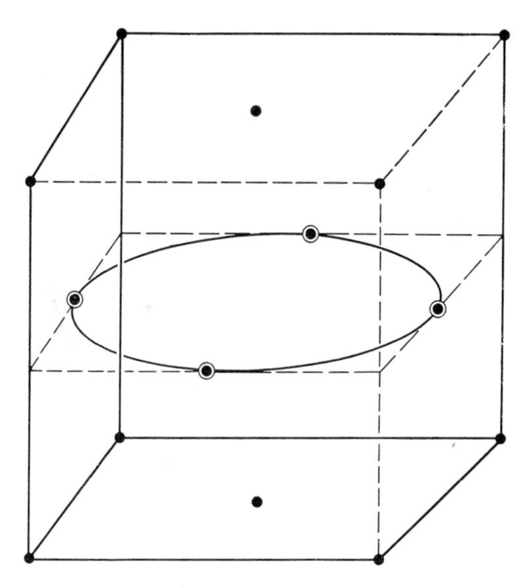

FIG. 7. Illustration of the four-ring mechanism of self-diffusion. (After Zener.[25])

Here ΔS_2 and H_2 are the entropy and heat of activation for the jumping of an atom from one site into an adjacent vacant site. ΔS_2 and H_2 will be related by the approximate equation

$$\Delta S_2 \simeq \beta(H_2/T_m), \tag{4.4}$$

with β given by equation (2.27) and Table 1. The atomic concentration of vacancies c will be given by

$$c = e^{\Delta S_1/k}e^{-H_1/kT}. \tag{4.5}$$

Here H_1 is the heat of formation of a vacancy, and ΔS_1 is the entropy of formation of a vacancy, exclusive of the entropy of mixing. ΔS_1 is certainly positive since the formation of a vacancy will allow more freedom of motion for the atoms surrounding the vacancy. When we now set

$$H = H_1 + H_2, \tag{4.6}$$

$$\Delta S = \Delta S_1 + \Delta S_2, \tag{4.7}$$

equation (4.3) becomes

$$D = a^2 \nu e^{\Delta S/k} e^{-H/kT}. \tag{4.8}$$

Since both ΔS_1 and ΔS_2 are positive, ΔS will likewise be positive. Since only the second part of ΔS obeys the relation (2.28), we can no longer anticipate a precise estimate of ΔS as in the case of interstitial diffusion. We can, however, anticipate a close correlation between ΔS and $\beta(H/T_m)$.

By a slight reinterpretation of ΔS the theoretical equation for D valid in the case of a four-atom ring may be reduced to the form of (4.8) valid for a vacancy mechanism. We interpret ΔG as the work necessary to bring atom A midway between two adjacent lattice cites P and P' by a four-atom ring rotation, without specifying the particular four-atom ring. The ΔS will then absorb the numerical coefficient of 2 (for face-centered cubic lattices) or of 3 (for body-centered cubic lattices).

Certain predictions may now be made concerning the experimental value of ΔS defined as

$$(\Delta S/k)_{\text{exp}} = \ln (D_0/a^2\nu), \tag{4.9}$$

where D_0 is given by experiment. First, irrespective of mechanism of self-diffusion, $(\Delta S)_{\text{exp}}$ must be positive. Second, for those metals having the same mechanism of self-diffusion, we anticipate a correlation between $(\Delta S/k)_{\text{exp}}$ and $\beta(H/kT_m)$. The experimental data are assembled in Fig. 8. It is seen that in all cases $(\Delta S/k)_{\text{exp}}$ is indeed positive. It is further seen that the anticipated correlation becomes better the more accurate the experimental data. Thus the equation

$$(\Delta S/k)_{\text{exp}} = \lambda\beta(H/kT_m) \tag{4.10}$$

correlates the data for the face-centered cubic metals with λ equal to 0.55, the body-centered cubic metals with λ equal to 1.0. Since we anticipate diffusion by the ring mechanism to be associated with a larger ΔS than diffusion by the vacancy mechanism, we are

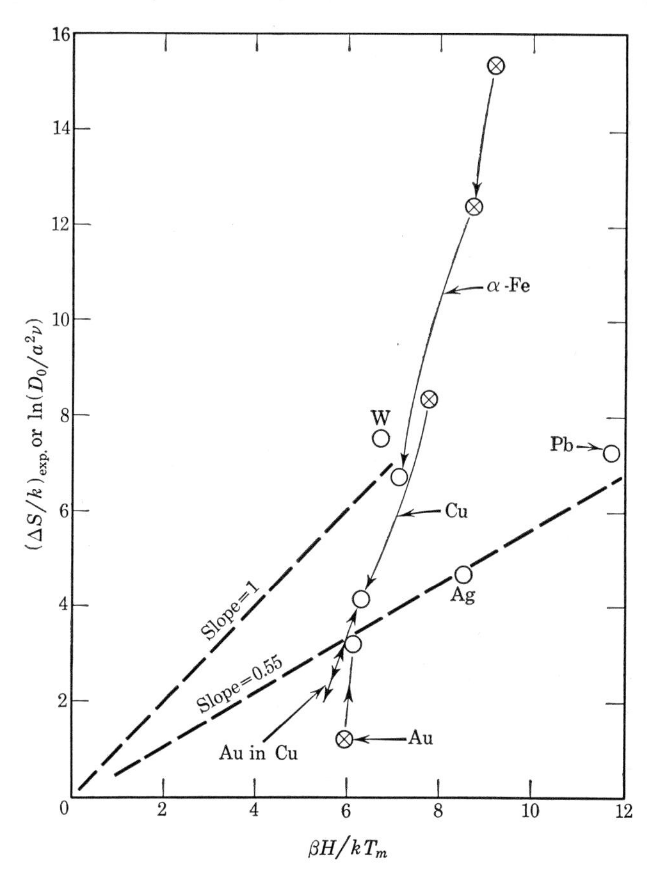

FIG. 8. Comparison of experimental values of $\Delta S/k$ with $\beta(H/kT_m)$ for self-diffusion of cubic metals and for chemical diffusion in very dilute solutions as determined by radioactive tracer technique. Successive experimental values on the same system are taken from the following references:

Alpha iron: Birchenall and Mehl[26] (1948); Birchenall and Mehl[27] (1950); Buffington, Bakalar, and Cohen[28] (1950).

Copper: Steigman, Shockley, and Nix[29] (1939); M. S. Maier and H. R. Nelson[30] (1942).

Gold: McKay[31] (1938, surface technique); Sagruboskij[32] (1937, slicing technique).

Au in Cu: Martin and Asaro[33] (1950).

led to suspect that the ring mechanism might operate for body-centered cubic metals, the vacancy mechanism for face-centered cubic metals. Direct computations of H for the face-centered cubic metal copper show a slight preference for the vacancy mechanism. Thus, upon taking the repulsive interaction between the inner shells of the copper ion to be of an exponential form, Huntington[24] has computed the vacancy mechanism to have an H of 81,000 cal/mole; Zener[25] has computed the ring mechanism to have an H of 91,000 cal/mole.

A third possible mechanism for self-diffusion is by the migration of interstitial atoms. This mechanism has been investigated by Huntington and Seitz[24] for the particular case of copper, and has been found to be quite inadequate. The work required to transfer an atom from the surface to an interstitial position was found to be nearly 300,000 cal/mole. It is anticipated that a similar result would be obtained for all metals which have strongly repulsive inner shells. The alkali metals are unique in that the radii of their inner shells are very small compared to the half distance between nearest neighbors in a lattice. Paneth[34] has found that in these metals only a comparatively small amount of work is required to transfer an atom from the surface into the interior of the lattice, namely, about 5000 cal/mole. The most obvious position for an interstitial atom is at the largest "hole," that is, at that point where the nearest lattice atoms are at a maximum distance. These largest holes are not, however, necessarily the most favorable sites for interstitial atoms. Thus in body-centered cubic metals the largest holes are at the (1/2, 1/4, 0) position, having four nearest neighbors at a distance of $0.56a$, whereas the interstitial solute atoms of carbon and nitrogen in α iron are located at the (1/2, 0, 0) position, having two nearest neighbors at a distance of $0.50a$. Detailed calculations have shown that the latter positions are preferred because of their relative "softness." Thus let W be the work required to push the nearest lattice atoms a small distance X away from the interstitial position. The reciprocal of the constant C defined by

$$W = (1/2)CX^2 \tag{4.11}$$

is a measure of the softness of the hole. In this terminology the (1/2, 0, 0) position is four times as soft as the (1/2, 1/4, 0) position. Paneth found that in the alkali metals the interstitial position midway between two atoms in a close-packed row is extremely soft. When an extra alkali metal is placed in such a position the relaxation of the lattice is confined essentially to this close-packed row, resulting in a localized crowding of the atoms in this row. The resulting configuration has been called a crowdion by Paneth. Self-diffusion in the alkali metals thus occurs by the motion of these crowdions.

5. CHEMICAL DIFFUSION AT VERY SMALL CONCENTRATIONS

By chemical diffusion we denote the diffusion of one type of atom into a matrix composed of chemically different atoms. One type of chemical diffusion was considered in Section 3, namely, the type in which the solute atom occupied interstitial positions. We shall now consider the case where the solute atoms occupy lattice sites.

Various complications are present at large concentrations of solute atoms which disappear as the concentration becomes very small. At sufficiently small concentration we may neglect both the interaction of the solute atoms with one another and also lattice imperfections necessitated by differences in lattice parameters across the diffusion region. Under these conditions diffusion again reduces to an example of the simple problem of a random walk. We are therefore tempted to apply to this type of diffusion the same considerations we adopted in the previous section for self-diffusion. However, if we adopt equation (4.8), then in most of the cases of chemical diffusion the experimental $\Delta S/k$, as computed from equation (4.9), is negative. Typical examples are listed in Table 2. We must therefore carefully examine the application of the foregoing theory to our present problem and thereby determine whether the mechanics of chemical diffusion are so radically different from those of self-diffusion as to demand a revision of our conclusions regarding the intrinsically positive character of ΔS, or whether the experiments have not satisfied our condition of a sufficiently dilute solution.

In the derivation of equation (2.5) it is implicitly assumed that the direction of successive jumps is random. This assumption is not strictly justified in the hole mechanism for self-diffusion. When an atom in a face-centered cubic lattice jumps from a site P into a vacancy at P', the next jump is more likely to be in the inverse direction than in any of the other possible eleven directions. This correlation of successive probabilities has been shown by Bardeen* to have only a very slight effect upon self-diffusion. In the commonly accepted Johnson[35] mechanism of the hole diffusion of foreign atoms, this correlation of successive probabilities is so great as to require a new analysis.

Johnson[35] has interpreted the frequently found low heat of activation for chemical diffusion as implying that less work is required to produce a lattice vacancy at a particular lattice site

TABLE 2

Examples of Negative Entropies of Activation
(After Dienes[17])

Solute Atom in Ag	$(\Delta S/k)_{\text{exp}}$
Cd	−4.4
Cu	−4.1
In	−4.0
Sb	−4.2
Sn	−3.9

adjacent to a solute atom than at any other particular lattice site. From this interpretation it follows that once a vacancy becomes a nearest neighbor of a particular solute atom, it will interchange places with this solute atom, and with the nearest neighbors of this solute atom, many times before it again wanders off into the lattice, leaving the solute atom behind. If we consider the temporary combination of solute atom and lattice vacancy as a molecule, Johnson has shown that the above-mentioned repeated interchanges will result in a diffusion of the molecule through the lattice. We shall now examine in detail the statistics of such diffusion.

We shall restrict ourselves to face-centered cubic lattices, and to the case where the vacancy interchanges much more frequently with the solute atom than with a nearest neighbor of the solute atom. We may then concentrate our attention on the migration of the center of gravity of the "solute atom-vacancy" molecule.

We denote by p the probability that a particular lattice site adjacent to the foreign atom A be vacant, and by Γ the rate at

* J. Bardeen, Paper 10 of this book.

which this vacancy jumps to a particular one of the four lattice sites which are adjacent both to the vacancy and to atom A. Whenever the vacancy makes such a jump the center of gravity of the A-vacancy molecule jumps by the distance $2^{-3/2}a$. We now rewrite equation (2.5) as

$$D = (1/6)\sum_i \Gamma_i \, \delta l_i^2, \tag{5.1}$$

where δl_i is the jump distance for the jump i, and Γ_i the corresponding jump rate. When we now take cognizance of the fact that the atom A has twelve neighboring lattice sites which may be occupied by a vacancy, and each such site has four jump directions with the jump rate Γ and jump distance $2^{-3/2}a$, we obtain

$$D = \Gamma a^2 p. \tag{5.2}$$

Upon setting

$$p = e^{-\Delta G_1/kT}, \tag{5.3}$$

$$\Gamma = \nu e^{-\Delta G_2/kT}, \tag{5.4}$$

where ΔG_1 and ΔG_2 have precisely the same meaning as used previously, we obtain for D precisely the equation (4.8) valid for self-diffusion. The experimental value for $\Delta S/k$, namely, $\ln (D_0/a^2 v)$, should therefore show the same correlation with $\beta H/kT_m$ as in the case of self-diffusion. Whenever $(\Delta S/k)_{\text{exp}}$ is negative, we must conclude therefore either that the experimental determination of D_0 is incorrect, or that the concentration of the solute atoms is not sufficiently small to justify the assumption of very dilute solutions.

The method of radioactive tracers is ideally suited for measuring chemical diffusion rates at very small concentrations. The only example of which the author is aware is that of Martin and Asaro[33] for gold into copper. Their data, presented in Fig. 8, are seen to be consistent with the slope of 0.55, which correlates all the data on self-diffusion in face-centered cubic metals.

6. GENERAL CHEMICAL DIFFUSION

In many examples of chemical diffusion the observed D_0 is much smaller, by several orders of magnitudes, than the theoretical value[31] (see also Table 2). Such anomalously low values of D_0 are invariably accompanied by values of H much lower than that for self-diffusion of the solvent matrix. Whereas the anomalously low D_0 tends, by itself, to lower the diffusion rate, the reverse effect of the anomalously low H more than compensates for the small D_0, resulting in a larger chemical diffusion rate than would be anticipated from self-diffusion rate. In the various mechanisms of diffusion which we have considered above, all lattice sites were considered as equivalent, and hence the diffusion* may be thought of as occurring in a homogeneous manner throughout the lattice. Anomalously low values of D_0 now lead us to suspect inhomogeneous diffusion through highly conducting paths which can be thought of as short-circuiting homogeneous diffusion.*

Such short-circuiting paths have previously been suspected in many systems. The most obvious method is by a network of highly conducting paths, homogeneous diffusion being confined to an interchange between the highly conducting paths and the neighboring crystalline regions. Grain boundaries form one possible system of highly conducting paths. The diffusion of thorium in tungsten has been interpreted as taking place by the above-mentioned combination of short-range homogeneous diffusion and of long-range grain boundary diffusion.[36,37] The disorganized regions introduced by plastic deformation also may, in certain cases, serve as highly conducting regions. Again, the diffusion of thorium in tungsten serves as an example which has received considerable study.[36] Further examples have been given by Matanno,[38] who showed that the annealing of certain cold-rolled copper alloys reduced their diffusion coefficient. Highly conducting paths appear to be formed also whenever large gradients in lattice parameters are introduced by large concentration gradients. The most familiar examples occur in the diffusion of hydrogen into and out of metals. Such diffusion is much greater in those specimens in which such diffusion has previously occurred than in virgin specimens. The literature on this subject has been reviewed by Smith.[39] Other cases of the formation of highly conducting paths by concentration gradients have been studied by Hedvall.[40]

In the above-mentioned examples of inhomogeneous diffusion the inhomogeneities were of a structural nature, grain boundaries,

* *Note added in proof.* This concept that in many cases of chemical diffusion short-circuiting paths are involved has been further confirmed by the extensive analysis of A. S. Nowick, *J. Appl. Phys.*, **22**, 1182 (1951).

or dislocations. The inhomogeneity may also be of a chemical nature. Thus, consider a copper-base alloy with 20 per cent of zinc, and suppose that a vacancy interchanges places much more readily with zinc atoms than with copper atoms. The motion of the vacancies will then be essentially confined to the network formed by the zinc atoms.

Inhomogeneous diffusion will, in general, be accompanied by a net diffusion flow of matter, irrespective as to whether the pertinent inhomogeneity is physical or chemical. In the former case one of the constituents will have a greater mobility along the structural inhomogeneity. In the latter case only one type of atom participates in diffusion, as zinc in the example cited. In certain types of experiments no net mass flow can occur. In such cases the diffusion flow must be exactly balanced by an overall lattice displacement in the direction opposite to the diffusion flow. Such displacements may occur, for example, by the motion of dislocations normal to their slip planes, such motion being caused by the generation or annihilation of vacancies.[41,42] It is this compensating lattice drift which probably is the origin of the Kirkendall effect.[43,44]

REFERENCES

1. C. J. Smithels, *Metals Reference Book*, pp. 390–408, Interscience Publishers, New York, 1949.
2. L. Onsager, *Ann. N. Y. Acad. Sci.*, **46**, 241 (1945).
3. A. Einstein, *Ann. Physik*, **17**, 549 (1950).
4. S. R. De Groot, *L'effet Soret*, N. V. Noord-Hollandsche Uitgevers Maatchapij, Amsterdam, 1945.
5. A. D. le Clair, *Progress in Metal Physics*, Vol. I, Chap. 7, Interscience Publishers, New York, 1949.
6. Lord Rayleigh, *The Theory of Sound*, Vol. 1, pp. 37–38, Macmillan & Co., London, 1894.
7. Riemann-Weber, *Differentialgleichungen der Physik*, 7th Ed., Vol. 2, pp. 203–205, Braunschweig, 1927.
8. E. Wigner, *Phys. Rev.*, **40**, 749 (1932).
9. S. Chandrasekhar, *Revs. Modern Phys.*, **15**, 63 (1943).
10. C. Wert and C. Zener, *Phys. Rev.*, **76**, 1169 (1949).
11. C. Wert, *Phys. Rev.*, **79**, 601 (1950).
12. T. S. Kê, *Phys. Rev.*, **71**, 533 (1947).
13. T. S. Kê, *Trans. AIME*, **176**, 448 (1948).
14. T. S. Kê, *Phys. Rev.*, **74**, 16 (1948).
15. T. S. Kê, *J. Appl. Phys.*, **20**, 1226 (1949).
16. W. Köster, *Z. Metallkunde*, **39**, 1 (1948).
17. G. J. Dienes, *J. Appl. Phys.*, **21**, 1189 (1950).

18. D. Polder, *Philips Research Reports*, **1**, 1 (1945).
19. C. Wert, *J. Appl. Phys.*, **21**, 1196 (1950).
20. J. Snoek, *Physica*, **6**, 591 (1939); **8**, 711 (1941).
21. J. K. Stanley, *Trans. AIME*, **185**, 752 (1949).
22. T. S. Kê, *Phys. Rev.*, **74**, 9 (1948).
23. T. S. Kê, *Phys. Rev.*, **74**, 914 (1948).
24. H. B. Huntington and F. Seitz, *Phys. Rev.*, **61**, 315 (1942); **76**, 1728 (1949).
25. C. Zener, *Acta Cryst.*, **3**, 346 (1950).
26. C. E. Birchenall and R. F. Mehl, *J. Appl. Phys.*, **19**, 217 (1948).
27. C. E. Birchenall and R. F. Mehl, *Trans. AIME*, **188**, 144 (1950).
28. F. S. Buffington, I. D. Bakalar, and M. Cohen, *Trans. AIME*, **188**, 1374 (1950).
29. J. Steigman, W. Shockley and F. C. Nix, *Phys. Rev.*, **56**, 13 (1939).
30. M. S. Maier and H. R. Nelson, *Trans. AIME*, **147**, 39 (1942).
31. H. A. C. McKay, *Trans. Faraday Soc.*, **34**, 845 (1938).
32. A. M. Sagruboskij, *Physikal. Z. Sowjetunion*, **12**, 118 (1937).
33. A. B. Martin and F. Asaro, *Phys. Rev.*, **80**, 123 (1950).
34. H. Paneth, *Phys. Rev.*, **80**, 708 (1950).
35. R. P. Johnson, *Phys. Rev.*, **56**, 814 (1939).
36. G. R. Fonda, A. H. Young, and A. Walker, *Physics*, **4**, 1 (1933).
37. I. Langmuir, *J. Franklin Inst.*, **217**, 543 (1934).
38. C. Matanno, *Japan J. Physics*, **9**, 41 (1934).
39. D. P. Smith, *Hydrogen in Metals*, University of Chicago Press, 1948.
40. I. A. Hedvall, *Reaktionsfähigkeit fester Stoffe*, J. A. Barth, Leipzig, 1938.
41. F. Seitz, *Phys. Rev.*, **74**, 1513 (1948).
42. F. Seitz, *Acta Cryst.*, **3**, 355 (1950).
43. E. O. Kirkendall, *Trans. AIME*, **147**, 104 (1942); A. D. Smigelskas and E. O. Kirkendall, *Trans. AIME*, **171**, 130 (1947).
44. L. C. C. da Silva and R. F. Mehl, *Trans. AIME*, **191**, 155 (1951).

IV. ON THE PROPERTIES AND EFFECTS OF EXTERNAL AND INTERNAL SURFACES OF CRYSTALS

12.

Surface and Interfacial Tensions of Single-Phase Solids

J. C. FISHER AND C. G. DUNN

General Electric Research Laboratory, Schenectady, N. Y.

ABSTRACT

The published values of surface and interfacial tensions of single-phase solids are collected, evaluated, and tabulated. Several errors in the literature are corrected. Reasonably good values are obtained for the surface tensions of solid copper, silver, and gold, for the grain and twin boundary tensions in copper, and for the variation in grain boundary tension with orientation of the adjacent grains in silicon iron, tin, and lead.

1. METHODS OF DETERMINING SURFACE TENSION

Determination of equilibrium surface and interfacial tensions of solids is difficult because of the long times required for equilibration and because of orientation effects related to crystal structure. Nevertheless, in the past few years, owing largely to C. S. Smith's paper[1] on the interpretation of the microstructure of metals and alloys in terms of interfacial tensions, a considerable amount of effort has been concentrated upon the problem. Fairly reliable values now are available for the surface, grain boundary, and twin boundary tensions of several solid metals, and for the influence of the relative orientation of adjacent grains upon the grain boundary tension.

The methods whereby interfacial tensions of solids have been studied are not new. Measurement of the dihedral angles at three interfaces meeting along a line has long been used for determining relative liquid/liquid interfacial tensions. Extension of this method to solids requires only longer waiting times for equilibrium and use of the microscope for measuring angles.

The force required to balance the surface tension of a solid has been measured by applying external force to a thin foil or wire that otherwise would shrink under the action of the tension.

2. SURFACE TENSIONS OF SOLIDS

Since the time of Faraday[2] it has been known that thin metal films shrink when heated. Chapman and Porter[3] ascribed the effect to surface tension, and several investigators[4-6] have attempted to determine the magnitude of the surface tension by opposing the shrinkage with known external forces.

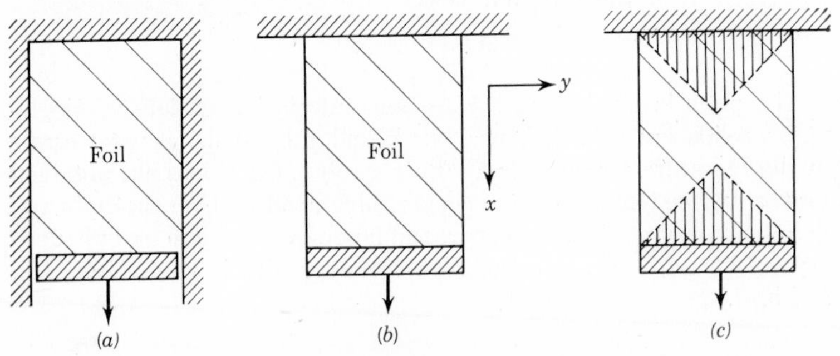

FIG. 1. Three types of constraint for the creep of thin metal foils.

Consider a rectangular metal foil supported as shown in Fig. 1*a*, with three edges constrained and the fourth edge free to move. The foil edges are supported so that they cannot pull away, although frictionless sliding is allowed. By varying the force applied to the movable constraint, it is possible to vary the rate of extension or contraction of the foil. The force P that just balances the surface tension at equilibrium is equal to twice the product of the surface tension γ and the foil width w,

$$P = 2\gamma w. \tag{2.1}$$

If now the two side constraints are removed, as in Fig. 1*b*, external lateral tensions no longer are present. The stresses in the foil then are

$$\sigma_x = P/wt - 2\gamma/t, \tag{2.2}$$

$$\sigma_y = -2\gamma/t, \tag{2.3}$$

$$\sigma_z = 0, \tag{2.4}$$

where t is the foil thickness and the axes are as in Fig. 1*b*. The strain rate in the length direction is proportional to $\sigma_x - \frac{1}{2}(\sigma_y + \sigma_z)$, and for zero strain rate

$$P = \gamma w. \tag{2.5}$$

Only half as much force is required to maintain zero creep rate in a foil with free sides as in a foil with supported sides.

The foils employed in surface tension studies are not free to move upon their supports. For such foils, with laterally constrained ends and unsupported sides, it is approximately correct to say that a triangular region of area $w^2/2$ at each end of the foil is constrained so that the lateral creep rate is zero, and that the remainder of the foil is unconstrained, as shown in Fig. 1*c*. If θ is the fraction of the foil that is constrained, the force required to maintain zero rate of extension is

$$P = 2\gamma w/(2 - \theta). \tag{2.6}$$

Schottky[4] fractured thin silver foils at elevated temperatures in an effort to determine the surface tension of silver. His measurements did not correspond to equilibrium conditions.

Sawai and Nishida[5] determined the surface tension of gold (98 per cent Au + 2 per cent Ag) and silver foil. Their foils were 0.5 cm wide, about 1.5 cm long, and $3.1(10)^{-5}$ to $7.7(10)^{-5}$ cm thick. The ends were attached to rigid parallel plates, and the sides were unsupported. The relative motion of gage marks 1.0 cm apart was measured, the gage marks being about 0.25 cm removed from the specimen ends. At each temperature the average strain rate $\Delta L/L\, \Delta t$ was plotted versus load. The maximum and minimum loads that gave unmeasurably small creep rates were averaged to give the load corresponding to zero creep rate. The measurements and calculated surface tension values are given in Table 1.

Although Sawai and Nishida used equation (2.1), it is evident that equation (2.5) is the proper one for their experiments. If this correction is made, the mean surface tension values of gold and silver are $\gamma_{\mathrm{Au}} = 1310$ dynes/cm and $\gamma_{\mathrm{Ag}} = 1140$ dynes/cm in the temperature range 650 to 850°C. The reported increases of surface tension with increasing temperature probably are not significant, although they may possibly result from the desorption of gases.

Tammann and Boehme[6] also determined the surface tension of gold foil. They used approximately square foils 0.5 cm wide,

TABLE 1

SUMMARY OF THE MEASUREMENTS OF SAWAI AND NISHIDA[5] IN DETERMINING THE SURFACE TENSIONS OF GOLD (98% AU + 2% AG) AND SILVER FOILS

(P is load in mg/mm of foil width. γ is surface tension in mg/mm.)

T, °C	Au, $7.7(10)^{-5}$ cm			Ag, $6.3(10)^{-5}$ cm			Ag, $3.1(10)^{-5}$ cm		
	P	γ(ref. 5)	γ(eq. 2.5)	P	γ(ref. 5)	γ(eq. 2.5)	P	γ(ref. 5)	γ(eq. 2.5)
650	5.6 211.6	54.3	108.6	30.0 144.8	43.7	87.4	40.2 151.2	47.9	95.7
700	77.2 171.8	61.0	124.5	77.4 133.2	52.7	105.3	77.6 138.0	53.7	107.8
750	125.6 141.4	66.8	133.5	118.0 ———	59.0	118.0	114.4 124.2	59.7	119.3
800	144.6	72.3	144.6	123.2	61.6	123.2	128.0	64.0	128.0
850	155.6	77.8	155.6	136.6*	68.3	136.6	137.0*	68.5	137.0

* Interpolated graphically.

Mean Surface Tension Values ± Probable Error of Mean

	mg/mm	dynes/cm
Gold	133.4 ± 5.5	1310 ± 55
Silver	115.8 ± 3.5	1140 ± 35

0.5 to 0.6 cm long, and $6.5(10)^{-5}$ cm thick. The foil ends were attached to rigid parallel wires, and the relative motion of the wires was observed. At each temperature, the average creep

TABLE 2

SUMMARY OF THE MEASUREMENTS OF TAMMANN AND BOEHME[6] IN DETERMINING THE SURFACE TENSION OF GOLD FOIL

T, °C	*Number of Specimens*	γ (*ref. 6*)	γ (*eq. 2.6*, $\theta = 0.5$)
700	5	1230 mg/cm	1845 mg/cm
750	7	1220 "	1830 "
800	5	1200 "	1800 "
850	5	1180 "	1770 "

The mean value of the surface tension of solid gold is 1780 ± 10 dynes/cm.

rate $\Delta L/L\ \Delta t$ was plotted versus load, and the load corresponding to zero creep was obtained by interpolation. The temperatures, number of specimens employed, and calculated surface tensions are given in Table 2.

Although Tammann and Boehme employed equation (2.1) in their calculations, it is evident that equation (2.6), with $\theta = 0.5$ corresponding to a square foil, is more nearly correct. With $\theta = 0.5$, the surface tension of gold is $\gamma_{Au} = 1780$ dynes/cm.

Udin, Shaler, and Wulff[7] determined the surface tension of copper by studying the creep of fine wires.

The equilibrium force that is transmitted along a noncreeping wire of circular cross section is made up of two parts. The first is a tensile force, $2\pi r\gamma$, the product of the surface tension γ and the length of the perimeter. The second is a compressive force, $\pi r\gamma$, the product of the cross-sectional area and the excess pressure γ/r in the interior of the wire. The net force is a tensile force of magnitude $\pi r\gamma$, which when balanced with a known external force P enables the calculation of γ according to the relationship

$$\gamma = P/\pi r. \tag{2.7}$$

Wires 3 and 5 mils in diameter (1 mil = 0.001 in.) were employed by Udin, Shaler, and Wulff. A pair of knots tied about 2 cm apart marked each gage length. The extension or contraction of each wire was measured after a fixed time of creep at constant temperature in a closed evacuated copper container, and a plot of creep strain versus load yielded by interpolation the value of the critical load for which there was no extension or contraction. Table 3 summarizes the measurements and the surface tension values found. They are well represented by the single value $\gamma_{Cu} = 1430$ dynes/cm in the temperature range 950 to 1050°C.

The creep of wires technique has been extended to gold by Alexander et al.[8] Two knots 10 to 12 cm apart formed the gage length in a wire $2.8(10)^{-3}$ cm in diameter and 30 cm long. Strain-time curves were obtained for creep in vacuum, and the stress corresponding to zero creep rate was determined by interpolation. Table 4 summarizes the experimental results. The mean value obtained for the surface tension is $\gamma_{Au} = 1450$ dynes/cm.

Rymer and Butler[9] have pointed out that the anomalous lattice spacings determined by electron diffraction from thin gold foil can be explained as a surface tension effect. They calculate that a surface tension of 500 dynes/cm, acting on a lamina of thickness $4(10)^{-7}$ cm, would cause strains consistent in order of magnitude with those observed.

Whenever three interfaces meet along a line, it is possible to

TABLE 3

SUMMARY OF THE MEASUREMENTS OF UDIN, SHALER, AND WULFF[7] IN DETERMINING THE SURFACE TENSION OF COPPER WIRE

(σ is stress in dynes/cm^2, ϵ is strain.)

Temperature, °C	950		999		1024		1049	
Time, 10^5 sec	5.15		1.80		1.08		0.874	
Wire radius, 10^{-3} cm	6.4		6.4		6.4		6.4	
Specimen number	$10^{-5}\sigma$	$10^3\epsilon$	$10^{-5}\sigma$	$10^3\epsilon$	$10^{-5}\sigma$	$10^3\epsilon$	$10^{-5}\sigma$	$10^3\epsilon$
1	0.076	−3.9	0.069	−4.4	0.091	−6.1	0.091	−4.5
2	0.777	−2.1	0.076	−4.2	0.738	−4.5	0.861	−3.3
3	1.774	−1.3	1.742	−1.8	1.461	−3.1	1.319	−2.5
4	2.755	+1.3	2.350	−0.5	2.368	−0.6	2.315	−0.5
5	2.313	−0.6	2.807	+0.6	2.535	0.0	2.865	+1.3
6	3.140	+1.9	3.180	+3.0	3.145	+3.7	2.842	+2.4
7	3.465	+2.1	3.810	+2.3	3.472	+4.2	3.520	+3.8
8	4.547	+4.1	4.603	+5.9	4.644	+3.8	4.545	+5.4
γ, dynes/cm	1460		1460		1540		1400	

Temperature, °C	950		1000		1050	
Time, 10^5 sec	5.35		2.60		1.69	
Wire radius, 10^{-3} cm	3.6		3.6		3.6	
Specimen number	$10^{-5}\sigma$	$10^3\epsilon$*	$10^{-5}\sigma$	$10^3\epsilon$	$10^{-5}\sigma$	$10^3\epsilon$
1	†		0.072	−10.7	0.096	−8.9
2	1.706	−3.10	1.179	−5.7	†	
3	3.508	−0.67	2.455	−2.1	2.428	−5.0
4	4.107	−0.32	3.393	−0.9	3.655	−0.8
5	5.459	+2.00	3.635	−0.6	4.545	+3.1
6	5.724	+3.22	4.235	+0.2	5.047	+4.1
7	6.682	+4.89	5.540	+4.6	†	
8	8.345	+6.30	8.135	+9.1	7.530	+9.3
γ, dynes/cm	1400		1410		1360	

The mean value for the surface tension of solid copper is $\gamma = 1430 \pm 15$.
* Accuracy of measuring microscope increased from ±0.001 cm to ±0.0002 cm.
† Specimen damaged during measurement.

TABLE 4

SUMMARY OF THE MEASUREMENTS OF ALEXANDER ET AL.[8] IN DETERMINING THE SURFACE TENSION OF GOLD WIRE

T, °C	*Number of Specimens*	γ *(dynes/cm)*
920	7	1680
970	6	1280
1020	7	1400

The mean value of the surface tension of gold is $\gamma_{Au} = 1450 \pm 80$ dynes/cm.

determine the ratios of the corresponding surface tensions (provided that they do not depend markedly upon orientation) by measuring the dihedral angles and calculating from the well-known relationship

$$\gamma_{12}/\sin\theta_{12} = \gamma_{23}/\sin\theta_{23} = \gamma_{31}/\sin\theta_{31}, \tag{2.8}$$

where θ_{ij} is the angle opposite the i/j interface. If one of the interfaces is a solid/vapor surface and another is a liquid/vapor surface, the ratio of the solid-surface tension to that of the liquid can be established. The liquid-surface tension can be determined if it is not already known, and this value will lead to an absolute value for the surface tension of the solid.

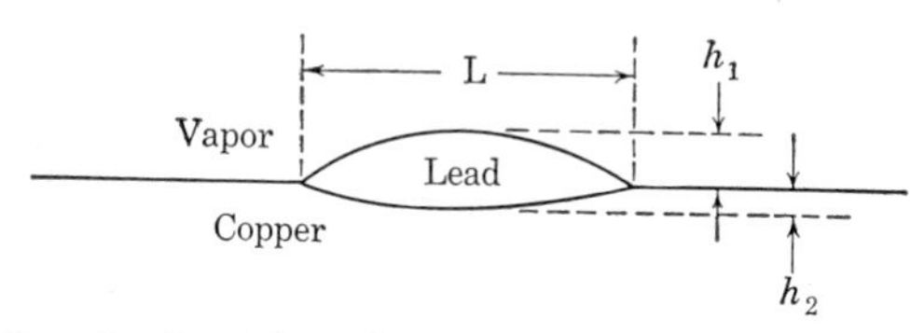

FIG. 2. Lead drop dimensions measured by Sears.[10]

The ratio of the surface tension of solid copper in lead vapor to that of liquid lead saturated with copper has been measured in this fashion by Sears.[10] He equilibrated small drops of liquid lead on copper surfaces for 8 hours at 800°C, then rapidly cooled the specimens to room temperature. The specimens then were copper-plated and sectioned at right angles to the original copper surface. It was believed that the overall relative dimensions of the drops had survived cooling and solidification of the lead better than the dihedral angles. For this reason, the dihedral angles were not measured directly, but were deduced from measurements of the quantities L, h_1, h_2, as shown in Fig. 2; the interfaces were assumed to be portions of spherical surfaces. Sears measured the dimensions of about 125 drop sections, and determined frequency distributions for the three interfacial angles from which he estimated the true dihedral angles. The corresponding ratio of the surface tension of solid copper to that of liquid lead, in the presence of lead vapor, was 1.8. Taking the surface tension of lead saturated with copper to be 400 dynes/cm at 800°C, Sears obtained 720 dynes/cm for the surface tension of copper in the presence of lead vapor. It is interesting to note that this value is only about half that for copper in its own vapor.

Bailey and Watkins[11] have determined the surface tension of solid copper by means of lead drop and thermal etching experiments that are described in the next section of this paper. Proceeding less directly than Sears, they obtained 780 dynes/cm for the surface tension of copper in lead vapor and 1800 dynes/cm for the surface tension of copper in hydrogen or argon. An alternate analysis of their data, described in the next section, gives 800 dynes/cm and 1800 dynes/cm for these values.

TABLE 5

EQUILIBRIUM SURFACE TENSIONS OF SOLID METALS: SUMMARY

Surface	Investigator	Value	Temperature, °C	Mean ± P.E. of Mean
Copper	Udin, Shaler, Wulff	1430 ± 15	950–1050	1430 ± 15*
	Bailey, Watkins	1800	800–900	
Gold	Sawai, Nishida	1310 ± 55	650–850	1510 ± 100
	Tammann, Boehme	1780 ± 10	700–850	
	Alexander, et al.	1450 ± 80	920–1020	
Silver	Sawai, Nishida	1140 ± 35	650–850	1140 ± 100 (est.)
Copper/Lead Vapor	Sears	720	800	760 ± 30
	Bailey, Watkins	800	800–900	

* Bailey and Watkins' value not included.

Most methods that have been proposed for the measurement of the surface tension or surface free energy of solids, aside from those just described, do not measure equilibrium values. Recent measurements of the work required for the comminution of quartz,[12] for example, lead to a surface free energy of 107,000 ergs/cm^2, a value that may be one hundred times larger than the equilibrium value. Similarly, Obreimoff's measurements of the surface free energy of mica,[13] obtained by measuring the work of cleavage, do not give equilibrium values.

It appears that the best values known for the equilibrium surface tensions of solids are those for gold, silver, copper, and copper in a lead vapor atmosphere.

The most accurately known value probably is that of solid

copper, as determined by Udin, Shaler, and Wulff. Next most accurately known is that of solid gold, as determined by Sawai and Nishida (corrected by a factor of 2), Tammann and Boehme (corrected by a factor of 1.5), and Alexander et al. Least accurately known probably are the surface tensions of solid silver as determined by Sawai and Nishida, and of copper in a lead vapor atmosphere as determined by Sears and by Bailey and Watkins (alternate analysis). The several measurements and their averages, together with estimated errors, are given in Table 5.

3. GRAIN AND TWIN BOUNDARY TENSIONS

All known grain and twin boundary tensions have been calculated from measurements of dihedral angles at the junction of three interfaces. Except for coherent twin boundaries, which have strongly orientation-dependent tensions, equation (2.8) has been employed in the calculation of relative boundary tensions. Usually a mean boundary tension for the particular texture present is determined from a large number of individual measurements.

Notation is simplified in the copper/lead/vapor systems if the phases of interest are denoted by subscripts as follows:

solid copper	1
liquid lead saturated with copper	2
lead vapor	3
copper vapor	none

The interfacial tensions then become

γ_{11} copper/copper (grain boundary)
γ_{12} copper/liquid lead
γ_{13} copper/lead vapor
γ_{1} copper/copper vapor
γ_{23} liquid lead/lead vapor

Ratios of many pairs of these tensions have been determined. They are:

	Ratio	*Investigator*
(1)	γ_{11}/γ_{12}	Smith[1]
(2)	γ_{11}/γ_{13}	Bailey and Watkins,[11] Fullman[14]
(3)	γ_{11}/γ_{1}	Bailey and Watkins[11]
(4)	γ_{12}/γ_{23}	Sears,[10] Bailey and Watkins[11]
(5)	γ_{13}/γ_{23}	Sears,[10] Bailey and Watkins[11]

A direct measurement of γ_1 is available from the work of Udin, Shaler, and Wulff,[7] and values for γ_{23} have been estimated by Sears[10] and by Bailey and Watkins.[11] Table 6 summarizes the

TABLE 6

SUMMARY OF INTERFACIAL TENSION RATIOS IN COPPER/LEAD/VAPOR SYSTEMS

$\gamma_{1'}$ = copper/copper tension
γ_{12} = copper/liquid lead tension
γ_{13} = copper/lead vapor tension
γ_1 = copper/copper vapor tension
γ_{23} = liquid lead/lead vapor tension

Investigator	Specimen	Interfaces	Time, Temperature	Ratio
Smith	99 Cu + 1 Pb	γ_{11}/γ_{12}	1 hr at 900°C	1.82
Smith	99 Cu + 1 Pb	γ_{11}/γ_{12}	2 hr at 700°C	1.69
Smith	99 Cu + 1 Pb	γ_{11}/γ_{12}	14 hr at 600°C	1.72
Smith	97 Cu + 3 Pb	γ_{11}/γ_{12}	24 hr at 600°C	1.64
				1.72
Bailey, Watkins	Cu in Pb vapor + Argon	γ_{11}/γ_{13}	2 hr at 900°C	0.65*
Bailey, Watkins	Cu in Pb vapor + H_2	γ_{11}/γ_{13}	2 hr at 900°C	0.86*
Bailey, Watkins	Cu in Pb vapor + H_2	γ_{11}/γ_{13}	8 hr at 800°C	0.86*
Fullman	Cu in Pb vapor + H_2	γ_{11}/γ_{13}	100 hr at 945°C	0.65 ±0.02
				0.65
Bailey, Watkins	Cu in Argon	γ_{11}/γ_1	2 hr at 900°C	0.35
Bailey, Watkins	Cu in H_2	γ_{11}/γ_1	2 hr at 900°C	0.35
Bailey, Watkins	Cu in H_2	γ_{11}/γ_1	14 hr at 800°C	0.38
				0.36
Sears	Pb drops on Cu	γ_{12}/γ_{23}†	8 hr at 800°C	1.28*
Bailey, Watkins	in Argon	γ_{12}/γ_{23}‡	900°C	0.56
Bailey, Watkins	in H_2	γ_{12}/γ_{23}‡	900°C	0.90
Bailey, Watkins	in H_2	γ_{12}/γ_{23}‡	800°C	0.92
				0.79
Sears	Pb drops on Cu	γ_{13}/γ_{23}†	8 hr at 800°C	1.80
Bailey, Watkins	in Argon	γ_{13}/γ_{23}‡	900°C	1.55
Bailey, Watkins	in H_2	γ_{13}/γ_{23}‡	900°C	1.89
Bailey, Watkins	in H_2	γ_{13}/γ_{23}‡	800°C	1.86
				1.78
Udin, Shaler, Wulff	See Table 3	γ_1	950–1050°C	1430 dynes/cm
Sears	See text	γ_{23}	800°C	400 dynes/cm
Bailey, Watkins	See text	γ_{23}	900°C	466 dynes/cm
Bailey, Watkins	See text	γ_{23}	800°C	435 dynes/cm
				435 dynes/cm

* Not averaged.

† Not independent. Determined simultaneously.

‡ Not independent. Determined simultaneously, using also values of γ_{11}/γ_{12} and γ_{11}/γ_{13}. Alternate analysis (see text).

values obtained for the five ratios, and for γ_1 and γ_{23}. Consideration of the relative accuracies of these values will facilitate estimation of the best value of the copper/copper grain boundary tension γ_{11}.

Smith measured dihedral angles at a large number of randomly selected copper/copper/lead interface junctions that had been equilibrated at high temperatures, where lead is liquid, and then cooled rapidly to room temperature. The angles were grouped according to size in steps of 5°, the group corresponding to 65°, for example, containing all angles in the range $62\frac{1}{2}° < \theta < 67\frac{1}{2}°$. The angle corresponding to the middle of the largest group was taken as the true dihedral angle.

TABLE 7

ANALYSIS OF BAILEY AND WATKINS' DIHEDRAL ANGLE MEASUREMENTS ON A TYPICAL SPECIMEN

(Copper heated 8 hr at 800°C in hydrogen plus unsaturated lead vapor, then sectioned normal to free surface)

Number of boundaries observed to intersect surface:	212
Discarded boundaries:	
Twin boundaries	154
Boundaries not normal to surface	12
Selected boundaries:	
Dihedral angles not measurable or too large	34
Dihedral angles photographed and measured	12

Measured angles in order of size:

119°	128°	129°	132°
123°	128°	129°	144°
124°	128°	132°	157°

Probable true angle: 129°

Bailey and Watkins measured three angles: (1) the thermally etched groove angle at the intersection of a grain boundary with a free copper surface in a lead vapor atmosphere, (2) the thermally etched groove angle at the intersection of a grain boundary with a free copper surface in a hydrogen or argon atmosphere, and (3) the advancing contact angle for liquid lead flowing over solid copper.

Their procedure in measuring dihedral angles is summarized in Table 7. Sections normal to the surface of a thermally etched and plated sample were examined, and boundaries intersecting the original surface were noted. Twin boundaries and boundaries not normal to the surface were discarded. Of the remaining boundaries the quarter having the smallest angles, and therefore being most nearly perpendicular to the plane of the section, were photographed and the angles measured. The angle about which the measurements clustered was taken as the true angle.

There is a fault in Bailey and Watkins' analysis of the advancing contact angle for liquid lead flowing over solid copper. Although they assume equilibration and balance of surface tensions parallel

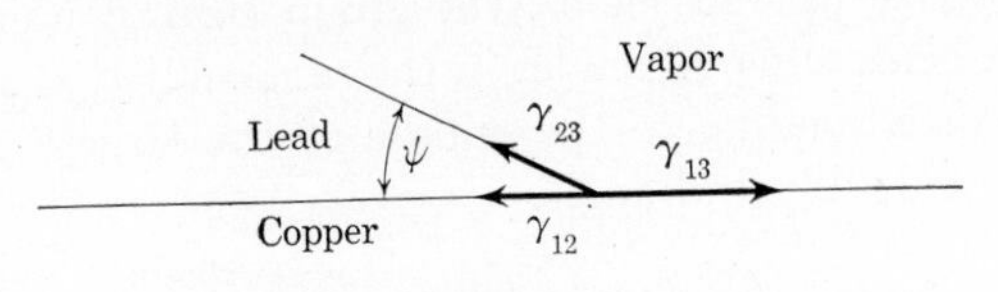

(*a*) Bailey and Watkins (11)

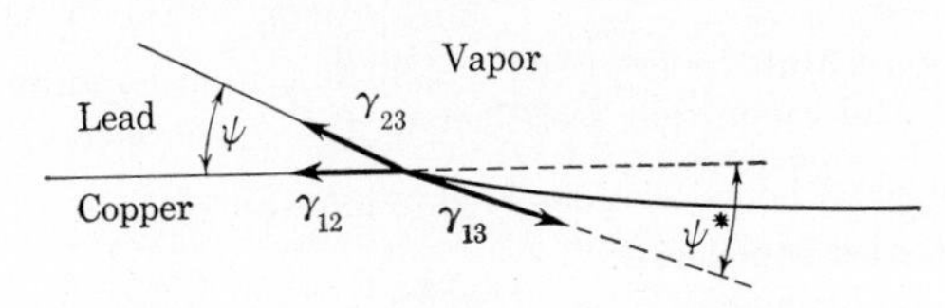

(*b*) Fisher and Sears (unpublished)

FIG. 3. Assumed interface configuration at the junction of the three phases: solid copper, liquid lead, vapor.

to the copper surface, they assume nonequilibrium dihedral angles and unbalance of surface tensions perpendicular to the surface. For orientation-independent tensions, such unbalance is not allowable at equilibrium. Figure 3 shows their assumed interface configuration and an alternative configuration proposed by Fisher and Sears.[15] The lead is advancing to the right.

Bailey and Watkins balanced surface tensions parallel to the copper surface according to the equation

$$\gamma_{13} = \gamma_{12} + \gamma_{23} \cos \psi, \tag{3.1}$$

whereas the alternate analysis balances surface tensions, both parallel and perpendicular to the surface, according to the two equations

$$\gamma_{13} \cos \psi^* = \gamma_{12} + \gamma_{23} \cos \psi, \tag{3.2}$$

$$\gamma_{13} \sin \psi^* = \gamma_{23} \sin \psi, \tag{3.3}$$

introducing at the same time the additional unknown ψ^*. The additional equations

$$\gamma_{11} = 2\gamma_{12} \cos (\theta/2), \tag{3.4}$$

$$\gamma_{11} = 2\gamma_{13} \cos (\phi/2), \tag{3.5}$$

$$\gamma_{23} = \text{known value}, \tag{3.6}$$

required in both analyses refer to the interface configurations shown in Fig. 4.

Although it is not certain that the alternate configuration is correct, or that an advancing contact angle measurement is ade-

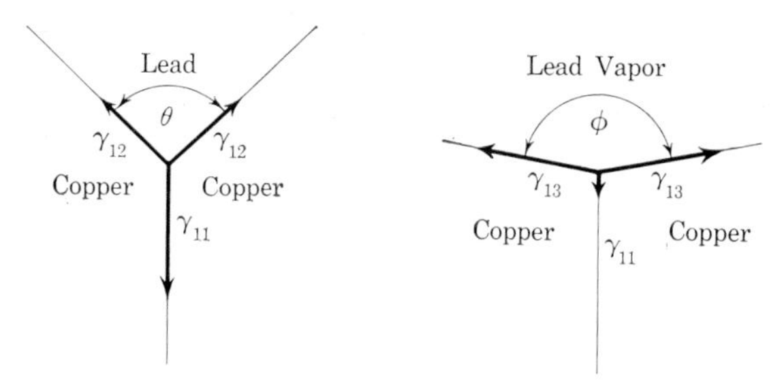

FIG. 4. Interface configurations at copper/copper/lead and copper/copper/vapor junctions.

quate for unique determination of the interfacial tensions in question, the alternate analysis probably is a step in the right direction. Surface tensions determined by both methods of analysis are compared in Table 8. Because the angle ψ^* is small, the two analyses lead to very similar results.

Fullman made a taper section at an angle of approximately 9° to the surface of a copper specimen that had been thermally etched in a lead vapor atmosphere, cooled, and copper-plated. He then measured interfacial angles at grain boundary intersections. Assuming that the grain boundaries were perpendicular to the free surface (they ran all the way through the thin sheet), and noting the angle between the grain boundary trace and the surface trace, he was able to calculate the true dihedral angle at each thermally etched groove. He obtained the frequency spectrum given in Fig. 5, for which the mean angle is $142.0 \pm 1.4°$.

The method whereby Sears determined dihedral angles already has been described, as has the determination of γ_1 by Udin, Shaler, and Wulff. The surface tension of liquid lead saturated with copper has been estimated by Sears to be $\gamma_{23} = 400$ dynes/cm at 800°C, and by Bailey and Watkins to be $\gamma_{23} = 435$ dynes/cm at 800°C and $\gamma_{23} = 466$ dynes/cm at 900°C. The latter estimates were based upon measurements of the surface tension of liquid lead by Bircumshaw[16] and by Sauerwald and Drath,[17]

TABLE 8

Comparison of Interfacial Tensions Calculated from Data of Bailey and Watkins[11]

(Upper values, original analysis; lower values, alternate analysis.)

γ_{11} = copper/copper tension
γ_{12} = copper/liquid lead tension
γ_{13} = copper/lead vapor tension
γ_{1} = copper/copper vapor tension
γ_{23} = liquid lead/lead vapor tension

Temperature, °C	Gas Phase	γ_{23}	γ_{13}	γ_{12}	γ_{11}	γ_{1}
800	H_2 + Pb	435	780 810	380 400	670 700	
800	H_2					1750 1840
900	H_2 + Pb	466	810 880	360 420	700 750	
900	H_2					2000 2170
900	Argon + Pb	466	740 720	290 260	560 470	
900	Argon					1600 1350

and of the surface tension of copper by Sauerwald and Drath,[17] using a simple mixtures rule. An independent estimate suggests that the value $\gamma_{23} = 435$ dynes/cm probably is very nearly correct in the temperature range of 800 to 900°C.

In obtaining mean values for the several ratios in Table 6, Bailey and Watkins' values of γ_{11}/γ_{13} were not averaged with Fullman's value for it was felt that Fullman's determination was significantly more accurate. Sears' value of γ_{12}/γ_{23} was not averaged with Bailey and Watkins' values, for there is evidence that Sears' value is not accurate. Examination of photographs of cross sections of Sears' lead drops[18] indicates that the interface configuration may be as sketched in Fig. 6, rather than as assumed in Fig. 2. Although the calculated ratio γ_{13}/γ_{23} is not strongly

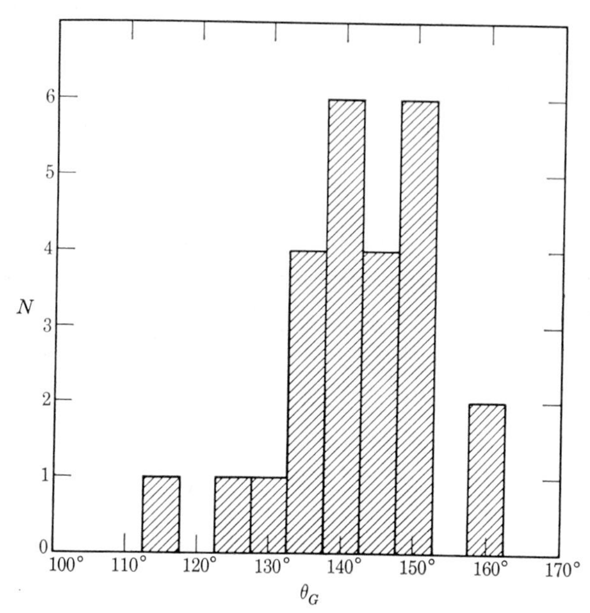

FIG. 5. Frequency spectrum for thermally etched groove angle at the intersection of a grain boundary with the free surface of copper in a lead vapor atmosphere. (After Fullman.[14])

influenced by such a change in configuration, the ratio γ_{12}/γ_{23} can change by a factor in the neighborhood of two when the angle α increases from zero to 5°.

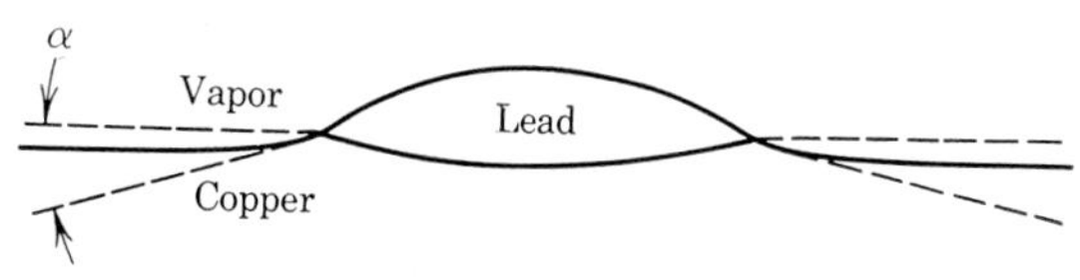

FIG. 6. Probable interface configuration for Sears' lead drop experiments.[10,18]

The copper/copper grain boundary tension γ_{11} can be obtained from any of the following relationships:

$$\gamma_{11} = \gamma_1(\gamma_{11}/\gamma_1), \tag{3.7}$$

$$\gamma_{11} = \gamma_{23}(\gamma_{12}/\gamma_{23})(\gamma_{11}/\gamma_{12}), \tag{3.8}$$

$$\gamma_{11} = \gamma_{23}(\gamma_{13}/\gamma_{23})(\gamma_{11}/\gamma_{13}), \tag{3.9}$$

together with the data in Table 6. The first relationship gives $\gamma_{11} = 515$ dynes/cm, the second gives $\gamma_{11} = 590$ dynes/cm, and the third gives $\gamma_{11} = 505$ dynes/cm. A fourth value of γ_{11} has been determined by Van Vlack,[19] using the methods described in Table 1 of C. S. Smith's paper (Paper 14). Starting with an absolute measurement of the interfacial tension between liquid Cu_2S and liquid Cu, Van Vlack determined $Fe_\gamma/Cu_{liq.}$, $Fe_\gamma/Cu_2S_{liq.}$, Fe_γ/Fe_γ, Fe_γ/Cu, and Cu/Cu interfacial tensions. His value of the Cu/Cu interfacial tension was $\gamma_{11} = 595$ dynes/cm. The four values of γ_{11} are summarized in Table 9, and the final mean value of γ_{11} is 550 ± 15 dynes/cm.

TABLE 9

Grain Boundary Tension in Copper: Summary

(Data from Table 6)

γ_{11} = Copper/copper tension

$\gamma_{11} = \gamma_1(\gamma_{11}/\gamma_1)$	$= 1430(0.36)$	$= 515$
$\gamma_{11} = \gamma_{23}(\gamma_{12}/\gamma_{23})(\gamma_{11}/\gamma_{12})$	$= 435(0.79)(1.72)$	$= 590$
$\gamma_{11} = \gamma_{23}(\gamma_{13}/\gamma_{23})(\gamma_{11}/\gamma_{13})$	$= 435(1.78)(0.65)$	$= 505$
Van Vlack[19]		$\gamma_{11} = 595$

The mean value of γ_{11} is 550 ± 15 dynes/cm.

Apparently the only other grain boundary tension known is that of gamma iron, determined by Van Vlack.[19] He obtained the value $\gamma_{Fe/Fe} = 850$ dynes/cm.

Twin boundary free energies have been measured by Dunn, Daniels, and Bolton[20] and by Fullman.[14,21,22]

Twin boundaries are said to be coherent when the composition plane and the twinning plane are identical. The boundary then is characteristically plane, and its surface tension has a fixed value in a single component system. Two complications arise in interpreting dihedral angle measurements when one of the interfaces is a coherent twin boundary. First, the coherent twin boundary tension is small relative to the variation of grain boundary tension with orientation, so that serious errors can be introduced by assuming an "average" grain boundary tension for two arbitrary grain boundaries meeting at a grain/twin/grain junction. Second, coherent twin boundaries are perfectly plane, coinciding with (111) planes of both a grain and its twin in face-centered cubic metals and with (112) planes in body-centered cubic metals, and they never have been observed to migrate normal to themselves.

The proper interpretation of these observations appears to be that the free energy of the boundary between twinned grains increases abruptly as the boundary is rotated from the coherent position. Because the work required to create a unit area of any interface equals its surface tension only for extensions parallel to the interface, it is essential, in employing the surface tension method, to avoid virtual displacements of a three-grain intersection that correspond to rotation of an interface having a highly orientation-dependent tension. In particular, virtual displacements that produce rotation of a coherent twin boundary do not correspond to zero work by equilibrium surface tensions, whereas displacements that produce rotation of noncoherent grain boundaries having only slight orientation dependence do. In order to determine coherent twin boundary tensions, therefore, only virtual displacements parallel to the twin boundary should be contemplated. Surface tensions, as forces, are equilibrated only parallel to twin boundaries and not perpendicular to them.

Dunn, Daniels, and Bolton[20] have measured the ratio of the coherent twin boundary tension to the grain boundary tension for a single twin in 3.5 per cent silicon iron. The particular grain boundaries chosen had relative interfacial tensions of approximately 1.0 according to Fig. 9, as determined from the orientation differences of the associated grains and the known dependence of interfacial tension upon orientation in silicon iron. The technique was that of producing a three-grain specimen of predetermined crystal orientation by a method of controlled grain growth in sheet material.[23] Two grains were grown having twinned orientation with respect to each other, and the third grain was grown with another known orientation. Upon annealing, the grain boundary separating the twinned grains migrated to the coherent position and became characteristically plane. Equilibration of interfacial tensions parallel to the coherent interface then led to $\gamma_t/\gamma_{gb} = 0.22$ for the ratio of the coherent (112) twin boundary tension to the mean grain boundary tension in 3.5 per cent silicon iron.

Fullman[14] has made extensive studies of the coherent twin boundary tension of copper. The first determinations were based upon measurements of the dihedral angles at junctions of twin boundaries and grain boundaries similar to those sketched in Fig. 7. Each grain group studied consisted of a grain and included twin abutting against another grain. The thin sheet specimen was deformed slightly, and the orientations of the various grains were deduced from the location of the twin boundaries and of the slip band traces. Measurement of the apparent interfacial angles then allowed calculation of the true dihedral angles, θ_1, θ_2, θ_3, θ_4.

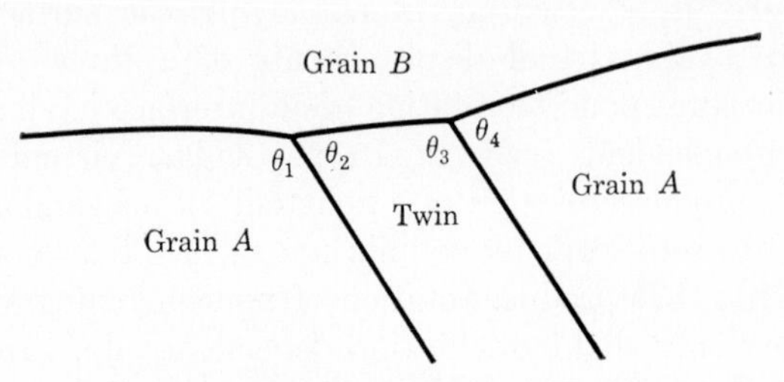

FIG. 7. Twin and grain boundary junctions examined by Fullman.[14]

If these four angles are known, equilibration of interfacial tensions parallel to the twin boundaries at the two intersections gives the equations

$$\gamma_{AB} \cos \theta_1 + \gamma_{tB} \cos \theta_2 + \gamma_t = 0 \quad (3.10)$$

$$\gamma_{AB} \cos \theta_3 + \gamma_{tB} \cos \theta_4 + \gamma_t = 0 \quad (3.11)$$

from which the surface tension ratios

$$\gamma_t/\gamma_{AB} = (\cos \theta_2 \cos \theta_4 - \cos \theta_1 \cos \theta_3)/(\cos \theta_3 - \cos \theta_2)$$

$$\gamma_t/\gamma_{tB} = (\cos \theta_2 \cos \theta_4 - \cos \theta_1 \cos \theta_3)/(\cos \theta_1 - \cos \theta_4)$$

can be calculated.

Measurement of such ratios at twenty-seven grain configurations similar to that in Fig. 7 gave a mean value $\gamma_t/\gamma_{gb} = 0.045$ (± 0.003 probable error of the mean) for the ratio of the coherent twin boundary tension to the grain boundary tension. Taking the copper grain boundary tension as 550 dynes/cm, we find the corresponding coherent twin boundary tension to be $\gamma_t =$ 25 dynes/cm.

An alternative method of measurement of the twin boundary tension, employed by Fullman,[14] is measuring the thermally etched groove angles at the intersection of a coherent twin boundary and a free copper surface in the presence of lead vapor. A thermally etched and copper-plated surface was sectioned at an angle of approximately 9°, to magnify the depth of the groove angle. It was assumed that all twin boundaries were normal to the copper surface, as had been demonstrated previously for the texture in question. Thirty-three measurements of the thermally etched

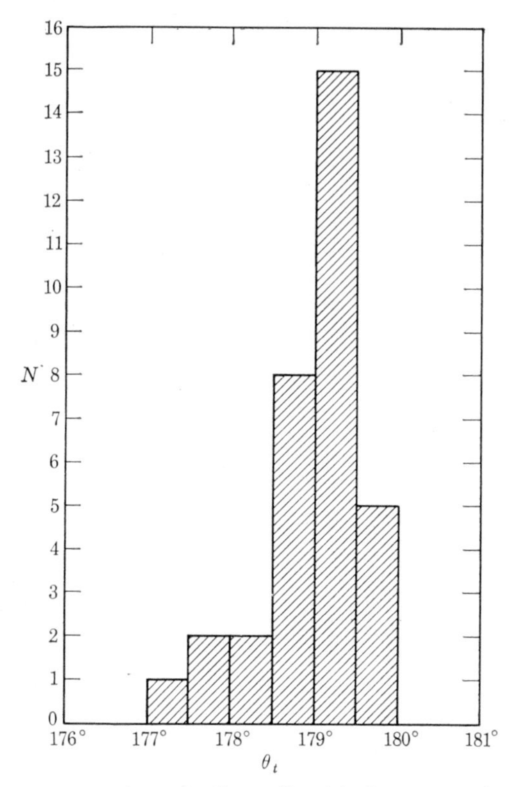

FIG. 8. Frequency spectrum for thermally etched groove angle at the intersection of a twin boundary with the free surface of copper in a lead vapor atmosphere. (After Fullman.[14])

groove angle, summarized graphically in Fig. 8, gave a mean ratio $\gamma_t/\gamma_{13} = 0.0168 \pm 0.0013$ of twin boundary tension to surface tension for copper in a lead vapor atmosphere. Taking a value of 760 dynes/cm for γ_{13}, the corresponding absolute value of the coherent twin boundary tension is $\gamma_t = 13$ dynes/cm. The mean of the two values, based upon Fullman's measurements, is $\gamma_t = 19 \pm 4$ dynes/cm.

The noncoherent twin boundary interface in copper, corresponding to the noncoherent interfaces at the steps in stepped twins or at the ends of twins that stop inside grains, has been shown by Fullman[21] to be an interface having a definite orientation relationship to the twin pair. The plane of the interface lies near a (113) plane of one twin and a (335) plane of the other. By measurement of the dihedral angles at forty-three junctions of a noncoherent twin boundary and two ordinary grain boundaries, he determined the ratio of the noncoherent twin boundary tension to

TABLE 10

Twin Boundary Tensions: Summary

γ_t = twin boundary tension
γ_{gb} = grain boundary tension
γ_{13} = copper/lead vapor tension

Investigator	Material	Boundary	Ratio	Absolute Value
Dunn, Daniels, Bolton	3.5% silicon iron	Coherent, (112)	$\gamma_t/\gamma_{gb} = 0.22$	
Fullman[14]	Copper	Coherent, (111)	$\gamma_t/\gamma_{gb} = 0.045$	25
Fullman[14]	Copper	Coherent, (111)	$\gamma_t/\gamma_{13} = 0.0168$	13
Fullman[22]	Aluminum	Coherent, (111)	$\gamma_t/\gamma_{gb} = 0.21$	
Fullman[21]	Copper	Noncoherent, ~ (113), (335)	$\gamma_t/\gamma_{gb} = 0.80$	440
Dunn, Daniels, Bolton	3.5% silicon iron	Noncoherent, arbitrary	$\gamma_t/\gamma_{gb} = 0.83$	

The mean value of the coherent (111) twin boundary tension in copper is $\gamma_t = 19 \pm 4$ dynes/cm.

the average grain boundary tension to be 0.80. The large value observed for the noncoherent twin boundary tension in copper is in agreement with the value 0.83 found by Dunn, Daniels, and Bolton[20] for the ratio of an arbitrary noncoherent twin boundary tension to the average grain boundary tension in 3.5 per cent silicon iron.

The coherent twin boundary energy of aluminum has been measured by Fullman[22] in the following manner. He examined a number of intersections where twin or near-twin interfaces joined two grain boundary interfaces, and measured the dihedral angle opposite the twin boundary. A plot of dihedral angle versus the departure from true twin orientation gave a curve from which the dihedral angle corresponding to a coherent twin could be determined. The corresponding ratio of coherent twin boundary tension to grain boundary tension is $(\gamma_t/\gamma_{gb})_{Al} = 0.21$.

The several measurements of relative twin boundary tensions are summarized in Table 10.

4. VARIATION OF GRAIN BOUNDARY TENSION WITH ORIENTATION

Relative grain boundary tensions in 3.5 per cent silicon iron have been determined by Dunn and Lionetti[24] and by Dunn, Daniels, and Bolton,[20,25] for known differences in orientation.

The method employed was high temperature equilibration of the boundaries of three grains in sheet specimens, each grain having been grown to a predetermined orientation by means of a controlled grain growth process. There are two groups of data corresponding to two series of measurements, in each of which a known crystallographic direction in each grain was held normal to the sheet surface. The first is a (110) series in the range 0 to 90° difference in orientation, and the second is a (100) series in the range 0 to 45° difference in orientation.

There are two degrees of freedom in a series such as the (110) series of Dunn and associates, in which each of the three grains involved has a (110) plane normal to the sheet, and the grain boundary also is normal to the sheet. First, and probably of greatest importance, a grain can be rotated through an angle Δ relative to coincidence with a neighbor. This angle Δ will be called the "orientation difference" between the two grains. Second, and probably of lesser importance, the interface between two grains of orientation difference Δ can assume an arbitrary angle with respect to the crystallographic axes of either grain. It is assumed that the variation of grain boundary tension with respect to orientation depends primarily upon Δ, particularly when Δ is small.

Dihedral angles were measured for each three-grain group, and relative grain boundary tensions were calculated. Equation 2.8 was employed except for highly orientation-dependent interfaces, where surface tensions were balanced only parallel to the orientation-dependent interface. Each specimen led, therefore, to two or three proportional (that is, in correct proportion but of unknown magnitude) grain boundary tensions for known orientation differences.

The (110) series contained five specimens, each with one boundary near $\Delta = 15°$ orientation difference. With the relative grain boundary tension of a 15° boundary in the (110) series defined as unity, a curve similar to that shown in Fig. 9 was constructed. The slope of the tentative curve near $\Delta = 15°$ allowed small corrections to be made in the relative tensions of the five boundaries near $\Delta = 15°$, and the final curve in Fig. 9 was obtained. In order to plot the data from three-grain groups not containing a

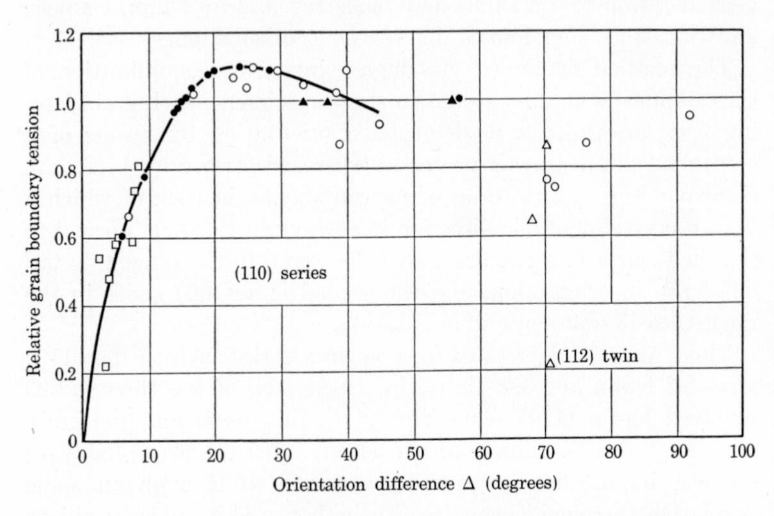

FIG. 9. Relative grain boundary tension versus orientation difference in silicon iron. (110) series. Open circles from reference 24, squares from reference 25, triangles from reference 20. Solid circles and triangles fitted to curve.

15° boundary, the proportional surface tensions of each group were multiplied by a factor that brought one of the two or three points in question into coincidence with the curve.

The curve corresponding to the (100) series, given in Fig. 10, was constructed entirely by the curve fitting method. It was assumed that a smooth curve of grain boundary tension versus Δ existed, and each set of proportional tensions from a single specimen was multiplied by an adjusting factor so that the smoothest curve was obtained. Although the shape of the curve in Fig. 10 was determined in part subjectively, it is probable that other investigators would arrive at substantially the same curve.

It should be pointed out that the relative grain boundary tensions in Figs. 9 and 10 are given to the same scale, a three-grain group connecting the two series having been prepared and measured by Dunn, Daniels, and Bolton.[25]

The most interesting fact made evident by the curves in Figs. 9 and 10 is the rapid decrease of boundary tension with orientation difference for small orientation differences.

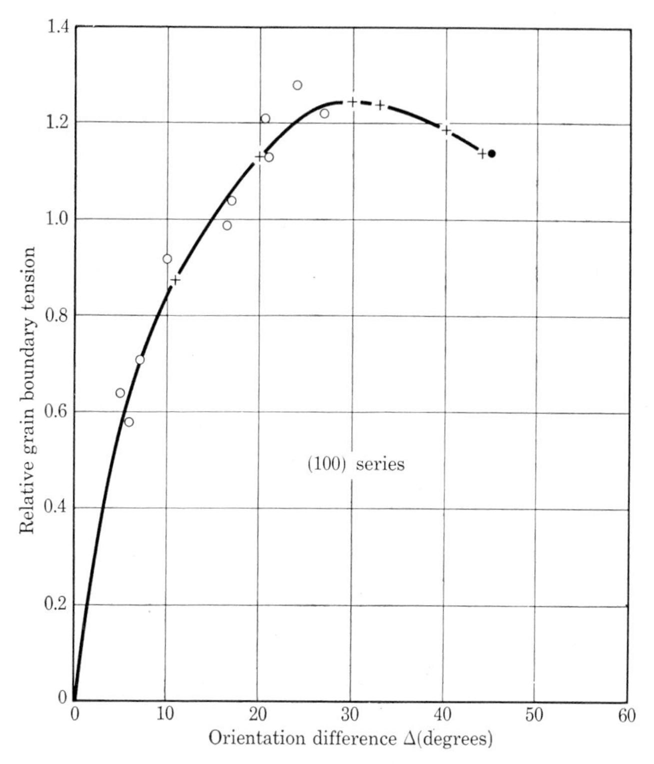

FIG. 10. Relative grain boundary tension versus orientation difference in silicon iron.[25] (100) series. Crosses fitted to curve. Solid circle is connecting point between (110) series and (100) series.

Beyond 45° orientation difference in the (110) series no curve can be drawn; near 70° a single curve would be meaningless, for variations of boundary orientation produce a wide range of interfacial tensions, as expected for boundaries separating twinned or nearly twinned grains.

Relative grain boundary tensions in tin (99.987 per cent purity) have been determined by Chalmers[26] and by Aust and Chalmers.[27]

Although the earlier work reported by Chalmers indicated no dependence of tension upon difference in orientation, the later work, extended to smaller orientation differences, showed a dependence similar to that for silicon iron.

Aust and Chalmers brought the boundaries of three-grain specimens to equilibrium by prolonged annealing at a temperature 10°

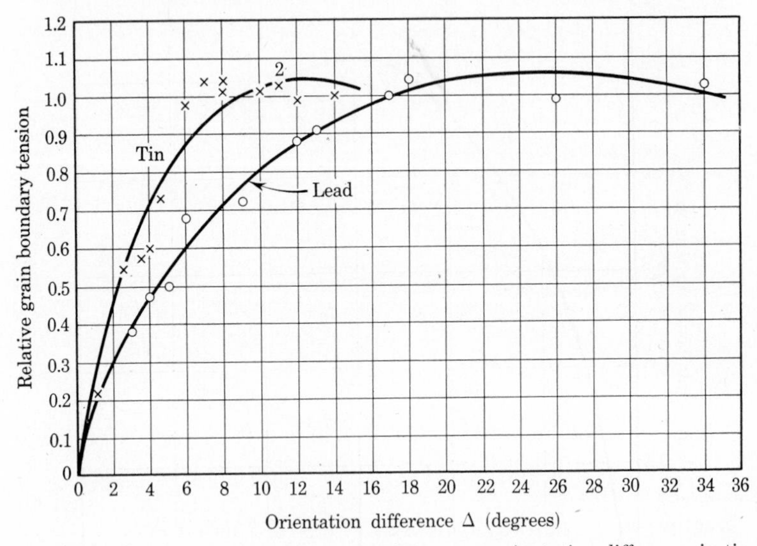

Fig. 11. Relative grain boundary tension versus orientation difference in tin (crosses), from data of Aust and Chalmers [27] and in lead (circles) from data of Aust and Chalmers.[28] Least square curves calculated from the formula $T = A\Delta - B\Delta \log \Delta$.[29]

below the melting point. The specimens were prepared by growing each grain from the melt with a predetermined orientation. In this way they prepared a series of specimens having the c-axes of two grains parallel, perpendicular to parallel flat specimen surfaces, and differing in orientation by a predetermined angle Δ. The c-axis of the third grain was rotated approximately 45° toward the boundary between the other two grains, providing two interfaces of practically constant tension independent of the value of Δ.

Results of the investigation of fourteen specimens having orientation differences from 0 to 15° are given in Table 11 and Fig. 11. As with silicon iron, the interfacial tension drops to zero as Δ approaches zero.

TABLE 11

SUMMARY OF AUST AND CHALMERS'[27] MEASUREMENTS OF THE INFLUENCE OF ORIENTATION DIFFERENCE UPON THE RELATIVE GRAIN BOUNDARY TENSION IN TIN

Orientation Difference, Δ	*Dihedral Angles (See Fig. 12)* e	c	b	*Relative Grain Boundary Tension,* γ_{gb}
14°	120°	119°	121°	1.00
12°	121°	121°	118°	0.99
11°	118°	119°	123°	1.03
11°	118°	120°	122°	1.03
10°	119°	121°	120°	1.01
8°	118°	122°	120°	1.03
8°	119°	118°	123°	1.01
7°	118°	124°	118°	1.03
6°	122°	116°	122°	0.97
4½°	137°	118°	105°	0.73
4°	145°	117°	98°	0.60
3½°	147°	119°	94°	0.57
2½°	149°	106°	105°	0.54
1°	168°	93°	99°	0.21

Aust and Chalmers have also determined the influence of orientation difference upon the interfacial tension of lead.[28] The experimental method was the same as that for tin, with the (100) direction of two grains being perpendicular to the plane faces of

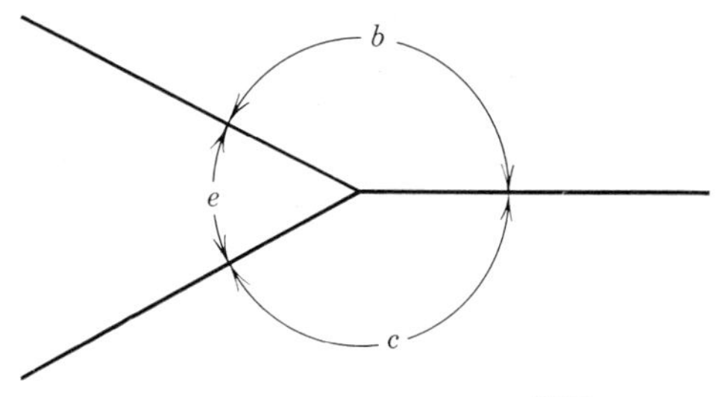

FIG. 12. Angles measured by Aust and Chalmers.[27,28] The two boundaries meeting with angle e are the standard boundaries; the third is the unknown with orientation difference Δ.

the specimen and the (100) direction of the third grain being rotated about 45° toward the interface between the other two. Table 12 and Fig. 11 summarize the data, which are in good agreement with those for silicon iron and tin.

TABLE 12

SUMMARY OF AUST AND CHALMERS'[28] MEASUREMENTS OF THE INFLUENCE OF ORIENTATION DIFFERENCE UPON THE RELATIVE GRAIN BOUNDARY TENSION IN LEAD

Orientation Difference Δ	*Dihedral Angles (See Fig. 12)* e	c	b	*Relative Grain Boundary Tension,* γ_{gb}
34°	119°	118°	123°	1.02
26°	121°	116°	123°	0.99
18°	117°	123°	120°	1.04
17°	120°	124°	116°	1.00
13°	126°	117°	117°	0.91
12°	128°	108°	124°	0.88
9°	138°	110°	112°	0.72
6°	140°	110°	110°	0.68
5°	151°	102°	107°	0.50
4°	153°	103°	104°	0.47
3°	158°	100°	102°	0.38

5. BEST VALUES FOR SURFACE TENSIONS

Fairly reliable values are known for the surface tensions of solid silver, copper, and gold, and for the surface tension of copper in a lead vapor atmosphere. They are:

$$\gamma_{Ag} = 1140 \text{ dynes/cm},$$
$$\gamma_{Cu} = 1430 \text{ dynes/cm},$$
$$\gamma_{Au} = 1510 \text{ dynes/cm},$$
$$\gamma_{Cu/Pb(v)} = 760 \text{ dynes/cm}.$$

Grain boundary tensions in copper and in gamma iron are also known:

$$\gamma_{Cu/Cu} = 550 \text{ dynes/cm},$$
$$\gamma_{Fe/Fe} = 850 \text{ dynes/cm},$$

as is the coherent twin boundary tension in copper,

$$\gamma_t = 19 \text{ dynes/cm}.$$

The relative variation of grain boundary tension with orientation difference of abutting grains has been measured for 3.5 per cent silicon iron, tin, and lead, as is shown graphically in Figs. 9–11. Table 10 lists a few twin-to-grain boundary tension ratios, for various boundary orientations, for twin related grains in copper, aluminum, and silicon iron.

REFERENCES

1. C. S. Smith, *Trans. AIME*, **175**, 15 (1948).
2. M. Faraday, *Trans. Roy. Soc. (London)*, **147**, 145 (1857).
3. J. C. Chapman and H. L. Porter, *Proc. Roy. Soc. (London)*, **83A**, 65 (1910).
4. H. Schottky, Gesell. Wiss. Göttingen, Nachr., *Math.—Phys. Klasse*, **4**, 480 (1912).
5. I. Sawai and M. Nishida, *Z. anorg. u. allgem. Chem.*, **190**, 375 (1930).
6. G. Tammann and W. Boehme, *Ann. phys.*, **12**, 820 (1932).
7. H. Udin, A. J. Shaler, and J. Wulff, *J. Metals*, **1**, 186 (1949).
8. B. H. Alexander, R. Baluffi, M. H. Dawson, H. P. Kling, and F. D. Rosi, "Self-Diffusion of Metals and Associated Phenomena III," Sylvania Electric Products, Inc., *Interim Technical Report*, May 8, 1950.
9. T. B. Rymer and C. C. Butler, *Proc. Phys. Soc. (London)*, **59**, 541 (1947).
10. G. W. Sears, *J. Appl. Phys.*, **21**, 721 (1950).
11. G. L. J. Bailey and H. C. Watkins, *Proc. Phys. Soc. (London)*, **63B**, 350 (1950).
12. A. K. Schellinger, *Science*, **111**, 693 (1950).
13. J. W. Obreimoff, *Proc. Roy. Soc. (London)*, **127A**, 290 (1930).
14. R. L. Fullman, *J. Appl. Phys.*, **22**, 448 (1951).
15. J. C. Fisher and G. W. Sears, to be published.
16. L. L. Bircumshaw, *Phil. Mag.*, **17**, 181 (1934).
17. F. Sauerwald and G. Drath, *Z. anorg. u. allgem. Chem.*, **162**, 301 (1927).
18. G. W. Sears, private communication.
19. L. H. Van Vlack, Thesis, University of Chicago, 1950.
20. C. G. Dunn, F. W. Daniels, and M. J. Bolton, *Trans. AIME*, **188**, 368 (1950).
21. R. L. Fullman, *J. Appl. Phys.*, **22**, 556 (1951).
22. R. L. Fullman, Unpublished research.
23. C. G. Dunn, *Trans. AIME*, **185**, 72 (1949).
24. C. G. Dunn and F. Lionetti, *Trans. AIME*, **185**, 125 (1949).
25. C. G. Dunn, F. W. Daniels, and M. J. Bolton, *Trans. AIME*, **188**, 1245 (1950).
26. B. Chalmers, *Proc. Roy. Soc. (London)*, **196A**, 64 (1949).
27. K. T. Aust and B. Chalmers, *Proc. Roy. Soc. (London)*, **201A**, 210(1950).
28. K. T. Aust and B. Chalmers, *Proc. Roy. Soc. (London)*, **204A**, 359 (1950).
29. W. T. Read, Jr., and W. Shockley, *Phys. Rev.*, **78**, 275 (1950).

DISCUSSION

ROY SHUTTLEWORTH (UNIVERSITY OF ILLINOIS):

The Equilibrium Shape of Crystals and Surface Forces

Every crystal surface (crystal-vapor boundary or grain boundary between two crystals of different orientation) has both a surface free energy (a scalar) and a surface tension (a symmetrical second-order tensor with, in general, three independent components). Although for a liquid the single independent component of the surface tension is numerically equal to the surface free energy, this is not so for a crystal.[1,2,3] Measurements have been made of the change in dimensions of metal wires due to surface forces;[4,5] of the equilibrium angles where three grain boundaries meet at a line;[6,7,8,9] and of the contact angle of a drop of one liquid metal resting on a crystal of another metal.[10,11] Since calculations have recently been made on the surface energies of grain boundaries[12,13] it is important to decide whether the experiments must be interpreted in terms of free energy or in terms of surface tension. It is concluded that the wire-pulling experiments[4,5] give a measure of $F_S - (R/L)F_B$ (where F_S and F_B are the free energies of the crystal surfaces and the grain boundaries, and R and L are the radius of the wire and the distance between grain boundaries); and that, since a solid can support a shear stress, the equilibrium angles between three crystal surfaces that meet at a line will depend on the surface free energies (not the tensions).

It is possible to write down explicit conditions for the equilibrium of a system subject to surface forces only if it is possible to neglect the strain energy in the interior of the system that is due to the surface forces. The strain energy can be neglected because of either of two assumptions: (*a*) *The system is supposed incompressible and unshearable, so that the strain is everywhere zero.* (*b*) *The system is supposed incompressible and viscous, so that in equilibrium the shear stress is everywhere zero.* Assumption *a* is usually an adequate approximation for a crystal;

[1] J. W. Gibbs, *Collected Works*, Vol. 1, p. 315, Longmans, Green and Co., London, 1876.

[2] R. Shuttleworth, *Proc. Phys. Soc.* (*London*), **63**, 444 (1950).

[3] C. Herring, *The Physics of Powder Metallurgy*, Chapter 8, McGraw-Hill Book Co., New York, 1950.

[4] H. Udin, A. J. Shaler, and J. Wulff, *J. Metals*, **1**, 186 (1949).

[5] B. H. Alexander, R. Baluffi, M. H. Dawson, H. P. Kling, and R. D. Rosi, "Self-diffusion of Metals and Associated Phenomena III," Sylvania Electric Products, Inc., *Interim Technical Report*, May 8, 1950.

[6] C. S. Smith, *Trans. AIME*, **175**, 15 (1948).

[7] C. G. Dunn and F. Lionetti, *Trans. AIME*, **185**, 125 (1949).

[8] C. G. Dunn, F. W. Daniels, and M. J. Bolton, *Trans. AIME*, **188**, 368 (1950).

[9] K. T. Aust and B. Chalmers, *Proc. Roy. Soc.* (*London*), **196A**, 64 (1949).

[10] G. L. J. Bailey and H. C. Watkins, *Proc. Phys. Soc.* (*London*), **A63**, 350 (1950).

[11] G. W. Sears, *J. Appl. Phys.*, **21**, 721 (1950).

[12] J. H. van der Merwe, *Proc. Phys. Soc.* (*London*), **A63**, 616 (1950).

[13] W. T. Read and W. Shockley, *Phys. Rev.*, **78**, 275 (1950). See also Paper 13 of this book.

assumption *b* is appropriate to a liquid. Assumption *b* will never be appropriate for a crystal because of the fundamental differences between a crystal and a liquid. In a liquid, but not in a crystal, there is no long-range order, and the atoms are in continuous movement. After a liquid has been sheared, the stresses can be relieved by independent local rearrangements of atoms; in a crystal strains must be relieved by a systematic movement of atoms. The force necessary to shear a liquid will be smaller the smaller the rate of shear, becoming zero in the limit. When a shearing stress is applied to a perfect crystal, reversible elastic deformations will first occur, and only at a finite critical shear stress will irreversible slip occur. Real crystals contain dislocations, which are not in thermal equilibrium, and movement of these dislocations will shear the crystal. If change of crystal shape occurs by the movement of dislocations due to surface forces, assumption *a* is not adequate, for besides the change in surface energy the change in energy of the dislocations must also be considered.

The fact that in a liquid the shear stresses can be relieved by local rearrangement is responsible for the equality between surface tension and surface free energy.

The mechanisms by which the equilibrium shapes are produced are quite different for liquids and crystals. In liquids the surface tension produces shear stresses, and there is a viscous flow of the whole liquid until these are relieved. In crystals the mechanisms of deformation involve changes only at the surface of the crystal, for example, evaporation-condensation, surface diffusion, volume diffusion of holes, grain growth.

Detailed Applications

Shape of an Isolated System. According to either assumption *a* or assumption *b*, the condition of minimum energy is that

$$\int F \, dA \text{ is a minimum,} \tag{D.1}$$

where dA is an element of area and F is the free energy per unit area of this element; the integral is taken over the whole surface of the system. For a crystal, F will be a function of crystal face, and, on the assumption of central forces, it is found that condition (D.1) predicts that the crystal will be a polyhedron with flat faces and sharp edges.[2] It is clear that because of surface tension in the crystal faces there will be dilatation stresses over the whole volume of the polyhedron and shear stresses in the edges and corners; however, for normal values of the elastic constants the energies associated with these stresses are negligible (see footnote 2, equation 10).

For a liquid, F is constant so that condition (D.1) predicts a sphere. For a liquid, but not for a crystal, the concept of surface tension can be used to calculate the equilibrium shape. When the surface tension has only one independent component* its effect at a point in a surface is that of a pressure, p, normal to the surface

$$p = \gamma(1/R_1 + 1/R_2), \tag{D.2}$$

where γ is the component of the surface tension, R_1 and R_2 are the radii of curvature in two perpendicular directions. Since a liquid cannot withstand a shear stress, p must be the same over the surface; γ is constant since the liquid is isotropic. The sphere is the only closed surface for which $1/R_1 + 1/R_2$ is constant.

Wire-pulling Experiments. Udin et al.[4] and Alexander et al.[5] have made experiments on the creep of thin polycrystalline wires at high temperatures. If no load is applied, the wires contract; under high load they extend viscously by as much as 5 per cent, whereas at an intermediate load they maintain constant length. Since neither assumption a nor assumption b is appropriate, it is necessary to know the change in energy of the imperfections during flow. Herring[15] has suggested that deformation occurs by the diffusion of holes from the grain boundaries to the surface of the wire. If this is so, there will be no change in the energy of imperfections other than the boundaries. Since the grain boundaries are perpendicular to the wire, the free energy of each crystal is

$$E_T = 2\pi RLF_S + \pi R^2 F_B, \tag{D.3}$$

where it is assumed that each crystal is cylindrical with dimensions R and L, and F_S and F_B are the free energies of the surfaces and the boundaries (assumed constant). The condition of minimum energy is

$$mg = \pi R[F_S - (R/L)F_B], \tag{D.4}$$

where mg is the load on the wire. Since initially $R/L \sim \frac{1}{2}$ and $F_B \sim \frac{1}{3}F_S$, the wire will contract if there is no load, decreasing the area of the surface and increasing the area of the grain boundaries.

Intersection of Three Crystal Surfaces. The condition of equilibrium where the interfaces between three fluids meet can be obtained by consideration of the mechanical equilibrium of the particles at the line

* The surface tension tensor of a crystal surface would have just one independent component provided it had a threefold (or greater) axis of symmetry.[2] (If this axis is taken as the z direction of a cartesian orthogonal reference frame, $x^2 + y^2$ is the only second-order polynomial in x, y that is invariant for such an axis.[14])

[14] F. G. Fumi, *Nuovo Cimento*, **5**, 59 (1949).

[15] C. Herring, *J. Appl. Phys.*, **21**, 437 (1950).

of intersection, since these particles are acted on only by the three surface tensions

$$\gamma_{12}/\sin\theta_3 = \gamma_{23}/\sin\theta_1 = \gamma_{31}/\sin\theta_2. \tag{D.5}$$

This result does not hold at the intersection of three crystal surfaces because, in general, shear stresses will contribute to the equilibrium of the particles at the line of intersection.

The original treatment[16] of the conditions of equilibrium at the intersection of three crystal surfaces was confused, and the result wrongly stated in the form of equation (D.5). Since any movement of the boundaries will occur by diffusion or grain growth, assumption *a* is appropriate. If it is supposed that the surface free energy of the boundary between two crystals depends only on the relative orientation between the crystals and not on the direction of the boundary, the condition of minimum energy is

$$F_{12}/\sin\theta_3 = F_{23}/\sin\theta_1 = F_{31}/\sin\theta_2. \tag{D.6}$$

For crystals, equations (D.5) and (D.6) cannot be satisfied simultaneously, and so there will be shear stresses around the line of intersection. Herring[3] generalized equation (D.6) to include the dependence of the free energy on the direction of the boundary.

If a liquid rests on a solid, equilibrium is rapidly established by the spreading of the liquid until the Dupré relation is satisfied:

$$F_S = F_{SL} + F_L\cos\theta. \tag{D.7}$$

During a much longer period of time, material is transported from one part of the solid to another until equation (D.6) is satisfied.

Bruce Chalmers (University of Toronto):

Little attention appears to have been paid so far to the importance of the atmosphere in relation to the surface tension of solids. There has been little or no direct experimental work on this topic, but there is indirect evidence in the study of the thermal etching of silver.[17] It was shown that the surface tended to be smooth when no oxygen was present and to become "corrugated" in the presence of oxygen. The processes are reversible. It follows that, in the presence of oxygen, the surface tension is considerably less for certain preferred crystallographic faces than for the random surface, whereas in the absence of oxygen this is not the case.

[16] R. Shuttleworth, R. King, and B. Chalmers, *Nature*, **158**, 482 (1946); *Proc. Roy. Soc.* (*London*), **A193**, 465 (1948).

[17] B. Chalmers, R. Shuttleworth, and R. King, *Proc. Roy. Soc.* (*London*), 1931, 465 (1948).

W. T. Read, Jr. (Bell Telephone Laboratories):

A. P. Greenough[18] has measured groove angles where grain boundaries meet the surface in silver bicrystals, the two grains having a variable orientation difference defined by a relative rotation about an axis lying in the boundary. A plot of the ratio of grain boundary to surface energy versus angle of misfit, together with the best-fit theoretical curve, is given in Paper 13 of this book.

W. Shockley (Bell Telephone Laboratories):

The striking difference between copper and aluminum regarding twin boundary energies as compared to grain boundary energies may be explained in terms of the difference in electronic structure of the two metals. If we assume, as seems probable, that the grain boundary energies are normal in the two cases, the data reported by Fisher and Dunn indicate that the twin boundary energy is about five times as large in aluminum as in copper. According to the work of Fuchs,[19] copper may be regarded as composed of a uniform electron gas in which positive copper ions float, interacting with each other with simple repulsive central force energies. For such a model, we would expect a very small energy difference to be produced by a fault on a (111) plane, which does not alter any of the distances between nearest neighbors. Aluminum, on the other hand, has three valence electrons per atom, which probably partially fill at least two Brillouin zones. Their wave functions thus resemble to some extent those which might arise in a crystal with valence bonding, and thus interactions between next nearest neighbors and in groups of more than two atoms might be important. This same line of reasoning has been followed at Bristol, according to Professor Mott, the work there having been stimulated by Barrett's report of the absence of twinning faults in aluminum. Professor Mott has suggested that the additional energy in aluminum may be interpreted in terms of extra reflections of electron waves at the twinning faults, which may be regarded as distorting the Brillouin zone boundaries.

C. Herring (Bell Telephone Laboratories):

Since some of the remarks made on this paper have evidenced an interest in the transport mechanism involved in the wire-pulling experiments, it may be worth calling attention to a paper[20] in which it is proposed that the elongation or shrinking of the wires is due to volume self-diffusion between the outer circumference and the grain boundaries,

[18] A. P. Greenough, *J. Inst. of Metals* (to be published).

[19] K. Fuchs, *Proc. Roy. Soc.* (*London*), **157**, 444 (1936); **153**, 622 (1936); **151**, 585 (1935).

[20] C. Herring, *J. Appl. Phys.*, **21**, 437 (1950).

a process first discussed by Nabarro.[21] The fairly good agreement obtained between the observed rates and those computed on this hypothesis suggests that most or all of the dislocations are unable to move very far out of their slip planes under the urging of the rather small departures of local vacancy concentration from equilibrium which occur in these experiments.

E. OROWAN (MASSACHUSETTS INSTITUTE OF TECHNOLOGY):

There is no reason for the suspicion, expressed in this paper, that the method of Obreimow for measuring the surface energy of mica may not satisfy the requirements of equilibrium and reversibility. In fact, the elastic curvature of the cleavage lamina from which the value of the surface energy is derived is determined while the cleaving knife blade rests. There can be little doubt that the value obtained for mica by the method of Obreimow represents the most accurately known surface energy of a solid. It is important to remark, however, that the original measurements of Obreimow have been improved in accuracy, and that his values were disfigured by a factor 4 due to a miscalculation. The main source of error in Obreimow's measurements was apparently the roughly cut edge of his mica lamellae; the present writer avoided this by using lamellae with ground edges. The corrected value of the surface energy of mica obtained in this way[22] was 4500 ergs/cm^2 in vacuum and 375 ergs/cm^2 in air.

The work of Udin, Shaler, and Wulff raises an interesting question. In the evaluation of their measurements it is assumed that the copper wires are cylinders which extend or contract uniformly at constant volume. Now these wires consisted of crystal grains the length of which has many times the diameter of the wire, and the grain boundaries were practically perpendicular to the wire axis, so that sliding of the grains along their boundaries did not occur. However, if a cylindrical crystal stretches or contracts by slip concentrated in slip planes, according to the usual picture of the process, the surface energy obtained from the measurements of Udin, Shaler, and Wulff is different from the value calculated with the assumption that the wire surface remains cylindrical and does not develop steps due to slip. Consider the simple case shown in Fig. D.1 of a slip plane at an angle α to the wire axis. The slip direction should be in the plane of the figure. If two parts of the crystal are displaced by the distance dx in the slip direction, the surface laid free is dx times the width of the crystal perpendicular to the slip direction, that is, $2r\,dx$, where r is its radius. The component of the displacement

[21] F. R. N. Nabarro, *Report of a Conference on the Strength of Solids*, p. 75, University of Bristol, England, Physical Society, London, 1948.

[22] E. Orowan, *Z. Physik*, **82**, 239 and 259 (1933).

parallel to the axis of the cylindrical crystal is $dL = dx \cos \alpha$, dL being the extension. Since the increase of the free energy is

$$2r\gamma\, dx = \frac{2\, r\gamma}{\cos \alpha}\, dL$$

the minimum force required for extension is $2r\gamma/\cos \alpha$, as against $\pi r\gamma$ in the case of the uniform extension of a cylinder. With $\alpha = 45°$, the difference is about 10 per cent; it may be considerably more if α is somewhat less. Besides, if the deformation mechanism is slip, the surface energy obtained is that of the slip plane (111). In the case of uniform extension, the measured value is a mean of the surface energies of the many high-indexed planes which make up the surface of the cylinder if this is assumed to be smooth. In reality, the surface of a metal annealed at a sufficiently high temperature is usually made up of submicroscopic facets of low-indexed planes, of which the total area may be as much as $\sqrt{3}$ times the macroscopic surface area if the facets are cube planes.

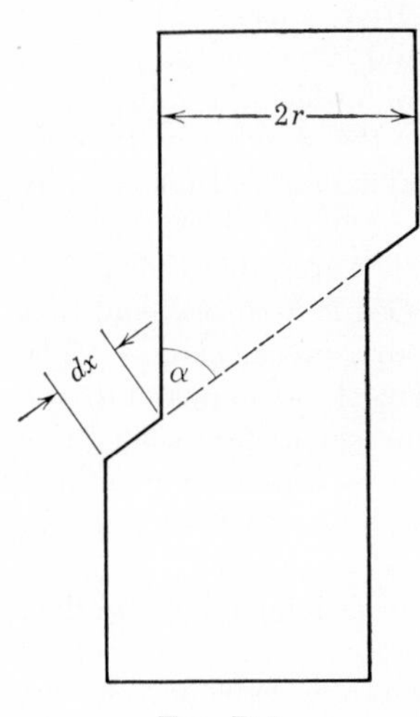

FIG. D.1

Although the order of magnitude of the final result is not in doubt, the surface energy cannot be determined with an uncertainty less than, for instance, plus or minus 15 or 20 per cent without knowledge of the deformation mechanism of the wires under the given experimental conditions; nor can it be recognized which crystallographic plane it is whose surface energy is measured. The surface energies of low-indexed planes may differ from those of high-indexed planes by factors of the order of 2 or even 3.

F. C. FISHER (*in reply*):

The authors appreciate the contributions of the several discussors, particularly that of Read, in calling their attention to Greenough's measurements, now summarized in Paper 13 of this book.

As pointed out by Shuttleworth, the influence of transverse grain boundaries should have been taken into consideration in calculating the surface tensions of solid metals from the forces required to prevent extension or contraction of wires and foils. The corresponding surface tension values summarized in the paper should be increased by a factor in the neighborhood of 1.15, as should the grain boundary tension values derived therefrom.

Regarding the question as to whether surface tensions or surface free energies have been measured, it should be pointed out that experimental investigations of surface and grain boundary tensions generally have proceeded with the assumption that metals behave like liquids. To this degree of approximation, tension and free energy presumably are interchangeable.

13.

Dislocation Models of Grain Boundaries

W. T. READ, JR., AND W. SHOCKLEY

Bell Telephone Laboratories, Murray Hill, N. J.

ABSTRACT

For grain boundaries joining two crystallites which have been rotated relative to one another by a small angle θ, the geometrical conditions rigidly limit the choice of the dislocation model and thus lead to definite predictions which can be compared with experiment. For any fixed arbitrary orientation of the grain boundary and axis of relative rotation of the adjoining grains, the energy per unit area satisfies the formula $E = E_0\theta[A - \ln \theta]$, where E_0 and A are parameters dependent on the model. E_0 is calculable directly from the elastic constants and the dislocation model, and A requires, in addition, the energy of atomic disorder at the core of a dislocation. The available experimental curves of relative E vs. θ for silicon-iron, tin, and lead are in good agreement with the formula, even for values of θ larger than are justified by the derivation. A theoretical estimate of the absolute energy of a random grain boundary in copper agrees within 30 per cent with the average experimental values. The difference between energy and free energy is shown to be unimportant for boundaries with small θ.

1. GEOMETRY OF A SIMPLE BOUNDARY

Grain boundaries with small angles of misfit provide a particularly suitable field for the application of dislocation theory. In most branches of metal physics, predictions from dislocation theory can be made to fit almost any experimental observations by choice of a suitable dislocation array. However, the geometry of a small-angle grain boundary rigidly limits the choice of a dislocation model. Usually crystal geometry does not uniquely determine the model but limits the choice to only a few reasonable possibilities. In the specific examples which we consider in Section 5 of this paper only two models are involved. The energies of the several models can be calculated, and the model giving the lowest energy can be taken as representing a grain boundary in a well-annealed specimen. Because grain boundary energies can be measured experimentally, a quantitative check between theory and experiment is possible. It will be shown that, by using anisotropic elasticity, an energy parameter E_0 can be calculated which can also be measured experimentally. The calculation of E_0 involves knowing the energy only in regions of elastic distortion, so that E_0 is uniquely determined by the elastic constants c_{ij} of the metal and the dislocation model. To illustrate the physical significance of E_0 and the other terms in the energy expression, we consider a grain boundary having a simple dislocation model, and then derive, by physical reasoning, a formula for the energy as a function of the angle of misfit of the adjoining grains. The formula will later be extended to the general case of an arbitrary grain boundary.

Figure 1*a* shows two crystals of cubic symmetry having a common cube axis and an angle of misfit θ, defined by the rotation of each crystal through $\theta/2$ radians away from the boundary, which is a plane of symmetry. If these two grains are joined to form a bicrystal, the misfit can be taken up in two ways: (1) by atomic misfit on the boundary, the crystals themselves being undistorted, and (2) by an elastic distortion of the grains extending over relatively large areas, the atomic disorder being confined to certain localized areas on the grain boundary, as illustrated in Fig. 1*b*. It is evident that, for small-angle grain boundaries, the second method of joining gives the lower total energy. The local regions of atomic disorder in Fig. 1*b* are line imperfections extending indefinitely at right angles to the figure. If a circuit is made around such a line imperfection, going from atom to atom along cube edges in such a way that the algebraic sum of the jumps along each cube edge vanishes, the circuit will have a closure failure defining an edge dislocation (Shockley and Read, Paper 2 of this book). Thus the line imperfections required by the geometry of a small-angle grain boundary are, by definition, dislocations. The type of model shown in Fig. 1*b* has been discussed by Bragg[1] and Burgers.[2]

The spacing D between dislocations is seen to be related to the angle of misfit and atomic spacing b* by

$$\frac{b}{D} = 2 \sin \frac{\theta}{2} \doteq \theta, \tag{1.1}$$

where the approximation holds for small angles. When θ is large, the dislocations are so close together that all the misfit is taken

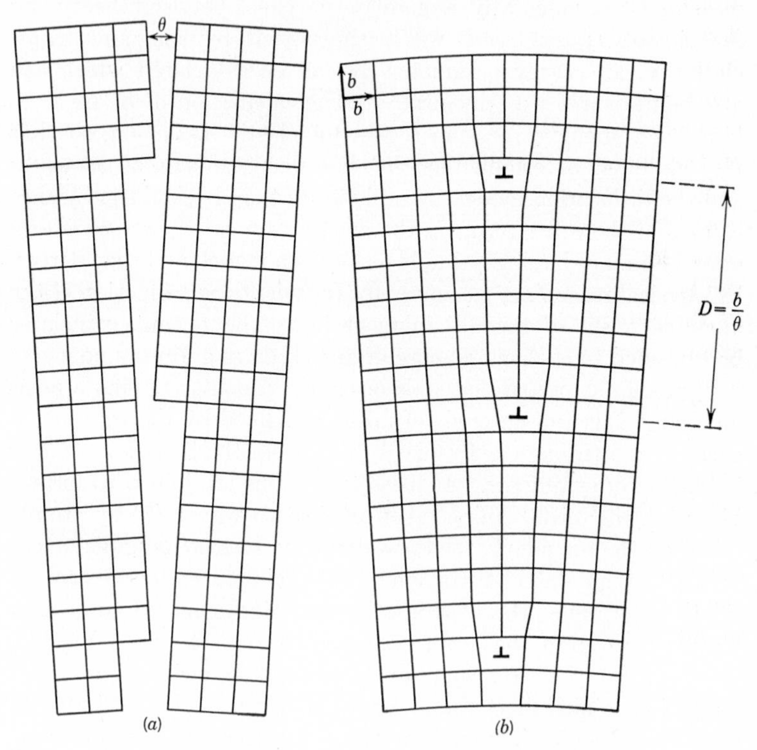

FIG. 1. Simple grain boundary showing (*a*) two grains with common crystal axis and (*b*) method of joining and dislocation model.

up by atomic disorder on the boundary, and the foregoing methods (1 and 2) of joining the grains are equivalent. In such a large-angle grain boundary, the relations between atoms on the boundary are similar to those existing in a liquid, so that a large-angle grain boundary is equivalent to a layer of liquid a few atomic spacings in

* We shall use b to mean the magnitude of the slip, or Burgers vector. In a previous paper[3] dealing with simple cubic lattices, $b = a =$ lattice constant.

thickness. However, the older theory of an amorphous phase of substantial width is now regarded as physically unreasonable.

Figure 1*b* illustrates the two types of energy in a grain boundary: (1) the energy of elastic distortion spread over regions of extent comparable to the spacing between dislocations and (2) the energy of atomic disorder confined to localized regions, each within a few atomic spacings of a dislocation. In the following section, we derive, by physical reasoning, a formula for the energy of the simple grain boundary in Fig. 1*b*. It is found that the formula contains two parameters: the energy parameter E_0, which can be evaluated by elasticity theory, and a parameter A, which depends on the energy of atomic disorder at a dislocation, and cannot be evaluated by elasticity theory. The form of the formula, however, is determined entirely by elasticity theory. That is, by considering only the elastic energy, a simple differential expression can be set up for the grain boundary energy as a function of angle; in the integration of this expression, the unknown energy of atomic misfit enters as an undetermined constant of integration.

2. DERIVATION OF THE ENERGY FORMULA FOR A SIMPLE GRAIN BOUNDARY

In deriving the energy of the simple grain boundary of Fig. 1*b*, we shall need only one result from anisotropic elasticity theory: the expression for the component τ of shearing stress in the slip direction and on the slip plane of a single dislocation. Letting R be the perpendicular distance from the dislocation axis, assumed to be an infinite straight line, we have*

$$\tau = \tau_0 \frac{b}{R} + \tau_1 \left(\frac{b}{R}\right)^2 \cdots \tau_n \left(\frac{b}{R}\right)^{n+1} \cdots, \tag{2.1}$$

where τ_0 is uniquely determined by the slip vector, whose length is b, and the elastic constants of the anisotropic material. The coefficients $\tau_1 \cdots \tau_n \cdots$ are determined by the interaction of the elastically strained material with the disordered material near the dislocation axis, where equation (2.1) does not apply. If we are interested in the stress only at distances of many atomic spacings from the dislocation, only the first term in equation (2.1) need be considered. Also the first term is the only one which contributes to the dependence of the energy on the size of the crystal; or, when

* It is planned to derive this result in a later paper.

many dislocations are present having stress fields which cancel at large distances, the first term in equation (2.1) is the only one which gives an energy dependence on the size of the stressed region. In contrast, the other terms in equation (2.1) represent a localized elastic energy, which may be added to the inelastic energy of the dislocation core to give a total concentrated energy per dislocation, depending on atomic misfit. This local energy will occur in the formula for the energy per dislocation in a grain boundary as an undetermined constant of integration.

The dislocation model of the grain boundary in Fig. 1*b* consists of a vertical row of edge dislocations, as indicated in the figure by the symbol $\perp$. Because of the symmetry of the boundary, only a single type of dislocation is required. To calculate the energy, we could sum the stress fields due to an infinite vertical row of dislocations and integrate the stress energy over the entire domain. However, a much simpler procedure is possible, based on the following physical reasoning. Let us consider the energy per dislocation as the sum of three energies, E_{I}, E_{II}, and E_{III}, as shown in Fig. 2*a*. E_{I} is the energy inside a circle of radius $r_l \sim b$, within which the distortion is inelastic. E_{II} is the energy in the region of elastic distortion between the circle of radius r_l and a circle of radius $R \gg b$, where R is proportional to, but sufficiently smaller than, D so that inside R the stress can be assumed to be due entirely to the included dislocation. E_{III} is the elastic energy in the remainder of the strip. Now let θ decrease by $d\theta$, so that D and R acquire increments given by

$$\frac{dR}{R} = \frac{dD}{D} = -\frac{d\theta}{\theta}, \tag{2.2}$$

and consider the changes in the three energies. By hypothesis, the energy E_{I} remains the same, since neither the area nor the energy density changes. The energy E_{III} also remains the same as a result of the following two compensating effects of increasing R: (1) corresponding elements of area vary as R^2; (2) the energy density at corresponding points varies as $1/R^2$. To prove the second effect, consider that all the linear dimensions, including b, increase in proportion to R. The energy density will then remain the same at corresponding distances from the dislocation; that is, the whole picture will simply be photographically enlarged. The effect of increasing b in proportion to R is to increase the energy density as R^2, since both stress and strain are proportional to b. Thus, for constant b, the energy density must vary as $1/R^2$. Hence we conclude that the energy E_{II} is the only energy which

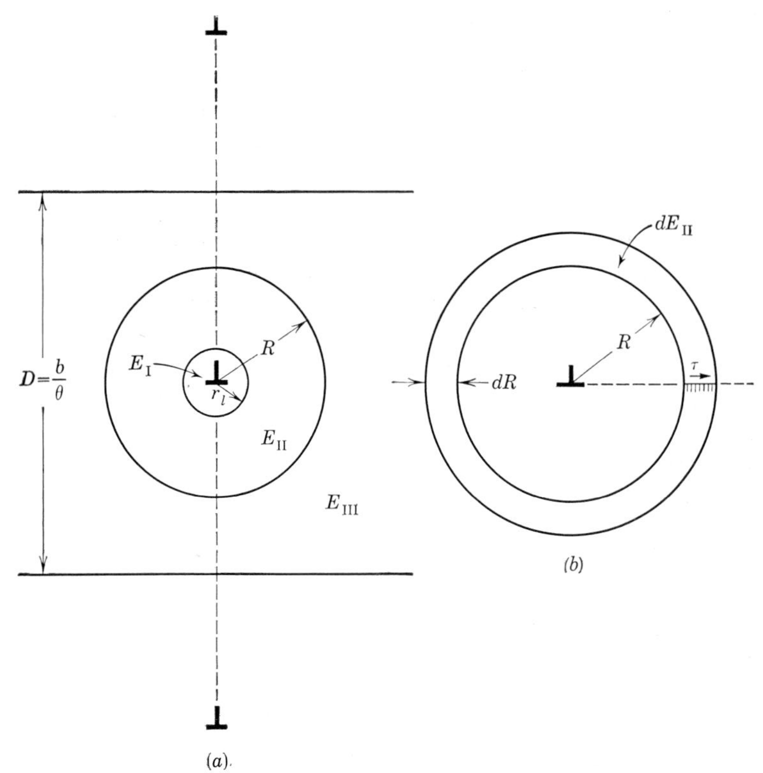

FIG. 2. Steps in calculating grain boundary energy. (a) The three types of energy, E_{I}, E_{II}, and E_{III}, in the grain boundary of Fig. 1b. (b) Change in energy per dislocation due to decrease in θ and corresponding increase in R, which is inversely proportional to θ.

varies with θ. If E is the energy per unit area of the boundary, $E/D = E\theta/b$ is the energy per dislocation per unit length, and

$$\frac{d}{d\theta}\left(\frac{E\theta}{b}\right) = \frac{dE_{\text{II}}}{d\theta}\,. \tag{2.3}$$

Because the stress inside the circle of radius R remains constant as θ changes, the increment dE_{II} is due to the increase in area alone and is equal to the energy in a ring bounded by circles of radii

R and $R + dR$, with their centers at the dislocation (Fig. 2b). In this ring the distortion is elastic, and the stress, by hypothesis, can be considered to be due entirely to the included dislocation; hence the energy is readily calculated if the elastic stress field around a single dislocation is known. The following simple calculation involves knowing only the shearing stress τ equation (2.1). The energy in the ring is equal to the work done on the boundary in the virtual (equilibrium) process of forming the dislocation. Thus it is equal to one half the product of surface stress and displacement integrated over the complete boundary, which includes not only the two circles, but also the connecting section of slip plane. According to dislocation theory, the stress varies as R and the displacement is independent of R, except for a rigid body translation of each circle. Hence the integrated product of stress and displacement is equal and opposite on the two circles, except for the contribution of the rigid body displacement, which vanishes since the net force on each circle necessarily vanishes. Thus the energy dE_{II} in the ring is equal to simply the work done by the force $\tau\, dR$ (Fig. 2), acting through the slip distance b, and we have

$$dE_{\text{II}} = \tfrac{1}{2}\tau b\, dR. \tag{2.4}$$

If we substitute equations (2.1), (2.2), and (2.3) in equation (2.4), and neglect higher order terms in b/R in equation (2.1), the simple differential expression (2.4) becomes

$$\frac{d}{d\theta}\left(\frac{E}{\theta}\right) = \frac{b\tau_0}{2}\frac{1}{\theta}. \tag{2.5}$$

Thus we have obtained from elasticity theory alone an expression for the variation in energy with angle. Integrating gives

$$\begin{aligned} E &= E_0\theta[A - \ln \theta] \\ &= E_0\theta[1 - \ln (\theta/\theta_m)], \end{aligned} \tag{2.6}$$

where θ_m, the angle of maximum E, is determined by the unknown constant of integration $A = 1 + \ln \theta_m$, which involves the energy of atomic disorder. The parameter

$$E_0 = \frac{b\tau_0}{2} \tag{2.7}$$

is uniquely determined by anisotropic elasticity in terms of the elastic constants and Burgers vector.

The unknown parameter A involves not only the unknown inelastic energy E_{I} inside the circle of radius r_l where Hooke's law fails, but also the contribution to the elastic energy, E_{II}, of terms dependent on the unknown boundary conditions on the boundary of the elastic region, for example, the higher order terms in equation (2.1). These terms give an unknown elastic energy $E_{\mathrm{II}'}$ independent of θ (for small θ) and probably comparable in magnitude to E_{I}. To determine the relative contributions to A of the unknown energy $E_{\mathrm{I}} + E_{\mathrm{II}'}$, dependent on interatomic forces, and the known elastic energy, it is necessary to calculate the elastic energy from the superimposed stress fields of an infinite array of dislocations. The authors have done this in a previous paper,[3] using isotropic elasticity. The result is

$$A = 1 + \ln \frac{b}{2\pi r_l} + \frac{2}{b^2 \tau_0} [E_{\mathrm{I}} + E_{\mathrm{II}'}], \tag{2.8a}$$

in which the first two terms include the contribution of E_{III} and

$$E_0 = \tfrac{1}{2} b\, \tau_0 = Gb/4\pi(1 - \sigma) \tag{2.8b}$$

where G is the rigidity modulus and τ is Poisson's ratio.

As discussed in the previous paper, the unknowns r_l and $E_{\mathrm{I}} + E_{\mathrm{II}'}$ can be represented by a single parameter $r_0 < r_l$, giving

$$A = 1 + \ln \frac{b}{2\pi r_0} . \tag{2.9}$$

From equation (2.6) we see that, if grain boundary energies are measured and plotted as E/θ vs. $\ln \theta$, the theory predicts that the points will fall on a straight line, of which the slope is given by E_0 (2.7). Hence the calculated value of E_0 can be directly compared with experimental measurements, and by such comparisons it should be possible to establish precisely what pattern of dislocations makes up the grain boundary. Another objective of comparing theory and experiment is to estimate and interpret the energy $E_{\mathrm{I}} \sim E_{\mathrm{II}'}$, which involves the region in which the strain is so large that Hooke's law fails.

The foregoing derivation assumes a uniform spacing of dislocations so that the energy per dislocation is the same for every dislocation. For example, in Fig. 1b, there is one dislocation every seven atomic planes, corresponding to $\theta = 1/7$ radian. However, when $1/\theta$ is not integral, the dislocations cannot be uniformly spaced; $1/\theta = 7.5$ would correspond to alternate spacings of seven and eight atomic planes. In reference 3 we have shown that this nonuniform spacing introduces an infinite number of cusps in the E vs. θ curve, but this fine structure is unimportant except for certain prominent cusps, such as correspond to twin or other symmetrical boundaries of low indices.

3. EXTENSION TO THE GENERAL CASE

The grain boundary in the last section was a particularly simple one having but a single degree of freedom. Actually, an arbitrary grain boundary has five degrees of freedom: three degrees of freedom of relative rotation of the adjoining grains and two degrees of freedom of rotation of the boundary with respect to the two grains. Read and Shockley[3] have treated the case of a two-degree-of-freedom boundary in which the grains have a common crystal axis and the plane of the boundary is allowed to rotate about the common axis. Frank[4] has given a formula for the dislocation content of an arbitrary, five-degree-of-freedom, grain boundary. When the misfit is small, this formula can be readily derived by the following simple physical reasoning. Let the arbitrary misfit between two grains A and B be defined by a relative rotation of magnitude θ about an axis parallel to the unit vector $\mathbf{u}$. Now choose an arbitrary vector $\mathbf{r}$ lying in the grain boundary, and define the vector $\mathbf{r}'$ having the same crystallographic indices in crystal B that $\mathbf{r}$ has in A. For small θ, the vectors $\mathbf{r}$ and $\mathbf{r}'$ are related by $\mathbf{r}' = \mathbf{r} + \mathbf{u} \times \mathbf{r}\theta$; that is, the relative rotation $\theta\mathbf{u}$ which brings the two grains into perfect register will bring $\mathbf{r}$ and $\mathbf{r}'$ into coincidence. We can, therefore, construct a Burgers circuit, or circuit which would close in a perfect crystal (Shockley and Read, second paper of this book), connecting the end points of the vectors $\mathbf{r}$ and $\mathbf{r}'$ and passing through the grain boundary at their common origin. The closure failure $\mathbf{r}' - \mathbf{r}$ is equal to the sum of the Burgers vectors of the dislocation lines enclosed by the loop, that is, cut by $\mathbf{r}$. Thus we have the theorem that the sum $\mathbf{S}$ of the Burgers vectors of the dislocation lines cut by an arbitrary vector $\mathbf{r}$ lying in the grain boundary is

$$\mathbf{S} = \mathbf{u} \times \mathbf{r}\theta. \tag{3.1}$$

By making two different choices of $\mathbf{r}$ in equation (3.1) we can determine the complete dislocation content of the boundary.

Clearly, if the axis of relative rotation **u** lines in the grain boundary, all the dislocation lines will be parallel to **u**. When the misfit has a twist component, the dislocation lines form a crossed grid.

If there are more than three possible Burgers vectors, several different dislocation arrays can be constructed, each of which satisfies the condition (3.1) for the resultant dislocation content. The best model is then taken to be the one giving the lowest grain boundary energy.

From equation (3.1) we see that the dislocation densities are proportional to θ. It will be convenient to define a quantity N_i as the density per unit θ of the ith dislocation type, the density being measured for each type in a direction normal to the dislocation axis.

To determine the energy in the general case, we can use, for each dislocation type separately, the same argument used for the single type in Fig. 1*b*. By summing over all types, we again obtain the general result

$$\begin{aligned} E &= E_0\theta[A - \ln \theta] \\ &= E_0[1 - \ln (\theta/\theta_m)], \end{aligned} \tag{3.2}$$

where now

$$E_0 = \tfrac{1}{2}\sum N_i b_i^2 \tau_{0i}, \tag{3.3}$$

the sum being taken over all dislocation types. For each type, the corresponding τ_0 is determined from elasticity theory in terms of the elastic constants and the orientation of the slip vector and dislocation axis.

Thus the two-parameter formula, derived for the simple grain boundary, applies in the general case of a boundary with five degrees of freedom, both the calculable parameter E_0 and (probably) also the unknown parameter A varying with the orientation of the grain boundary and axis of relative rotation.

The foregoing derivation assumes that the dislocation model of the grain boundary consists entirely of complete, or perfect, dislocations. In a face-centered cubic metal, it is possible that a boundary containing dislocation lines lying on (111) type planes might lower its energy by dissociating into two boundaries consisting of partial dislocations* and connected by stacking faults.

* See Paper 2 in this volume, Section 5. Partial dislocations are also called half dislocations and complementary pairs are called extended dislocations. These are discussed more fully in reference 5 of this paper.

Even in an arbitrary boundary some dislocations might lower their energies by making a zigzag course running alternately along different (111) type planes and dissociating into partial dislocations on each plane, the partial dislocations coming together whenever there is a shift from one plane to another, as discussed by Shockley and Read (second paper in this book). In the special case of a pure twist boundary on a (111) type plane, the boundary could be made up entirely of partial dislocations and stacking faults. These possibilities constitute an interesting field for investigation, in which comparison of theoretical and experimental results might lead to a better understanding of the role played by partial dislocations in metals. In the present paper, however, only boundaries containing complete dislocations will be considered.

4. COMPARISON WITH EXPERIMENTAL MEASUREMENTS OF RELATIVE ENERGIES

The quantities E_0 and A vary with the orientation of the grain boundary. Read and Shockley[3] estimate that A varies by about $\pm$ 0.15 for a two-degree-of-freedom boundary as the plane of the boundary rotates about the common crystal axis of the adjoining grains. If all the dislocations are of the same type crystallographically, E_0 will vary with grain boundary orientation in proportion to the total density of dislocations, since in equation (3.2) E_0 multiplies the term representing the constant localized energy per dislocation. For the two-degree-of-freedom boundary considered by Read and Shockley,[3] E_0 is proportional to $(\sin \phi + \cos \phi)$, where ϕ lies between 0° and 90° and represents the angle between the grain boundary and the average [100] axis of the adjoining grains.

Thus experimental measurements of grain boundary energy vs. θ would be expected to show some scatter if the orientation of both the grain boundary and the axis of relative rotation were not kept constant. However, by taking a large number of points, we can obtain an average experimental curve to compare with the theory.

Recently Dunn and co-workers[6] measured grain boundary energies in silicon ferrite (about 3.5 weight per cent silicon, body-centered cubic) on a relative scale as a function of the angle of misfit, θ. These experiments were especially well suited for comparison with the theory, since the orientation of the axis of relative rotation was held constant, in one set of measurements along a [110] direction, in another set along a [100] direction. The grain boundary, therefore, had only two degrees of freedom. The orientation of the boundary plane about the common axis was not measured, and varied at random. Using a similar experimental technique, Aust and Chalmers[7,8] measured relative grain boundary energies in tin and lead.

All four sets of measurements, which are tabulated and discussed by Fisher and Dunn in Paper 12 of this book, were well fitted with curves of the form (3.2). Since all the measurements were on a relative scale, the values of E_0 were unknown, and therefore cannot be compared with the numerical predictions of the theory. However, by putting equation (3.2) in the dimensionless form

$$\frac{E}{E_m} = \frac{\theta}{\theta_m}[1 - \ln(\theta/\theta_m)], \tag{4.1}$$

where

$$E_m = E_0\theta_m, \tag{4.2}$$

the form of the theoretical curve can be checked. If the measured relative energies are plotted as E/E_m vs. θ/θ_m, where θ_m is obtained from the maximum of the best-fit curve for each set of measurements, then the theory predicts that all the points should be represented by the single formula (4.1). Figure 3 is a plot of the experimental points, together with the equation (4.1). The values of θ_m for the four sets of measurements are listed on the figure.

We see that the theoretical curve fits the data over a much larger range of angles than would be expected from the assumptions made in the derivation. This is probably due to a fortunate cancellation of errors, as well as to the fact that θ_m, which is important at large angles, is arbitrary in the theory, and is chosen to make the curve fit at large angles.*

The fact that the form of the theoretical curve is followed up to the maximum energy suggests that the theoretical value of the

* Van der Merwe[9] has given a more detailed mathematical analysis of intercrystalline boundary energies, making use of a number of approximate assumptions regarding interatomic forces, including a sine law of stress and strain for planes of atoms on the boundary. The resulting energy versus θ curve agrees with the present one at small angles, but has no maximum, and consequently gives a poor fit to the data at large angles. This may be explained in part on the basis of criticisms of the sine law by W. M. Lomer.[10]

maximum energy $E_m = E_0\theta_m$ may give a good approximation to the relatively constant energy in the flat part of the curve at large angles. The energy level of this part of the curve is important because a grain boundary, picked at random, would probably have an energy in this range. In order for the boundary to have an energy appreciably less than the maximum, all three of the

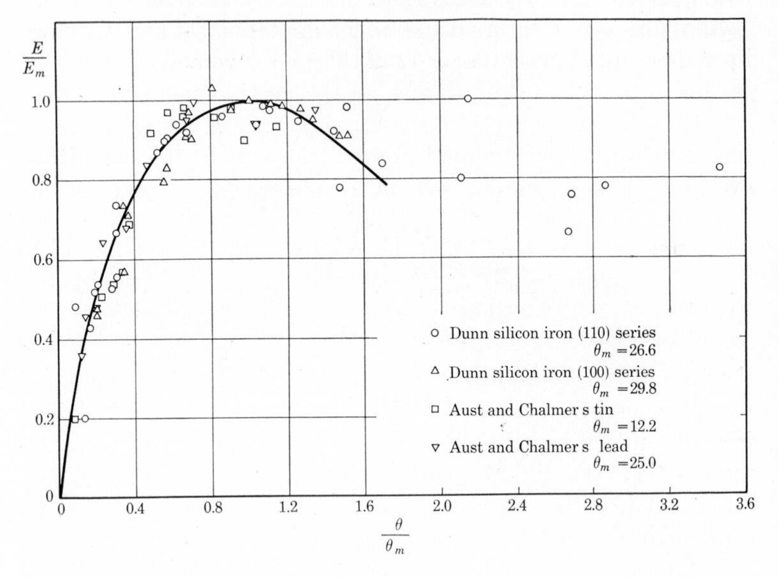

FIG. 3. Comparison of experimental data with the $E_m\theta(1 - \ln \theta/\theta_m)$ formula.

angles which specify the relative orientation of the grains must be small; and this is unlikely except in a controlled boundary. A statistical analysis by C. S. Smith[11] is in agreement with the view that random grain boundaries have approximately the same energies. The absolute values of measured grain boundary energy in copper discussed by Fisher and Dunn (in Paper 12 of this book) apply to a random grain boundary and consequently can be compared with the theoretical values of $E_m = E_0\theta_m$. In Section 5 we calculate E_0 for several boundaries, using anisotropic elasticity. In Section 6 we compare the calculations with the experimental measurements, thus providing a quantitive check on the theory.

5. CALCULATION OF E_0

To evaluate E_0 for most actual metals, it is necessary to use anisotropic elasticity in calculating τ_0 for the various dislocation types required. For almost isotropic crystals, such as aluminum and tungsten, isotropic elasticity is a good approximation, and involves considerably less computation, especially when the dislocation axis is not parallel to a simple crystallographic direction. We shall review briefly the general isotropic case, and then consider a few simple grain boundaries in anisotropic crystals.

For a pure edge dislocation,[12]

$$\tau_0 = \frac{G}{2\pi(1 - \sigma)}, \tag{5.1}$$

where G is the shear modulus and σ is Poisson's ratio. For a pure screw,

$$\tau_0 = G/2\pi. \tag{5.2}$$

In all cases it is to be remembered that $b\tau_0/R$ is the component of shearing stress on the slip plane and in the slip direction (Section 2). In the general case, where the dislocation axis makes an angle α with the slip vector, the slip vector may be resolved into edge and screw components leading to

$$\tau_0 = \frac{G}{2\pi}\left[\frac{\sin^2 \alpha}{1 - \sigma} + \cos^2 \alpha\right] \tag{5.3}$$

from which the shear stress in the slip direction can be obtained for any orientation of the dislocation axis.*

In an anisotropic crystal the shear stress in the slip direction depends on the orientation of the dislocation axis, not only in respect to the slip vector [as in (5.3)], but also in respect to the crystal axes. Eshelby[13] has treated the case of edge dislocations in anisotropic materials, the orientation of the dislocation axis being arbitrary in the plane normal to the slip vector. In most cases, however, it is necessary to consider also screw components. When the dislocation axis is normal to a plane of crystal symmetry,

* The slip plane is the plane containing both the slip vector and the dislocation axis. When these coincide, that is, for a pure screw dislocation, the slip plane is arbitrary, and, in the isotropic case, the shear stress is found to be the same on all planes containing the dislocation axis.

the screw components can be treated separately and added to the edge components. If the dislocation axis is parallel to one of the crystal axes of a cubic crystal, the shearing stress associated with the screw component is given by the same formula as in the isotropic case, taking $G = c_{44}$.

For an edge dislocation in a cubic crystal with the dislocation axis [001], as in Fig. 1, and the slip vector [100], Eshelby's results give

$$\tau_0 = (c_{11} + c_{12})(c_{44}c_{44}'/c_{11}c_{11}')^{1/2}/2\pi, \tag{5.4}$$

where the primed quantities are the elastic constants referred to the set of axes, [110], [1̄10], [001], and are given in terms of c_{11}, c_{12}, and c_{44} by

$$\begin{aligned} c_{11}' + c_{12}' &= c_{11} + c_{12}, \\ c_{44}' &= \frac{c_{11} - c_{12}}{2}, \\ c_{11}' &= \frac{c_{11} + c_{12} + 2c_{44}}{2}. \end{aligned} \tag{5.5}$$

Clearly τ_0 is the same for both [100] and [110] Burgers vectors when the dislocation axis is [001].

In this section we shall consider, as an example, a grain boundary between two face-centered cubic crystallites having a common [001] axis and an angle of misfit θ, as in Fig. 1. Now, however, we introduce another degree of freedom by letting the boundary rotate about [001], making an angle ϕ with the mean of the [100] directions in the two grains. Taking $\mathbf{r}$ in equation (3.1) parallel to the axis of relative rotation [001] gives $\mathbf{S} = 0$, which means that the dislocation lines run parallel to [001]. Taking $\mathbf{r}$ in (3.1) as a unit vector at right angles to the [001] axis, we obtain

$$\mathbf{S} = [\theta \sin \phi, \ -\theta \cos \phi, \ 0]. \tag{5.6}$$

We can now choose either of two physically reasonable dislocation models, both of which satisfy condition 5.6 for the resultant dislocation content of the boundary.

Model 1 consists of two sets of dislocations with Burgers vectors $(b/\sqrt{2})$ [110] and $(b/\sqrt{2})$ [1̄10], respectively, where $\sqrt{2}b$ is the lattice constant. For both sets τ_0 is given by equation (5.5). To determine the dislocation densities we refer the vector $\mathbf{S}$ to the

[110], [1$\bar{1}$0] axes by replacing ϕ in equation (5.4) by $\phi' = \phi \pm 45°$, the sign of 45° being chosen so that both ϕ and ϕ' lie between 0° and 90°. The densities of the two sets per unit θ are then readily found. Their sum is

$$\Sigma N_i = \frac{\cos \phi' + \sin \phi'}{b} . \tag{5.7}$$

Substituting equations (5.5) and (5.7) into equation (3.3), we have

$$E_0 = \frac{(\cos \phi' + \sin \phi')}{4\pi} b(c_{11} + c_{12}) \sqrt{\frac{c_{44}c_{44}'}{c_{11}c_{11}'}} \cdot \tag{5.8}$$

Model 2 consists of four sets of dislocations, all of which are half screw and half edge. One set has slip vectors $(b/\sqrt{2})$ [101] and alternates with another set having $(b/\sqrt{2})$ [10$\bar{1}$]. The other two sets have slip vectors $(b/\sqrt{2})$ [011] and $(b/\sqrt{2})$ [01$\bar{1}$], respectively, and also alternate. We thus have two sets of edge components. The screw components associated with each set alternate in sign so that the screws give no contribution to the resultant dislocation content, as required by equation (5.6).

The τ_0's are the same for all the dislocations. From equation (5.6) the total dislocation density per unit θ is readily found to be

$$\Sigma N_i = \left(\frac{\sin \phi + \cos \phi}{b}\right) \sqrt{2}. \tag{5.9}$$

Multiplying this by the τ_0 for a dislocation with equal screw and edge components, we have

$$E_0 = \frac{(\sin \phi + \cos \phi)}{4\pi} \frac{b}{\sqrt{2}} \left[c_{44} + (c_{11} + c_{12}) \sqrt{\frac{c_{44}c_{44}'}{c_{11}c_{11}'}} \right] \cdot \tag{5.10}$$

Using the elastic constants for the face-centered cubic metals aluminum, copper, lead, gold, and silver, we find that model 1 gives a lower energy except when the plane of the grain boundary is so close to a (100) type plane in gold that ϕ is less than 20′. For $\phi = 45°$, corresponding to a (110) boundary, model 2 has about twice the energy of model 1.

We could carry out the same analysis for body-centered cubic crystals, using several different models for each boundary. For example, we could determine under what conditions a boundary consisting of dislocations with [100] Burgers vectors would be better than one having [111] vectors.

6. COMPARISON WITH EXPERIMENT FOR ABSOLUTE ENERGIES

In Section 4 we have seen that the form of the theoretical curve of E vs. θ agrees very well with experimental measurements, even at relatively large angles, where the assumptions made in the derivation are no longer valid. If the theoretical curve of energy vs. angle of misfit is assumed to hold up to $\theta = \theta_m$, the maximum energy can be calculated from

$$E_m = E_0 \theta_m, \tag{6.1}$$

where E_0 is evaluated by elasticity theory, as illustrated in Section 5, and θ_m is determined from an experimental curve of the type obtained by Dunn and co-workers and Aust and Chalmers. As mentioned in Section 4, a random grain boundary will have an energy near the maximum. Consequently, the calculated E_m can be compared with the measurement of the energy of a random grain boundary. The only absolute measurements of grain boundary energy recorded by Fisher and Dunn (Paper 12 of this book) are for a random boundary in copper. Four independent determinations give a mean of 550 ergs/cm². The value of θ_m is not known for copper. However, as the best available estimate, we shall take $\theta_m = 25°$ obtained for lead, which has the same lattice structure, face-centered cubic, as copper. The quantity E_0 for an arbitrary boundary depends on the four variables specifying the orientation of the boundary and axis of relative rotation. At present we know E_0 as a function of only one of these four degrees of freedom: namely, ϕ' in equation (5.6). Taking an average over ϕ' and using the elastic constants and slip distance for copper, we have, from equation (5.8),

$$\frac{2}{\pi}\int_0^{\pi/2} E_0(\phi')\, d\phi' = \frac{5150}{\pi}, \tag{6.2}$$

which for $\theta_m = 25° = 0.436$ radian gives $E_m = 715$ ergs/cm². Thus the calculated value is 30 per cent higher than the mean of the measured values. However, in view of the approximations and averages involved in the theoretical calculation, this degree of agreement with experiment is considered encouraging.*

* *Note added in proof.* The elastic constants for copper were obtained from Schmid and Boas, *Plasticity of Crystals*, Hughes and Co., London (1950), and

A crucial experimental check of the theory would be provided by an accurate measurement of absolute grain boundary energies for small angles of misfit. In this case the unknown parameter $A = 1 + \ln \theta_m$ would be small in comparison with $\ln \theta$, and only the part of the theory which depends on elasticity theory and the dislocation model would be involved in the quantitative theoretical predictions. An agreement between theory and experiment in this area would constitute very strong evidence for the dislocation model.

It should be pointed out that the energy calculations discussed in this paper correspond to the absolute zero of temperature because the effect of the dislocations upon the energy rather than the free energy is evaluated. The difference is unimportant for small angle boundaries, as is shown by the following argument. The free energy at the elevated temperatures, at which the grain boundaries come to equilibrium configurations in the experiments, may be taken as the sum of the energy at absolute zero U_0 plus a sum of free energies of the form

$$kT \ln [1 - \exp (-h\nu/kT)], \tag{6.3}$$

one from each mode of vibration. The energy U_0 is increased by the energies of the grain boundaries calculated at absolute zero. In addition, the presence of dislocations affects the frequency of the normal modes. This effect can be estimated by thinking in terms of an Einstein model in which each atom is imagined to have its own frequency. For such a model, we should expect appreciable changes in frequency to occur only for the atoms in the regions in which Hooke's law fails. As a rough estimate, we shall assume that for each lattice constant of length along a dislocation, six atoms have a change in frequency of 15 per cent. This will contribute a change in free energy at high temperatures, $h\nu/kT \ll 1$, of $6kT \ln 1.15 \doteq kT$ per unit length of dislocation. This free energy change will contribute additively to E_{I}, however, and will therefore not affect comparisons with experiment in regard to E_0. Physically this is because E_0 arises from regions which are deformed elastically so that the change in their free energy may be deter-

refer to room temperature. H. Brooks has called the authors' attention to the fact that the values of the elastic constants at the high temperatures where the boundaries come to equilibrium are probably about 15 per cent lower. This would reduce the disagreement to 15 per cent.

mined from the elastic energy calculated from their isothermal elastic constants.

The contribution to E_{I} due to the change in frequency may be appreciable, as may be seen from the rough estimate given above and also by a more intuitive argument. For a large angle boundary, the energies E_{II} and E_{III} are small compared to E_{I} because the E_{I} regions are in contact or overlapping. Hence the free energy due to E_{I} per unit length of dislocation will be of the order of $E_m 2a$ because dislocations will be only a few atomic distances apart. This leads to free energies per lattice constant length of dislocation of $500 \cdot 2 \cdot b^2 \doteq 4 \times 10^{-13}$ erg. At 1000°K the lattice frequency term estimated above would be 1.39×10^{-13} erg and would be comparable. Another way of suggesting the importance of the free energy terms is to compare the added free energy of a large angle boundary with the free energy required to melt a layer of metal two atomic planes thick. It is then found that those energies are comparable, suggesting that the disorder at a large angle grain boundary is comparable to that in a liquid. At the melting point, of course, changes in entropy and energy make equal contributions to the free energy. This argument thus leads to the conclusion that entropy effects will be comparable to energy effects in the term E_{I} and will be of such a sign as to decrease the free energy.

Another phenomenon which may affect the term E_{I} is the formation near the dislocations of concentration gradients in alloys. It appears probable that an argument, similar to that presented above for vibrational free energy, can be applied to these atmospheres. For example, in a very dilute alloy an appreciable concentration of the solute atoms close to an isolated dislocation line can occur.* The presence of these atoms will produce local variations in the stress field that will contribute terms in $(b/R)^n$ with $n > 1$ in equation (2.1). For small angle boundaries, r_l can be taken large enough so that overlap of these terms from one dislocation to another can be neglected; hence they can be considered as simply adding to E_{I}. At large distances, the effect of stress on concentration will produce only linear effects, and the energy E_{II} may be calculated as before. The elastic constants employed, however,

* Such concentrations have been considered by Cottrell in connection with the hardening of steel (*Report of a Conference on the Strength of Solids*, University of Bristol, England, Physical Society, London, 1948).

should be those corresponding to isothermal processes in which diffusion effects are allowed to come to equilibrium. This reasoning suggests that the methods used in this paper for calculating grain boundary energies can be employed for alloys as well. However, a far more thorough analysis then we have carried out would be necessary to establish the conclusion rigorously.

REFERENCES

1. W. L. Bragg, *Proc. Phys. Soc. (London)*, **52**, 54 (1940).
2. J. M. Burgers, *Proc. Phys. Soc. (London)*, **52**, 23 (1940); *Proc. Kon. Ned. Akad. v. Wet. Amsterdam*, **42**, 293 (1939). See also W. G. Burgers, *ibid.*, **50**, 595 (1947).
3. W. T. Read and W. Shockley, *Phys. Rev.*, **78**, 275 (1950). See also a preliminary report, *ibid.*, **75**, 692 (1949).
4. F. C. Frank, *Carnegie Institute of Technology Symposium on the Plastic Deformation of Crystalline Solids*, Office of Naval Research, 1950.
5. R. D. Heidenreich and W. Shockley, *Report of a Conference on the Strength of Solids*, University of Bristol, England, Physical Society, London, 1948.
6. C. G. Dunn and F. Lionetti, *Trans. AIME*, **185**, 125 (1949). Also C. G. Dunn, F. W. Daniels, and M. J. Bolton, *Trans. AIME*, **188**, 1245 (1950).
7. K. T. Aust and B. Chalmers, *Proc. Roy. Soc. (London)*, **A201**, 210 (1950).
8. K. T. Aust and B. Chalmers, *Proc. Roy. Soc. (London)*, **A204**, 359 (1950).
9. J. H. van der Merwe, *Proc. Phys. Soc. (London)*, **A63**, pt. 6, 616 (1950).
10. W. M. Lomer, *Proc. Roy. Soc. (London)*, **A196**, 135 (1949).
11. C. S. Smith, "Grains, Phases and Interphases: An Interpretation of Microstructure," *Metals Tech.* (June, 1948).
12. A. H. Cottrell, *Progress in Metal Physics*, Vol. I, Chapter II (editor, Bruce Chalmers), Interscience Publishers, New York, 1949.
13. J. D. Eshelby, *Phil. Mag.*, **40**, 903 (1949).

DISCUSSION

Bruce Chalmers (University of Toronto):

The paper under discussion is concerned primarily with the energy of grain boundaries in pure metals, and the effects of impurities are not considered. It is possible, however, that the specific free energy of a grain boundary may be affected by the presence of atoms of different sizes in small concentrations. An atom of greater or smaller size has associated with it an amount of strain energy due to misfit.[1] This is reduced if the atom is in a region where the matrix lattice has volume

[1] A. H. Cottrell, *Progress in Metal Physics* (Bruce Chalmers, editor), Vol. I, p. 77, Interscience Publishers, New York, 1949.

strain of the appropriate sign. It is, therefore, appropriate to consider the volume strain near a boundary in terms of the dislocation model. The volume strain near a single edge dislocation in iron is shown in Fig. D.1.[1]

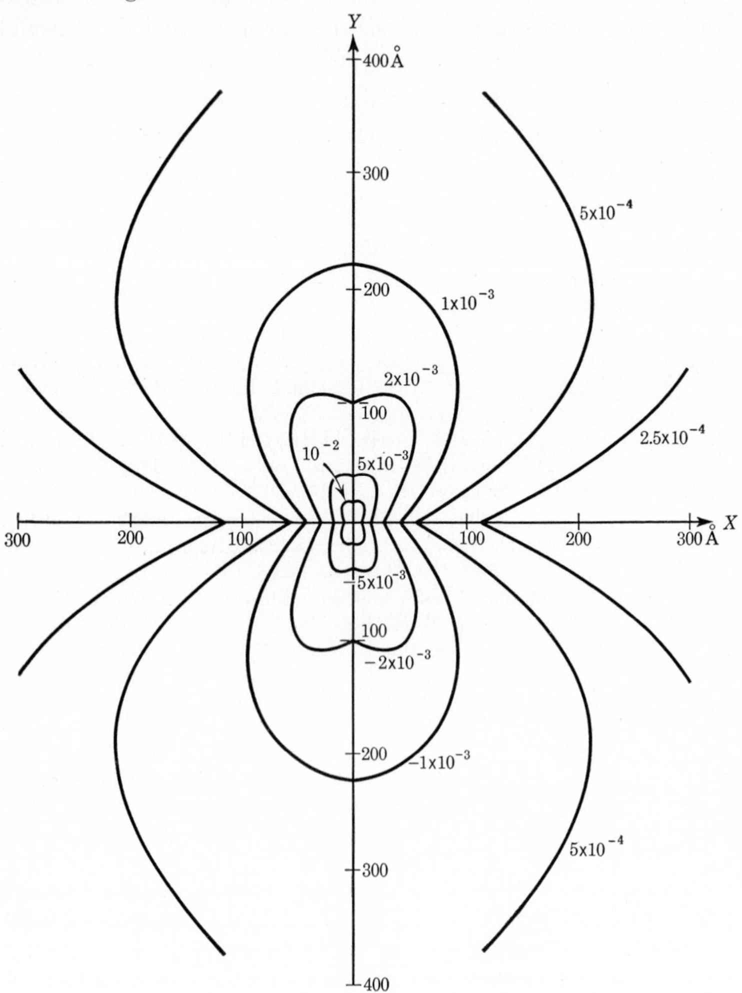

FIG. D.1. Volume strain near a single edge dislocation in iron.

If we consider an array of dislocations of the type represented in Fig. 1 of the paper under discussion, there will be some cancellation of the volume strains, especially when the dislocations are close together.

If attention is confined to a single crystallographic plane, there is an area around each dislocation in which the "volume" strain is greater than an arbitrary amount v/V. Let this area be A_s. The area A_s per dislocation will decrease as the dislocations are brought closer together. The product of the area A_s and the number of dislocations n per unit distance gives the strained volume per unit area of boundary.

Preliminary calculations[2] of the volume nA_s with more than 10^{-3} volume strain as a function of dislocation spacing have shown that nA_s passes through a maximum when the spacing of the dislocations

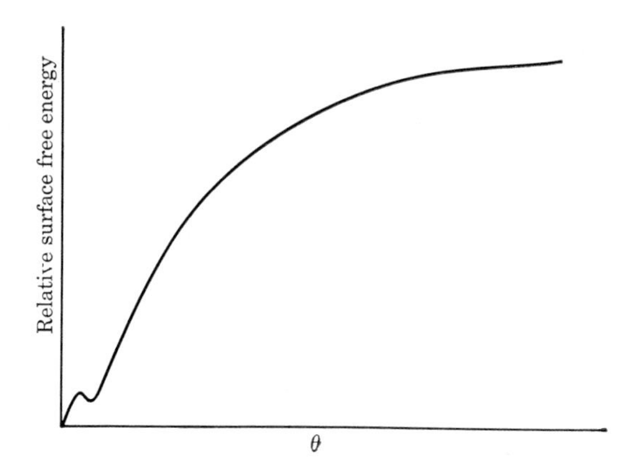

FIG. D.2. Possible form of dependence upon difference in orientation of relative surface free energy.

corresponds to a boundary with a difference of orientation of about 0.5°. This suggests that the strain energy due to misfit atoms would be reduced if the difference of orientation had a value corresponding to the maximum on a curve of this kind. If the volume strain is given a higher value, the maximum occurs at smaller spacing, that is, larger angle between the crystal lattices.

If we consider the free energy of a system which contains "misfit" atoms and a boundary, it may follow that the free energy varies with the difference of orientation θ at the boundary in a more complex manner than would be expected for a pure metal, and that the form of the curve should be that shown in Fig. D.2, the minimum corresponding to the maximum in the strained volume vs. angle relationship. The persistence of certain low-angle substructure boundaries appears to lend some support to this suggestion.

[2] U. Martius and B. Chalmers. Unpublished.

W. T. READ, JR., AND W. SHOCKLEY (*in reply*):

Professor Chalmer's viewpoint differs somewhat from the remarks in the last section of our article, remarks which were incorporated after the meeting. The chief difference is that we emphasize the possibility of a local atmosphere building up near each individual dislocation so that the composite dislocation plus atmosphere acts as a unit. It is to be hoped that further theoretical and experimental work will determine the exact role of concentration gradients near grain boundaries.

C. HERRING (BELL TELEPHONE LABORATORIES):

An appreciable inaccuracy is introduced into all existing measurements of grain boundary energies because, to get a unique answer from these measurements, it has been necessary to assume equilibration of only three vectors, an assumption which is not correct if any of the three interfacial tensions varies appreciably with orientation of the interface. For the general case of three intersecting interfaces a straightforward calculation[3] of the variation of total interfacial free energy with position of the intersection line gives as the equilibrium condition

$$\sum_{i=1}^{3} (E_i\mathbf{t}_i + \partial E_i/\partial \mathbf{t}_i) = 0, \qquad \text{(D.1)}$$

where E_i is the specific surface free energy of the ith boundary, $\mathbf{t}_i$ is a unit vector in the plane of the ith boundary pointing normally outward from the line of intersection of the three boundaries, and $\partial E_i/\partial \mathbf{t}_i$ is a vector normal to $\mathbf{t}_i$ and to the intersection line, whose magnitude measures the rate of change of E_i with the orientation of the ith interface. Both theory and experiment suggest that the terms $\partial E_i/\partial \mathbf{t}_i$ are quite appreciable compared with the terms $E_i\mathbf{t}_i$. For example, the dislocation model of Read and Shockley[4] indicates that, in the limit of small orientation difference, $\partial E/\partial \mathbf{t}$ can get as large as E itself. Dr. B. H. Alexander has called my attention to another piece of evidence, namely, occasional photographs which show a twin boundary meeting a grain boundary that curves away from the twinned grain as it approaches the twin boundary from either side. In such a case all three of the $\mathbf{t}_i$ point into the same semicircle, so that no equilibrium would be possible without appreciable terms of the type $\partial E_i/\partial \mathbf{t}_i$. Dr. Alexander has kindly supplied me with the accompanying photograph, which shows an example of this effect, Fig. D.3.

[3] C. Herring, *The Physics of Powder Metallurgy* (W. E. Kingston, Editor), Chapter 8, McGraw-Hill Book Co., New York, 1951.

[4] W. T. Read and W. Shockley, *Phys. Rev.*, **78**, 275 (1950), Eqs. (5) and (6).

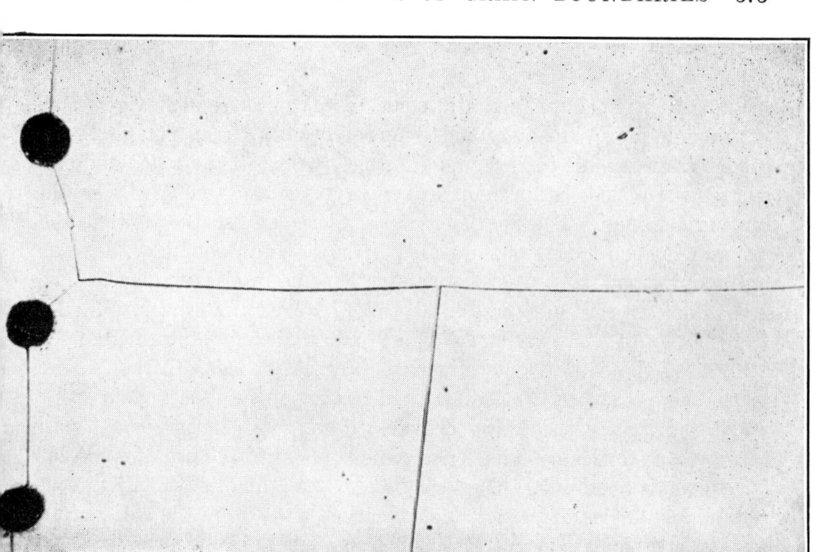

Fig. D.3. Intersection of a twin boundary with a grain boundary, in copper annealed 400 hours at 1075°C. (From Alexander.)

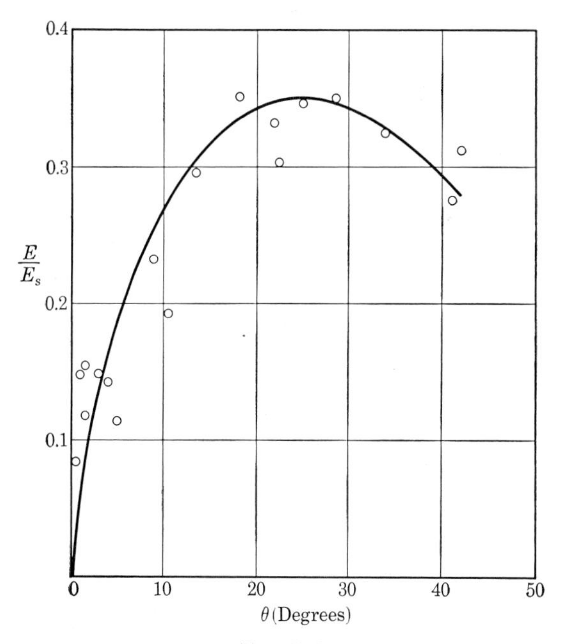

Fig. D.4

W. T. Read

Since this paper was written, some recent measurements, by A. P. Greenough,[5] on silver have come to my attention. Greenough measured groove angles where grain boundaries met the external surface and calculated the ratio of grain boundary energy to surface energy by equilibrating tensions. The specimens were bicrystals, so grown that the axis of relative rotation of the grains lay in the grain boundary, but was not a simple crystal axis and was not the same in all specimens. The groove angles were measured in all cases by several methods. Figure D.4 is a plot of E/E_S vs. θ, each value of E/E_S being obtained from the average of the several determinations of groove angle. Although the scatter here is somewhat greater than in Fig. 4, the data appear to be well fitted by the theoretical curve with $\theta_m = 25°$, in agreement with the θ_m value for lead. This lends some support to the use of $\theta_m = 25°$ for copper in Section 5. The data in Fig. D.4 are not sufficiently accurate at low angles to permit determination of E_0 from the slope of an E/θ vs. $\ln \theta$ plot at small angles. The curve of Fig. D.4 corresponds to $E_m = 0.35E_S$. Using the value $E_S = 1140$ from Fisher and Dunn (Paper 12 of this book), we obtain $E_m = 400$ ergs/cm^2. Calculating E_m from the theory by the same procedure used for copper in Section 5 gives $E_m = 516$ ergs/cm^2. Thus the calculated value is high by 29 per cent. Again this degree of agreement is considered encouraging.*

* *Note added in proof.* Again the elastic constants were the Schmid and Boas values for room temperature and are probably 15 per cent high. This would reduce the disagreement to 14 per cent. If the value of 1140 for E_S is multiplied by a factor of 1.15 to correct for the effect of transverse grain boundaries in the measurements of silver foils (see Shuttleworth's discussion of Paper 12 and Fisher's reply), then the theoretical and experimental values are in almost perfect agreement.

[5] A. P. Greenough and R. King, "Grain Boundary Energies in Silver," *Journal Inst. Met.* **79**, pt. 6, 415 (1951).

14.

Interphase Interfaces

CYRIL STANLEY SMITH

Institute for the Study of Metals, University of Chicago

ABSTRACT

In systems that can be heated to temperatures where change of shape by diffusion can occur, the free energy of the interface between a crystal and a liquid may be obtained by measuring the equilibrium angles at the point of junction with a liquid-vapor or a liquid-liquid interface, the surface tension of which can be measured by conventional methods. The liquid-solid interface can in turn be equilibrated with the boundary between two crystals. In two-phase solids, the equilibrium angle between a grain boundary and an interface boundary is of importance for it determines the equilibrium microstructure. Tables of interface energies or energy ratios for many alloy systems are given. The energy of the interface between crystals of different metallic phases in contact with each other is generally less than that of the interface between two differently oriented crystals of the same phase. It is shown that two-dimensional lattices which differ in the number of sides of the unit cell (for example, lattices of triangles and squares) can be fitted together without "dislocations" at the boundary, even though the lattices differ in orientation and spacing. This principle may be of importance in connection with transformations of the diffusionless variety.

1. THE ROLE OF INTERFACE ENERGIES

The interface between two crystals not of the same phase differs in some respects from the interface between two crystals of the same phase, that is, the grain boundary treated in the present symposium by W. T. Read and W. Shockley* and by J. C. Fisher and C. G. Dunn.† It might be expected that the addition of asymmetrical chemical binding forces to the energy resulting

* W. T. Read and W. Shockley, Paper 13 of this book.

† J. C. Fisher and C. G. Dunn, Paper 12 of this book.

from the geometrical misfit of the lattices would result in a higher energy for the interphase interface. In actuality, this is not always the case; indeed, in common two-phase alloys the converse is invariably true.

The metallurgist, the ceramist, and the geologist are all vitally concerned with these interfaces, for the structure of their materials, always polycrystalline and frequently polyphase, de-

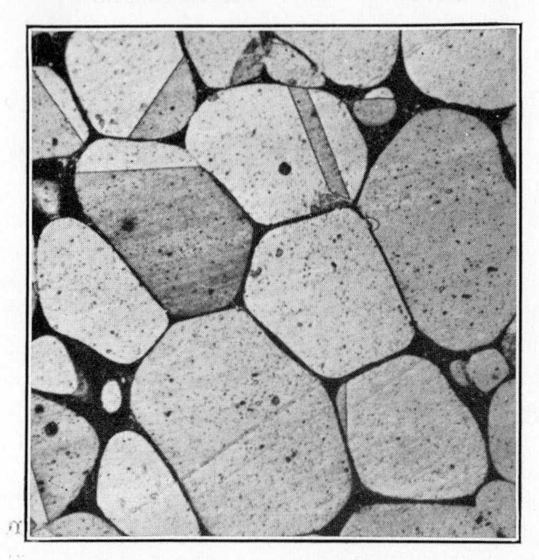

Fig. 1. Microstructure of Cu-Ag alloy, 15 per cent Ag, quenched from 850°C. ×400.

pends in very large degree on the local geometry of interface equilibrium, following the simple laws of vectorial balance of surface tensions. The difference between a hopelessly brittle alloy and a ductile one is often no more than the distribution of a minor amount of a liquid or brittle phase in films between the grains instead of in the less harmful form of nearly spherical inclusions. Compare, for example, the appearance of the microstructure (Fig. 1) of a Cu-Ag alloy heated just above the eutectic temperature, which is hopelessly "hot short," with that of a beta brass containing lead (Fig. 2), which is perfectly plastic when hot. In both cases there is liquid present, but in Fig. 1 it is harmfully and in Fig. 2 harmlessly distributed. The difference in structure and properties is entirely due to the relative differences in the interface energies involved.

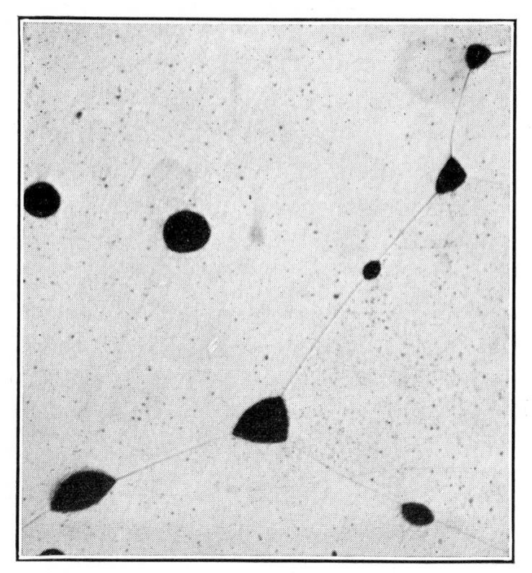

FIG. 2. Microstructure of leaded brass (51-46-3 Cu-Zn-Pb), quenched from 700°C. ×500.

2. THE GEOMETRY OF INTERFACE EQUILIBRIUM IN POLYCRYSTALLINE SOLIDS

If three grains meet along a common edge, the boundaries between the three grains will reach local equilibrium at angles determined by the requirements of vectorial equilibrium of the surface tensions; that is, in Fig. 3*a*,

$$\gamma_{12} + \gamma_{13} \cdot \cos\theta_1 + \gamma_{23} \cdot \cos\theta_2 = 0 \tag{2.1}$$

or

$$\frac{\gamma_{12}}{\sin\theta_3} = \frac{\gamma_{23}}{\sin\theta_1} = \frac{\gamma_{13}}{\sin\theta_2}\,. \tag{2.2}$$

Although the value of the interfacial tension* of a boundary two

* Surface tension, interfacial tension, and interfacial free energy are, in this paper, regarded as equivalent terms. The elastic stresses in the surface of crystals do not necessarily correspond to the free energy (cf., for example, Shuttleworth[1]), but the geometry of the equilibrium of such surfaces, and the force necessary to cause additional atoms to diffuse to the surface under "creep" conditions, can be treated, as in liquids, by either free energy or equivalent tension concepts. Even if the grains themselves have a time independent yield point, the interface between two crystals does not have a definite rigidity at high temperatures. It behaves as a viscous liquid and hence will adjust to a geometry identical with that resulting from the surface tension concept.

crystals of the same phase depends upon orientation, and small angles between the adjacent crystals result in low energy boundaries,*,† these will be statistically rare, and the most frequent boundaries are those between crystals differing so greatly in orientation that variations in this orientation are unimportant. To a first approximation, therefore, all interfaces may be regarded as the same, uninfluenced either by orientation of the crystal or by the direction of the boundary between them. If this is so, then $\gamma_{12} = \gamma_{23} = \gamma_{13}$, and $\theta_1 = \theta_2 = \theta_3 = 120°$. The grain boundaries in a polycrystalline single-phase metal will therefore meet at

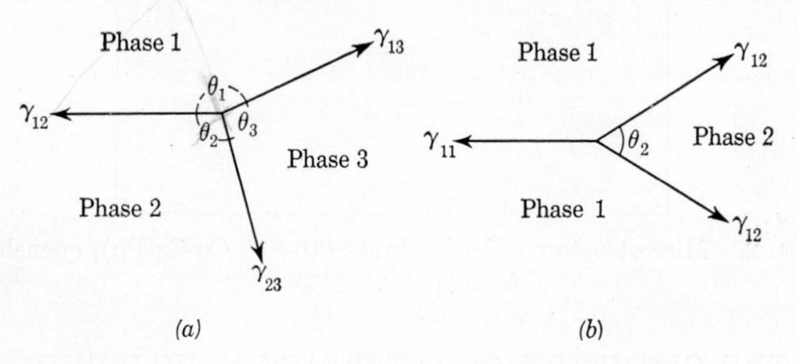

FIG. 3. Geometry of interfaces at three-grain corners.

120°, and the three-dimensional polycrystalline array of such grains will consist of a continuous network of surfaces meeting at 120° to each other along a continuous network of edges. The geometry is, in fact, nearly identical with that of a froth of soap bubbles.

Consider now two-phase alloys. There may still be edges at which three grains of a single phase meet, but in addition there will be lines along which two grains of one phase meet one grain of a different phase with which they are in chemical equilibrium (Fig. 3*b*). There is now one interface of a grain boundary character and one interface between two crystals that must differ in crystal structure, and will also differ in composition except at a transition point in a pure substance. This interface also possesses free energy, two-dimensional continuity, and all other characteristics of a grain boundary, with the additional property that for both structural and chemical reasons it can never disappear as does a grain boundary when the orientation of the crystals on the two

* W. T. Read and W. Shockley, Paper 13 of this book.

† J. C. Fisher and C. G. Dunn, Paper 12 of this book.

sides of it becomes the same. These interfaces will reach equilibrium at an angle determined by the following relation:

$$\cos \frac{\theta_2}{2} = \frac{\gamma_{11}}{2\gamma_{12}} \cdot \tag{2.3}$$

If γ_{12} is less than $0.5\gamma_{11}$, $\cos \theta_2$ would be greater than one, and no physical solution is possible. Above this value, θ increases progressively with increasing ratio of the interface energies. This angle, the *dihedral angle*, is a characteristic of a given two-phase material, and is dominant in determining the microstructure of alloys or other materials such as ceramics and rocks. This simple picture ignores the crystallinity of phases and applies equally well to a system of immiscible fluids with one more phase. Superimposed on this is the effect of orientation on interphase energies; this is sometimes dominant, as in the case of the Widmannstäten structure of meteorites and many alloys containing phases precipitated in the solid, and is sometimes insignificant, as in the case of most worked and annealed alloys.

3. EXPERIMENTAL METHODS OF STUDYING INTERFACES AND INTERFACIAL ENERGIES

The interface between two solids is less accessible to study than the surface or the interface between two fluids. Direct structure determinations are impossible. Adsorption and diffusion of solutes or of radioactive tracers may give information interpretable in terms of structure, but no such work has yet been done. The nucleation of a third phase constitutes another possible indirect approach.

Though the structures of solid interfaces are mostly beyond our reach, their energies are not. As discussed above, it is possible by the study of dihedral angles of polycrystalline materials to obtain relative energies of a large number of interfaces. Sometimes these can be compared directly with known or measurable interfaces of a liquid-vapor or liquid-liquid character, and thus their own energies obtained in absolute units. Solid-liquid interface energies may also be computed from undercooling data, for the size of an effective nucleus for solidification depends on the energy of this interface.

The first method is based on the fact that after sufficiently long heat treatment at a sufficiently high temperature even solids will conform to surface forces.* Once equilibrium has been established, all that is necessary is to quench the sample and measure under the microscope the equilibrium angles between any two surfaces. If surface energies could be determined directly, for example, by measuring the heat of solution, evaporation, or condensation of finely divided solids, the method could become widely applicable. Currently the only reliable absolute methods involve liquid interfaces and necessitate the introduction of additional components whose presence may modify the energies of the solid substances under study. At present writing even this method has been used only on copper-copper-lead and on iron-copper-copper sulphide interfaces.

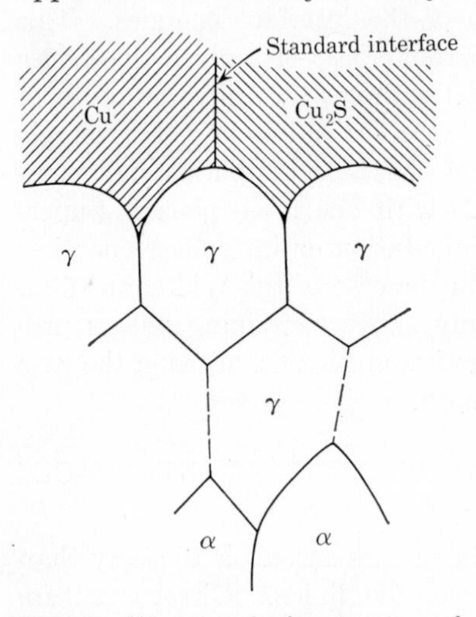

FIG. 4. Diagram of microstructure of Fe-Cu-Cu_2S alloy showing relation of various interfaces and measurable dihedral angles.

Bailey and Watkins[3] measured the contact angle of molten lead against a solid plane copper surface, the dihedral angle of a lead-saturated copper surface against a grain boundary, and that of liquid lead against a copper grain boundary. Sears[4] measured the diameter and height of a lens-shaped drop of lead in equilibrium on the surface of a copper crystal, and thus computed the three angles relating the three interfaces. Both investigators utilized the accepted value of the surface tension of molten lead, arbitrarily corrected for its copper content, and the same microscopic measurement of the dihedral angle of lead against the copper grain boundary. The results of the two methods agree reasonably well, as can be seen in Table 1.

* This adjustment is achieved by diffusion of atoms, either along the interface or through the crystals themselves. Although plastic deformation of the body of the crystal by surface forces is not impossible, the fact that readjustment of shape occurs far more rapidly with low interface energies in a system with considerable solubility than in a system with high interface energies and low solubility, suggests that diffusion is the chief mechanism involved.[2]

Van Vlack[2] used the capillary method to determine the energy of the interface between two immiscible liquids, copper and copper sulphide (using radiography to make it visible), and equilibrated this interface with gamma iron, measuring the appropriate angles (Fig. 4) under the microscope. All phases were in equilibrium,

TABLE 1

MEASUREMENTS OF INTERFACIAL TENSIONS INVOLVING SOLIDS, OBTAINED BY EQUILIBRIUM DIRECTLY AGAINST A LIQUID INTERFACE OF KNOWN ABSOLUTE ENERGY

Interface	Interface Energy, ergs/cm²		
All phases in chemical equilibrium with each other	Bailey and Watkins[3] 900°C	Sears[4] 800°C	Van Vlack[2] 1100°C
Pb-vapor (standard)	466	not stated	
Cu-Pb vapor	780	720	
Cu-Pb liquid	340	510	
Cu-Cu	640	860	595 (1000°C)*
In equilibrium with each other			
Cu_2S_L-Cu liquid (standard)			100†
Fe_γ-Cu liquid			430
Fe_γ-Cu_2S liquid			470
Fe_γ-Fe_γ			850

* Derived through Fe-Fe, Fe-Cu, and Cu-Cu equilibrium angles at 1000°C.
† Determined by capillary method.

mutually saturated with iron, copper, and sulphur. His results are also given in Table 1. For comparison with Bailey and Watkins', Van Vlack's value of the copper-copper grain boundary is also given, determined in a separate experiment by the equilibration of gamma iron and copper at 1000°C, assuming the gamma iron boundary to be the same as at 1100°C. Bailey and Watkins measured the dihedral angle of the surface of pure copper against its grain boundaries (which they assumed to be the same as in the alloy with lead) and derived a figure of 1800 ergs/cm² for the surface energy of pure copper. All these values are somewhat

TABLE 2

VALUES OF RELATIVE INTERFACIAL ENERGIES

System	Temperature, °C	Interface between		Grain Boundary Used as a Comparison Interface, C	$\frac{\gamma_{A/B}}{\gamma_c}$	Reference
		Phase A	Phase B			
Cu-Zn	700	αFCC	βBCC	α/α	0.78	5
	"	αFCC	βBCC	β/β	1.00	5
Cu-Al	600	αFCC	βBCC	α/α	0.71	5
	"	βBCC	γCC	γ/γ	0.78	5
Cu-Sn	750	αFCC	βBCC	α/α	0.76	5
	"	αFCC	βBCC	β/β	0.93	5
Cu-Sn-Pb	600	αFCC	βBCC	β/β	1.00	5
	"	αFCC	βFCC	α/α	0.74	5
Cu-Sb	600	αFCC	βBCT	α/α	0.71	6
Cu-Ag	750	α(Cu)FCC	β(Ag)FCC	α/α	0.65	6
	750	α(Cu)FCC	β(Ag)FCC	β/β	0.74	6
Cu-Si	845	αFCC	βBCC	α/α	0.53	6
	"	αFCC	βBCC	β/β	1.18	6
	830	αFCC	κHCP	α/α	0.82*	6
	"	αFCC	κHCP	κ/κ	0.87*	6
Fe-C	690	αBCC	Fe_3C OR	α/α	0.93	5
	750	αBCC	γFCC	α/α	0.71	5
	950	αBCC	γFCC	γ/γ	0.74	2
FeCu	825	αBCC	"Cu" FCC	α/α	0.74	2
	"	αBCC	"Cu" FCC	Cu/Cu	0.86	2
	1000	γFCC	"Cu" FCC	γ/γ	0.61	2
	"	γFCC	"Cu" FCC	Cu/Cu	0.87	2
Zn Cu-Al	375	ηHCP	ϵHCP	ϵ/ϵ	0.93	5
(three	"	ηHCP	ϵHCP	η/η	0.93	5
phase	"	ϵHCP	β_1FCC	β_1/β_1	0.87	5
alloy)	"	ϵHCP	β_1FCC	ϵ/ϵ	0.74	5
	"	ηHCP	β_1FCC	β_1/β_1	1.00	5
	"	ηHCP	β_1FCC	η/η	0.87	5
Zn-Sn	160	β(Sn)BCT	α(Zn)HCP	α/α	0.74	6
	"	β(Sn)BCT	α(Zn)HCP	β/β	1.18	6

* This applies only to randomly oriented kappa produced by transformation of random beta. The oriented alpha-kappa interface is of extremely low energy—probably even less than that of a twin interface in a face-centered cubic structure because of the insensitivity to second nearest neighbor interaction.

FCC = face-centered cubic
BCC = body-centered cubic
CC = complex cubic γ-brass structure
HCP = hexagonal close-packed
BCT = body-centered tetragonal
OR = orthorhombic

uncertain; nevertheless, for the first time solid-solid interface energies have become measurable, and the theory of such interfaces must be developed to conform with experiment.

The foregoing constitute all available values of interface energies measured by direct equilibrium with an interface (liquid-liquid or liquid-gas) that could be studied independently by capillary or

TABLE 3

RELATIVE VALUES OF SOME SOLID-LIQUID INTERFACES COMPARED WITH GRAIN BOUNDARY ENERGIES

System*	Temperature, °C	Solid Grain Boundary	$\frac{\gamma_{SL}}{\gamma_{LL}}$	Reference
Cu-Pb	750	α/α FCC	0.58	7†
Cu-Zn-Pb	750	α/α (30% Zn,FCC)	0.65	5
Cu-Zn-Pb	750	β/β (49% Zn,BCC)	0.87	5
Cu-Ag	850	α/α (FCC)	$\leq$0.50	6
Fe-Cu	1125	γ/γ (FCC)	0.51	2, 5
Fe-Ag	1100	γ/γ (FCC)	>4	2
Al-Sn	350	Al/Al (FCC)	0.56	7†
	600	Al/Al (FCC)	0.50	7†
$Fe\text{-}Cu_2S$	1100	γ/γ (FCC)	0.55	2
Fe-FeS	1026	γ/γ (FCC)	0.52	2
	1300	γ/γ (FCC)	$\leq$0.50	2

* The last-named element is the principal component of the liquid phase.
† See also Fig. 6.

other absolute methods. Many more interfaces have been measured in relation to each other and are of particular interest in connection with the problem of the difference between interphase interfaces and single-phase grain boundaries. These values, all based on dihedral angle measurements on annealed polycrystalline microsamples of two- or three-phase alloys, are summarized in Table 2 (for the interface between two solid phases) and Table 3 (for interfaces between a solid phase and a liquid).

It is to be noted that in nearly every case the interface between two different solids has a lower energy than the grain boundary in either phase involved. Supposedly this would not be true if data from widely differing phases had been included (for example, crystals with metallic and homopolar bonds), but it is significant that so many metallic phases in equilibrium with each other have such low energy boundaries, and that the entire variation is relatively small.

The interface of a crystal with a liquid is generally of lower energy (Table 3). The ratio of the solid-liquid interface energy to that of the grain boundary has been studied (on quenched samples) as a function of both temperature and composition in a few systems, notably copper-lead and aluminum-tin (Fig. 5).[7] Although the grain boundary energy must vary somewhat with

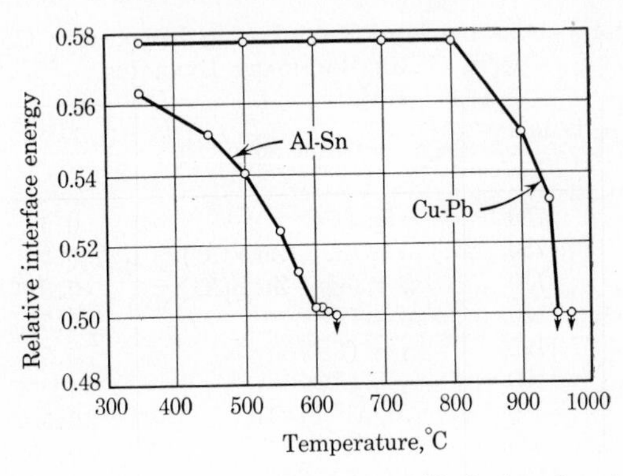

FIG. 5. Interface energy ratios deduced from dihedral angles of liquid phase in Cu-Pb and Al-Sn alloys at various temperatures.

temperature, it appears that the major change is that of the liquid-solid interface, and that this is chiefly a result of the changing composition of the liquid. Note that the Cu-Pb dihedral angle does not change with increasing temperature until near the monotectic temperature, when the copper content of the liquid discontinuously increases. Figure 6 shows the Al-Sn alloy data of Fig. 5 replotted as a function of the composition of the liquid at the various temperatures of anneal. As the aluminum content of the liquid increases, the energy of the interface with solid aluminum decreases. The form of curve is markedly similar to the well-known variation with composition of the surface tension of a binary liquid solution at a fixed temperature—small amounts of the component of lower surface tension lowering the surface tension of the mixture markedly, whereas converse additions produce little effect. Note that in Fig. 6 the ratio of interface energies extrapolated to pure aluminum at its melting point is very nearly 0.5, a condition that seems to be approximated in other metals. In a ternary alloy consisting of a solid component and a liquid containing two miscible low-melting elements, both insoluble in the solid, the solid-liquid interface energy varies with composition of the liquid in a similar manner.[7] This is shown by the aluminum alloys with Sn and Cd, Sn and Pb, and Sn and Bi in Fig. 7. In-

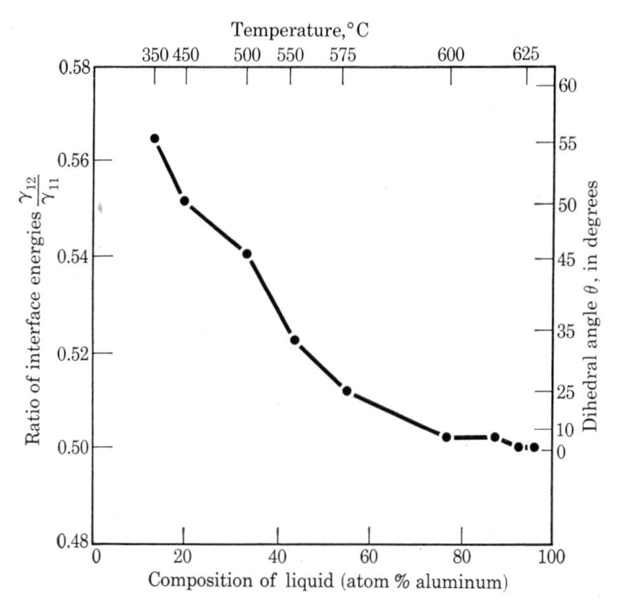

FIG. 6. Variation of interface energy ratio with temperature and with composition of liquid phase in Al-Sn alloys.

creasing mutual solubility of the solid and liquid phases tends to lower the interface energies, as might be expected (Al-Sn-Zn and Al-Sn-Cu alloys, Fig. 7).

It is often of considerable practical importance to control the degree of continuity of a minor second phase. It should be noted that if the dihedral angle is 60° or less, the second phase will form prisms along the grain edges, perfectly continuous throughout the entire sample and providing ever-open channels for liquid circulation and diffusion.[5] This is certainly a factor in the diffusion of bismuth in copper studied by Scheil and Schiessl[8] and may be a factor in the long-range diffusion of minerogenetic solutions frequently observed in geological formations. If the dihedral angle is greater than 60°, the second phase will be discontinuous unless in major amount, while as the angle decreases below 60° the phase will spread progressively over the grain surfaces and at 0° separate the grains entirely. The coagulation of solid particles in a slurry—

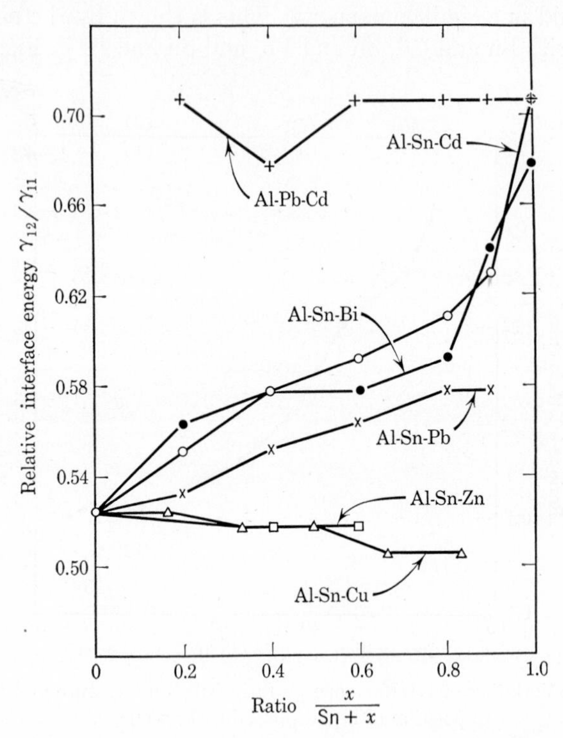

FIG. 7. Variation of interface energies in Al-Sn-x alloys at 550°C. Aluminum constant at 95 per cent (excepting △, 94 per cent Al).

or the adhesion of crystals in the mushy stage of solidification in alloy casting—cannot take place if the dihedral angle of the liquid is zero.

4. SOLID–LIQUID INTERFACIAL ENERGIES FROM UNDERCOOLING EXPERIMENTS

Turnbull and Fisher[9] have extended the classic theory of nucleation of Volmer, Becker, Frenkel, and others to provide the basis of a method of determining the free energy of the interface between a solid and a liquid. The critical size of the nucleus of a second phase forming from a previously homogeneous matrix is clearly dependent upon the balance between the volume-dependent free energy of transformation and the surface-dependent interfacial free energy. Turnbull[10] gives the following equation for the rate of nucleation:

$$I = n(kT/h)\exp[-\Delta F_A/kT]\exp[-16\pi\gamma^3 T_0^2/3\lambda^2(\Delta T)^2 kT], \quad (4.1)$$

where I is the rate of nucleation in number of nuclei per second, n is the number of atoms in the sample, ΔF_A is the free energy of activation for transport across the liquid-solid interface, γ is the interfacial energy between crystal nucleus and liquid, T_0 is the melting temperature, °K, λ is the heat of fusion for unit volume, and ΔT is the undercooling. There are two unknown parameters in equation (2.1), the liquid-solid interfacial energy, γ, and ΔF_A. Making the reasonable assumption that the value of $\exp[-\Delta F_A/kT]$ is of the order of 10^{-2}, we can calculate the interface energy from the value of the nucleation rate at a known temperature. Turnbull carried out actual nucleation rate experiments only on mercury and tin. For the other metals he used the simpler method of determining the maximum degree of undercooling of small droplets, which gives the temperature corresponding to a nucleation frequency of the order of $10^{-1\pm1}$ per second. In Table 4 are included Turnbull's data on undercooling of several metals, together with the computed values of the interfacial energy between solid and liquid. Also included in Table 4 are Turnbull's values of the "gram atomic interfacial energy" divided by the heat of fusion, that is,

$$\frac{\gamma_g}{\Delta H_f} = \frac{N^{1/3} V^{2/3} \gamma_{SL}}{\Delta H_f}, \quad (4.2)$$

where V is the gram atomic volume and N is Avogadro's number. (This ignores the difference of packing of the interface atoms compared with the volume.) This function is approximately the same for all metals except mercury, antimony, germanium, and bismuth. The interface energies are nearly one-half the heat of fusion, an empirical observation that must have some fundamental significance. If this relation is combined with that between heat of fusion and absolute melting point, the maximum degree of undercooling that can be obtained with any pure metal is also nearly constant, and is approximately equal to one-fifth of its melting temperature.

In samples of appreciable volume of any real metal there are likely to be present nuclei of foreign material which will initiate solidification at temperatures considerably above the temperature corresponding to homogeneous nucleation. If the contact angle of the solid against the impurity surface in a liquid is less than

TABLE 4

SOLID-LIQUID INTERFACE ENERGIES OF PURE SUBSTANCES DERIVED FROM SUPERCOOLING DATA

Metal	Maximum Undercooling Observed, ΔT, °K	Computed γ_{SL}, ergs/cm^2	$\frac{\gamma_g}{\Delta H}$
Mercury	58	24.4	0.53
Gallium	76	56	0.44
Tin	105	54.5	0.42
Bismuth	90	54	0.33
Lead	80	33	0.39
Antimony	135	101	0.30
Germanium	227	181	0.35
Silver	227	126	0.46
Gold	230	132	0.44
Copper	236	177	0.44
Manganese	308	206	0.48
Nickel	319	255	0.44
Cobalt	330	234	0.40
Iron	295	204	0.45
Palladium	332	209	0.45
Platinum	370	240	0.46
Water*	39	32.8	0.33

* From Fisher et al.[11] All other data from Turnbull.[10]

180° it is obvious that a much smaller volume of material is necessary to give the critical curvature; and, if the contact angle becomes zero, undercooling is dependent only on the energy necessary to compensate for the linear tension at the boundary, which is usually neglected. As Turnbull has shown, a study of undercooling on various surfaces should provide a means of determining contact angles, and hence (if solid-liquid energies are known for the pure materials from homogeneous nucleation experiments) to obtain interface energies between many pairs of solids. At present this approach has been used only to show qualitatively that the energy of the solid copper-solid lead interface is less than the solid copper-liquid copper one, that the silver iodide-ice interface is less than that of silver iodide-water, and that solid aluminum-solid tin is not greatly different from solid aluminum-liquid tin. The method merits fuller exploitation.

By a similar analysis of undercooling and nucleation in solid steel, Fisher et al.[12] have derived a value of 24 ergs/cm^2 for the free energy of the *coherent* interface between austenite (FCC) and martensite (BCT). Though this figure is not unreasonable, it is somewhat uncertain because of the difficulties of treating elastic strain energy thermodynamically.

5. THE PROPERTIES OF INTERFACES

It will be noted from Tables 1 and 2 that the interface energy between two differing crystals in the case of alloys, which alone have been studied, is never greater than the grain boundary between two crystals of either phase involved, and in all cases but those involving the alloys of beta brass structure is actually lower. In the next section it will be shown that there is no topological necessity for dislocations at an interface between crystals differing in coordination number. Though this does not mean that dislocations must be absent from such interfaces, the degree of coherence is, nevertheless, probably greater than at a typical grain boundary. We would therefore anticipate that the properties of at least some interphase interfaces of alloys would be different from those of grain boundaries. We would anticipate a lower corrodibility, less easy slip, and less rapid diffusion along such interfaces than along grain boundaries. The interfaces should provide a less ready source or sink for dislocations during deformation. Except in specific cases of structural matching, such interfaces should be less likely to nucleate a third phase than would a grain boundary.

Because of the difference of chemical binding, we would anticipate that the interface between metals and nonmetallic lattices would have high energy and, at least when the nonmetal is homopolar, be higher than grain boundaries in either phase. Beyond occasional data on contact angles of liquids, nothing seems to be known. The microstructure of two-phase meteorites (pallasites) shows rather infrequently definite three-grain corners, where two olivine crystals are in apparent surface tension equilibrium with the iron-nickel phase, which was supposedly molten at the time the structure was established. The dihedral angle is in the vicinity of 70°, indicating that the interphase interface has appreciably less energy than the grain boundary between olivine crystals, and is not much greater, as might have been expected for the interface between such chemically different substances.

The interface between metallic and ionic solids is of great industrial importance. The successful "ceramets"—mixed ceramic and metallic materials—are those where solid wetting occurs. Successful corrosion-resistant materials are probably those whereon a film is formed (by oxidation or other reaction) which has an interface energy such that it cannot be displaced by capillarity. The aggregation and elimination of inclusions in molten metals similarly depend on the interface energy, and troublesome drosses, such as those that can occur when melting aluminum and magnesium alloys, are formed only under conditions of oxidation that give a low energy interface, an interface that supposedly is both topologically and electronically intermediate between the structure of the oxide and that of the metal.

6. THE TOPOLOGY OF LATTICE INTERFACES

It will be noticed that, in almost every case included in Table 2, the energy of the interphase interface is less than that of a grain boundary in one of the phases. This, which certainly would not have been anticipated, may be in part a result of the fact that varying coordination numbers of atoms at the interface can minimize lattice strains at the boundary, a situation impossible in crystals composed of only one kind of atom, though perhaps possible in solid solutions. A preliminary approach to this problem can be made by considering, in two dimensions, the topology of the boundary between two networks of polygons meeting each other. The characteristic of any two-dimensional connected array of polygons and intersecting lines is

$$P - E + C = 1, \tag{6.1}$$

where P, E, and C denote the total number of polygons, edges, and corners, respectively, in the array.* Since each edge joins two corners,

$$2E = \sum rC_r, \tag{6.2}$$

* For proof of this, see O. Veblen, *Analysis Situs*, or any textbook on topology.

where C_r is the number of corners at which r edges meet. Since each edge is shared by two polygons, except those edges that constitute the boundary of the array, which belong to only one polygon,

$$2E = \sum nP_n + E_b, \tag{6.3}$$

where P_n is the number of polygons of n sides and E_b is the number of edges at the boundary of the array being considered. Equation (6.1) can be combined with either (6.2) or (6.3), or both, and simplified to give the following relations:*

$$2P + \sum(2 - r)C_r = 2, \tag{6.4}$$

$$\sum(2 - n)P_n + 2C = E_b + 2, \tag{6.5}$$

$$\sum(4 - n)P_n + \sum(4 - r)C_r = E_b + 4. \tag{6.6}$$

Equation (6.4) is universally applicable, even to a network of lines that form no closed polygons, whereas equations (6.5) and (6.6) apply only when each line constitutes an edge of some polygon.

These equations can be applied to two lattices of polygons meeting along a common boundary. It is always possible to find points of such coherence in such a boundary, and we shall restrict our

*Equation (6.4) should be useful to the organic chemist in determining from the empirical formula of a complex molecule, with atoms of several valences, the number of benzene rings or double bonds (that is, the number of hydrogens needed to saturate).

Another useful relation appears when only three-ray corners are permitted, as in a froth of bubbles or in grains of a polycrystalline material controlled by surface tension:

$$\sum(6 - n)P_n - E_b = 6.$$

If, as in the usual case of polycrystalline aggregates, the boundary is drawn around separated cells, some corners on the boundary will have only two edges meeting at them, for when separated from the neighboring mass they belong to only one polygon. Designating these as C_2, the relation then becomes

$$\sum(6 - n)P_n + 2C_2 - E_b = 6.$$

If

$$2C_2 = E_b + 6,$$

then

$$\sum(6 - n)P_n = 0,$$

and the average number of sides to a grain within the boundary must be six. The array of cells could then be fitted into a hole cut in an infinite network of hexagons. This latter relation is useful in selecting limited samples of grains for study of shape and size distribution.

consideration to the area between two such. We then have a row of cells of one lattice of such length that there are N edges at the boundary, another row of cells of the same length but with $N+1$ edges of the other type of cell. These cells meet along the interface, which has $N + 1$ cell edges (Fig. 8) and are made to coin-

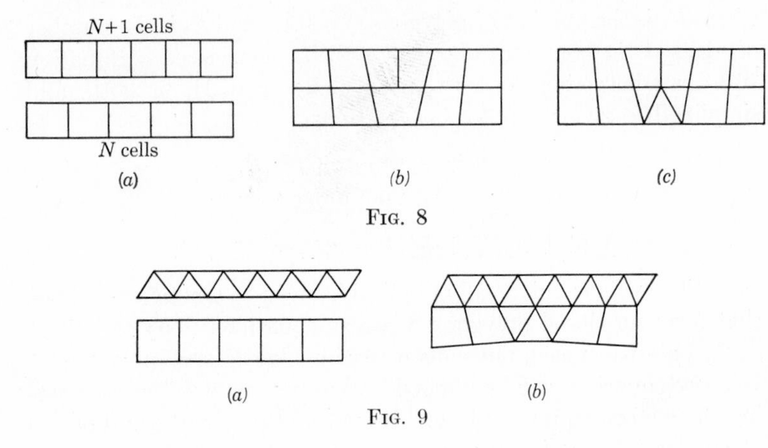

FIG. 8

FIG. 9

Junctions of Two Rows of Lattice Cells Differing in Parameter.

cide as well as possible, leaving one "dislocation." The total number of polygon edges at the external boundary of the two joined rows of cells is then

$$E_b = 2N + 5, \tag{6.7}$$

and the total number of polygon corners (atoms in crystal lattices) is

$$C = 3N + 5. \tag{6.8}$$

Substituting these values in equation (6.5), we get

$$\sum (n - 2)P_n = 4N + 3 \tag{6.9}$$

or

$$1P_3 + 2P_4 + 3P_5 + 4P_6 + 5P_7 \cdots + (n-2)P_n = 4N+3. \tag{6.10}$$

It is at once apparent that the number of polygons of various number of sides cannot be arbitrarily chosen. Because $(4N + 3)$ must be odd, there can be no number of rectangles which meet these conditions; consequently lattices of rectangles meeting along a boundary under the conditions of unit misfit specified must produce either one pentagon or three triangles in place of one of them, as shown in Fig. 8*b* or 8*c*. Similar complications arise with hexagons but not necessarily with triangles.

This may seem trivial or obvious. Less obvious, however, is the fact that, if two lattices of different types meet along an interface, then equation (6.9) can be satisfied without introducing any new type of polygon, but merely by varying the numbers of those already there. In crystallographic terms, we can obtain a *perfectly coherent boundary between the two lattices when the coordination numbers are different.* This can be seen better in Fig. 9*a* and 9*b* and in the lattices of larger extent in Fig. 10*a* and 10*b*.

It is to be noticed that in any boundary between lattices of differing coordination number, the boundary has atoms of coordination numbers intermediate between those that characterize the two lattices. A difference of parameter—or of orientation which requires the same addition of one cell in occasional rows—merely requires an increase in the number of atoms of intermediate coordination at the expense of those in one or the other lattice. This will result in a departure from a linear interface, but it does not necessitate atoms' acquiring a different coordination number from those already present in a strainless, perfectly matched, and oriented interface.

An alternative approach is to consider only the atoms at corners of lattice cells and not the shape of the lattice cells. A coherent interface between two oriented lattices of the same spacing would consist of a complete row of atoms of coordination number intermediate between the coordination number of atoms in the two lattices. Any change, either in orientation or in spacing of the lattices, will result in the introduction of additional atoms on one side or the other of the boundary. Topologically, only the atoms that are immediately adjacent to these additional atoms need be considered, for the rest of the lattice, however strained, remains topologically the same. The effect of any degree of disorientation or of lattice disregistry can be considered as merely multiplying the number, not the type, of these misfit polygons, each consisting of one of the "extra" atoms with its nearest neighbors.

The smallest group of atoms that must be considered is five—two of one lattice, two of the boundary layer of intermediate co-

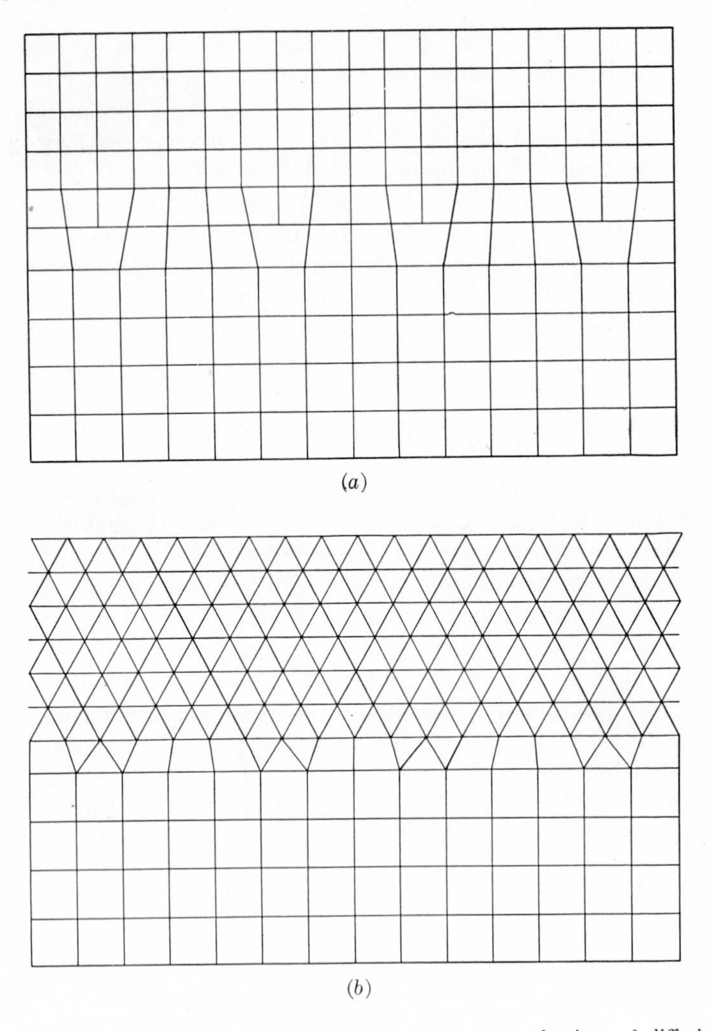

Fig. 10. (*a*) Incoherent interface between two square lattices of differing spacing. (*b*) Coherent interface between square and triangular lattices of different spacing.

ordination, and the "extra" atom (Fig. 11). The five atoms considered together must have external bonds to equal in number those available in the external perfect lattices. These bonds form topologically an array of external radiating lines, not intersecting each other, and can be considered as being terminated each by a

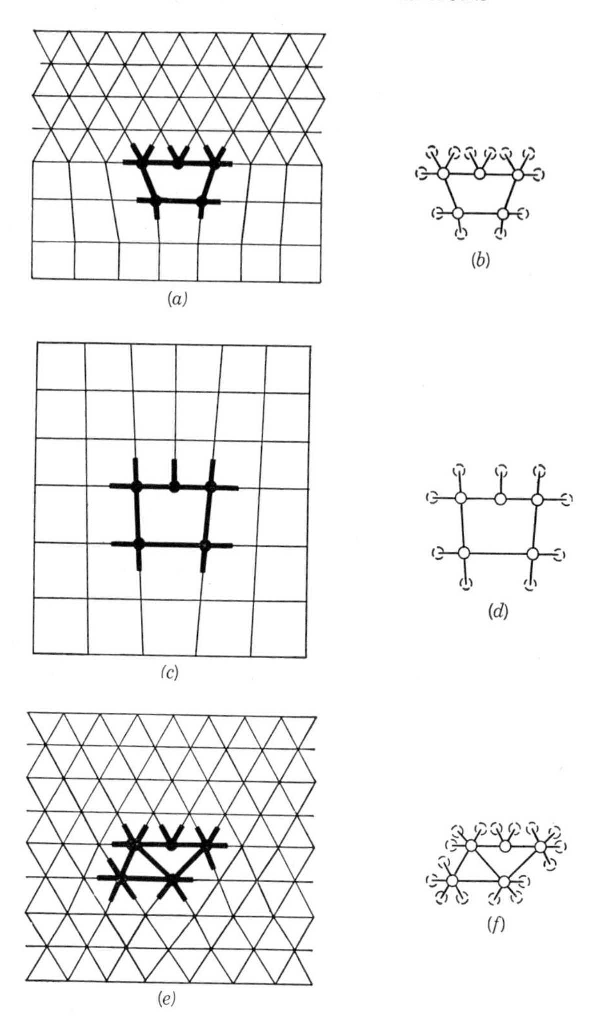

FIG. 11. Polygon of misfit formed by five atoms.

fictitious atom of coordination number one (Fig. 11*b*, 11*d*, and 11*f*).

Consider now equation (6.4), which we will rewrite in the form

$$0C_2 + 1C_3 + 2C_4 + 3C_5 + 4C_6 \cdots + \sum (r - 2)C_r = 2P + C_1 - 2. \tag{6.11}$$

In our polygon of misfit (Fig. 11) C_1 is the total number of external bonds, that is, the bonds not satisfied within the polygon itself, namely,

$$C_1 = 2(A - 2) + 2\left(\frac{A + B}{2} - 2\right) + \left(\frac{B}{2} + 1 - 2\right) - 2(p - 1)$$

$$= 3\left(A + \frac{B}{2}\right) - 2p - 7, \qquad (6.12)$$

where A and B are the normal coordination numbers corresponding to atoms in lattices A and B, respectively, and p is the number of polygons necessarily formed, by $(p - 1)$ cross linkages between the five atoms considered, in order initially to give normal valence to both A atoms. Equation (6.11) then becomes

$$C_3 + 2C_4 + 3C_5 + 4C_6 \cdots + (r - 2)C_r = 3\left(A + \frac{B}{2}\right) + 2(P - p) - 9. \qquad (6.13)$$

In this equation P is the total number of polygons formed by any arrangement and does not necessarily relate to p, which was needed to allow A atoms correct initial coordination. p will be 1 for $A = 4$, 2 for $A = 6$. P can be chosen arbitrarily, but each choice fixes certain coordination numbers. If the lattices are of the same coordination number (that is, if we are considering a grain boundary, not an interface boundary), then

$$C_3 + 2C_4 + 3C_5 + 4C_6 \cdots + (r - 2)C_r = 9\left(\frac{A}{2} - 1\right) + 2(P - p). \qquad (6.14)$$

It is at once obvious from equations (6.13) and (6.14) that the coordination number of atoms in the misfit area cannot be arbitrarily selected. Certain possible solutions are shown in Figs. 12, 13, and 14, including some which, though topologically possible, are most unlikely in any real lattice. The conclusion can be drawn that an additional atom in one of two adjacent atom rows of the same lattice must be accompanied by some atoms not of normal coordination (Figs. 12 and 13). Where, however, the coordination numbers of the two lattices initially differ (Fig. 14), the boundary can conform to any degree of misfit or orientation change solely by varying the number of atoms with allegiance to each lattice. This will produce a jog in the interface, which will no longer be linear, but no amount of displacement will produce registry in the case of lattices of the same coordination.

Although the examples above have principally treated the change in spacing of the two lattices meeting at the interface, precisely the same arguments apply to a change of orientation between two lattices, for this can also be broken down into a number

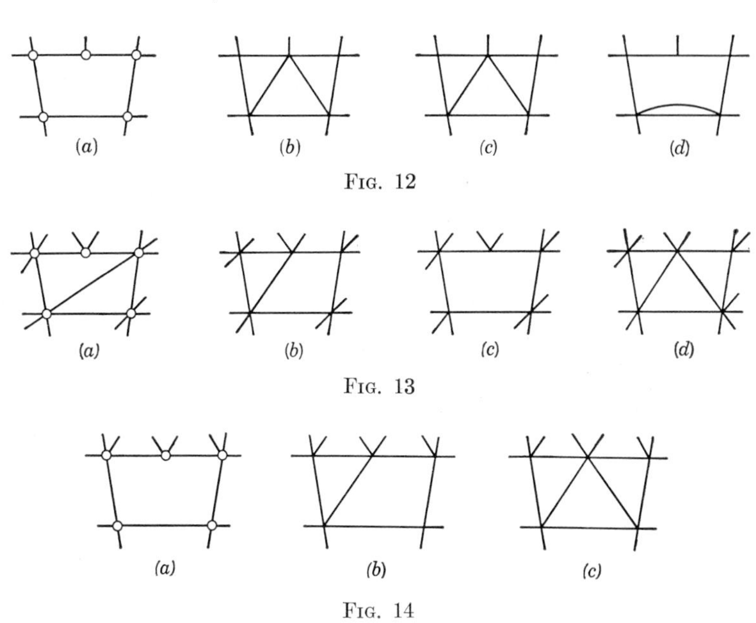

FIG. 12

FIG. 13

FIG. 14

Some Possible Coordination Numbers of Atoms in the Misfit Region.

of topological misfits with complete registry between. There are obviously critical geometries possible with integral relations between lattices and at critical orientations corresponding to twinning and the like, and the simple approach also breaks down when the lattice spacing of one lattice is less than half or more than twice the other.

The extension of these relations into three dimensions is more complex because of the possible adjustment of both two- and three-dimensional cells. Nevertheless, it is as necessary in three dimensions as it is in two that a boundary have atoms of different coordination number if the lattices are of the same coordination type, and that there need be no discontinuity beyond the intermediate coordination of the atoms everywhere at the interface if the coordination numbers differ.

The possibility of a nonlinear interface (or nonplanar in three dimensions) must be taken into account in considering coherency stresses, for example, in the formation of thin oxide films. It must permit much lower local lattice stresses than would be the case with planar interfaces. The motion of an interface along which complete coherence is maintained could occur at the speed of sound, for no diffusion is involved, whereas an interface composed of dislocations or vacancies would be much slower to migrate, for it can do so only if atoms change neighbors. The writer believes that this is the essential difference between a shear type (martensite) transformation and one of the slow nucleation-growth types, which have a largely incoherent interface. The prediction is hazarded that no rapid transformation will be found that does not involve a change of lattice coordination, except for perfectly oriented twin-like interfaces between lattices of identical spacing.

The fact that coherence between two lattices is topologically possible does not, of course, necessarily mean that it is the lowest energy form. If time for diffusion is allowed, the interface will take the lowest energy form, in which, to relieve local strain energy, some dislocations may be introduced. It is premature—at least for the present writer—to attempt to compute interfacial energies based on these assumptions, but it at least seems likely that with atom diameters varying with coordination number the possibility of an intermediate state both of size and number of neighbors will have a great influence on the elastic and chemical free energy of the interface. It is, however, to be noted that even interfaces between identical lattice types differing only chemically and in spacing still have an interphase interface energy less than that of the grain boundary in either phase. See, for example, the gamma Fe-Cu and Ag-Cu alloys in Table 2. The problem of interfaces is a complex, difficult, and fascinating one!

SUMMARY

Values are given for the interfacial free energy for interfaces involving one solid and a second solid or liquid phase. The data are fragmentary. Additional data, mostly from alloy systems, are tabulated, showing the ratio between two solid-solid interfaces, one of which is usually a grain boundary. It is noted experimentally that the energy of the interface between two different crystal lattices in metallic phases is almost invariably lower than the energy of a grain boundary between two crystals of the same phase differing only in orientation. It is shown topologically that a grain boundary interface must have some atoms differing in coordination number, but that an interface between crystals differing in coordination number can have perfect coherence regardless of lattice parameter or orientation, and without any atoms having coordination different from that of either lattice or the intermediate layer. The interface is not necessarily plane, but involves an added number of one or the other type of cell above those in the plane projection.

REFERENCES

1. R. Shuttleworth, "The Surface Tension of Solids," *Proc. Phys. Soc. (London)*, **63A**, 444–457 (1950).
2. L. H. Van Vlack, Thesis, University of Chicago, 1950. Published as "Intergranular Energy of Iron and Some Iron Alloys," *Trans. AIME*, 251–259 (March 1951).
3. G. L. J. Bailey and H. C. Watkins, "Surface Tensions in the System Solid Copper-Molten Lead," *Proc. Phys. Soc. (London)*, **B63**, 350–358 (1950).
4. G. W. Sears, "An Absolute Measurement of Copper-Copper Interfacial Free Energy," *J. Appl. Phys.*, **21**, 721 (1950).
5. C. S. Smith, "Grains, Phases, and Interfaces: An Interpretation of Microstructure," *Trans. AIME*, **175**, 15–51 (1948).
6. C. S. Smith, unpublished. Based on metallographic data by L. Heikkinen and K. K. Ikeuye.
7. K. K. Ikeuye and C. S. Smith, "Studies of Interface Energies in Some Aluminum and Copper Alloys," *Trans. AIME*, **185**, 762–768 (1949).
8. E. Scheil and K. E. Schiessl, "Über die Korngrenzendiffusion von flüssigem Wismut in Kupfer," *Z. Naturforschung*, **4a**, 524–526 (1949).
9. D. Turnbull and J. C. Fisher, "Rate of Nucleation in Condensed Systems," *J. Phys. Chem.*, **17**, 71–73 (1949).
10. D. Turnbull, "Correlation of Liquid-Solid Interfacial Energies Calculated from Supercooling of Small Droplets," *J. Chem. Phys.*, **18**, 769 (1950).
11. J. C. Fisher, J. H. Hollomon, and D. Turnbull, "Rate of Nucleation of Solid Particles in a Subcooled Liquid," *Science*, **109**, 168 (1949).
12. J. C. Fisher, J. H. Hollomon, and D. Turnbull, "Kinetics of the Austenite-Martensite Transformation," *Trans. AIME*, **185**, 691–700 (1949).

15.

Substructures in Crystals

A. GUINIER

Conservatoire des Arts et Métiers

ABSTRACT

Subboundaries divide the crystalline grains into smaller elements, called subgrains, which are slightly disoriented (a few minutes). The subboundaries are revealed with the optical or electron microscope by special etching reagents or by their property of favoring the formation of precipitates in supersaturated solid solutions or the gathering of impurities. Sensitive x-ray techniques give the relative orientations of the subgrains.

In most cases, the subgrains are formed by an annealing following a slight deformation of the metal (polygonization). The deformation may be due to external causes or internal stresses produced by quenching, allotropic transformation, solidification of the melt, etc. Subgrains are also formed during creep, when deformation and annealing are simultaneous.

Along the subboundaries the dislocations of the same sign are regularly spaced at rather great distances from each other. This model accounts for the properties of subboundaries: easy mobility, atomic disorder concentrated at special points.

The substructured crystal is characterized by the localization of imperfections in special planes between rather perfect lattices. That is realized in the polygonized state, but not in the cold-worked or in the recrystallized state. The substructure is a metastable stage of intermediate energy between the cold-worked and the recrystallized metal.

1. GRAINS, SUBGRAINS, AND SUBBOUNDARIES

We call crystalline grains in a metal the domains which appear upon observation after a macrographic etching of the polished surface. The reflecting power, or the tint of these domains, when coloring reagents are used, is almost uniform, and they are separated from their neighbors by well-defined limits called grain boundaries. Their dimensions are very variable, from 0.01 mm to the great lengths of the single crystals prepared specially.

If a Laue diagram is made so that the area touched by the beam is completely within the limits of the grain, we find a single crystal pattern. Each of the spots can be sharp if the crystal is perfect, or slightly enlarged by asterism if the crystal has been deformed. We shall consider here only perfect crystals or those slightly deformed, and we shall omit (except in the last part) the case of heavily cold-worked metals, in which the crystallites cannot be discovered by the microscope but are disclosed by the diffraction of x-rays.

Under certain experimental conditions, the grain defined above appears subdivided *into subgrains*, that is to say, it is divided into smaller domains by a network of limiting lines of generally closed contours. We call these limits *subboundaries*. The individuality of the grain subsists in the whole, and these subboundaries stop at the joints of the grains.

There are a very great number of widely varied cases where intergranular lines appear, the origin of which is more or less well known. For example, there are slip bands and the deformation bands, strain markings, etc. We shall not consider these lines in this paper, and we shall reserve the name of subboundaries for the lines of which Fig. 1 gives a very good example. Their characteristic is to form a network bounding the subgrains with *closed contours*, but of varied sizes and forms.

The aim of this article is to describe the experimental methods which reveal the subboundaries, to describe their properties as well as the atomic models proposed to explain them, and finally to discuss their origins and the mechanisms of their formation.

2. METHODS OF OBSERVATION OF SUBBOUNDARIES

MICROSCOPIC METHODS

Subboundaries were first observed many years ago by means of observations with the microscope. Early investigators have sometimes given these boundaries different names. By way of example, we shall quote some characteristic works without trying to write a full history of the subject. A sufficiently complete bibliography will be found in the article of Hultgren and Herrlander.[1]

On iron or soft steel crystals, numerous authors (see reference 1) have found subboundaries, which have been called "veining." These intragranular lines appear on the metal surface after mechanical, or preferably electrolytical, polishing. We shall analyze further the details of these observations. In this case, the subboundaries seem to be outlined by the precipitation of a constituent which Northcott[2] identified as an oxide. The phenomenon becomes more intense when the metal is oxidized in the molten state, and, on the other hand, disappears after annealing in hydrogen.

But what must be deduced from these observations is the fact that they prove that the oxide precipitate accompanies the "veining," but not that it is necessarily the cause of it. Such precipitation would not explain the formation of these networks of subboundaries. Northcott has made analogous observations on a large number of metals (cadmium, zinc, magnesium, aluminum, nickel, iron, silver); tin and lead were the only ones never to produce this phenomenon.

Hultgren and Herrlander[1] have observed subboundaries (which they call veining) by the micrographic method in steels deformed at a high temperature. They mention also a "veining constituent" but do not specify its nature. We shall return later to their observations in reference to the discussion of the formation of the veining.

Lacombe and Beaujard[3,4] carried out their observations on aluminum. The reasons for this choice were, first of all, the fact that the phenomenon is not complicated, as in iron, by the allotropy $\alpha \rightleftharpoons \gamma$, and, moreover, that the metal had a high degree of purity. The high purity permitted the study of the subboundaries in the absence of the additions which had complicated the interpretation of experiments on iron.

The specimens of refined aluminum (99.99 per cent) are recrystallized by a critical annealing, followed by a long heat treatment at 600°C, and a slow cooling in the furnace. The clearest experiments have been performed by Lacombe and Beaujard by developing etch pits on the metal after electrolytic polishing. It is found that, on certain crystals, these pits do not divide themselves up at random, but are grouped on lines cutting the grains in polygons of extremely variable dimensions (from less than 0.1 mm to several millimeters) (Fig. 1). Other reagents have

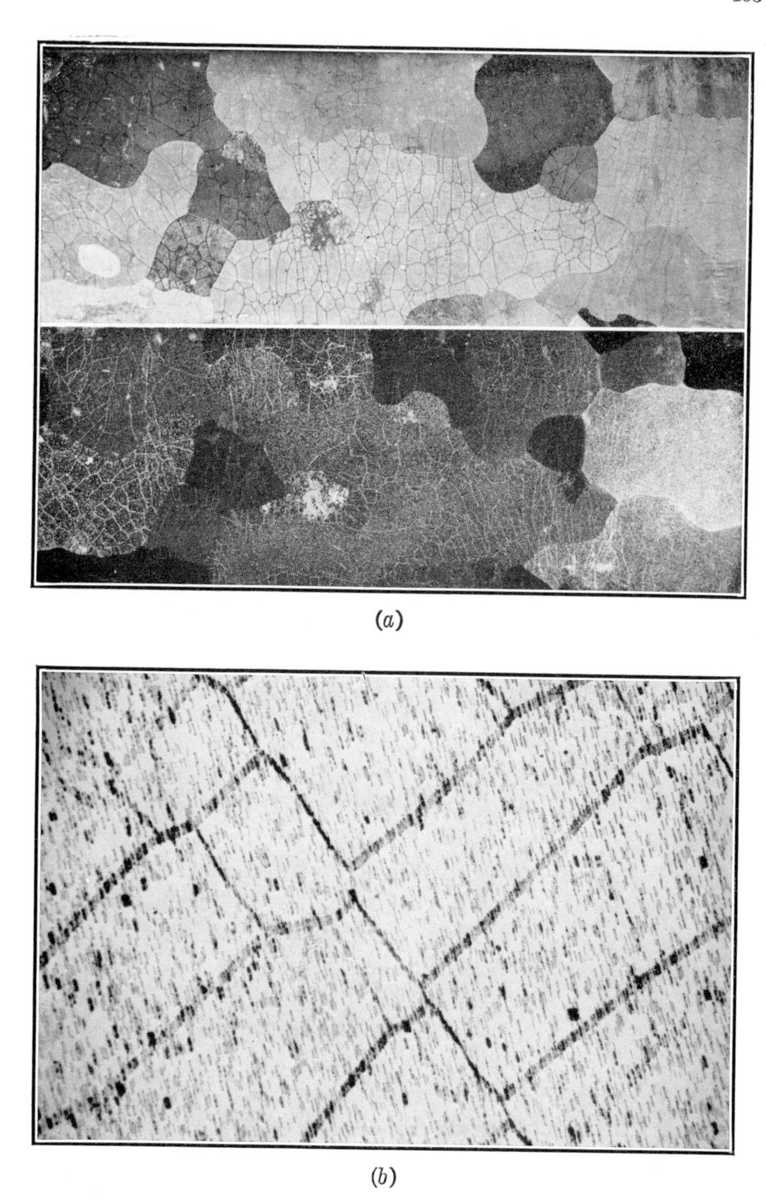

(a)

(b)

FIG. 1. (a) Polygonized crystal of pure aluminum. Natural size. (b) Subboundaries are revealed by etch pits. ×100. (Photographs by Lacombe.)

been indicated by Lacombe to produce evidence of subboundaries on pure aluminum. They should produce quite a gentle etching so that only the particularly sensitive points are marked: water solution of HCl at 10 per cent, solution of NaCl at 3 per cent, or again oxidization of the surface between 500° and 600°C. According to the procedure the subboundaries appear as discontinuous lines or continued lines.

The characteristics of these subboundaries are as follows:

(1) There are great irregularities of size among the diverse subgrains. In addition, certain grains are traversed only by very rare boundaries. Often their directions seem to be arranged at random; however, in certain cases, the domains are all clearly aligned in a similar direction.

(2) These lines are not only superficial. In the case of an aluminum specimen 1 mm thick, the two opposite faces show designs that are nearly identical, indicating that the subboundaries correspond to the subgrains of which the thickness is that of the sheet (that is to say, their thickness is much greater than their other dimensions).

(3) The subboundaries stop at the grain boundaries; therefore, they cannot be considered the remains of an old crystallization; it is certainly a question of the structure of the grains being observed.

Finally, the high degree of purity of the metal makes it impossible that the primary cause of the subboundaries arises from impurities. It is clear that, in Northcott's experiments, oxidation of the metal served only to reveal the existence of a phenomenon in which impurities do not play the primary role. Other investigators have employed Lacombe's micrographic method. Cahn[5] obtained very similar results with aluminum; he has also studied subboundaries in single crystals of zinc.

X-RAY METHODS

X-ray studies have permitted the establishment of the fundamental nature of these subgrains into which the subboundaries divide the crystal. These subgrains have *lattices very slightly disoriented relative to each other*. This conclusion results from the successive observations of many investigators; we shall describe only the conclusions.

The first studies on the orientation of subgrains, made by studying the direction of slip lines, showed that they had a uniform orientation, but the sensitivity of the method was insufficient. Laue diagrams indicated to Greninger[6] that ferrite grains with veining gave rise to broadened diffraction spots, this broadening corresponding to an orientation dispersion of 1° to 10°. Goss[7] found also that the grains of iron gave spots with asterism, but the splitting of the spot was not very clear.

It is conceivable that, if the individual blocks are very numerous and if their angular deviation is very small, the geometric conditions ordinarily realized in a Laue camera do not permit the resolution of the asterism into as many distinct spots as there are subgrains.

One of the methods to increase the resolving power is to decrease the number of subgrains contacted by the incident x-ray beam. In a sample with very developed subgrains, Lacombe and Beaujard[4] were able to make the x-ray beam fall exactly on a subboundary. Laue spots are then doubled, and the angular disorientation measured between the two adjacent subgrains is nearly a few minutes.

The resolving power of the Laue pattern is increased by the use of a fine-focused tube and a large distance between sample and source so that the divergence of the primary beam is very small. From back-reflection Laue diagrams obtained with this technique, orientation differences of about 0.1° can be detected.[8,9]

For transmission studies, we have used a more sensitive device, taking advantage of geometrical focusing of the diffracted rays.[10] A fine x-ray source irradiates a sample which should present itself in the form of a lamella thin enough to be traversed by a radiation of wavelength of the order of 0.4 to 0.7 Å. Whatever the size of the crystal, the rays reflected on a series of reticular planes converge on a small area, the size of which depends only on the size of the source. By choosing large enough distances (50 cm) between the source and the sample, we can separate the diffracted rays issuing from two crystals for which the lattices have an angular deviation of only 15″. This method, applied to certain crystals of recrystallized aluminum prepared with all possible precautions, shows that their lattices are defined to better than 30 seconds of arc over regions having areas of many square millimeters. Certain large crystals of iron prepared in the same way by recrystallization have also shown a perfection of the same order.

If the crystals are distorted, even very slightly (for example, a straining of 0.5 per cent), the spot broadens and transforms itself into a streak of *continuous* darkening, more or less uniform.

On the other hand, a crystal containing subgrains gives a striated spot. It is natural to think that each one of the striae corresponds to a subgrain. Besides we have verified that the number of the individual striae was of an order of magnitude compatible with the observed size of the subgrains.

Thus the two observations which reveal the subgrains, the micrographic etching and the x-ray analysis which defines the relative crystallographic orientations, can be correlated. Later on, we shall consider numerous experiments on subgrained crystals which make use of only one of these techniques. These are two partial but complementary methods of the study of the fragmentation of a single crystal. It is important to fix the limits of the two experimental methods. In the micrographs, according to Lacombe's method, the dimension of the etch pits is of the order of 0.01 mm. Consequently, the subgrains must have dimensions of several hundredths of a millimeter so that their limits are clearly revealed. It is certain that the nature of the etching reagent is of primary importance, but difficult to evaluate quantitatively. X-rays are less sensitive from this point of view. In our experiments, if the subgrains were smaller than 0.1 mm, the striae of the blocks were so numerous and so close together that they could not be separated. Then the Laue spot was the same as a spot from a crystal showing ordinary asterism.

STUDY WITH ELECTRON MICROSCOPE METHODS

We can use the electron microscope to disclose the subgrains of a smaller size. Several experiments, still not very numerous, have shown that this method might be fruitful.

(1) First of all, etch pits can be made by a method analogous to Lacombe's, but on a much smaller scale. On certain pictures, obtained by Castaing and Guinier[11] with aluminium alloys, etch pits of diameter of the order of 0.1 μ can be seen. It would, therefore, be possible to study subgrains having dimensions at least ten times smaller than those which may be studied with the optical microscope. But experiments of this kind have not yet been performed with success, to our knowledge.

(2) On the other hand, another technique employed by Castaing[12]

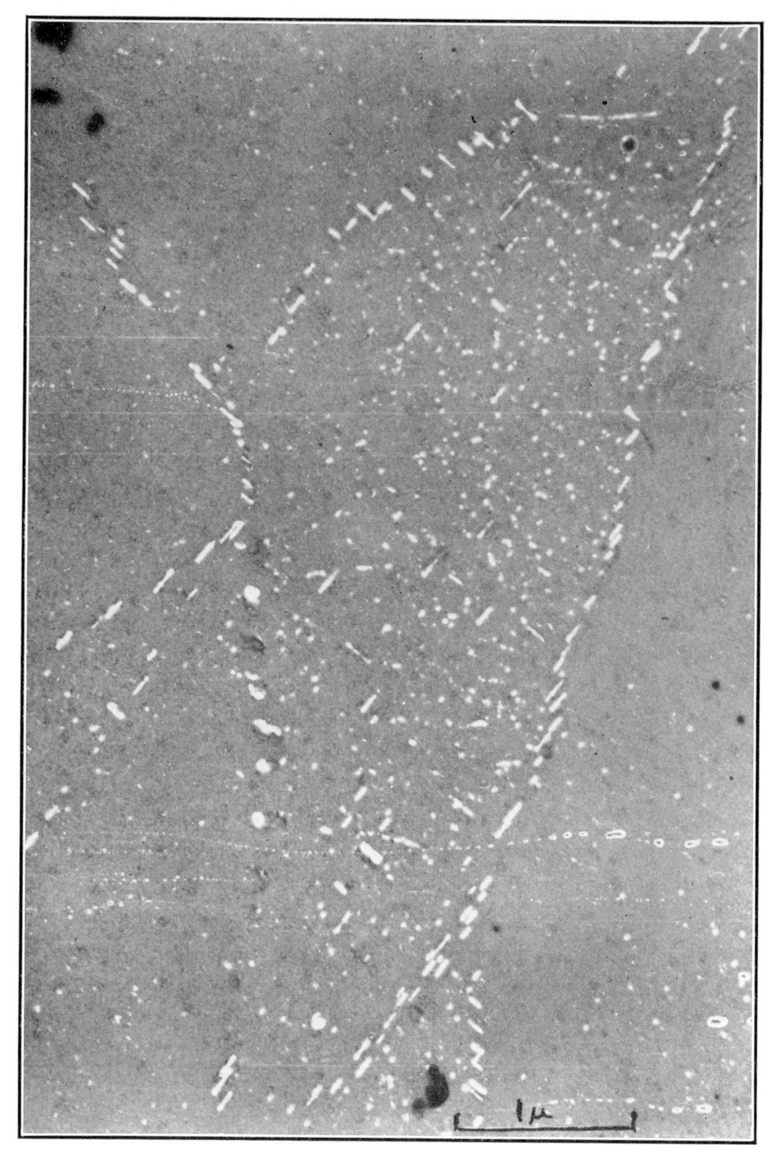

FIG. 2. Electron microscope photograph of a polygonized crystal of Cu-Al alloy. Subboundaries are marked by plates of Al_2Cu θ' precipitate. (Photograph by Castaing.)

has given interesting results. The metal was an Al-Cu alloy (4 per cent Cu), that is to say, susceptible to age hardening. After quenching, the alloy was submitted to an annealing insufficient to produce a precipitate in an appreciable quantity in the bulk of the crystal. Nevertheless, a series of little plates of the precipitated phase appears on the electron micrograph (oxide film replica), which are aligned and delineate closed contours very analogous to the contours of subgrains (Fig. 2). As in the observations of veining in iron, the precipitation takes place preferentially along the subboundaries. However, the electron microscope has a resolving power sufficient to distinguish individual precipitates, which often give the impression of a continuous line to the optical microscope.

Another example of the use of a precipitating phase to reveal the subboundaries is the work of Lacombe and Berghezan[13] on an Al-Zn alloy aged at room temperature. In this case there is no need of any attack; the simple electrolytic polishing reveals the subboundaries very clearly (Fig. 5). For, in the Al-Zn alloy, as in the Al-Cu alloy, the rate of precipitation of the supersaturated solid solution varies not only with the concentration of the dissolved metal but also with the state of perfection of the lattice.

The presence of a precipitate, therefore, reveals the presence of a crystalline imperfection. We shall dwell later on the consequences of these observations on the subject of the constitution of subboundaries, but from the simple experimental point of view the method seems to be extremely sensitive and of a great resolving power. It has the inconvenience of being practicable on only certain alloys which have undergone well-determined heat treatments.

3. ORIGIN OF SUBBOUNDARIES

The structure of a crystal divided into small disoriented grains is exactly what has been so often described as *mosaic structure*.[14] However, there is an essential difference: the dimensions of the coherent blocks of the mosaic structure are much smaller than those of subgrains. For another thing, according to these measurements of intensity, the mosaic structure of Darwin[15] and of Ewald[16] would exist in every metallic crystal. On the contrary, the division into subgrains is not always realized in the crystal. Much clarification on this subject can be obtained by carefully studying the relations between the subboundaries and the treatments undergone by the crystal.

Many among the first observers of substructures do not give any résumé of the conditions of preparation of the crystal which are necessary to make the substructures appear. Thus it is not possible to evolve an unambiguous conclusion from the observations on the veining of iron. In the same way, Lacombe has carried out his observations on crystals formed by recrystallization, but he mentions that all of them are not broken up into subgrains, without indicating where the difference might lie.

POLYGONIZATION

It seems that the key to the origin of subgrains has been found in the systematic study of *polygonization*. We shall enlarge a little on the polygonized state of the metal.

X-rays have shown that it was possible to obtain, by recrystallization, crystals that were quasi-perfect from the point of view of reticular orientation[10] (Fig. 3*a*).

But when the perfect crystal is slightly deformed, then annealed sufficiently, although without producing recrystallization, the Laue spot elongated by asterism after the deformation (Fig. 3*b*), is broken up into a large number of striae. The x-ray results indicate the formation of subgrains (Fig. 3*c*). These subgrains can also be observed by micrography. This treatment produces what Cahn and Orowan have named *polygonization*.[17,18] The distorted metal is transformed into a number of slightly disoriented subgrains as a result of local small modifications of the arrangement of the atoms; the curvature of the reticular planes are suppressed and replaced by multiple discontinuous changes of orientation. Polygonization of the metal therefore certainly brings about the formation of subboundaries. Polygonization was observed many years ago with sodium chloride crystals by x-ray examination by Andrade,[19] on rock salt by Konobeevski and Mirer,[20] and later on aluminum by Crussard,[21] who called the phenomenon "recrystallization in situ." Finally, Cahn[17] has carefully studied polygonization of crystals of zinc deformed by bending. The bending makes the lamellae slip over each other along the slip planes (Fig. 4). The annealing polygonizes the lamellae, and, in this case, it is predicted that the subboundaries should be perpendicular to the slip lines. It is just this that the micrographs show: the subgrains are in this particular case elongated and parallel. Cahn[5] has indicated some conditions for the appearance of subboundaries (strong curvature of the crystal, high annealing temperature (30°C below the melting point), and high purity of the metal).

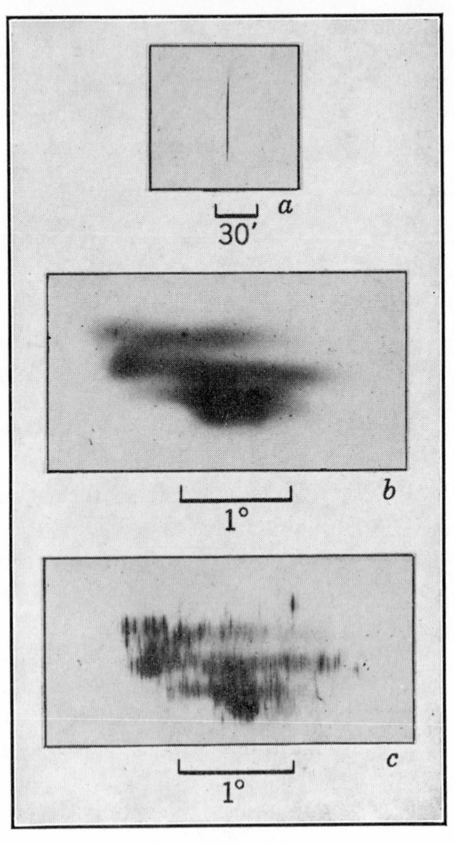

FIG. 3. Focalized Laue spots of an aluminum crystal: (*a*) perfect state (before deformation); (*b*) cold-worked state (after 5 per cent stretching); (*c*) polygonized state (after 30 hours' annealing at 590°C).

Actually these conditions are necessary only so that the subgrains are few in number and large. We have undertaken the study of the same metal with the sensitive method of focused Laue diagrams, and have found the metal in polygonized state after weak curvature and annealing at a low temperature. In this case the subgrains are very numerous, are very slightly disoriented relative to each other, and are not apparent from an ordinary Laue diagram.

We have studied aluminum principally. Any deformation (stretching, flexure, compression) produces asterism, and, after annealing, the crystal polygonizes. Pure aluminum or commercial aluminum is equally convenient. The micrographic observation shows subgrains of which the subboundaries often seem oriented at random. This proceeds from the multiplicity of the slip planes of aluminum. In certain cases, when one of these

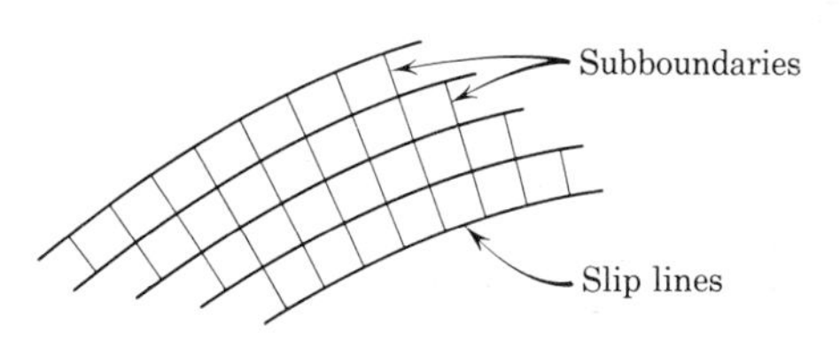

FIG. 4. Scheme of the relative positions of slip lines and subboundaries in a bent crystal of zinc. (After R. W. Cahn,[5].)

planes has a preponderant influence in the deformation of a region, it produces a special direction for the sublimits, and the subgrains have an elongated form.

We shall not discuss here the influence of the conditions of deformation and annealing on the size of the subgrains (for this subject, see reference 18).

Polygonization of a deformed metal occurs when recrystallization has not yet taken place. But when the annealing temperature is high enough, recrystallization can take place. The new crystals then develop at the expense of the polygonized crystals and are *perfect;* they are no longer divided into subgrains.

The phenomenon of polygonization is quite general and is related to the old observations on veining or substructures. Thus Hultgren and Herrlander[1] have obtained veining by a deformation of ferrite at elevated temperatures whereas, in the experiments of polygonization described above, the deformation was carried out at room temperature and the annealing followed the deformation; but it is obvious that the conditions and the results are very nearly the same. When the deformation is rapid, that is, when the heating time is short, the subgrains are finer, which is in agreement with the results of the polygonization experiments.

For another thing, these authors, as well as many others,[22,23] point out that the veining disappears when recrystallization occurs, which again agrees with what occurs in polygonization.

From this point of view, we must also quote the observations of Northcott,[2] who did not discover veining in tin and lead, which are the two metals recrystallizing most easily at room temperature. In this case we would expect that polygonization would be very easily masked.

FORMATION OF SUBGRAINS WITHOUT INTENTIONED DEFORMATION OF THE CRYSTAL

Is polygonization the mechanism necessary for the formation of substructures in the crystals? Is it necessary to deform and to anneal a crystal in order to form subgrains? In particular, subgrains have sometimes been observed in crystals that have not been subjected to intentional deformation. Such is the case in the experiments described by Lacombe and Beaujard[3] and Northcott.[2] Even in these experiments the formation of subgrains can be accounted for by polygonization.

First of all, in a specimen recrystallized after critical cold work and annealing, we often observe "insular" crystals which are the remains of the old crystallization imbedded in the new crystals, and which, on account of their orientation, have resisted absorption by the main new crystal.[24] These crystals, having undergone cold work and annealing, are therefore polygonized. This can explain the existence, in the middle of a specimen containing large crystals, of small crystals covered with subboundaries (Fig. 5). As for the large crystals themselves, which have been formed during the heating, they have been able to undergo little *accidental* deformations during the annealing. For example, if the sheet does not rest on an absolutely plane support, it can bend. It is sufficient in a specimen of length 20 mm for an irregularity of 15 μ to produce a curvature of reticular planes of 20′. These weak curvatures are polygonized at high temperature or on the slow cooling. Thus the small number of subgrains observed in the "undeformed" aluminum crystals (for the lattice with very small curvature is polygonized in large elements) is explained. Crussard (private communication) has verified that we can succeed, thanks to special precautions in the manipulation of the specimen, in obtaining the grains without any subboundaries.

Other distortions can occur unintentionally. For example, the quenching following the solution treatment can set up internal stresses, and polygonization can occur during the subsequent annealings. It must not be forgotten that, once polygonization is produced, it is impossible to make the crystal perfect again, unless recrystallization makes new grains form. Therefore, the sub-

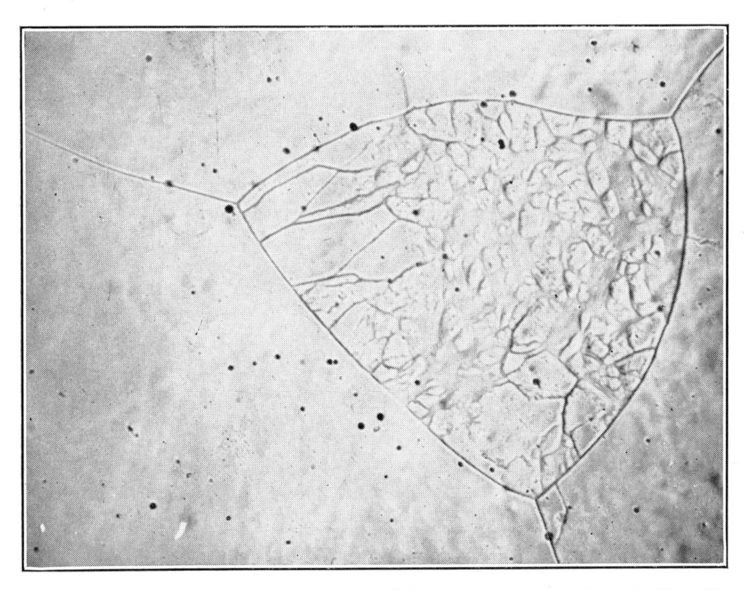

Fig. 5. Subgrained crystal surrounded by perfect crystals. Al-Zn alloy. Subboundaries appear after electropolishing without etching. ×100. (Photograph by Lacombe.)

grains formed at the beginning of the preparation of the metal remain throughout all the operations. Another factor which plays a part in the subgrains of ferrite (veining) is the allotropic transformation $\alpha \rightleftharpoons \gamma$.[25] When this transformation is too sudden, because of the volume changes which accompany it, certain grains can undergo stresses which deform them slightly. The curvatures of the lattice are finally polygonized during the time the metal is kept at a high temperature.

Finally, there are some observations on substructures where it is difficult to discover what deformation the grains would have been able to undergo. We have sometimes observed some recrystallized grains polygonized in the middle of many perfect grains;

similar observations were obtained by Lacombe (private communication), Northcott[2] also reports some observations of substructures in a recrystallized metal. These rather rare exceptions, still obscure, do not actually leave any doubt that the subgrains are usually due to polygonization.

CRYSTALS GROWN FROM THE MELT

The crystals which are formed from the liquid *are never perfect.*[10] Micrographic observation often discloses dendritic figures. These figures are generally revealed by the impurities which are localized in their contours, but they have as a primary cause the irregulari-

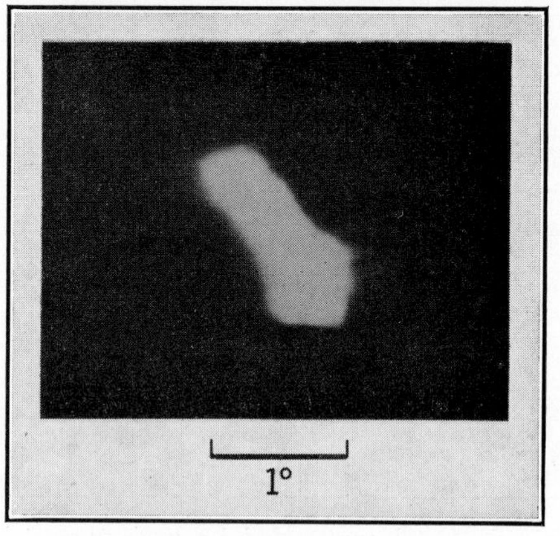

Fig. 6. Focalized Laue spots of an aluminum crystal grown from the melt.

ties of the crystal's growth from the nucleus. Buerger[26] developed first of all the *lineage structure* theory, and, more recently, Frank et al.[27] emphasized the essential role of the lattice imperfections (screw dislocations) in the growth of the crystal.

Experimentally, x-rays show that the reticular disorientations in the crystals grown from the melt are in general very important.[28] Micrographic examination shows that limits exist between portions of the crystal having slightly different lattice orientations. But we cannot in this case speak of subgrains, for each portion of the lattice still contains many defects. Thus, in rock salt crystallized from the melt, even with many precautions, there are internal stresses revealed by optical birefringence. The Laue spots (in diagrams with focused x-rays) obtained from rock salt or aluminum crystals are broad streaks, corresponding to an angular width greater than one degree, where the blackening is continuous but nonuniform (Fig. 6).

The usual treatment to remove the internal stresses consists in holding the crystal for a long time at a high temperature, followed by slow cooling. This treatment does not make the crystal perfect, but, during this annealing, polygonization of the distortions arising from solidification takes place.

Subgrains are formed, and the internal stresses, as well as the curvatures of the reticular planes, disappear. This is a very important mode of formation of subgrains.

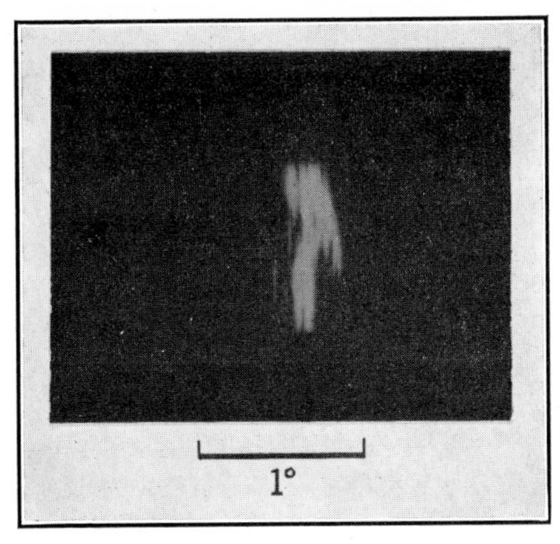

FIG. 7. Focalized Laue spots of sodium chloride crystal grown from the melt, annealed a very long time at 775°C, and very slowly cooled.

A long time ago Renninger[29] stated that a block of rock salt is composed of a mosaic of perfect subgrains of dimensions that can sometimes attain one millimeter. We have verified that continued asterism shown by crystals obtained from the melt (Al and NaCl) is broken up into very serried striae (Fig. 7). But the individual striae are not very sharp, that is, the subgrains are themselves divided into smaller blocks (they contain crystalline imperfections). The greater part of the subgrains observed by Northcott[2] probably were formed by this process.

Because of the change of volume accompanying the solidification, it is very difficult to realize such temperature conditions that no distortion is produced during the solidification. The distortions, once produced, can no longer be obliterated in the solid state. Perhaps it must be concluded that the few natural crystals that are perfect (quartz, for example) are formed after a transformation in the solid state (as the recrystallization of metals) and not from the liquid state.

To summarize the different ways of formation of subgrains, the essential fact is the necessity for plastic deformation followed by annealing. The deformation must be small enough and the temperature of annealing low enough that recrystallization does not take place.

THE SUBGRAINS CREATED BY CREEP

In creep, deformation and annealing occur simultaneously rather than consecutively. During this process it has been observed that the grains are broken up into subgrains; but the phenomena are sufficiently different from polygonization that Wood and Rachinger[30] are of the opinion that the two mechanisms should not be confused.

These authors deformed specimens of aluminum at a constant rate of straining and at different temperatures. They found that, in the case of slow strainings (0.1 per cent per hour and 8 per cent in all), the grain was broken up into subgrains.

On back reflection Debye-Scherrer diagrams, the isolated spots of the crystals were broken into a series of very sharp spots, distributed along an arc corresponding to a disorientation of 4 to 5°; the deviation between the individual spots was 0.1 to 0.2°. This dispersion remained, moreover, of the same order, even after a much stronger elongation. The perfection of the grains, according to the sharpness of the spots, should be as good as that of the initial grain.

For a given temperature and a given rate of deformation, the size of the crystal element tends towards a fixed limit. The number of spots on the arc of the Debye-Scherrer pattern remains the same for an elongation of 50 per cent (fracture) as for 4 per cent. This size depends on the temperature at which the deformation takes place. According to the number of observed spots, Wood estimates that the diameter of the subgrains is 7 μ at 350°, 5 μ at 300°, 2 μ at 150°, and 1 μ at 20°.

A microscopic examination of the polished surface shows irregular lines forming a rather confused network. According to the reproduction of the photograph published in Wood's paper, it seems that the mesh of this network is definitely bigger than the size of the subgrains determined by x-rays.

When the deformation takes place at a temperature above 250°C, there are no slip bands in evidence. But at a low temperature the slip lines are very marked, and they appear until 200°C. Wood has concluded from this that at each temperature the mechanism of deformation requires the formation of a substructure, but the boundaries of the element tend to become defined by specific crystallographic slip planes as the size of the substructure becomes small.

When the deformation is rapid (10 per cent per minute), ordinary deformation (slip bands, continuous asterism) occurs up to 200°C. At higher temperatures the Debye-Scherrer rings become spotty, but the spots only become really sharp and well defined around 500°. Thus, at a given temperature, the fragmentation occurs in smaller and probably less perfect elements than in the slow deformation.

Some recent experiments of Crussard[31] confirm the formation of subgrains during creep. Figure 8*a* is very similar to Wood's photograph. The aluminum specimen (after a straining of 5.5 per cent at 308°C) exhibits, besides the broadened grain boundaries, some subboundaries, cutting the grain into irregular cells. These cells are more visible after repolishing and etching (Fig. 8*b*—stretching 5.5 per cent—256°C). But after a further repolishing and new etching (Fig. 8*c*), the subboundaries have quite a different aspect, and the subgrains appear more irregular.

Let us now compare the subgrains formed during creep with those formed by polygonization.

(1) In both cases, the size of the subgrain increases as the temperature and the time of annealing increase. Indeed, during the slow deformation, the sample undergoes a long annealing, for example, 7 per cent extension at 0.1 per cent per hour represents a heating time of 70 hours, that is, a longer time than those we used in our polygonization experiments. In the case of the rapid hot deformation, the metal remains only a very short time at high temperature.

(2) The subgrains are formed during creep at temperatures where polygonization does not take place, or, at any rate, is not

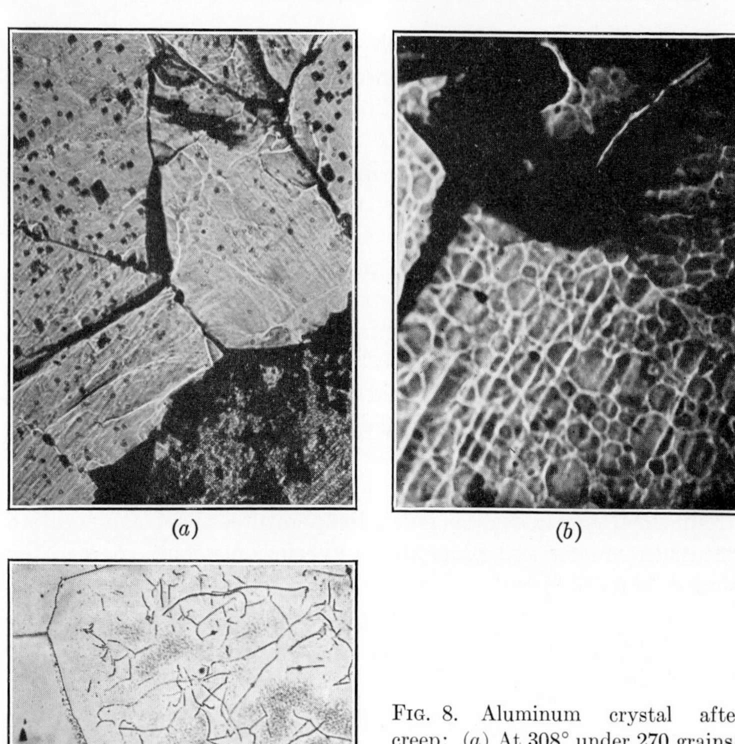

(a) (b) (c)

FIG. 8. Aluminum crystal after creep: (a) At 308° under 270 grains/mm², specimen not repolished after creep. (b) At 256° under 271 grains/mm², very short repolishing after creep (the surface is slightly outfocused). (c) Same condition as (b), but normally polished and etched after creep. (Photograph by Crussard.)

visible to x-rays. For another thing, during creep recrystallization is retarded. Thus, while there is a strong analogy, there is not perfect agreement between the effects of deformation at low temperature, followed by annealing, and those of a slow deformation at elevated temperature.

(3) The aspect of the subboundaries is very different. The

etching technique used by Crussard for obtaining Fig. 8*c* is exactly the same as that used by Lacombe; nevertheless, the subboundaries are quite different in appearance. In Fig. 8*b*, the subgrains (the "cells" of Wood) are separated by wide grooves, which, besides, can become broader during creep, as do the ordinary grain boundaries.[30] Crussard thinks that definite subboundaries are seen only after small amounts of creep. When the deformation is large, the division of grains into cells as described by Wood occurs.

We can conclude that there is no fundamental difference *in principle* between the formation of subgrains by creep and by polygonization. In both cases they result from the combined action of temperature and deformation. However, there are quite large differences in details, that is, the rate of deformation and the temperature at which the deformation takes place have a certain influence. Further experiments are still necessary to establish the exact nature of the subgrains arising from creep.

4. PROPERTIES OF SUBGRAINS AND SUBBOUNDARIES

The subboundaries can easily be distinguished from grain boundaries metallographically. The difference in appearance of the two sorts of boundaries arises from the differences between the action of the reagents on boundaries and subboundaries or, in other words, from the differences of the activity of the metal at these points. It is known that the grain boundary is attacked more markedly as the misfit between the two adjacent lattices increases; the minimum rate of attack occurs at a boundary between two twin crystals. The subboundary has a misfit greater than a twin boundary and less than an ordinary boundary. It is marked metallographically only by a very fine line, or even by a discontinuous succession of etch pits.

When precipitates are visible at subboundaries they occur at certain points spaced almost regularly along the subboundary. On the contrary, at grain boundaries, large precipitates are seen widely separated from each other. Moreover, often the boundary is surrounded by a band without any precipitate as if the dissolved atoms were all gathered in the large precipitates and the solid solution, depleted of solute atoms, had attained a concentration in equilibrium with the surroundings.

These observations, because of the irregularities in the position of the atoms, explain why the rate of diffusion and the rate of growth of the precipitate nuclei are greater at the grain boundary than in the bulk of the crystal itself. Along a subboundary, the disorder is certainly less, hence the weak reactivity of these subboundaries. More exactly, it seems that the atomic disorder occurs only around special points aligned on the subboundary. It is this very important experimental fact that justifies the model of the subboundary which will be given later.

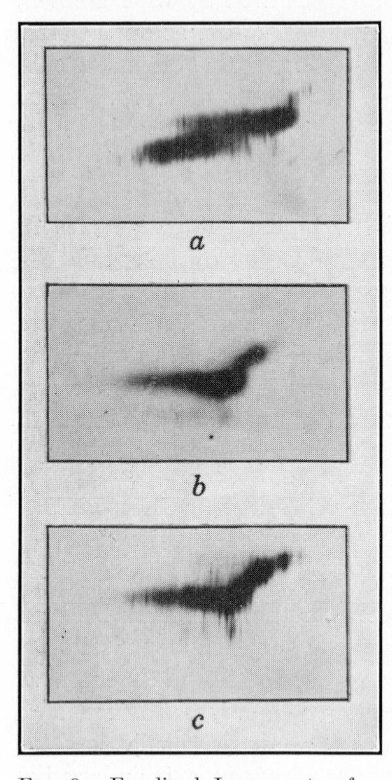

FIG. 9. Focalized Laue spots of a polygonized aluminum crystal: (*a*) taken at room temperature; (*b*) taken during the annealing at 580°C; (*c*) taken at room temperature after an annealing of 8 hours at 580°C.

Another consequence of the weak disturbances caused by the subboundaries is the relative ease with which these sublimits move. Lacombe and Beaujard[3] have shown that the contours of the subgrains disclosed by the etch pits could be completely modified by a new heating of the crystal. For another thing (Fig. 9), we have taken focused Laue patterns of a polygonized aluminum crystal, first of all at room temperature, then at 580°C, and again at the room temperature after a heating time which was equal to the time required to take the diagram at high temperature, that is, about one hour. In the first diagram the spot is clearly marked with numerous fine striae; in the second diagram, at elevated temperature, the striae are no longer clear; and they become clear again in the third diagram, but they are not exactly superposable on the initial ones. These observations prove that the distribution of the direction of the normals to the reticular planes has been modified during the heating and their angular displacement is perceptible from the beginning to the end of the exposure. Thus, not only do the subboundaries migrate, but also the orientations of the subgrains vary. These displacements happened especially at the beginning of the annealing for a given temperature. At the same time that the subgrains are displaced, there can be a disappearance of the smallest elements to the advantage of their neighbors; but the subgrains tend towards a limiting size and become more stable during prolonged heatings.

If the metal is heated to a higher temperature and if there is no recrystallization, an important change can take place. Some of the subgrains can grow and absorb all the others. Laue diagrams show only a few spots, but these spots are no longer very sharp, which shows that the subgrain, in growing, has lost its crystalline perfection. This condition should be connected with the fact that the ordinary recrystallized grains become less perfect during the normal "grain growth." The subgrains have, therefore, like the grains, the property of growing gradually when the temperature rises (Fig. 10) and also of sometimes presenting a phenomenon of exaggerated growth (Fig. 11). We have observed this exaggerated growth of subgrains only in aluminum of high purity,

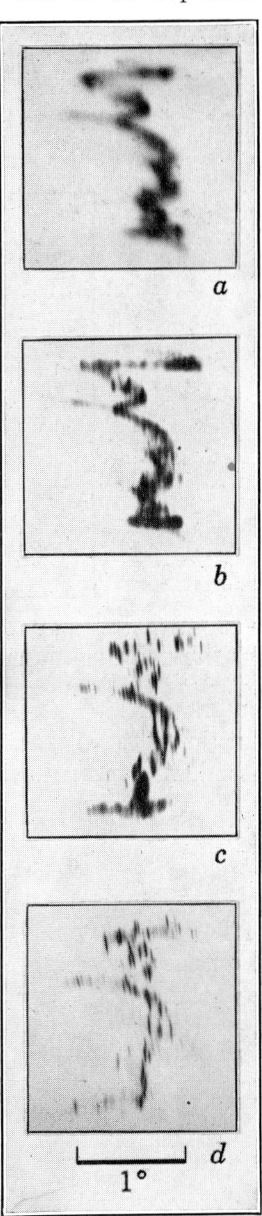

FIG. 10. Focalized Laue spots of an aluminum crystal showing the progressive growth of the subgrains: (*a*) cold-worked state; (*b*) annealed 14 hours at 520°C; (*c*) annealed 14 hours at 565°C; (*d*) annealed 14 hours at 610°C.

as if the impurities, localized in the subboundaries, retarded their motion.

Let us point out that, during all these heat treatments, the boundaries of the grains themselves have not undergone any modification.

This easy mobility of subboundaries compared to that of true boundaries indicates that these subboundaries have low energy. This low energy is due to the very small difference of orientation

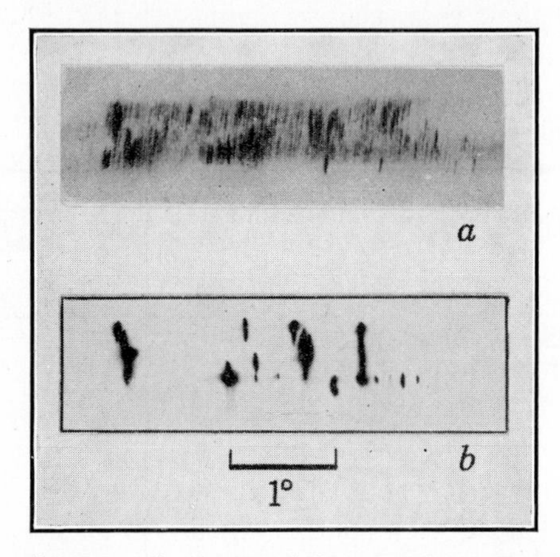

FIG. 11. Anomalous growth of some of the subgrains. Focalized Laue spots of a polygonized aluminum crystal: (*a*) after an annealing of 2 hours at 640°C; (*b*) after an annealing of 14 hours at 640°C.

existing between the contiguous lattices. It is not easy to understand why there should not be a continuous transition from an ordinary grain boundary to a zero-degree boundary and a subboundary. It is extremely rare to find two contiguous crystals formed by recrystallization, whose orientation is as close as those of the two subgrains.

The most favorable case is found in specimens having a pronounced recrystallization texture, like the so-called cube texture of certain metals after cold rolling. In fact x-rays show from these textures Laue patterns which bear much resemblance to those of polygonized grains; nevertheless the two cases are quite distinct. This difference can be accounted for in the following way:

(1) The extent of the angular disorientation in the best-marked texture is still large when compared to the total disorientation of a polygonized grain.

(2) Moreover, a subgrain is surrounded by subgrains of very close orientations, whereas a crystallite can have as nearest neighbors other crystallites, chosen at random among those of the collection. Therefore, the limits correspond to a change of orientation much larger than in a crystal with substructure. Figure 12 gives the two schematic models, and shows that the whole can in the two cases give the same separation of normals, that is, the same Laue diagram, in spite of the great differences of structure on a small scale.

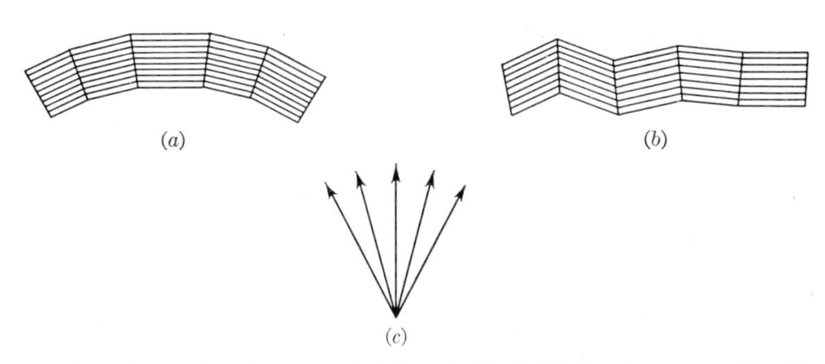

FIG. 12. Comparison between: (a) A grain divided into subgrains. (b) Different grains in a strongly orientated metal. The directions of the normals (c) are the same in both samples.

An important question which has been very little studied, to our knowledge, until now is the influence of subboundaries on the mechanical properties of metals. The measurements which have generally been made on recrystallized metals have been performed with perfect or subgrained crystals, but generally the authors were not concerned with the state of perfection of their specimens so that we still have few data indicating the relations between the macroscopic properties and the substructures.

Wood has established a correlation between the size of the subgrains which tend to be formed during creep and the mechanical strength. The bigger the subgrains, the smaller the resistance, which becomes negligible when the substructure is sufficiently large. Wood has even tried to relate the subgrain size, measured by x-rays, to the mechanical strength, by Bragg's theory,[32] and he finds a satisfactory agreement. The experimental fact which is most in favor of these views is that as the size of the subgrain, at a given temperature, tends towards a limit, so the resistance to the deformation cannot pass a certain limit. There is then continuous creep under constant stress. Crussard[31] has compared the elongation versus time curves during creep at constant temperature for aluminum specimens with and without substructure. There is certainly a difference in the shape of the curves, but a greater number of experiments are required to enable us to draw definite conclusions.

In a second series of experiments, Crussard[33] compared the stress-strain curves at room temperature. For the specimen constituted with perfect crystals, the equation of the curve can be written $\sigma = \sigma_0 + a\epsilon^m$ up to a transition point (for $\epsilon \sim 1$ per cent); then, for greater elongations, the equation is of the same type, but the exponent m changes from 0.5–0.8 to 0.1–0.2. This transition point does not exist if the crystals are polygonized. Lacombe and Berghezan[34] have shown that the rate of hardening in a polygonized Cu-Al alloy is less than in a recrystallized specimen.

5. CONSTITUTION OF SUBBOUNDARIES

All the observations described in the preceding paragraphs are well explained by adopting the model initially proposed by Burgers[35] for grain boundaries, and then discussed by numerous authors.[36] As this question is treated by Read and Shockley in this book, we will not treat it in detail here. However, let us remember that, according to the dislocation model, we can create a boundary between two crystals which have an angle between them of a/h, by introducing dislocations separated by a distance h (a is the lattice parameter). The simplest case produced by the scheme of Fig. 13 corresponds to the rotation about an axis situated in the plane of the junction of the two blocks, this plane being a symmetry plane for the two blocks. But it is possible to build valid models of boundaries in the general case by combining the dislocations of different types (screw and edge dislocations) and of different directions (see Paper 13).

The essential point to note is that this model, which has been proposed for all grain boundaries, seems to be especially well adapted to the cases of *subboundaries*, where the disorientations are very small. It is very important to emphasize that the observations on these subboundaries seem to give it an experimental confirmation of the model.

Indeed, the principal characteristic of subboundaries is the very small energy connected with them and also the discontinuous character of the irregularities (precipitates or etch pits) which mark them. If it is supposed that the lattices make an angle of 1′, it leads to a distance of 0.6 μ between dislocations; and between these two dislocations there is a region where the lattices are quasi-continuous.

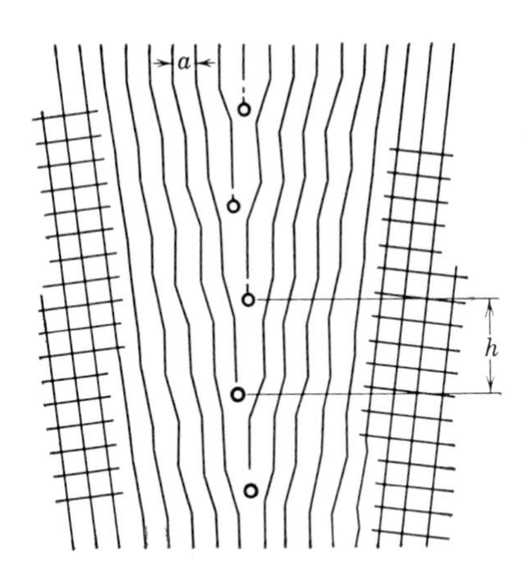

FIG. 13. Model of a subboundary as a line of dislocations. (After Burgers,[35].)

In the photograph obtained with the electron microscope (Fig. 2) the distance between the dislocations is of the order of several tenths of a micron, which corresponds to an angle between subgrains of the expected order of magnitude. A rigorous verification is unfortunately not possible as we cannot know precisely the orientation of the two subgrains of the photograph. It is noticed* on this same figure that the precipitates are directed sometimes in one direction, sometimes in another, the relationship of the two sorts of precipitate varying with the direction of the sublimits. We are tempted to see dislocations in the two directions that Shockley and Read introduce to construct subboundaries in the general case.[36] Unfortunately, the precipitates are formed in the plane (100), and there is no reason for supposing that these planes play a particular role in the dislocations, where it is more likely that the directions [111] intervene.

* This remark and the attempt at interpretation are due to W. Shockley and W. T. Read (private communication).

Another difficulty in the interpretation of those photographs is that we know only the trace of the joining plane but not its direction in space. Whatever may come of it, the existence of distinct dislocations of different natures seems to be well in accordance with the observations of the electron microscope. The size of the etch pits in the optical micrographs does not permit as clear an interpretation.

If we pass from the purely geometric point of view to the energetic point of view, we must take account of the fact that the

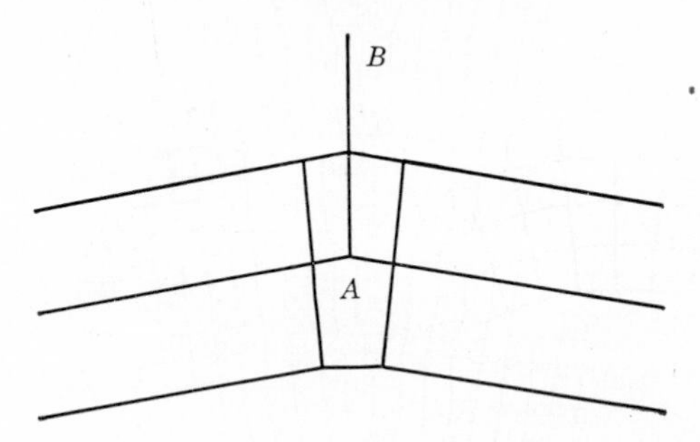

FIG. 14. Distribution of the stresses along a subboundary. (After Cottrell,[37].)

dislocations of the same sign have a tendency to group themselves in certain planes, which will form the joints between subgrains. It appears at first sight difficult to explain the stability of such an assembly of dislocations since it is generally admitted that two dislocations of the same sign exert a repulsive force on each other. But Cottrell[37] has noticed that this last result has been established for an infinite crystal containing a small number of dislocations. We must here consider the action of the two blocks on each other resulting from the curvature introduced by the dislocations. In the state of equilibrium there is a tension in the upper part, and a compression in the lower part (Fig. 14). If, therefore, a new positive dislocation is placed on the line AB, so as to increase the angle of the two subgrains, the arrival of the dislocation corresponds to a decrease of energy, and the subboundaries are stabilized.

For this model the condition of the formation of subboundaries can be understood. Suppose we start from a perfect crystal and deform it plastically; for example, we bend it. The crystal will contain a greater number of dislocations *of a given sign* distributed at random in the crystal. If the deformed crystal is heated to a temperature insufficient to make it recrystallize, it will tend towards a state of less energy. The temperature allows enough mobility to the dislocations so that, if some of them align, the others will move to the same planes. These planes will be discontinuities of orientation of the reticular planes. At the same time, since the two blocks which they limit will contain fewer dislocations, their curvatures will be diminished. That is, the block becomes progressively more perfect; this is polygonization (Fig. 15).

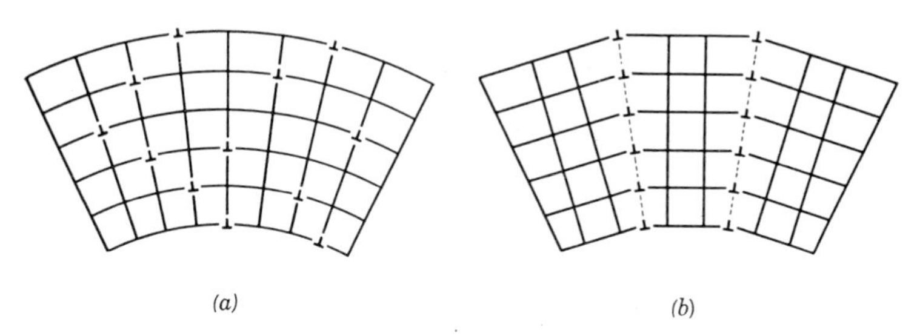

FIG. 15. Distribution of the dislocations: (*a*) in the bent crystal; (*b*) in the polygonized crystal. (After Cottrell,[37].)

The larger the time and the higher the temperature of annealing, the more considerable can be the movements of the dislocations. The subgrains are more extensive, and the disorientations between contiguous subgrains are greater. This is just the phenomenon observed.

If the crystal is not deformed by simple bending but by any other method, for example, tension, curvatures are again produced, but they are irregular and more or less localized (deformation bands). There are then, in the metal, dislocations of two signs, but such that, according to the regions, the one or the other type is in excess. Annealing, in this case, will have two effects: the mutual annihilation of dislocations of opposite signs, and the grouping in one plane of the dislocations of the same sign remaining in excess. There is, therefore, in this general case, at the same time, fragmentation into subgrains and progressive perfecting of the lattice within the subgrains. This corresponds to the stage where the asterism spot breaks up, but where the individual striae are not yet sharp.

According to this scheme, polygonization should be more definite when there is a marked and regular curvature. This prediction is confirmed experimentally. Polygonization is easier to produce by bending than by tension, and, in the general case, it is particularly distinct in the deformation bands, where the curvatures are concentrated.[5]

According to the mechanism which has just been described, the fragmentation of the cold-worked crystal into subgrains appears as an intermediate stage in its return to the state of least energy. However, the polygonized state still has an energy higher than that after recrystallization. Thus there can be recrystallization of the polygonized metal when nuclei able to grow are formed. The formation of nuclei is easier in the polycrystalline metal than in single crystals, and easier the larger the plastic deformation. Thus subgrains are specially observed in large slightly deformed crystals, for polygonization can be well developed without being masked by recrystallization.

The description of subboundaries as planes of gathering of dislocations at a distance from each other, separating really perfect crystals, is naturally only valid in the case of well-formed subgrains after an advanced polygonization.

But among the substructures that we have described there are less simple cases.

(1) The imperfections of crystals of first solidification are still distributed throughout the bulk of the crystal, and the subboundaries are less regular. This can be interpreted by the theory of dislocations, which holds that they are only partly concentrated on the subboundaries, the others being in the bulk of the subgrains. Along the subboundaries themselves, the dislocations are not regularly spaced.

(2) In the case of creep, the lattice of subgrains is quite perfect (according to Wood and Rachinger[30]), since x-rays give fine images of them. But the subboundaries are not defined enough that they can be represented by a simple line of dislocations. It must be noted, besides, that, since the angle between neighboring subgrains is greater, the dislocations would have to be closer together, leading to an increase in the disorder of the atoms in the transition layer. However, the picture is not sufficient to explain grooves of microscopic size (see Fig. 8*b*). It is likely that between the grains there exists a rather perturbed zone of transition, where

the dislocations are accumulated, without being in a single plane, these passage zones permitting the viscous sliding of the subgrains over each other and also their rotation, for the total disorientations obtained by creep by a given extension are very much bigger than those obtained by rapid tensile deformation at room temperature.

The easy mobility of subboundaries, in contrast with the relative stability of grain boundaries, shows that the mechanisms of displacement of the two sorts of limits are different. Beck et al.[38] see in this experimental fact a justification of the model of subboundaries. For the subboundary moves by the propagation of dislocations, but, on the other hand, the displacement of a grain boundary involves the diffusion of individual atoms from the nodes of one lattice to the nodes of the other lattice. This process requires a much greater activation energy.

6. EXTENSION OF THE NOTION OF SUBGRAIN

Until now, we have mentioned only subgrains that could be clearly made visible by a direct experimental method. But the notion of subgrains has been introduced in other cases, either as a result of theoretical hypothesis or of indirect experiments.

COLD-WORKED METAL

In the cold-worked state, before any annealing, is the metal already broken up into subgrains of very small dimensions? This is the theory which Wood and Rachinger[39] have proposed as a result of their experiments of x-ray diffraction; and it was used by W. L. Bragg[32] in his attempt to calculate the mechanical strength of metals from the value of the limiting size of the crystalline elements.

It has never been possible, by optical microscopy, to distinguish distinct domains in the cold-worked metal. With the electron microscope, Heidenreich[40] has disclosed some kinds of domains which should have dimensions of about 200 Å in a thin foil of aluminum. But it is difficult to draw conclusions as to the nature of these domains from the result of these preliminary experiments.

The only x-rays diagrams obtained with cold-worked metals are Debye-Scherrer diagrams; and these patterns are characterized by the broadening of the lines. One of the ways of explaining this broadening is that the metal is broken up into very small crystallites. If it is supposed that these are perfect and that they diffract the x-ray beam incoherently, the measure of the width of the lines gives an average value of their size. This is the opinion that Wood has defended in many papers. He has shown that the size of the crystallite tended towards an inferior limit when the degree of cold working increased (of the order of 2 to 4.10^{-6} cm or 200 to 400 Å).

But another interpretation of the broadening of the lines exists: it is to admit variations of the crystalline parameter from one block to another because of the internal irregular stresses. Certain experiments are clearly in favor of this second hypothesis.[41,42] Thus, even if the effect of the small size of the crystallites contributes to the line broadening, this effect is only partial. It is not therefore possible to deduce the size of the crystallite from the measurement of a line width.

It seems that, at the present, we cannot consider as proved the fragmentation of a metallic cold-worked crystal into perfect crystallites, or at least without too many defects. An experiment of diffraction,[43] with a microbeam of 30 μ diameter, has shown that the continuous Debye-Scherrer rings of cold-rolled aluminum are resolved into distinct spots. The authors have estimated, according to the number of spots observed, the diameter of the elementary aluminum crystallites at around 2 μ, that is, one hundred times greater than the value given by Wood. Furthermore, each individual spot is not very sharp, which proves the existence of distortions inside the individual grains.

In consequence, it is very probably too simple to consider the cold-worked metal as an assembly of subgrains, small but little deformed. A more likely model is to suppose the existence of domains having an average orientation rather badly defined on account of the internal distortions and stresses; these domains, being of variable size, could be quite small. But it is not possible to speak of well-defined *subgrains* in the cold-worked state.

THE RECOVERY

Subgrains are formed in a definite manner only after an annealing. But the question arises as to when and how the subgrains appear. In particular, what happens during recovery? In the study of the polygonization of deformed aluminum crystals,[18] traces of polygonization were observed at a temperature of the order of 450°C. And the recovery of the mechanical properties occurs at a very much lower temperature, above 200° and 300°C, temperatures for which Laue asterisms are still discontinuous without visible striation. This can be interpreted in two ways: either there is polygonization on a scale small enough so that the striae given by the subgrains cannot be distinguished, or the subgrains are rather large but too imperfect to give sharp striae. Either there is at first the formation of very small subgrains and their subsequent growth to the stage of visible polygonization, or there is a progressive improvement of the lattice of subgrains which does not vary much in size. We cannot at the present moment give an answer to these questions. New experiments will be necessary to elucidate this point, not only with x-rays, but also with optical and electron microscopes, with an improved resolving power to be able to detect the smallest possible crystalline domains.

MOSAIC STRUCTURE OF "PERFECT" CRYSTALS

To explain the reflecting power for x-rays of a nondeformed crystal as perfect as possible, Darwin[15] proposed the scheme of the mosaic structure, which has had a very great success since its proposal. The scheme is very like that of a polygonized metal, with two differences.

(1) The subgrains are supposed to have dimensions of 10^{-4} cm. That is, they are much smaller than the observed subgrains (they are bigger than Wood's "crystallites").

(2) The differences of orientation are certainly much smaller than in the polygonized metal.

We have determined[10] that a very good aluminum or iron crystal could not present disorientations greater than 1′ in a volume of several cubic millimeters. Two contiguous subgrains have therefore at the most a disorientation of this order between them. The joint between the two grains would then be made up of dislocations separated by several tenths of a micron, that is, by a distance at least of the order of magnitude of the dimensions of the block. It is therefore not possible to build a model of subgrains which might agree with the only two data which we have:

the total disorientation in as good a crystal as possible, and the maximum dimension of the coherent crystalline blocks deduced from the measurements of intensity of the reflected x-rays. Let us remember besides that the model of the mosaic structure was proposed by Darwin only because it permitted an easy calculation, but it is not necessary to interpret thoroughly the x-ray data. They require only that there are ruptures of coherence at intervals of the order of 10^{-4} cm. It is not then necessary to suppose the existence of perfect domains which are bounded by continuous limits.

It is more probable to admit that the lattice of the metal contains faults, for example, dislocations, rarer as the crystal is more perfect. The existence of these sparse dislocations takes account of the slight disorientation of the reticular planes; and, on the other hand, it destroys the coherence of the lattice, of which the reflecting power ceases to be that of the perfect crystal. But there are not any genuine subgrains in the crystal before deformation. Thus in the perfect crystal, as in the cold-worked crystal, we can conclude that there are not truly any subgrains. What characterizes the subgrain is that it is surrounded by subboundaries which cut the crystal in closed cells and that the subboundaries contain in large part of the imperfections of the crystal. The subgrains have a good internal perfection.

The existence of these well-defined subgrains corresponds to a particular state of the metal, in which the energy is intermediate between that of the cold-worked state and the well-recrystallized state. Besides the crystals in which experiment shows the existence of a well-defined substructure, there exist in addition some vague substructures, for which the internal imperfections are not negligible compared to the imperfections localized in the boundaries. These vague substructures correspond to the cases where the imperfections are distributed throughout the whole crystal; either they are very numerous as in cold-worked metal or extremely rare as in fully recrystallized specimens.

I thank Professor Crussard, Dr. Lacombe, and Dr. R. Castaing for having been kind enough to give me permission to reproduce some of their photographs, for having communicated to me some yet unpublished results, and for their many helpful discussions of the manuscript.

REFERENCES

1. A. Hultgren and B. Herrlander, *AIME Tech. Publ.* 2106 (1946).
2. L. Northcott, *J. Inst. Metals*, **59**, 225 (1936).
3. P. Lacombe and L. Beaujard, *J. Inst. Metals*, **74**, 1 (1947).
4. P. Lacombe and L. Beaujard, *Rev. mét.*, **45**, 317 (1948).
5. R. W. Cahn, *J. Inst. Metals*, **76**, 121 (1949). See also *Report of a Conference on the Strength of Solids*, p. 136, University of Bristol, England, Physical Society, London, 1948.
6. A. Greninger, *Trans. AIME*, **120**, 293 (1936).
7. N. Goss, *Trans. AIME*, **145**, 272 (1941).
8. C. Crussard, *Rev. mét.*, **41**, 111 (1944).
9. H. J. Gough, and W. A. Wood, *J. Roy. Aeronaut. Soc.*, **40**, 586 (1936).
10. A. Guinier and J. Tennevin, *Acta Cryst.*, **2**, 133 (1949).
11. R. Castaing and A. Guinier, *Compt. rend. acad. sci.*, **228**, 2033 (1949).
12. R. Castaing, *Compt. rend. acad. sci.*, **228**, 1341 (1949).
13. P. Lacombe and A. Berghezan, *Compt. rend. acad. sci.*, **226**, 2152 (1948).
14. C. Crussard and A. Guinier, *Rev. mét.*, **46**, 61 (1949).
15. C. G. Darwin, *Phil. Mag.*, **27**, 315 (1914).
16. P. P. Ewald, *Ann. phys.*, **54**, 519 (1918).
17. R. W. Cahn, *Progress in Metal Physics*, Vol. II, Interscience Publishers, New York, 1950.
18. A. Guinier and J. Tennevin, *Progress in Metal Physics*, Vol. II, Interscience Publishers, New York, 1950.
19. D. C. Andrade and L. C. Tsien, *Proc. Roy. Soc. (London)*, **A163**, 3 (1937).
20. S. Konobeevski and I. Mirer, *Z. Krist.*, **81**, 69 (1932).
21. C. Crussard, *Rev. mét.*, **41**, 133 (1944).
22. H. S. Rawdon and T. Berglund, *Natl. Bureau Standards Sci. Paper* 571, p. 649 (1928).
23. E. Ammermann and T. Kornfeld, *Arch. Eisenhüttenw.*, **3**, 307 (1929).
24. W. May, T. Tiedema, and W. Berger, *Nature*, **162**, 740 (1948); P. Lacombe and A. Berghezan, *Métaux & Corrosion*, **24**, 1 (1949).
25. L. Northcott, *J. Iron Steel Inst.*, **126**, 267 (1932).
26. M. J. Buerger, *Z. Krist.*, **89**, 195 (1934).
27. W. K. Burton, N. Cabrera, and F. C. Frank, *Nature*, **163**, 398 (1949).
28. P. Lacombe and L. Beaujard, *Rev. mét.*, **44**, 65 (1947).
29. M. Renninger, *Z. Krist.*, **89**, 344 (1934).
30. W. A. Wood and W. A. Rachinger, *J. Inst. Metals*, **76**, 237 (1949).
31. G. Wyon and C. Crussard, *Rev. mét.*, **48**, 121 (1951).
32. W. L. Bragg, *Symposium on Internal Stresses*, p. 221, Institute of Metals, 1948.
33. C. Crussard and B. Jaoul, *Rev. mét.*, **47**, 589 (1950).
34. P. Lacombe and A. Berghezan, *Compt. rend.*, **228**, 1733 (1949).
35. J. M. Burgers, *Proc. Phys. Soc. (London)*, **52**, 23 (1940).
36. W. Shockley and W. T. Read, *Phys. Rev.*, **78**, 275 (1950).
37. A. H. Cottrell, *Progress in Metal Physics*, Vol. I, p. 94, Interscience Publishers, New York, 1949.
38. P. A. Beck, P. R. Sperry, and Hsun Hu, *J. Appl. Phys.*, **21**, 420 (1950).

39. W. A. Wood and W. A. Rachinger, *J. Inst. Metals*, **75**, 571 (1949).
40. R. D. Heidenreich, *J. Appl. Phys.*, **20**, 993 (1949).
41. H. Lipson, *Symposium on Internal Stresses*, p. 35, Institute of Metals, 1948.
42. C. S. Smith and E. E. Stickley, *Phys. Rev.*, **64**, 191 (1943).
43. J. N. Kellar, P. H. Hirsch, and J. S. Thorp, *Nature*, **165**, 554 (1950).

DISCUSSION

Bruce Chalmers (University of Toronto):

A study[1] of the type of substructure previously referred to as *macromosaic* has shown that crystals grown from the melt under linear heat-flow conditions usually consist of strips of slightly different orientation. The orientations differ by about 1°, and the strips are of the order of 1 mm wide. It has been found that the differences of orientation increase gradually over a distance of about 1 cm from zero up to the final value in regions where they cannot derive directly from previously existing crystal.

The following mechanism has been suggested[2] for their origin. The solid at the melting point is believed to contain a considerable concentration of lattice vacancies, and it is suggested that some of them condense in the solid-liquid interface in the form of lines of vacancies.[3] Successive layers of atoms superimposed on such a structure would tend to perpetuate it, resulting in a dislocation line, parallel to the interface, with its Burgers vector parallel to the interface and perpendicular to the line. The line is terminated by two dislocation lines, perpendicular to the interface with their Burgers vectors parallel to the interface and perpendicular to the original line of vacancies. The loop formed by these three dislocation lines is closed by the liquid in contact with the solid at the growing interface. We thus have two edge-type dislocations which extend in a direction that is perpendicular to the interface. A suitable array of such dislocations would result in a substructure of the type under discussion. It is, therefore, suggested that the gradual increase in angle is due to the gradual production of dislocation pairs. It is not clear why they form the particular array that is observed, or why the angles reach stable values. These effects may be due to the stabilizing effects of impurities (see Discussion of Paper 13, by Read, in this book). It would seem that a more detailed study of the substructure should throw more light on the origin of these dislocations during solidification.

[1] E. Teghtsoonian and B. Chalmers, *Canadian Journal of Physics*, September, 1951.

[2] U. Martius, E. Teghtsoonian, and B. Chalmers, unpublished.

[3] F. Seitz, *Phys. Rev.*, **79**, 890 (1950).

R. Smoluchowski (Carnegie Institute of Technology):

In our laboratory Dr. Newkirk has observed, in the course of ordering of a Co-Pt alloy, effects similar to polygonization. Both microscopic and x-ray evidence resembles much of that presented by Dr. Guinier. The proper interpretation is not certain, but presumably in that case the ordering reaction which is accompanied by high strains leads to formation of mosaic boundaries which may be the site of preferential ordering.

C. G. Dunn (General Electric Co.):

There are several observations made within recent years on deformed and annealed silicon iron crystals (3.3 to 3.5 per cent silicon) that are interesting in connection with the subject of subboundaries. I should like to mention them briefly and refer to work either published or about to be published for the fuller details.

The first phenomenon is that of the removal of asterism in Laue patterns for cold-rolled crystals, which was reported several years ago under crystal recovery.[4,5] Figure D.1 illustrates this phenomenon. Recently, however, we have observed with the aid of improved micrographic methods that *polygonization* actually is part of the process of Laue spot sharpening, and *coarsening of the subgrains formed by polygonization* is the other process.[6] During polygonization there is little change in the asterism of Laue patterns. However, with coarsening of the subgrains, the spread in Laue spots decreases. Sometimes close doublets are observed, but often the spots are relatively sharp as in Fig. D.1*e*. It seems almost certain that the removal of orientation spread occurs by a selective growth process of the subgrains, which is governed by orientation difference and size of subgrains. Since energy in the subboundaries increases with orientation difference, the driving energy for removal of orientation spread is greater than for random growth.

The second phenomenon is that of polygonization and subgrain coarsening in large-grained polycrystalline specimens, where either (*a*) the ordinary boundaries remain fixed or (*b*) boundary migration occurs. The sharpening of Laue spots in connection with the foregoing phenomenon was reported earlier, but the presence of the subboundaries was noted only recently. We have observed that subboundaries are "pulled along" with movement of a boundary leading to imperfections in the area swept over. We also believe that boundary movement is largely determined by the difference in subboundary energy

[4] C. G. Dunn, *Trans. AIME*, **158**, 372 (1944).

[5] C. G. Dunn, *Trans. AIME*, **167**, 373 (1946).

[6] C. G. Dunn and F. W. Daniels, "Formation and Behavior of Sub-boundaries in Silicon Iron," *Trans. AIME*, **191**, 147 (1951).

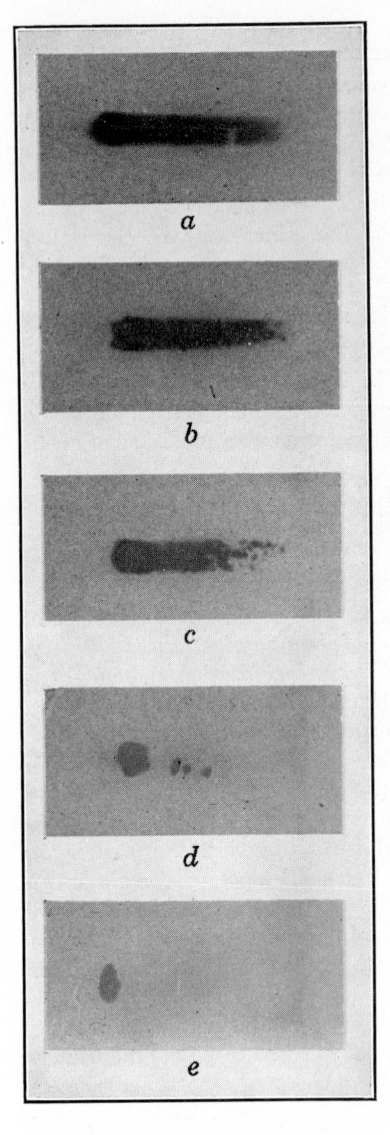

FIG. D.1. X-ray Laue spot showing the removal of asterism. (*a*) cold-rolled specimen; (*b*) after 10 minutes at 950°C; (*c*) after 5 hours at 1000°C; (*d*) after 1 hour at 1200°C; (*e*) after 48 hours at 1400°C.

per unit volume between adjacent crystals. When the difference is small, no movement occurs; when the difference is large, movement is possible.

The third phenomenon is that of polygonization in bent specimens, which we have observed between 800 and 1400°C. The boundaries form 90° to the active slip planes. At early stages of forming they are not particularly straight or continuous. Boundaries that are more or less straight develop only after prolonged annealing, which also coarsens the substructure. At a temperature of 950°C the subgrains readily increase in size. One instance was noted (see Fig. D.2) where the lamellar width increased from 3.5 μ to 18 μ during 24 hours. It can be concluded, therefore, that high purities such as those reported for aluminum and zinc are not necessary for subboundary movements and subgrain coarsening in silicon iron.

As to mechanisms and driving forces for the foregoing phenomenon, our information is either incomplete or theoretical. Evidence so far indicates that subboundaries probably interact like ordinary boundaries with coarsening leading to a reduction in subboundary energy. The number of interacting points decreases with coarsening, and this leads apparently to a limiting size. The grain boundary energy equation of Shockley and Read* provides a means of deter-

* W. T. Read and W. Shockley, Paper 13 of this book.

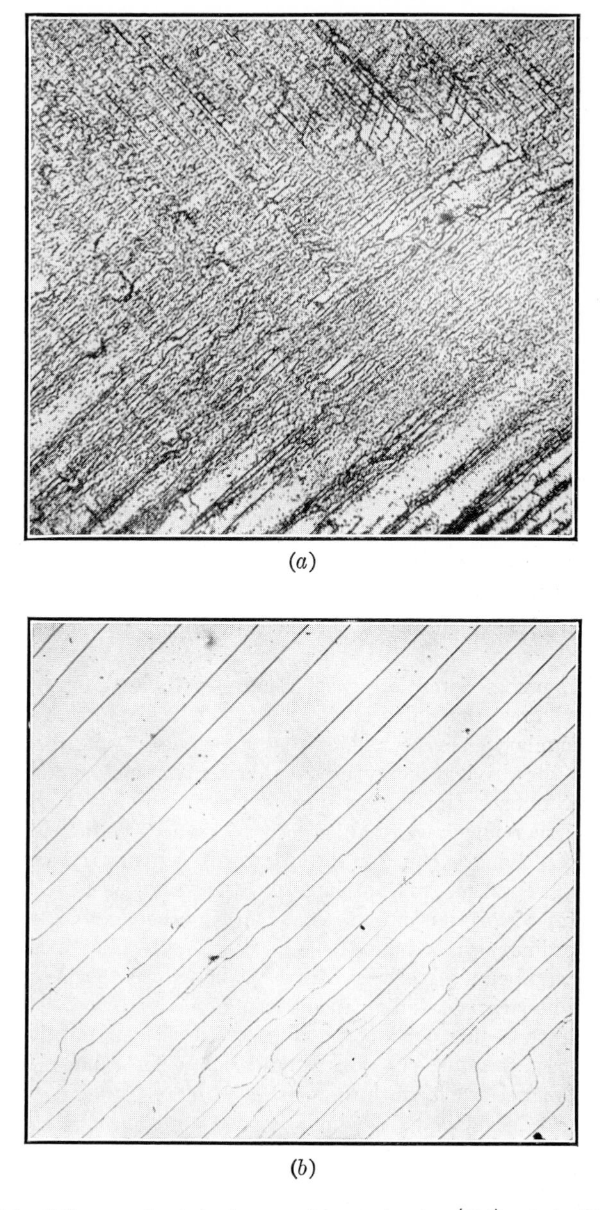

(a)

(b)

Fig. D.2. Micrograph of single crystal bent about a ⟨121⟩ axis to 21/32 in. (16.5 mm) radius and then annealed. Electro etch. ×200. (a) After 10 minutes at 950°C. (b) After 24 hours at 950°C.

mining the energy per unit volume for some idealized conditions. For example, the energy per unit volume can be found readily, at least on a relative basis for a bent specimen with uniform lamellae of width w, orientation difference steps of θ, boundaries at an angle ϕ to the radius, and a radius of bend R.

$$\text{Energy per unit volume} = \frac{E_0\theta(A - \ln \theta)}{R\theta \cos \phi} = \frac{E_0(A - \ln \theta)}{R \cos \phi},$$

where E_0 and A are essentially constants.

The first interesting conclusion to be drawn from this quantity is that a constant energy per unit volume appears for doubling of the substructure. Numerically this constant energy difference turns out to be slightly more than one tenth the residual energy for the case when θ is 0.2°—approximately the maximum average degree of coarsening found so far in silicon iron. The actual driving force for doubling is slightly more than one fifth of this number because only half the volume transforms for each stage of doubling. Stated another way, the process is one of coalescence of subboundaries in such a way that two θ-boundaries become one 2θ-boundary.

In another type of coalescence (a threefold increase) three boundaries coalesce with only half the total volume transforming. The driving energy for this is about one third the 0.2°-boundary residual mentioned above.

Another process is coalescence in succession, with only one lamella growing, the rest remaining inactive. In this case the first step leads to a 2θ-boundary; the second step to a 3θ-boundary, and so on. After each step the driving energy becomes larger, but not at a high rate. The effect is one of boundary type and not size of growing lamella, though these would tend to go together. Because of the slow rate of increase of driving energy for the distance the boundary must move, it seems very unlikely that a single large grain would develop by the step-by-step absorption of the rest. On the other hand, a new grain with an ordinary grain boundary would generally have available the average grain boundary energy per unit volume for a driving force, and this could be large, depending on subgrain size.

Another consequence of Shockley and Read's equation is that we should expect very low-energy subboundaries. The value of θ equal to 0.2° is about one twenty-fifth that of the ordinary boundary and therefore of the order of the twin boundary energy in copper.* It probably is lower than the twin boundary energy in aluminum.* If the boundary energies in the uncoarsened samples obey the energy equation, it follows that there are subboundaries with energies considerably below that of the coherent twin boundary.

* J. C. Fisher and C. G. Dunn, Paper 12 of this book.

16.

The Properties and Effects of Grain Boundaries

BRUCE CHALMERS

University of Toronto

ABSTRACT

A distinction is made between the properties and the effects of grain boundaries; the effects of boundaries on plastic deformation are discussed, and the possibility of a noncrystallographic mode of deformation is considered. The following properties are also considered: strength (shear and normal) and fusion (chemical and electrochemical).

1. INTRODUCTION

One of the first results of the study of individual or "single" metal crystals was the realization that they behave quite differently from polycrystalline samples of the same metals. In order to explain such differences, it is first necessary to recognize that there are two ways in which the single crystal differs from the polycrystal. In the first place, there are no crystal boundaries, and therefore any contribution to the properties of the polycrystal that is directly due to the boundaries would be absent in the single crystal. In addition, we must consider the possibility that a single crystal may behave differently if it is surrounded by other crystals in contact with it. Such an effect would not depend directly on the intrinsic properties of the intercrystalline boundaries, but would nevertheless occur as a result of the existence of the boundaries. It could be described as an effect of the boundaries in distinction to the previously mentioned properties of the boundaries. It is convenient to discuss in sequence the effects and the properties of grain boundaries, although it is recognized that the effects can be understood only in terms of certain of the properties.

2. THE EFFECTS OF GRAIN BOUNDARIES

The physical properties of metals are, for many purposes, divided into those which are *structure-sensitive* and those which are *non-structure-sensitive*. The structure-sensitive properties are those which are greatly affected by small departures from the ideal structure; in metals, the most important structure-sensitive properties are associated with plasticity. The elastic constants and the electrical and thermal properties are to a considerable degree nonstructure-sensitive; the difference between the single and polycrystalline forms is, from this point of view, a difference in structure. The plastic properties are profoundly changed, whereas the density, specific heat, thermal expansion, thermal conductivity, and electrical conductivity are affected to an extent which is too small for detection by existing methods. It is possible, therefore, to calculate the values of these properties for the polycrystal from the single-crystal data, provided that proper allowance is made for the anisotropy of some of these effects.

On the other hand, the plastic behavior of a polycrystalline specimen cannot be predicted directly from single-crystal data. This is attributed to the effects which each crystal exerts on its neighbors. In order to examine these effects, it is first necessary to review the experimental evidence. This is of two kinds. In the first place, there have been many observations which have led to the general conclusion that the stress-strain curve is raised as the crystal size is reduced. A few of these observations have been the results of systematic experiments. For example, Edwards and Pfeil[1] have studied the influence of grain size on the tensile properties of iron; Pell-Walpole[2] has investigated the effect of grain size on the tensile strength of tin and tin alloys; Northcott[3] has conducted similar experiments on copper alloys and zinc and magnesium in the cast condition; Herenquel and Lacombe[4] have investigated high-purity magnesium from the same point of view; and Sugihara[5] has reported results on the effect of grain size on the elastic limit of aluminum.

Experiments such as these are necessarily concerned with the integrated effect of many regions of intercrystalline influence. Such regions may differ from each other in at least two ways.

The difference between the orientations of the neighboring crystals has a value that is defined by two independent angles, both of which may vary; and the orientation of the boundary itself, both with respect to the stress and to the crystals, can also vary from one boundary to another. Any attempt, therefore, to deduce detailed quantitative relationships or mechanisms from experiments on polycrystalline specimens is unlikely to succeed. The converse procedure, however, has met with considerable, but not complete, success. G. I. Taylor[6] made an analysis of the stress-strain curve that would characterize a polycrystalline specimen of aluminum, on the assumption that each crystal deforms in a manner that is geometrically similar to the deformation of the whole specimen. It is implicit in this assumption that each crystal remains in conformity with its neighbors throughout the process. If the specimen as a whole deforms as an isotropic plastic medium, then each crystal must do the same. In general, this necessitates the simultaneous operation of slip on three sets of planes; two directions are active in two out of the three planes. It follows that slip must occur in some directions and planes that are less favorably oriented with respect to the stress than would be the case for the most favorably situated set in a single crystal. A higher stress, therefore, is necessary to produce a given resolved shear stress on such planes, and the stress necessary to initiate plastic deformation is therefore higher in the polycrystalline material than for the single crystal. An analysis on the same lines for the remainder of the stress-strain curve gave fair agreement with experiment in the case of aluminum.

The same analysis predicts the orientation of each crystal after deformation in terms of the original orientation and the amount of strain. These predictions were not completely satisfied; as indeed is to be expected when the essential oversimplification of the initial assumptions is recognized. It is not, in fact, always possible to specify accurately the orientation of a particular crystal after deformation, because of the departure from complete homogeneity in the deformation of the crystal. Furthermore, it should be observed that this analysis does not predict any variation of the stress-strain curve with crystal size, so long as the specimen is polycrystalline.

The partial but not complete success of Taylor's method of attack on this problem suggests that there is an additional effect of a crystal on its neighbors. The study of such effects cannot be carried very far with specimens containing many crystals and many boundaries, and we are therefore led to consider the second type of experiment, namely, that in which a single boundary between two crystals is investigated.

Such experiments may be carried out on the boundaries in large-grained specimens, usually prepared by controlled grain growth. Boas and Hargreaves[7] investigated the inhomogeneity of deformation in the neighborhood of boundaries that were transverse to the axis of the tensile stress. They found that different crystals suffered different average amounts of strain and that the strain was not uniform throughout any one crystal, but varied near the boundary with a neighboring crystal in such a way that both crystals tended to have equal strain at their mutual boundary. These experiments, and those of Miller[8] on the influence of a grain boundary on the deformation of zinc and of Hibbard[9] on plastic deformation in large-grained copper specimens, show that effects occur near crystal boundaries but not elsewhere. These effects may include the suppression of lamellar slip on slip planes because, in general, lamellar slip at the boundary would not be compatible with the retention of a coherent interface. Thus, whatever it is that causes slip in single crystals to be lamellar (that is, concentrated in relatively widely spaced planes or groups of planes) is superseded near the boundary by the cohesion of the two crystals with each other. Deformation near the boundary is therefore subject to constraints that do not exist elsewhere and may no longer be definable in strict crystallographic terms. It may be simpler to regard it as "noncrystallographic" deformation, the occurrence of which in certain circumstances has been postulated by Schmid.[10]

It is not, perhaps, unreasonable to consider that noncrystallographic deformation can occur if the maximum shear stress reaches a critical value. This is usually prevented by the previous occurrence of ordinary crystallographic slip. If the proximity of crystal boundaries or previous extensive plastic deformation causes sufficient increase in the critical shear stress for crystallographic plasticity, the alternative process may occur. It is, then, suggested that one of the effects of the crystal boundary is to cause such a high local increase in the stress required for ordinary plastic processes that the other process occurs instead. The properties by virtue of which this can take place will be discussed in the next section.

A potentially even more revealing type of experiment is that in which the specimen consists of two crystals and a single boundary —that is, a bicrystal. Techniques have been developed for producing bicrystals with predetermined orientations, and experiments by Chalmers[11] on such specimens in tin have shown that the yield stress is considerably influenced by the difference in orientation of the two crystals. When the orientations are nearly identical, the yield stress approaches the single crystal value. Larger differences in orientation correspond to greater yield stresses.

3. PROPERTIES OF GRAIN BOUNDARIES

It is evident from the very high mechanical strength of some polycrystalline metals that the crystal boundaries can support quite high stresses, and there is direct experimental evidence that this is the case. It is convenient to consider shear stresses and normal stresses separately.

SHEAR STRESSES

Two quite different methods of approaching the problem of the mechanical properties of crystal boundaries under shear stresses have been adopted. By far the more fruitful so far has been that of Kê,[12] who has compared the relaxation spectra of large- and small-grained wires of various metals. The experimental method was to measure the internal friction in torsion as a function of temperature, and thence to deduce the time of relaxation of whatever anelastic phenomenon is responsible for the energy dissipation. The only difference between the large- and small-grained specimens was assumed to be the grain size, and the damping was attributed to relative shear movement of neighboring grains, opposed by forces with the characteristics of viscosity. On these assumptions, an expression was derived for the viscosity of the boundary material on the basis of a viscous boundary layer about 2 Å thick. In the case of aluminum, the numerical value of the viscosity at the melting point was found to coincide, approximately, with that of the liquid metal. The temperature dependence, however, is quite different, and the equality at the melting point should not be taken to mean that the boundary material shares the properties of the liquid.

Another approach to the problem of the stress-strain-time relationships for crystal boundaries under shear stresses is that of Cahn, King, and Chalmers,[13] who applied shear stresses to "bicrystals"—that is, specimens consisting of two crystals and one boundary. The relative movement of the crystals was determined as a function of time by observation of fiducial marks on the surface of the bicrystal. It was found that the rate of strain decreases with time; this would not be predicted from the apparently viscous behavior deduced by Kê. It is recognized that the phenomenon investigated on the bicrystals is of a different order of magnitude, as regards both linear extent and time scale, from that of Kê. Bicrystal experiments have been conducted on tin and on aluminum, with qualitatively similar results.

NORMAL STRESSES

It is evident that the grain boundaries must also be able to support normal stresses. There is no problem in connection with compressive stresses; the effect of tensile stress is not so readily determined. It is not uncommon for failure in creep to occur as a result of intergranular separation; and at high temperatures (relatively to the melting point) there is a tendency for tensile failure to occur in the same way. This has led to the concept of the *equicohesive temperature*[14] at which the tensile strength of the boundary is equal to that of the crystal; at lower temperatures the situation is reversed. It should be pointed out, however, that the equicohesion temperature is not a precise constant for a given metal; it depends to quite a large extent on the conditions of observation, and in particular on the rate at which a test is conducted. Furthermore, under some conditions, it is possible to produce a mixture of transgranular and intergranular fractures. This may be related to the complexity of a polycrystalline solid under tension, in which the normal component of tension varies from one boundary to another, whereas the relative orientation of the two crystals at a boundary also varies in a random and unrelated way.

More detailed information about the normal strength of the boundaries is likely to be obtained from "bicrystal" experiments, in which the variables are separated and under control. A difficulty arises, however, if an attempt is made to conduct simple tension experiments on bicrystals from this point of view; the individual crystals deform under relatively low stresses, and it is difficult, if not impossible, to apply sufficient stress to cause boundary failure. A possible way round this difficulty is to apply the stress locally to a small part of the boundary in a bicrystal, so that general deformation of the crystals is prevented. This has been done[15] in a preliminary way, in lead and tin at room temperature, by the following procedure. A bicrystal is prepared, with known orientations and a smooth surface. An indentation is then made close to the boundary by means of a microhardness indentor. As the indentor is removed, or else subsequently, separation of the two crystals may occur locally. This is attributed, tentatively, to the tension resulting from the elastic recovery of the deformed material near the indentor. A more thorough examination of this effect is in progress.

4. FUSION OF GRAIN BOUNDARIES

It has frequently been observed that the strength of crystal boundaries becomes negligibly small at a temperature distinctly below that at which the crystals melt. This is generally regarded as equivalent to the statement that the boundaries melt at a lower temperature than the crystals. Experiments on bicrystals of tin[16] have given considerable support to the view, as it was shown that the temperature difference is independent of the stress over a range of three to one and for a very wide range of rates of heating. It was also shown that the temperature difference was independent of the impurity content within the range 20 to 140 parts per million, and of the relative orientation over a wide range, which did not, however, include any angles less than 14°.

Qualitative support for these observations comes from the work of Chaudron, Lacombe, and Yannaquis,[17] who maintained a slight temperature gradient in polycrystalline aluminum and found evidence that the boundaries had melted in a zone in which the crystals were still solid.

5. CHEMICAL PROPERTIES OF GRAIN BOUNDARIES

It is to be expected, on any theory of the grain boundary structure that has yet been proposed, that there would be a tendency for solute atoms to have a higher concentration at the boundaries than elsewhere. The theoretical extent of this effect depends on the particular model that is adopted, and therefore experimental data might provide an additional means of discriminating between various theories. The only experimental evidence, however, is very difficult to reconcile with current views on the extent of the boundary zone. Dean and Davey[18] have examined the copper content of zinc-rich Cu-Zn alloys by electrolytic solution of quantities of the order of 1 mg. The samples were taken from the surface at regions which included crystal boundaries and at regions which did not. A significant but inconsistent difference was found in the copper content; for example, in one case, the "boundary" sample showed 1.6 per cent copper, while the comparison sample contained 2.1 per cent copper. Interpretation of the results is complicated by the fact that the particular alloys used were two-phase at room temperature and had to be annealed at elevated temperatures, and then quenched in order to have an effective single-phase solid solution alloy. A simple approximate analysis shows that even if the boundary consists only of zinc (that is, zero copper content) its thickness would be of the order of 10^{-3} cm. This analysis involves several assumptions, but is not likely to be wrong by a factor of 10. If the copper content of the boundary were not zero, its thickness would be even greater. It appears that some other explanation of the results must be found, although efforts were made to avoid the foreseeable sources of error.

This conclusion is supported by the results of C. S. Smith and D. F. Clifton,[19] who found no significant difference in composition between successive slices of thickness 0.02 mm taken parallel to a grain boundary in a Cu-Sn alloy.

6. ELECTROCHEMICAL EFFECTS

Preferential electrolytic attack at grain boundaries is quite common, and it is also found that the presence of tensile stress, either externally applied or residual, accelerates the process. It seems that these effects generally occur when there is a second phase which has precipitated at the boundaries. The electrochemical characteristics of the second phase and, sometimes, of the depleted solid solution zone surrounding it provide an explanation of the intercrystalline corrosion which occurs. The only property of the boundary that is relevant is associated with the preferential formation of the second phase, either as a precipitate or otherwise. Little seems to be known about this effect, which may be associated with the nucleation of the precipitating particle. Nucleation should be easier where the surface energy of the particle is a minimum, and this may occur at the crystal boundaries because of the less ordered structure that exists there. This matter does not appear to have been investigated systematically.

7. OTHER POSSIBILITIES

It will be appreciated that very few of the intrinsic properties of grain boundaries have so far been measured; there are indeed not many properties that can be measured when they reside in a very thin layer within an opaque solid. There are, however, certain other types of measurement that might be made; for example, the optical properties of grain boundaries could be studied in a transparent crystalline material, such as silver chloride, which behaves in some ways analogously to metals.

Analogously, it should be possible to measure the reflectivity of boundaries to elastic waves by means of the ultrasonic pulse technique. This might give some information on the extent to which the elasticity and density of the boundary differ from those of the crystals. In conclusion, it should perhaps be observed that the recent work on boundary free energy, which is discussed by Fisher in Paper 12 of this book, has given more information about the boundary than any other method so far devised.

REFERENCES

1. C. A. Edwards and C. P. Pfeil, *J. Iron Steel Inst.*, **112**, 79 (1925).
2. W. T. Pell-Walpole, *J. Inst. Metals*, **69**, 131 (1943).
3. L. Northcott, *J. Inst. Metals*, **68**, 189 (1942).
4. J. Herenquel and P. Lacombe, *Métaux & Corrosion*, **11**, 185 (1936).
5. M. Sugihara, *Mem. Coll. Sci. Kjoto Imp. Univ.*, (A)**20**, 173 (1937).
6. G. I. Taylor, *J. Inst. Metals*, **62**, 307 (1938); *Stephen Timoshenko 60th Anniversary Volume*, The Macmillan Co., New York, 1938.
7. W. Boas and M. E. Hargreaves, *Proc. Roy. Soc. (London)*, **A193**, 89 (1948).
8. R. F. Miller, *Trans. AIME*, **111**, 135 (1934).
9. W. R. Hibbard, Jr., *Trans. AIME*, **180**, 52 (1949).
10. E. Schmid, *Proc. Inter Conf. on Physics, (London)*, p. 161 (1934).
11. B. Chalmers, *Proc. Roy. Soc.*, **A162**, 120 (1937).
12. T'ing-Sui Kê, *Phys. Rev.*, **71** (No. 8), 533 (1947).
13. R. W. Cahn, R. King, and B. Chalmers, *Nature*, **161**, 682 (1948).
14 Z. Jeffries and R. S. Archer, *The Science of Metals*, McGraw-Hill Book Co., New York, 1924.

15. J. Becker, Private communication.
16. B. Chalmers, *Proc. Roy. Soc.* (*London*), **A175**, 100 (1940).
17. G. Chaudron, P. Lacombe, and N. Yannaquis, *Compt. rend.*, **226**, 1392 (1948).
18. G. R. Dean and W. P. Davey, *Trans. Am. Soc. Metals*, **26**, 267 (1938).
19. C. S. Smith and D. F. Clifton, *Rev. Sci. Instruments*, **20**, 583 (1949).

DISCUSSION

R. Smoluchowski (Carnegie Institute of Technology):

The author of this paper stated that strains and deformation surrounding a grain boundary affect a relatively wide layer of metal on both sides of the boundary. I would like to mention in that connection that known, but not well-understood, phenomenon that under certain etching conditions etch pits appear on the surface of a polycrystalline material, except in the vicinity of grain boundaries. The band free of etch pits is usually quite smooth and uniform and seems to have different widths for different pairs of grains. It is also observable along twin boundaries. Off hand, one would expect a layer of strained metal to etch more easily than the unstrained interior of a grain. Assumption of localized potential differences also does not lead to a satisfactory interpretation.

E. Orowan (Massachusetts Institute of Technology):

Many years ago, the present speaker had repeatedly discussed the question whether a crystal could be superheated above its melting point, and whether melting could start at a surface or an interface at a slightly lower temperature, with Professor Max Volmer, then Head of the Institute of Physical Chemistry at the Technical University Berlin-Charlottenburg. Under the influence of these discussions, he carried out the simple experiment of heating a rod of chemically pure lead over a gas flame and at the same time pulling it apart. Invariably, the rod parted cleanly along grain boundaries if the heating was sufficiently slow and uniform. When this experiment was repeated with spectroscopically pure lead, however, it never worked, proving that the premature melting at the boundaries was due to the small amount of impurity in the "chemically pure" metal, but did not occur to any observable extent in the absence of impurities.

17.

Movement and Diffusion Phenomena in Grain Boundaries

R. SMOLUCHOWSKI

Carnegie Institute of Technology

ABSTRACT

Mott suggested that the grain boundary can be described as a sequence of "islands" of good and bad fit between the grains. On that basis, a theory of the mobility of grain boundaries is proposed. Experimental data for silver, aluminum, and brass are in agreement with the theoretical calculations of mobility due to surface tension in a curved boundary. The mobility of grain boundaries have also been estimated by Read and Shockley on the basis of the dislocation model.

The various physical factors such as surface energy, state of strain, external stresses, time and temperature, the relative orientation are considered, and their influence on the mobility of grain boundaries is interpreted and illustrated. Further geometrical factors such as thickness of specimen and grain size are also considered, together with the influence of obstacles and impurities on mobility of grain boundaries.

The mechanism of grain boundary diffusion is discussed from the point of view of the current theories of volume diffusion. The experimental results are described, and their interpretation is suggested. Finally the influence of the relative orientation of grains and of grain boundary itself on diffusion is discussed, and the recent experimental results in that field are described. The relationship between grain boundary diffusion and the dislocation model as well as the recent observations of anisotropy of diffusion in a grain boundary are discussed.

1. MOVEMENT OF GRAIN BOUNDARIES

The importance of grain boundaries lies not only in their presence as static boundaries between individual grains, but also in the fact that under the influence of various factors the boundaries can move and affect the properties of a polycrystalline material. This mobility of the grain boundaries themselves is related to diffusion, within static grain boundaries, which plays a basic role in many metallic reactions.

MECHANISM OF GRAIN-BOUNDARY MOVEMENT

The ideas about the mechanism of the movement of grain boundaries are closely related to the various points of view on the structure of grain boundaries themselves. Two groups of theories can be distinguished. In one of them the existence of a more or less undefined layer of misfit between two grains is assumed. This region can be treated either as a viscous pseudo-liquid[1] or as a sequence of "islands" of good and bad fit.[2] Based on this concept, the movement of a grain boundary can be pictured as a gradual transfer of atoms from one grain into the viscous layer by a process somewhat analogous to melting, and a simultaneous transfer of atoms from that layer to the other grain by a process analogous to solidification. The theories of the other group are based on the dislocation model of grain boundaries,[3] and the motion of the boundaries is analyzed in terms of the motion of arrays of dislocations.

Let us consider in more detail a theory of the first group based on a viscous or disordered nature of the grain boundary. A quantitative treatment of the "melting" and of "solidification" of atoms in the grain boundary, in accord with the viscous liquid model, is hampered by the absence of a detailed theory of melting and solidification. In addition, there is the basic objection that the temperature dependence of the viscosity of a grain boundary appears to be much higher than that of the liquid metal.[4] The analogy to a liquid is thus not very fruitful. The movement of a boundary according to the "island" theory can be pictured as a sequence of disordering of a group of atoms of one crystal on one side of the boundary, and ordering them according to the lattice of the growing crystal on the other side of the boundary. This process can be put into semi-quantitative theory in the following manner:[5] A group of n atoms forms a layer of monatomic thickness almost parallel to the grain boundary. Let us assume, similarly to Mott's theory of viscous slip along grain boundaries, that the free energy for disordering these n atoms at absolute zero is $F = nL$, where L is the heat of fusion, and it is zero at the melting point T_m. However, instead of Mott's relation,

$$F = nL(1 - T/T_m), \tag{1.1}$$

we put

$$F = nL(1 - T/T_m) - \gamma nvT/T_m, \tag{1.2}$$

where v is the area of the layer per atom and γ is the orientation dependent surface energy of the grain boundary. The higher the energy, the easier it is to disorder the atoms. The justification for the assumption is the observation that mobility of grain boundaries depends strongly upon the orientation of the boundary and on the orientation of the grains. Energy of a grain boundary[3] is proportional to the shear modulus G, which, in general, does not disappear at the melting point, although it reaches very small values at that temperature (the author is indebted to Dr. C. Herring for pointing out this fact). In view of the approximate character of the assumption (1.2) we shall put $\gamma = 0$ at $T = T_m$; a more elaborate relationship does not seem to have sufficient theoretical justification.

In the absence of any driving force, the number of atoms ordering and disordering on each side of the boundary is the same, and the boundary is stable. It is known, however, that in certain conditions a grain boundary migrates under the influence of its surface energy or surface tension γ; this case will be considered here in more detail. Depending upon the curvature of the boundary, the driving force for this migration is given by

$$\tau_s = 2\gamma/r \tag{1.3}$$

or by

$$\tau_c = \gamma/r \tag{1.4}$$

for spherical and cylindrical curvatures, respectively. The average distance between the equilibrium positions of the atoms before and after the motion is a fraction, f, of the atomic diameter. After the atoms have moved, the boundary itself has moved by one atomic diameter, a. The work done by the force, τ, is thus

$$\tau nfav. \tag{1.5}$$

According to rate theory, we have thus, in the usual manner, for the rate of motion of the boundary,

$$\begin{aligned} V &= \nu a \exp\left[(-F + \tau nfav)/kT\right] - \nu a \exp\left[(-F - \tau nfav)/kT\right] \\ &= 2\nu a \exp\left(-F/kT\right) \sin h\left(\tau nfav/kT\right) \\ &\cong (2\nu\tau a^2 nfv/kT) \exp\left(-F/kT\right), \end{aligned} \tag{1.6}$$

where ν is the atomic frequency. Clearly the driving force and, thus, the rate of motion depend upon the radius of curvature and, hence, upon the grain size. We have, thus, for a spherical grain:

$$V \simeq (4\nu a^2 \gamma n f v / rkT) \exp(-F/kT) \tag{1.7}$$

or, using (1.2), we have an exponential law

$$V = V_0 \exp(-Q/kT), \tag{1.8}$$

with

$$V_0 = (4\nu a^2 \gamma n f v / rkT) \exp[(nL + \gamma n v)/kT_m] \tag{1.9}$$

and

$$Q = nL. \tag{1.10}$$

Experimental data of Alexander and co-workers[6] for silver, of Beck and co-workers[7] for aluminum and brass, and of Walker[8] and Burke[9] for brass can be expressed in the form (1.8) with the constants shown in Table 1. These values were obtained directly from the published data or by replotting them in the usual manner: ln V (not the diameter of the grain!) against $1/T$. The latent heats of fusion, L, for silver, aluminum, and brass were taken as 2.73, 2.52, and 3.0, respectively, giving from (1.1) for n the values 10, 29 to 35, and 18 atoms, respectively. The surface energy γ was put equal to 400 ergs/cm^2, which is of the order of the best value for copper given by Fisher and Dunn,* similar measurements for aluminum not being available. There are no data available which would permit a quantitative correlation of surface energy and rate of motion as a function of orientation. For that reason the surface energy used here is to be understood as a typical average value. The average grain radius in the various experiments was 0.05, 0.05, and 0.005 cm for the three metals. The factor, f, was put equal to 0.5. The other values are as usual $\nu = 10^{12}$ sec^{-1} and $a = 10^{-8}$ cm. All experiments were made in the proximity of 500°C, and so this temperature was chosen for T in (1.9). With these numerical values we obtain for V_0 the values shown in the last column of Table 1. In comparing with experiment, we should remember that a relatively small uncertainty of Q affects V_0 a great deal, so that together with other sources of error an agreement better than within one or two orders of magnitude should be considered fortuitous. Many factors, such as possible stress magnifications, have been left out entirely from consideration.

* Paper 12 of this book.

It is interesting to look into the influence of surface tension γ on mobility. As shown by Dunn and Lionetti,[10] grain-boundary energies can vary, depending on orientation of the grains, from zero to a maximum value. Let us assume that $\gamma_{max} = 400$ erg/cm^2 and that for another grain boundary it is only 100 erg/cm^2. If we use all the numerical values applicable to silver in the previous calculation, we obtain a rate of mobility twenty-five times lower. For a twin boundary with an energy of the order of 1 per cent of the maximum value, the mobility is one thousand times lower.

Now let us return to the other group of theories, based on the dislocation model of grain boundaries.[3] According to this picture,

TABLE 1

OBSERVED AND CALCULATED MOBILITIES OF GRAIN BOUNDARIES

	Q, cal/mole	V_0*(obs.), cm/sec*	V_0*(calc.), cm/sec*
Ag	38,000	2×10^3	1.5×10^4
Al	71,000–85,000	10^{18}–10^{19}	1.3×10^{20}
Brass	55,000	10^8–10^9	1.6×10^{10}

the basic mechanism of motion of a grain boundary is the movement of dislocations rather than the movement of individual atoms. A dislocation can move either in its slip plane or by a process of self-diffusion in a direction perpendicular to the slip plane. Thus, as analyzed extensively by Read and Shockley,[3] a movement of a grain boundary of general orientation and shape is a sum of these two kinds of movements of dislocations. The observed activation energies are reasonably close to the known energies for self-diffusion.

Whichever of the foregoing two points of view, or their compromise, finally proves to be the best, it is clear that temperature, orientation, impurities, composition, state of perfection of the two grains, etc., will play an important role in determining the mobility of a grain boundary.

PHYSICAL FACTORS

The basic physical factors affecting motion of grain boundaries will be briefly described and illustrated in the following survey, without any attempt at completeness. In particular, problems of nucleation of new grains, of texture, of ultimate structures, etc., will be mentioned only if they illustrate the mobility of a grain boundary and the roles of the various factors.

Surface Energy. Since the grain boundary is a distorted or imperfect quasi-crystalline array, the energy per atom situated there is higher than that of an atom within either one of the neighboring grains. The number of neighbors of each atom at the grain boundary and the distances between are in general different than they are within the interior of the crystal. Only the relative position of the nearest or of the second nearest neighbors of the atoms along a twin boundary are altered; the number of neighbors and their distances are preserved. For these reasons, the energy of a twin boundary is small compared to the energy of a grain boundary. In general, the energy of a grain boundary depends not only on the orientation of the grain but also on the orientation of the grain boundary itself with respect to the two grains. Thus, if there is enough atomic mobility, the grain bound-

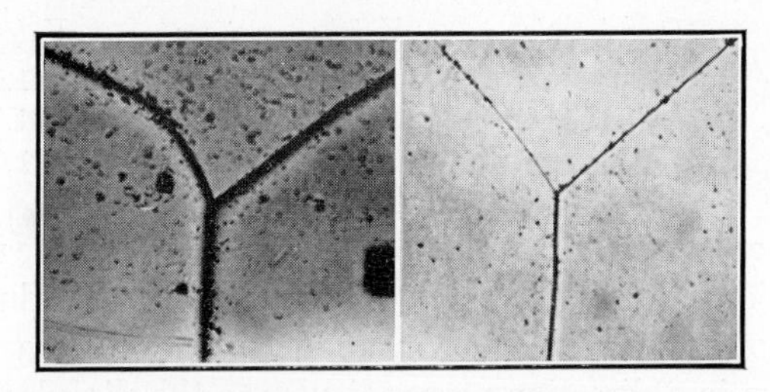

FIG. 1. Displacement of grain boundaries in Fe-Si. (After Dunn, Daniels, and Bolton.[10])

aries will tend to move in such a way as to lower the total boundary area and also to increase the area of the low-energy configurations at the expense of high energy boundaries. Thus it follows that grain boundaries of high energy will tend to be flat whereas those of lower energies may have appreciable curvatures. This geometry has been observed experimentally.[11] From the foregoing it follows also that, if the influence of the orientation of a boundary, with respect to the grains, on the energy of the boundary is small, the boundaries will tend to straighten out and to be short. If, on the contrary, the orientation effect is strong, then a longer curved boundary of the proper orientation may be more stable than a straight one. This is particularly true when part of the boundary can be a twin boundary.

Evidence of the tendency of grain boundaries having one end fixed to shorten and to straighten is found in the work of Dunn and co-workers on Fe-Si crystals.[10] The progress of the motion of grain boundaries is illustrated in Fig. 1. If both ends of a boundary are rather immobile, the boundary moves towards its center of curvature, as is well illustrated by Fig. 2, taken from the work of Beck and Sperry.[12]

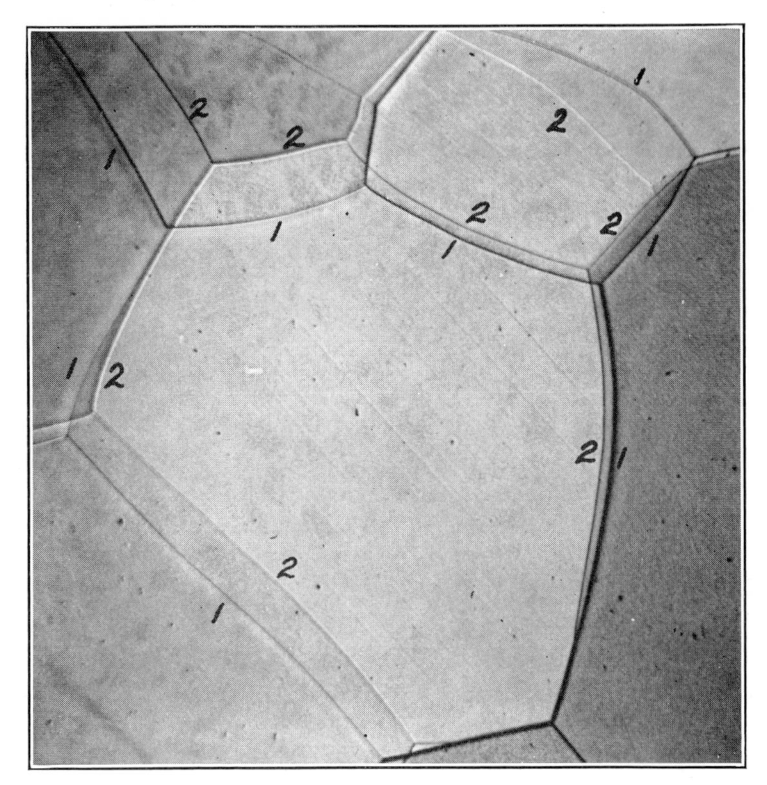

FIG. 2. Migration of grain boundaries toward their centers of curvature in aluminum. (1) 2 minutes at 600°C. (2) Additional 30 seconds at 600°C. (After Beck and Sperry.[12])

The influence of soluble additions on surface energy is especially strong when these additions tend to concentrate at the boundaries. The mobility of the solute atoms, through long-range diffusion, may be much smaller than the mobility of the atoms of the pure metal at the boundary, where the movements required may be fractions of an interatomic distance. The influence of solute atoms on the mobility of dislocations has often been pointed out.

Thus we may expect the mobility of grain boundaries due to surface tension to be composition-sensitive even at low concentrations.

State of Strain. Another basic driving force for the motion of grain boundaries is the state of strain of individual grains. We expect a grain which is less strained, and thus having a lower energy, to grow at the expense of a neighboring grain which has a higher strain energy. This difference in state of strain can be due to a uniform deformation of a polycrystalline material in which the strain varies from grain to grain, depending upon its orientation. It can also be obtained in a recrystallized material in which the various grains grew in a highly inhomogeneous stress field of the original cold-worked material. These effects have been much studied and are (often erroneously) called coarsening or secondary recrystallization. The latter is applied, strictly speaking, only to material which has been recrystallized and is further annealed at higher temperature without additional deformation.

The driving force, obtained from the release of the strain energy of the less perfect grain, is often much greater than the surface energy. It can happen, thus, that a boundary will move against the surface tension; for instance, away from its center of curvature. The boundary will increase its curvature and its length as long as there is enough energy gained by absorbing the imperfect grain by a more perfect one. A beautiful illustration of this effect is provided by Beck and Sperry[12] and shown in Fig. 3. The successive positions of the boundary between grains A and B are clearly seen. It should be noted that, as shown by a stronger etching, the part of grain B swept by the moving boundary is practically strain-free whereas its parent and the disappearing grain are both cold-worked. The same specimen provides, in another area, examples of typical new recrystallization grains, which, judging by the number of visible outlines, have started much later than the movement of the grain boundary shown in Fig. 3. This is quite natural since we would expect a strain-free nucleus to be more stable if it has a backing of a parent grain rather than if it has an orientation different from any neighboring material.

External Stress. On the basis of the dislocation model, we would expect an external elastic stress to affect the stability of grain boundaries. No clear-cut examples of this effect have been reported, though some indications in the case of zinc have been observed.[13]

Temperature and Time. The influence of temperature on the mobility of grain boundaries is very basic not only because temperature enters into the usual Boltzman-type dependence, as discussed in the early part of this paper, but also because it influences the state of strain through recovery. This role of temperature is often

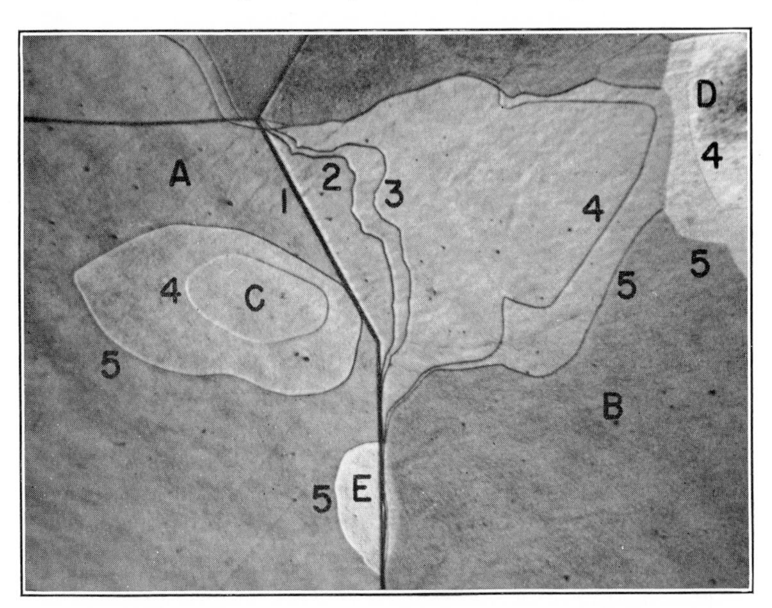

FIG. 3. Migration of grain boundaries due to strain in aluminum. Grain *A* grows at the expense of grain *B*. Recrystallization at 500°C after 0, 5, 10, 25, and 32 seconds corresponds to stages (1), (2), (3), (4), and (5), respectively. (After Beck and Sperry.[12])

forgotten. In many instances, especially in studies of recrystallization, it is erroneous to assume that the unrecrystallized material remains unchanged until it itself recrystallizes. This gradual relief of strain and change of strain gradients can influence greatly the rate of growth as a function of time at a temperature. Many empirical relationships have been proposed to express the relationship between grain growth and time. One of the most frequently used is Becks:[14]

$$D = Kt^n, \tag{1.11}$$

where D is grain diameter, t is time, K and n are constants. For high-purity aluminum n varies from 0.056 at 350°C to 0.32 at

600°C. The rate of growth decreases with time according to the relation

$$V = \frac{dD}{dt} = Knt^{n-1}, \tag{1.12}$$

which also indicates that at low temperatures the rate decreases faster than at high.

The role of time and temperature is also very important in relation to impurities, as will be discussed later.

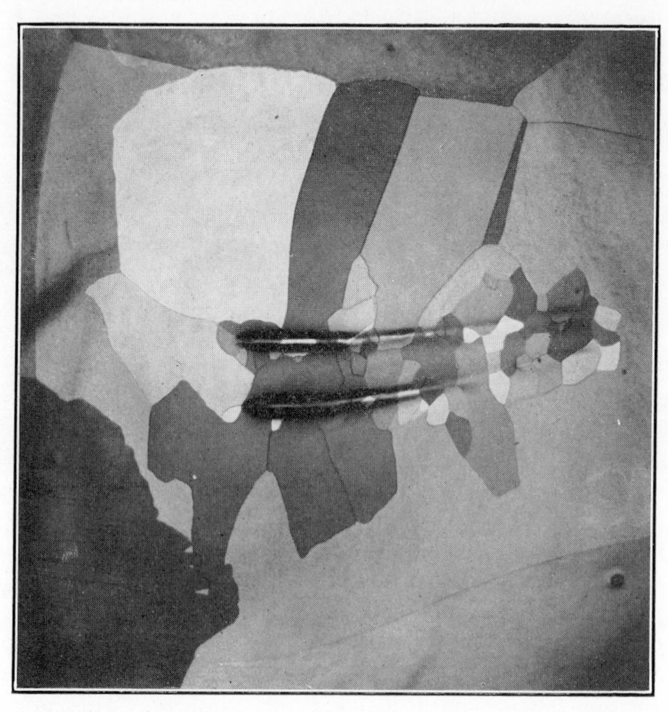

Fig. 4. Preferred growth of recrystallized grain originating in two scratches in aluminum. (After Beck, Sperry, and Hu.[16])

Relative Orientation. There is ample evidence that the rate of motion of a grain boundary is strongly dependent upon mutual orientation of the two grains. In many cases, this could be interpreted as due to a difference in surface energy or to a difference in the amount of strain, which itself is a function of orientation. However, most likely the orientation effect is due to the ease with which particular movements of the groups of atoms can be accomplished. This latter point of view was investigated by Kronberg and Wilson[15] in terms of oriented nucleation. Beck,[16] however, has evidence that seems to show that it is rather the rate of growth which is orientation-dependent rather than the nucleation. A good illustration of this fact is given as Fig. 4 which shows a number of grains of copper artificially nucleated by a scratch. All those which are long have a similar orientation relationship with respect to the old grain, and the particular orientation corresponds to a rotation of about 40° around the [111] direction. A quantitative explanation of this effect is still missing, though some of the arguments forwarded by Kronberg and Wilson are very plausible.

GEOMETRICAL FACTORS

There are many purely geometrical factors which affect mobility of a grain boundary. One of them is, of course, curvature, which was discussed in connection with surface tension. Furthermore, such factors as shape of grain and grain-size distribution can influence the motion of a grain boundary. These tendencies are probably best observed in the famous soap bubble analogy. As C. S. Smith pointed out in Paper 14 of this book, there is a preferred number of neighbors which each grain wants to attain and also a tendency to equalize grain size.

A factor worth specific mentioning is sample thickness. It has frequently been observed that the ultimate grain size obtained by grain growth is strongly influenced by the dimensions of the specimen. An illustration of this fact is Fig. 5, made by Beck[17] on the basis of Burke's data. The dotted line shows that at small grain sizes the ultimate grain is commensurate with specimen thickness. The deviation from the straight line at larger grain sizes is, according to Beck, due to an inclusion effect, as discussed later. The specimen thickness limitation may be related to the fact that in grains larger than the thickness of the specimen the grain boundary is a small part of the total grain surface. It is clear that, whenever the average grain size begins to approach a limiting size of that sort, the motion of the grain boundaries must slow down.

The decrease of the rate of growth with increasing grain size, which was studied by Beck, may be due to the increasing concentration of impurities swept by the moving boundary. It can be also related to equations (1.11) and (1.12), which give

$$V \sim D^{(n-1)/n}. \tag{1.13}$$

OBSTACLES IN THE MOTION OF GRAIN BOUNDARIES

All crystalline imperfections, such as cracks and inclusions, act as anchors for a grain boundary. A boundary tends to pass through such obstacles, using their areas to decrease its own sur-

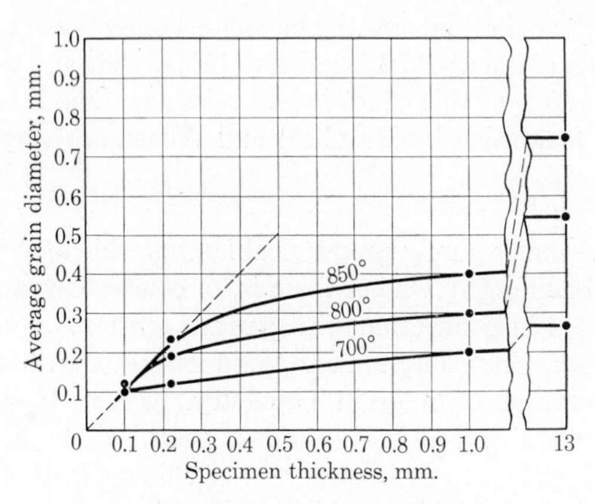

FIG. 5. Ultimate grain diameter as a function of specimen thickness in brass. (After Beck from data by Burke.[17])

face. Strong concentration of force is required to tear a boundary away from an imperfection. Once it is free, the boundary will move rapidly until it is stopped by another obstacle. This effect of imperfections is the most likely reason for the very frequently observed rapid jumps of grain boundaries. In some instances, it has been shown that on repeating the movement the boundary stops and then jumps in the same place, thus pointing to a local feature rather than to a statistical fluctuation.

An important type of obstacle is surface inhomogeneity, which often prevents grain growth on the surface of specimens. In particular, scratches and etch pits can slow down the rate of migration of boundaries appreciably. An illustration of this effect is Fig. 6, taken from the work of Rathenau and Custers.[18]

Probably the most frequently encountered obstacles are mosaic boundaries (or polygonization[19]), which, of course, are strongly influenced by cold work, and in general depend on the history of the crystal. If the metal is not pure, then there can also be insoluble impurities. As mentioned before, the rate of growth of a grain slows down with time and thus, for various reasons, when the density of impurities is sufficient, they may stop the growth completely. This has been particularly studied by Beck,[17] and this

FIG. 6. Influence of etching on grain growth in Ni-Fe: (*a*) 44 μ; (*b*) 59 μ; (*c*) 83 μ; (*d*) 115 μ. (After Rathenau and Custers.[18])

also, according to him, explains the limiting grain sizes which are much smaller than specimen thickness, as observed by Burke (Fig. 5).

The role of imperfections ties in very closely with the influence of temperature on the mobility of grain boundaries. With increasing temperature, many inclusions will dissolve, and the grain boundaries will be able to move again more easily. Also a sufficiently long time at a temperature may lead to a better homogenization of composition and to elimination of many inclusions. We should not forget, however, that grain boundaries are the "garbage cans" of metals.

2. DIFFUSION ALONG GRAIN BOUNDARIES

Although visual and qualitative observations of preferential diffusion along grain boundaries have often been made, it is only recently that the subject has been studied in a more quantitative manner.

MECHANISM OF GRAIN-BOUNDARY DIFFUSION

Intuitively it is not surprising at all that the mobility of atoms along a grain boundary is different from the mobility in a perfect crystalline lattice. Without examining the details of the mechanism of diffusion in solids, still much argued, we may point out that there are three basic groups of theories. One group is based on the assumption that diffusion occurs by an interchange of an atom and a vacancy in the lattice. The second group assumes that diffusion occurs through the simultaneous interchange of positions of two atoms, or more than two moving in the form of a "ring."[20] Finally, the third group assumes that diffusion can occur by a penetration of the diffusing atom through interstitial spaces in the lattice. The activation energies for the various processes have been theoretically calculated by Huntington,[21] Seitz,[22] Zener,[20] and others. As general conclusion, we may safely say that in close-packed lattices, such as copper, silver, or zinc, the vacancy mechanism requires least energy and is the predominant phenomenon. In other lattices, such as body-centered iron, etc., the interchange mechanisms may be of primary importance. The interstitial mechanism is likely to occur only at very high temperatures.

If we have to do with diffusion along a grain boundary, the conclusion as to its nature will depend upon the mechanism of volume diffusion. The easiest to use here is the vacancy mechanism. A grain boundary undoubtedly is an agglomeration of vacancies and imperfections either in the form of areas of "misfit" or as dislocations. Thus, we would conclude that there is an abundance of the necessary "carriers" and a low energy of activation. The interchange model is difficult to use since the instantaneous configuration of the interchanging atoms is rather indefinite. It may be, however, the main mechanism of diffusion along grain boundaries of not-close-packed metals, especially when the angle between the two grains, and thus the boundary energy, is low. The third mechanism, the interstitial migration along a grain boundary, does not differ much from the vacancy mechanism. In a highly imperfect lattice, the distinction between a vacancy and an interstitial position largely disappears. A particularly interesting aspect of the dislocation model of a grain boundary is the possibility of a different diffusion rate along the dislocations and in a direction perpendicular to them. To be sure, a similar difference could be expected on the Mott's "island" model since the islands, themselves, the distances between them, etc., can be highly anisotropic within the plane of the grain boundary. As yet no quantitative evidence of such a difference is known although there are several qualitative indications that in certain instances an anisotropy of that kind exists.[11]

DIFFUSION EQUATION

In order to be able to interpret in a quantitative manner experimental data on grain-boundary diffusion, it is necessary to solve the standard diffusion equation. Ideally, we should use its generalized form

$$\frac{\partial c}{\partial t} = \frac{\partial}{\partial x}\left(D\,\frac{\partial c}{\partial x}\right), \tag{2.1}$$

in which the diffusion coefficient is concentration dependent. However, even assuming D constant, as yet no rigorous solution has been given. The only published solution has been obtained by Fisher[23] with the help of several simplifying assumptions. He considers the case of a flat boundary perpendicular to the surface of a specimen and possessing a definite thickness, δ, a uniform structure, and concentration which does not vary across the thickness. The diffusing substance, for instance a radioactive isotope, is deposited on the surface of the sample and allowed to diffuse. If the diffusion along the grain boundary is faster than volume diffusion, we obtain the outline shown in Fig. 7. Fisher assumes, further, that, at large enough distances from the surface, the diffusion can be considered as taking place along the grain boundary (direction y) and simultaneously away from the grain boundary. The latter is assumed to occur into the two grains, *only* in the direction (direction x) perpendicular to the boundary.

Under these assumptions, he obtains:

$$C = C_0 \exp\left(-2^{1/2} y_1/\pi^{1/4} t_1^{1/4}\right) \operatorname{erfc}\left(x_1/2t_1^{1/2}\right), \tag{2.2}$$

where

$$y_1 = y/\delta (D_B/D_V)^{1/2}; \qquad t_1 = D_V t/\delta^2; \qquad x_1 = x/\delta, \tag{2.3}$$

and erfc stands for the complementary error function. The coefficients D_B and D_V refer to boundary and volume diffusion,

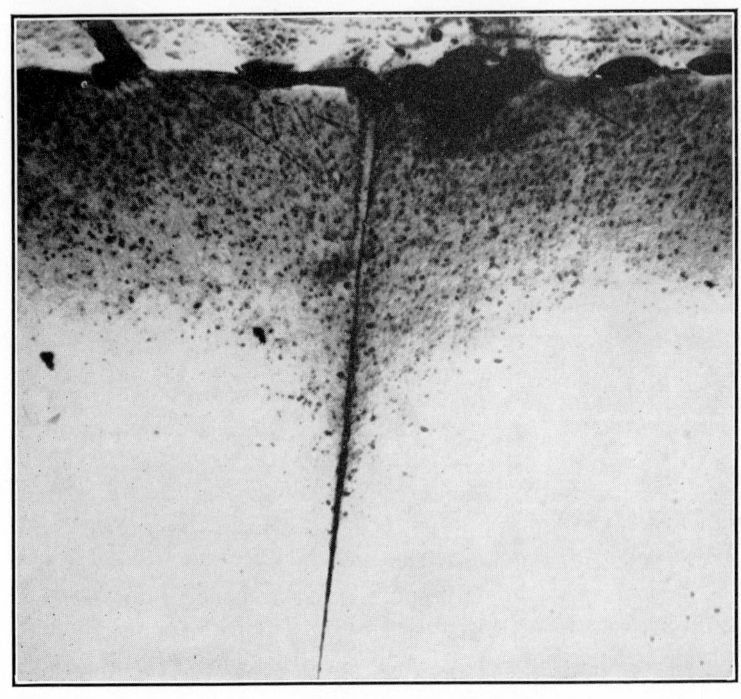

FIG. 7. Diffusion of silver along a grain boundary of columnar copper for 260 hours at 675°C cut perpendicular to the interface. (After Achter and Smoluchowski.[11])

respectively. A calculation of the total amount of material which has diffused into a thin layer sufficiently distant from the original surface gives

$$\overline{C} = C_0 t_1^{1/2} \exp\left(-2^{1/2} y_1/\pi^{1/4} t_1^{1/4}\right) dy_1, \tag{2.4}$$

which indicates that $\overline{C}$ is a simple exponential function of the distance y. This relationship has been experimentally confirmed (assuming $\delta = 5$ Å) by Hoffman and Turnbull.[24] Equation (2.2) is not accurate enough to describe the shape of the concentration distribution near the original surface; however, as a step to obtain the experimentally verified equation (2.4), it is very useful.

EXPERIMENTAL RESULTS

Without attempting to describe the various experimental data, we may mention that probably the first quantitative estimates of the activation energy of grain-boundary diffusion were made by Langmuir.[25] Using the electron emissivity of thoriated tungsten as an indication of surface concentration and comparing materials with various grain sizes, he obtained for grain-boundary diffusion $Q = 90{,}000$ cal/mole as compared to $Q = 120{,}000$ cal/mole for volume diffusion. The absolute values of diffusion coefficients were then obtained, using the Langmuir-Dushman relationship ($D_0 \sim 1$).

Qualitative observations of grain boundary diffusion were made on the aluminum-copper[26] and copper-silver[27] systems. They indicated that, at low temperatures, the diffusion along grain boundaries is faster than volume diffusion, as evidenced by formation of cusps similar to those shown in Fig. 7. The fact that at high temperatures this phenomenon disappears confirms the expectation that the activation energy for grain-boundary diffusion is lower than for volume diffusion. Some evidence to the contrary was obtained in a rather indirect way[1] or on materials of doubtful purity.

Diffusion studies have been made on the copper-bismuth system by Voce and Hallowes[28] and by Scheil and Schiessl.[29] It is, however, very doubtful whether phenomena occurring in this system should be classified as typical diffusion. Bismuth in these experiments is either in the vapor or in the liquid state, and the penetration process appears to be very complicated. The last-mentioned authors obtained for the rate of penetration of bismuth $Q = 20{,}000$ cal/mole.

Diffusion of silver along individual grain boundaries of columnar copper was studied by Achter and Smoluchowski,[11] with particular emphasis on the orientation effect. The details will be described later; here it need only be mentioned that the activation energy for grain-bound diffusion appears to be around 23,000 cal/mole, as compared to 38,000 cal/mole for volume diffusion.

Grain-boundary diffusion phenomena in silver were studied by Hoffman and Turnbull,[24] using radioactive silver as the diffusing substance. This self-diffusion appears to follow the same general behavior as diffusion of two different elements. By studying self-diffusion in fine-grained (35 μ) polycrystalline material and in single crystals, they obtained for the activation energies 26,400 and 46,000, respectively (D_0 = 0.17 and 0.895, respectively). Furthermore, using equation (2.4) and assuming the width of the boundary to be 5 Å, they obtained, from a study of surface activities, for the grain-boundary diffusion Q = 21,400 (D_0 = 0.06), in reasonably good agreement with the previous values.

ORIENTATION EFFECT

It is clear, from previous considerations of mobility of grain boundaries and of the mechanism of diffusion, that an influence of grain orientation on grain-boundary diffusion would be expected. Various experiments point to a strong orientation dependence of grain boundary surface energies, and the variation near small angles of disorientation should be especially pronounced.

Achter and Smoluchowski[11] have made a study of these orientation effects, using silver as the element diffusing along grain boundaries of columnar copper. By using columnar copper, in which all grains have one common cubic direction, the relative orientation of two grains can be described by one parameter. This was chosen to be the smallest angle θ formed by those remaining cubic directions, which include the grain boundary. The orientation of the grains was determined by x-rays, and it appeared that the parallelity of the columnar grains was often not perfect. The silver was supplied by a 2 atomic per cent solid solution of silver in copper. In other experiments radioactive silver was plated on the copper samples. After diffusion, in the range of 675° to 725°C, the sample can be sliced either parallel or perpendicular to the direction of diffusion, as illustrated in Figs. 7 and 8. The presence of silver as a precipitate at higher concentrations or in solution at lower concentrations is easily revealed by proper etching. The etching appeared to be orientation-sensitive, as can be seen from the different blackening of the diffusion zone in two adjacent grains in Fig. 7. For that reason, all comparisons of the width of the diffusion zone, obtained by etching in a standardized manner, were made on surfaces perpendicular to the columnar direction. The relative amount of diffusion was estimated by measuring either the width of the diffusion zone surrounding a boundary or that distance from the surface at which all visible penetration disappeared.

The results are shown in Fig. 9, indicating a strong orientation effect. The most striking result is the practical absence of diffusion at angles smaller than 20° or larger than 70°. It seems

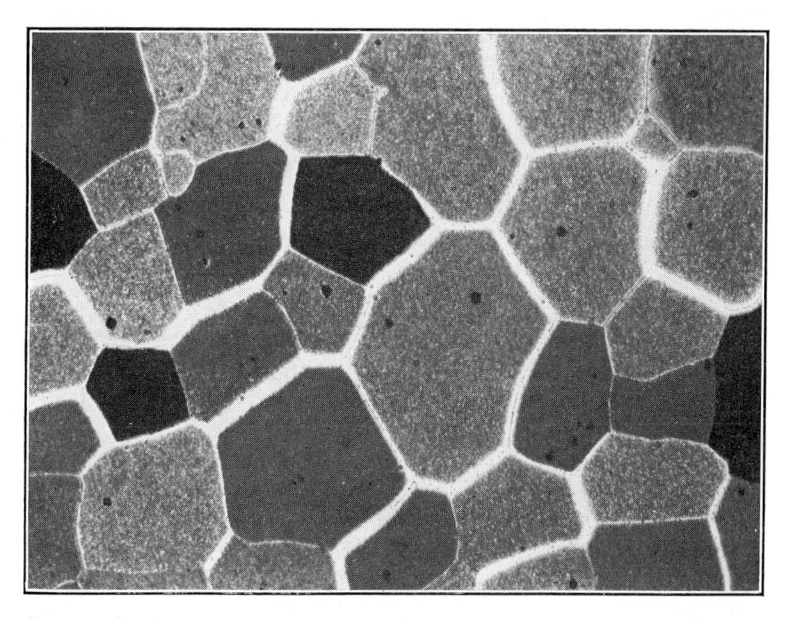

FIG. 8. Various amounts of silver showing along grain boundaries of columnar copper after diffusion for 260 hours at 675°C. Cut parallel to the interface at a depth of 0.02 cm. (After Achter and Smoluchowski.[11])

plausible to interpret this effect in the following way. At small angles of misfit the crystalline arrays of the two grains fit reasonably well, the boundary can be described in terms of dislocations, and the diffusion rate is very low. As the angle increases, the density of dislocations increases, and finally their identity is in effect lost. This stage, which presumably occurs around 20°, corresponds to an onset of large distortion and to an appreciable increase of the grain-boundary diffusion. At these angles the statistical approach, along the lines suggested by Mott in his "island" model, is probably more suitable for a description of these phenomena. It should be noted that the angle of 20° agrees well with the angles at which Dunn and co-workers[10] found a marked break in the energy vs. angle curve. It is plausible to assume that in both cases the limiting angles are due to the same cause. The cusp in the curves on Fig. 9 corresponds to an angle at which the two grains are in a twin relationship [plane (210)]. As expected, the energy and the diffusion along such a boundary would be quite low. As far as the influence of the orientation of

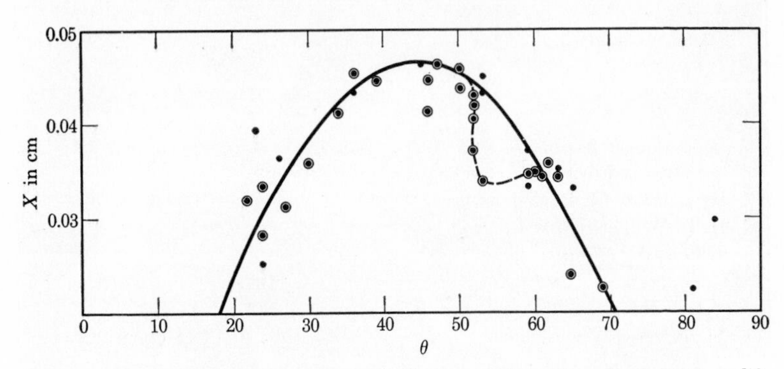

FIG. 9. Intergranular penetration of silver as a function of orientation difference of two columnar grains of copper after 141 hours at 725°C. (After Achter and Smoluchowski.[11])

the boundary itself between two fixed grains is concerned, the results indicate that diffusion increases with increasing deviation from a position bisecting the angle θ.

The grain boundaries used in obtaining Fig. 9 were only those between grains which were close to being truly columnar. It appeared that, when grains were not truly columnar, grain-boundary diffusion was observed in a direction perpendicular to the columnar direction, the silver being in that case supplied by an adjoining, silver-rich, boundary at a junction. This effect was observed only when the two cubic directions, which are not quite parallel, were in a plane which was close to being perpendicular to the grain boundary. Thus a deviation consisting of a small relative rotation of two ideally columnar grains in the plane of the grain boundary does not increase the diffusion rate. A rotation in a plane perpendicular to the boundary increases the diffusion appreciably, especially when it is as large as 20° or more. This result confirms experimentally the theoretical expectation that diffusion along a grain boundary is easier in the direction of the dislocations rather than in the direction perpendicular to them.

Experiments with radioactive silver performed by Couling and Schafer[30] confirmed the above results obtained first by microscopic technique.

REFERENCES

1. T. S. Kê, *Phys. Rev.*, **71**, 533 (1947); *J. Appl. Phys.*, **20**, 274 (1949).
2. N. F. Mott, *Proc. Phys. Soc. (London)*, **60**, 391 (1948).
3. J. M. Burgers, *Proc. Phys. Soc. (London)*, **52**, 23 (1940). W. T. Read and W. Shockley, *Phys. Rev.*, **78**, 275 (1950). T. H. van der Merwe, *Proc. Phys. Soc. (London)*, **63**, 616 (1950).
4. J. Frenkel, *Theory of Liquids*, Clarendon Press, Oxford University, 1946.
5. R. Smoluchowski, *Phys. Rev.*, **83**, 69 (1951).
6. B. H. Alexander, R. Baluffi, M. H. Dawson, H. P. Kling, and F. D. Rossi, Sylvania Electric Products Co. *Report* NYO-663.
7. P. A. Beck, M. L. Holzworth, and H. Hu, *Phys. Rev.*, **73**, 526 (1948).
8. H. L. Walker, *Univ. Ill. Eng. Exp. Stat. Bull.* 359 (1945).
9. J. E. Burke, *Trans. AIME*, **180**, 73 (1949).
10. C. G. Dunn and F. Lionetti, *J. Metals*, **1**, 125 (1949); C. G. Dunn, F. W. Daniels, and M. J. Bolton. *Trans. AIME*, **188**, 1256 (1950).
11. M. R. Achter and R. Smoluchowski, *Phys. Rev.*, **76**, 470 (1949); M. R. Achter, Carnegie Institute of Technology Thesis, 1950. *J. Appl. Phys.*, October, 1951; *Phys. Rev.*, **83**, 163 (1951).
12. P. A. Beck and P. R. Sperry, *J. Appl. Phys.*, **21**, 150 (1950).
13. D. Nulk and R. Smoluchowski (unpublished research).
14. P. A. Beck, J. C. Kremer, L. J. Demer, and M. L. Holzworth, *Metals Tech.*, TP 2280 (1947).
15. M. L. Kronberg and F. H. Wilson, *Trans. AIME*, **185**, 501 (1949).
16. P. A. Beck, P. R. Sperry, and H. Hu, *J. Appl. Phys.*, **21**, 420 (1950).
17. P. A. Beck, *Trans. AIME*, **185**, 882 (1949).
18. G. W. Rathenau and J. F. H. Custers, *Philips Research Report 4*, 241 (1949).
19. P. Lacombe, *Report of a Conference on the Strength of Solids*, University of Bristol, England, Physical Society, London, 1948.
20. C. Zener, *Acta Cryst.*, **3**, 34 (1950).
21. H. B. Huntington, *Phys. Rev.*, **61**, 325 (1942); H. B. Huntington and F. Seitz, *Phys. Rev.*, **61**, 315 (1942).
22. F. Seitz, *Phys. Rev.*, **74**, 1513 (1948); *Acta Cryst.*, **3**, 355 (1950).
23. J. C. Fisher, *J. Appl. Phys.*, **22**, 74 (1951).
24. R. E. Hoffman and D. Turnbull, *J. Appl. Phys.*, **22**, 634 (1951).
25. I. Langmuir, *J. Franklin Inst.*, **217**, 543 (1934).
26. F. Keller and R. H. Brown, *Trans. AIME*, **156**, 377 (1944).
27. F. Berman and R. H. Harrington, *Trans. ASM*, **34**, 143 (1945).
28. E. Voce and A. P. C. Hallowes, *J. Inst. Metals*, **73**, 323 (1947).
29. E. Scheil and K. E. Schiessl, *Z. Naturforsch.*, **4a**, 524 (1949).
30. L. Couling and D. Schafer (to be published).

DISCUSSION

W. SHOCKLEY (BELL TELEPHONE LABORATORIES):

In connection with Dr. Smoluchowski's paper, it is appropriate to mention some unpublished results obtained at the University of Delft by Dr. Tiedema, working under the direction of Professor W. G. Burgers. Tiedema has investigated the grains which form in recrystallized aluminum. He has found that the crystal grains are imperfect and that portions of them differ in orientation by the order of ¼ degree. He advises that this difference in orientation occurs at the nucleus for recrystallization, which may consist of three or more regions having the small difference in orientation. It has been proposed by the researchers at Delft that the nucleus for crystallization may form by condensation of the dislocations into grain boundaries, thus producing a region of low stress and low free energy. This view is very similar to that proposed by Cahn in connection with his studies of polygonization.

BRUCE CHALMERS (UNIVERSITY OF TORONTO):

The influence of impurities on the rate of grain boundary migration was seen very clearly in the work of Aust and Chalmers[1] on the grain-boundary energy in lead. The specimens were prepared in such a way that the position of the boundaries immediately after solidification was considerably removed from the position of equilibrium. It was observed that, when lead of 99.999 per cent purity was used, the point of junction of the three boundaries frequently moved through a distance of several millimeters during the process of cooling from the freezing point. Lead of lower purity did not show any visible movement under the same conditions.

An attempt has been made to determine the energy of activation for the process of boundary migration from experiments of this type. Preliminary work by Leaver and Siscoe and Aust[2] has given the following results: the rate of movement of the boundary in tin was observed under conditions where the only driving force is believed to be the change in area of the boundary. By making certain assumptions, it was possible to determine the rate of movement as a function of temperature and, therefore, to estimate the activation energy of the process. The values given by Leaver, Siscoe, and Aust for the activation energy showed some scatter, possibly due to different relative orientations in different specimens, and varied from 5.2 to 9.3 Kcal/gram atom. It is of interest to compare these figures with those published by Fensham[3]

[1] K. T. Aust and B. Chalmers, *Proc. Roy. Soc. (London)*, **204**, 359 (1950).

[2] G. R. Leaver, S. F. Siscoe, and K. T. Aust, unpublished.

[3] P. J. Fensham, *Australian J. Sci. Research*, **3**, 91 (1950).

for the self-diffusion of tin. He found $Q = 5.9 \pm 0.4$ Kcal/gram, atom for self-diffusion parallel to the a-axis and 10.5 ± 0.5 Kcal/gram atom for self-diffusion parallel to the c-axis. The unexpectedly close agreement between these figures may be significant. It does not appear as if Q is very sensitive to impurity content, but it is probable, on the basis of the observations quoted above, that A may be.

C. G. Dunn (General Electric Company):

Although relative orientation may affect the rate of growth through the way surface tension enters equations (1.7) and (1.8), since surface tension itself is orientation dependent, it is furthermore fairly clear, as the author points out, that there is also an orientation effect apart from this. The observation that grains often exhibit anisotropic growth (they become highly elliptical rather than circular in shape) is a crystallographic direction type of orientation relationship which is commonly seen for secondary recrystallization occurring in a highly oriented single-texture matrix of fine grains. On the other hand, the anisotropy of growth may exhibit itself, not in terms of the shape of a single growing grain, but rather in terms of a volume rate of growth which varies from grain to grain.[4–7,*] This phenomenon may occur for growth in weak- or strong-texture matrices.

Somewhat more quantitative data on relative orientation effects in a weak texture matrix of silicon iron have been obtained.[4] Figure D.1 shows how rate of growth of a single crystal grain (exaggerated grain growth) varies as the orientation of the growing grain is varied. In obtaining these data, seed crystals were reoriented to provide a series with the [001] direction held constant in the direction of growth. The orientation of each grain was then determined by the angle of tilt of the (100) plane from the plane of the sheet specimen. We note that the driving energy for growth resides in the fine-grained matrix, presumably as grain boundary energy, and this is constant for each of the growing grains. Neglected here, of course, is the change in the surface due to the tilt of the (100) plane which might alter the driving energy. However, data obtained for constant crystallographic surface also show orientation dependence of a similar type, so it is reasonable to attribute the effect to an orientation relationship and not to a difference in driving energy.

* See also reference 16 of this paper.

[4] A. E. van Arkel, *Rev. Mét., Mém.*, **33**, 197 (1936).

[5] W. G. Burgers, *Z. Metallkunde*, **41**, 2 (1950).

[6] Paper by C. G. Dunn, in *Cold Working of Metals*, p. 113, American Society for Metals, Cleveland, Ohio, 1949.

[7] W. May, *Röntgenografisch Onderzoek van Aluminiumkristallen Onstaan door Rekristallisatie*, Doctoral Dissertation, Technische Hogeschool, Delft, p. 92, 1950.

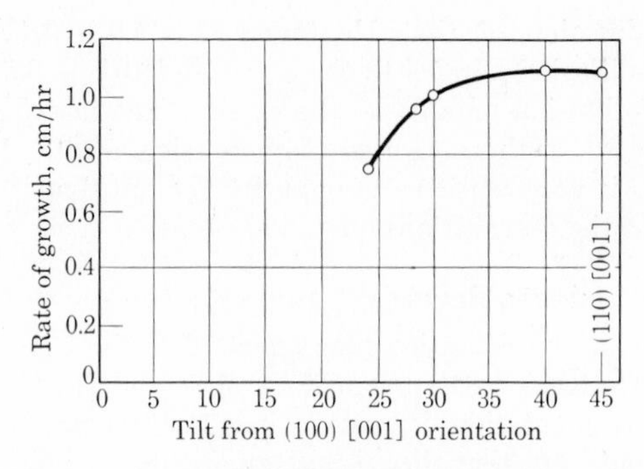

FIG. D.1. Variation of rate of growth with orientation of growing grain. (After Dunn.[6])

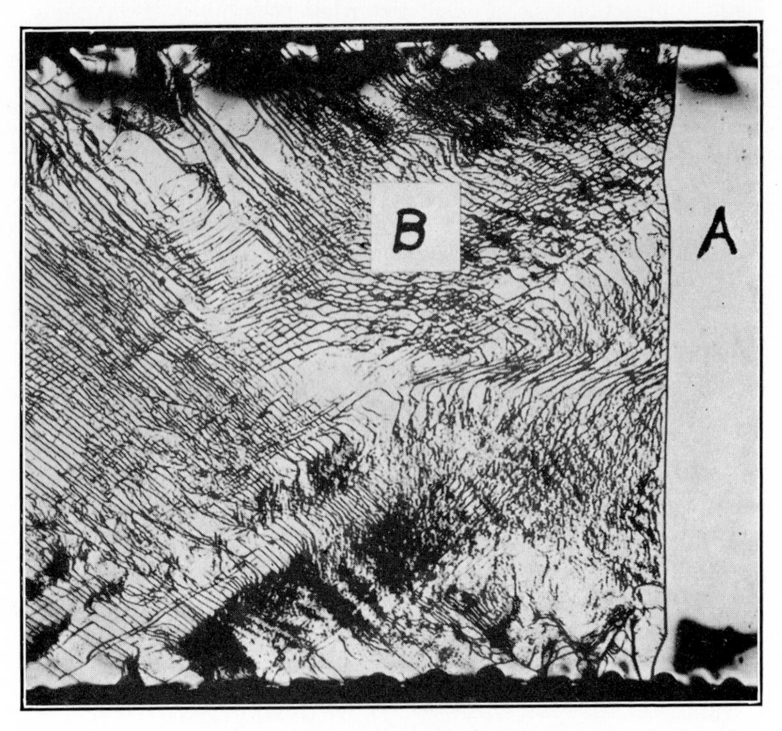

FIG. D.2. Micrograph of a bicrystal specimen with grain *B* in a complex polygonized state and grain *A* free of subboundaries. ×130. (After Dunn and Daniels.[8])

At the present time we are planning experiments with more complete control of the variables. For example, we hope to study rates of growth as a function of orientation in essentially bicrystal specimens. Figure D.2 gives an illustration of one type of bicrystal where one grain B contains a subgrain structure (and therefore subboundaries), and the other grain A, which at high temperatures grows at the expense of grain B, is free of such subboundaries.[8] The orientations of both grains may be predetermined, which is to say that such specimens can be made to order, and orientation relationships therefore can be made a controllable variable in growth or grain-boundary migration studies.

[8] C. G. Dunn and F. W. Daniels, "Formation and Behavior of Subboundaries in Silicon Iron," *Trans. AIME*, **191**, 147 (1951).

Author Index

(Numbers set in bold-face type show the pagination of the authors' own papers in this book.)

Subject Index